Projective Geometry

VOLUME II

BY OSWALD VEBLEN

OSWALD VEBLEN

Late Professor of Mathematics, Princeton University

JOHN WESLEY YOUNG

Late Professor of Mathematics, Dartmouth College

BLAISDELL PUBLISHING COMPANY

A DIVISION OF GINN AND COMPANY

New York · Toronto · London

PRINTED IN THE UNITED STATES OF AMERICA

PREFACE

The present volume is an attempt to carry out the program outlined in the preface to Volume I. Unfortunately, Professor Young was obliged by the pressure of other duties to cease his collaboration at an early stage of the composition of this volume. Much of the work on the first chapters had already been done when this happened, but the form of exposition has been changed so much since then that although Professor Young deserves credit for constructive work, he cannot fairly be held responsible for mistakes or oversights.

Professor Young has kindly read the proof sheets of this volume, as have also Professors A. B. Coble and A. A. Bennett. Most of the drawings were made by Dr. J. W. Alexander. I offer my thanks to all of these gentlemen and also to Messrs. Ginn and Company, who have shown their usual courtesy and efficiency while converting the manuscript into a book.

The second volume has been arranged so that one may pass on a first reading from the end of Chapter VII, Volume I, to the beginning of Volume II. The later chapters of Volume I may well be read in connection with the part of Volume II from Chapter V onward.

I shall pass by the opportunity to discuss any of the pedagogical questions which have been raised in connection with the first volume and which may easily be foreseen for the second. It is to be expected that there will continue to be a general agreement among those who have not made the experiment, that an abstract method of treatment of geometry is unsuited to beginning students.

In this book, however, we are committed to the abstract point of view. We have in mind two principles for the classification of any theorem of geometry: (*a*) the axiomatic basis, or bases, from which it can be derived, or, in other words, the class of spaces in which it can be valid; and (*b*) the group to which it belongs in a given space.

PREFACE

In the first volume we were always concerned with theorems belonging to the projective group, and these theorems were classified according as they were consequences of the groups of Assumptions A, E; A, E, H_0; A, E, P; or A, E, P, H_0. Among the spaces satisfying A, E, P (the properly projective spaces) may be mentioned the modular spaces, the rational nonmodular space, the real space, and the complex space. Any one of these may be specified categorically by adding the proper assumptions to A, E, P. The passage from the point of view of general projective geometry to that of the particular spaces is made in the first chapter of this volume.

Having fixed attention on any particular space, we have a set of groups of transformations to each of which belongs its geometry. For example, in the complex projective plane we find among others, (1) the group of all-continuous one-to-one reciprocal transformations (analysis situs), (2) the group of birational transformations (algebraic geometry), (3) the projective group, (4) the group of non-Euclidean geometry, (5) a sequence of groups connected with Euclidean geometry (cf. § 54). The groups (2), (3), (4), and (5) all have analogues in the other spaces mentioned in the paragraphs above, and consequently it is desirable to develop the theorems of the corresponding geometries in such a way that the assumptions required for their proofs are put in evidence in each case. This will be found illustrated in the chapters on affine and Euclidean geometry.

The two principles of classification, (*a*) and (*b*), give rise to a double sequence of geometries, most of which are of consequence in present-day mathematics. It is the purpose of this book to give an elementary account of the foundations and interrelations of the more important of these geometries (with the notable exception of (2)). May I venture to suggest the desirability of other books taking account of this logical structure, but dealing with particular types of geometric figures?

The ideal of such books should be not merely to prove every theorem rigorously but to prove it in such a fashion as to show in which spaces it is true and to which geometries it belongs. Some idea of the form which would be assumed by a treatise on conic sections written in this fashion can be obtained from § 83 below. Other subjects for which this type of exposition would be feasible at the present time are quadric surfaces, cubic and quartic curves, rational curves, configurations, linear line geometry, collineation groups, vector analysis.

Books of this type could take for granted the foundational and coördinating work of such a book as this one, and thus be free to use all the different points of view right from the beginning. On the other hand, a general work like this one could be much abbreviated if there were corresponding treatises on particular geometric figures (for example, conic sections) to which cross references could be made.

OSWALD VEBLEN

BROOKLIN, MAINE
AUGUST, 1917

CONTENTS

CHAPTER I

FOUNDATIONS

SECTION PAGE

1. Plan of the chapter . . . 1
2. List of Assumptions A, E, P, and H_0 . . . 1
3. Assumption K . . . 3
4. Double points of projectivities . . . 5
5. Complex geometry . . . 6
6. Imaginary elements adjoined to a real space . . . 7
7. Harmonic sequence . . . 9
8. Assumption H . . . 11
9. Order in a net of rationality . . . 13
*10. Cuts in a net of rationality . . . 14
*11. Assumption of continuity . . . 16
*12. Chains in general . . . 21
*13. Consistency, categoricalness, and independence of the assumptions . . . 23
*14. Foundations of the complex geometry . . . 29
*15. Ordered projective spaces . . . 32
*16. Modular projective spaces . . . 33
17. Recapitulation . . . 36

CHAPTER II

ELEMENTARY THEOREMS ON ORDER

18. Direct and opposite projectivities on a line . . . 37
19. The two sense-classes on a line . . . 40
20. Sense in any one-dimensional form . . . 43
21. Separation of point pairs . . . 44
22. Segments and intervals . . . 45
23. Linear regions . . . 47
24. Algebraic criteria of sense . . . 49
25. Pairs of lines and of planes . . . 50
26. The triangle and the tetrahedron . . . 52
27. Algebraic criteria of separation. Cross ratios of points in space . . . 55
28. Euclidean spaces . . . 58
29. Assumptions for a Euclidean space . . . 59
30. Sense in a Euclidean plane . . . 61
*31. Sense in Euclidean spaces . . . 63
*32. Sense in a projective space . . . 64
33. Intuitional description of the projective plane . . . 67

CHAPTER III

THE AFFINE GROUP IN THE PLANE

SECTION PAGE

34. The geometry corresponding to a given group of transformations . . . 70
35. Euclidean plane and the affine group 71
36. Parallel lines 72
37. Ellipse, hyperbola, parabola 73
38. The group of translations 74
39. Self-conjugate subgroups. Congruence 78
40. Congruence of parallel point pairs 80
41. Metric properties of conics 81
42. Vectors 82
43. Ratios of collinear vectors 85
44. Theorems of Menelaus, Ceva, and Carnot 89
45. Point reflections 92
46. Extension of the definition of congruence 94
47. The homothetic group 95
48. Equivalence of ordered point triads 96
49. Measure of ordered point triads 99
50. The equiaffine group 105
*51. Algebraic formula for measure. Barycentric coördinates 106
*52. Line reflections 109
*53. Algebraic formulas for line reflections 115
54. Subgroups of the affine group 116

CHAPTER IV

EUCLIDEAN PLANE GEOMETRY

55. Geometries of the Euclidean type 119
56. Orthogonal lines 120
57. Displacements and symmetries. Congruence 123
58. Pairs of orthogonal line reflections 126
59. The group of displacements 129
60. Circles 131
61. Congruent and similar triangles 134
62. Algebraic formulas for certain parabolic metric groups 135
63. Introduction of order relations 138
64. The real plane 140
65. Intersectional properties of circles 142
66. The Euclidean geometry. A set of assumptions 144
67. Distance 147
68. Area 149
69. The measure of angles 151
70. The complex plane 154
71. Pencils of circles 157
72. Measure of line pairs 163
73. Generalization by projection 167

CHAPTER V

ORDINAL AND METRIC PROPERTIES OF CONICS

SECTION PAGE
74. One-dimensional projectivities 170
75. Interior and exterior of a conic 174
76. Double points of projectivities 177
77. Ruler-and-compass constructions 180
78. Conjugate imaginary elements 182
79. Projective, affine, and Euclidean classification of conics 186
80. Foci of the ellipse and hyperbola 189
81. Focus and axis of a parabola 193
82. Eccentricity of a conic 196
83. Synoptic remarks on conic sections 199
84. Focal properties of collineations 201
85. Homogeneous quadratic equations in three variables 202
86. Nonhomogeneous quadratic equations in two variables 208
87. Euclidean classification of point conics 210
88. Classification of line conics 212
*89. Polar systems 215

CHAPTER VI

INVERSION GEOMETRY AND RELATED TOPICS

90. Vectors and complex numbers 219
91. Correspondence between the complex line and the real Euclidean plane . 222
92. The inversion group in the real Euclidean plane 225
93. Generalization by inversion 231
94. Inversions in the complex Euclidean plane 235
95. Correspondence between the real Euclidean plane and a complex pencil of lines 238
96. The real inversion plane 241
97. Order relations in the real inversion plane 244
98. Types of circular transformations 246
99. Chains and antiprojectivities 250
100. Tetracyclic coördinates 253
101. Involutoric collineations 257
102. The projective group of a quadric 259
103. Real quadrics 262
104. The complex inversion plane 264
105. Function plane, inversion plane, and projective plane 268
106. Projectivities of one-dimensional forms in general 271
*107. Projectivities of a quadric 273
*108. Products of pairs of involutoric projectivities 277
109. Conjugate imaginary lines of the second kind 281
110. The principle of transference 284

CONTENTS

CHAPTER VII

AFFINE AND EUCLIDEAN GEOMETRY OF THREE DIMENSIONS

SECTION PAGE

111. Affine geometry 287
112. Vectors, equivalence of point triads, etc. 288
113. The parabolic metric group. Orthogonal lines and planes 293
114. Orthogonal plane reflections 295
115. Displacements and symmetries. Congruence 297
116. Euclidean geometry of three dimensions 301
*117. Generalization to n dimensions 304
118. Equations of the affine and Euclidean groups 305
119. Distance, area, volume, angular measure 311
120. The sphere and other quadrics 315
121. Resolution of a displacement into orthogonal line reflections 317
122. Rotation, translation, twist 321
123. Properties of displacements 325
124. Correspondence between the rotations and the points of space 328
125. Algebra of matrices 333
126. Rotations of an imaginary sphere 335
127. Quaternions 337
128. Quaternions and the one-dimensional projective group 339
*129. Representation of rotations and one-dimensional projectivities by points 342
130. Parameter representation of displacements 344

CHAPTER VIII

NON-EUCLIDEAN GEOMETRIES

131. Hyperbolic metric geometry in the plane 350
132. Orthogonal lines, displacements, and congruence 352
133. Types of hyperbolic displacements 355
134. Interpretation of hyperbolic geometry in the inversion plane 357
135. Significance and history of non-Euclidean geometry 360
136. Angular measure 362
137. Distance 364
138. Algebraic formulas for distance and angle 365
*139. Differential of arc 366
140. Hyperbolic geometry of three dimensions 369
141. Elliptic plane geometry. Definition 371
142. Elliptic geometry of three dimensions 373
143. Double elliptic geometry 375
144. Euclidean geometry as a limiting case of non-Euclidean 375
145. Parameter representation of elliptic displacements 377
146. Parameter representation of hyperbolic displacements 380

CONTENTS

CHAPTER IX

THEOREMS ON SENSE AND SEPARATION

SECTION		PAGE
147.	Plan of the chapter	385
148.	Convex regions	385
149.	Further theorems on convex regions	388
150.	Boundary of a convex region	392
151.	Triangular regions	395
152.	The tetrahedron	397
153.	Generalization to n dimensions	400
154.	Curves	401
155.	Connected sets, regions, etc.	404
156.	Continuous families of sets of points	405
157.	Continuous families of transformations	406
158.	Affine theorems on sense	407
159.	Elementary transformations on a Euclidean line	409
160.	Elementary transformations in the Euclidean plane and space	411
161.	Sense in a convex region	413
162.	Euclidean theorems on sense	414
163.	Positive and negative displacements	416
164.	Sense-classes in projective spaces	418
165.	Elementary transformations on a projective line	419
166.	Elementary transformations in a projective plane	421
167.	Elementary transformations in a projective space	423
*168.	Sense in overlapping convex regions	424
*169.	Oriented points in a plane	425
*170.	Pencils of rays	429
*171.	Pencils of segments and directions	433
*172.	Bundles of rays, segments, and directions	435
*173.	One- and two-sided regions	436
174.	Sense-classes on a sphere	437
175.	Order relations on complex lines	437
176.	Direct and opposite collineations in space	438
177.	Right- and left-handed figures	441
178.	Right- and left-handed reguli, congruences, and complexes	443
*179.	Elementary transformations of triads of lines	446
*180.	Doubly oriented lines	447
*181.	More general theory of sense	451
182.	Broken lines and polygons	454
183.	A theorem on simple polygons	457
184.	Polygons in a plane	458
185.	Subdivision of a plane by lines	460
186.	The modular equations and matrices	464
187.	Regions determined by a polygon	467
188.	Polygonal regions and polyhedra	473
189.	Subdivision of space by planes	475
190.	The matrices H_1, H_2, and H_3	477
191.	The rank of H_2	479

CONTENTS

SECTION PAGE
192. Polygons in space 480
193. Odd and even polyhedra 482
194. Regions bounded by a polyhedron 483
195. The matrices E_1 and E_2 for the projective plane 484
196. Odd and even polygons in the projective plane 489
197. One- and two-sided polygonal regions 490
198. One- and two-sided polyhedra 493
199. Orientation of space 496

INDEX 501

PROJECTIVE GEOMETRY

CHAPTER I

FOUNDATIONS

1. Plan of the chapter. In the first volume of this book we have been concerned with general projective geometry, that is to say, with those theorems which are consequences of Assumptions A, E, P. In many cases we also made use of Assumption H_0, but most of the theorems which we proved by the aid of this assumption remain true (though trivial) when this assumption is false. The class of spaces to which the geometry of Vol. I applies is very large, and the set of assumptions used is therefore far from categorical.

The main purpose of geometry is, of course, to serve as a theory of that space in which we envisage ourselves and external nature. This purpose can be accomplished only partially by a geometry based on a set of assumptions which is not categorical. We therefore proceed to add the assumptions which are necessary in order to limit attention to the geometry of reals, the geometry in which the number system is the real number system of analysis.

These assumptions are stated in two ways, the one (§ 3) dependent on the theory of the real number system and the other (§§ 7–13) independent of it. We also state the assumptions (§§ 5, 14, 15, 16) necessary for certain other geometries which are of importance because of their relations to the real geometry and to other branches of mathematics. At the end of the chapter we give a summary of the assumptions for the various projective geometries which we are considering.

2. List of Assumptions A, E, P, and H_0. For the sake of having all the assumptions before us in the present chapter, we reprint A, E, P, and H_0. The assumptions serve to determine a class S of elements called points, and a class of subclasses of S called lines. The phrase "a point is on a line" or "a line is on a point" means that the point belongs to the line (cf. p. 16, Vol. I).

ASSUMPTIONS OF ALIGNMENT:

A 1. *If A and B are distinct points, there is at least one line on both A and B.*

A 2. *If A and B are distinct points, there is not more than one line on both A and B.*

A 3. *If A, B, C are points not all on the same line, and D and E ($D \neq E$) are points such that B, C, D are on a line and C, A, E are on a line, there is a point F such that A, B, F are on a line and also D, E, F are on a line.*

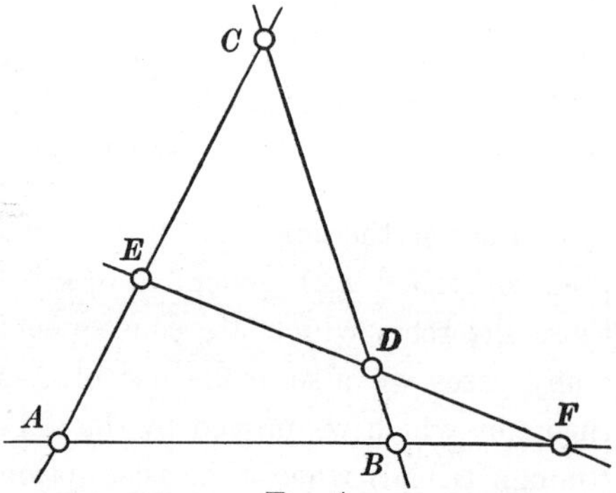

FIG. 1

ASSUMPTIONS OF EXTENSION:

E 0. *There are at least three points on every line.*

E 1. *There exists at least one line.*

E 2. *All points are not on the same line.*

E 3. *All points are not on the same plane.**

E 3′. *If S_3 is a three-space,† every point is on S_3.*

ASSUMPTION OF PROJECTIVITY:

P. *If a projectivity leaves each of three distinct points of a line invariant, it leaves every point of the line invariant.‡*

ASSUMPTION H_0:

H_0. *The diagonal points of a complete quadrangle are noncollinear.§*

As was explained when Assumption P was first introduced, this assumption does not appear in the complete list of assumptions for the geometry of reals, but is replaced by certain other assumptions from which it (as well as H_0) can be derived as a theorem. The list of assumptions for this geometry will consist of Assumptions A, E, and the new assumptions.

* Cf. § 7, Vol. I.

† Cf. § 9, Vol. I.

‡ Cf. § 35, Vol. I.

§ Cf. § 18, Vol. I.

3. Assumption K. The most summary way of completing the list of assumptions for the geometry of reals is to introduce the following:

K. *A geometric number system* (Chap. VI, Vol. I) *is isomorphic* with the real number system of analysis.*

Thus a complete list of assumptions for the geometry of reals is A, E, K.

The use of Assumption K implies a previous knowledge of the real number system.† Its apparent simplicity therefore masks certain real difficulties. What these difficulties are from a geometric point of view will be found on reading §§ 7–13, where K is analyzed into independent statements H, C, R. These sections, however, may be omitted, if desired, on a first reading.

Since a geometric number system in one one-dimensional form is isomorphic with any geometric number system in any one-dimensional form in the same space, it is evident that the principle of duality is valid for all theorems deducible from Assumptions A, E, K.

In order that the results of Vol. I be applicable to the geometry of reals, it must be shown that Assumption P is a logical consequence of Assumptions A, E, K. Since multiplication is commutative in the real number system, this result would follow directly from Theorem 7, Chap. VI, Vol. I. The proof there given is, however, incomplete. It is shown (Theorem 6, loc. cit.) that if P holds, multiplication is commutative; but it is not there proved that if multiplication is commutative, P is satisfied. The needed proof may be made as follows:

THEOREM 1. *Assumption* P *is valid in any space satisfying Assumptions* A *and* E *and such that multiplication is commutative in a geometric number system* (Chap. VI, Vol. I).

Proof. It is obvious that the number systems determined by any two choices of the fundamental points $H_0H_1H_\infty$ are isomorphic (cf. Theorems 1 and 3, Chap. VI, Vol. I), so that we may base our argument on an arbitrary choice of these points. We are assuming that multiplication is commutative, and are to prove that any projectivity Π

* This term is defined in § 52, Vol. I.

† The real number system is to be thought of either as defined in terms which rest ultimately on the positive integers (cf. Pierpont, Theory of Functions of Real Variables, pp. 1–94; or Fine, College Algebra, pp. 1–70) or by means of a set of postulates (cf. E. V. Huntington, Transactions of the American Mathematical Society, Vol. VI (1905), p. 17).

which leaves three distinct points of a line fixed is the identity. By definition, Π is the resultant of a sequence of perspectivities

$$[H] \overset{S_1}{\underset{\wedge}{=}} [P_1] \overset{S_2}{\underset{\wedge}{=}} \cdots \overset{S_n}{\underset{\wedge}{=}} [\Pi(H)]$$

where $[H]$ denotes the points of the given line. By Theorem 5, Chap. III, Vol. I, this chain of perspectivities may be replaced by three perspectivities

$$[H] \overset{S}{\underset{\wedge}{=}} [P] \overset{T}{\underset{\wedge}{=}} [Q] \overset{U}{\underset{\wedge}{=}} [\Pi(H)].$$

Moreover, by Theorem 4, Chap. III, Vol. I, the pencils $[P]$ and $[Q]$ may be chosen so that their respective axes pass through two of the given fixed points of Π. Let us denote these points by H_x and H_y

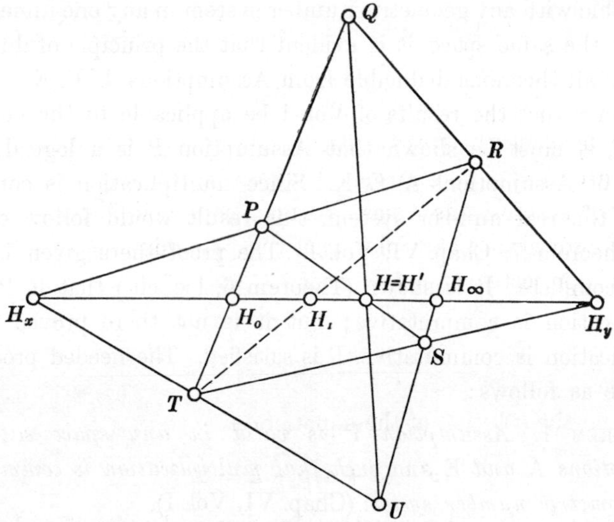

FIG. 2

respectively and let H_∞ be the third fixed point. By another application of Theorem 4 the pencils $[P]$ and $[Q]$ may be chosen so that their common point R is on the line SH_∞ (fig. 2).

Now, since H_∞ is transformed into itself, S, H_∞, and U must be collinear. Since H_x is fixed, T, H_x, and U must be collinear. Since H_y is fixed, S, T, and H_y are collinear. If H is any point of the line H_xH_y, it is transformed by the perspectivity with S as center to a point P of the line H_xR; the perspectivity with T as center transforms P to a point Q of the line RH_y; the perspectivity with U as center transforms Q back to a point H' of the line H_xH_y. We have to show that $H' = H$.

Let H_0 be the trace on the line H_xH_y of PT; let H_1 be the trace of RT; and H' is the trace of UQ.

The complete quadrangle $TRSP$ determines Q $(H_0H_yH_1,\ H_\infty H_xH)$, and hence (Theorem 3, Chap. VI, Vol. I) in the scale $H_0H_1H_\infty$

$$H_y \cdot H_x = H.$$

The complete quadrangle $TRQU$ determines Q $(H_0H_xH_1,\ H_\infty H_yH')$, and hence in the scale $H_0H_1H_\infty$

$$H_x \cdot H_y = H'.$$

Since multiplication is commutative, $H = H'$, which proves the theorem

The reader will find no difficulty in using the construction above to prove that the validity of the theorem of Pappus (§ 36, Vol. I) is necessary and sufficient for the commutative law of multiplication and for Assumption P.

4. Double points of projectivities. Definition. A projective transformation of a real line into itself is said to be *hyperbolic*, *parabolic*, or *elliptic*,* according as it has two, one, or no double points.

It was proved in § 58, Vol. I, that the determination of the double points of a projective transformation†

$$(1)\qquad \begin{aligned} \rho x_0' &= ax_0 + bx_1 \\ \rho x_1' &= cx_0 + dx_1 \end{aligned}$$

depends on the solution of the equation

$$(2)\qquad \rho^2 - (a+d)\rho + \Delta = 0,$$

where $\Delta = ad - bc$. This equation has two real roots if and only if its discriminant

$$(a+d)^2 - 4\Delta$$

is positive. Hence we have

If $\Delta < 0$, *the transformation* (1) *is hyperbolic. For an elliptic or parabolic projectivity* Δ *is always positive.*

* These terms are derived from the corresponding types of conic sections (see § 37). In a complex one-dimensional form a somewhat different terminology is used (cf. § 98).

† In this volume we shall generally write homogeneous coördinates in the form (x_0, x_1), whereas in Vol. I we used (x_1, x_2).

In case the projectivity (1) is an involution, $a = -d$ (§ 54, Vol. I), and hence -4Δ is the discriminant of (2). Hence

An involution is elliptic or hyperbolic according as Δ *is positive or negative.*

The intimate connection of these theorems with the theory of linear order is evident on comparison with the first sections of Chap. II. A deduction of the corresponding theorems from the intuitive conceptions of order is to be found in Chap. IV of the Geometria Projettiva of Enriques.

EXERCISE

A projectivity for which $\Delta > 0$ is a product of two hyperbolic involutions. A projectivity for which $\Delta < 0$ is a product of three hyperbolic involutions.

5. Complex geometry. Assumption K provides for the solution of many problems of construction which could not be solved in a net of rationality. But even in the real space the fundamental problem of finding the double points of an involution has no general solution.

To see this it is only necessary to set up an involution for which $\Delta > 0$. Take any involution of which two pairs of conjugate points AA' and BB' form a harmonic set $H(AA', BB')$. If the scale P_0, P_1, P_∞ is chosen so that $A = P_0$, $A' = P_\infty$, $B = P_1$, then $B' = P_{-1}$ and the involution is represented by the bilinear equation (§ 54, Vol. I)

$$xx' = -1.$$

The double points of this involution, if existent, would satisfy the equation

$$x^2 = -1,$$

which has no real roots.

An effect of Assumption K is thus to deny the possibility of solving this problem. If, however, we negate Assumption K and replace it by properly chosen other assumptions, we are led to a geometry in which this problem is always soluble, namely, the geometry of the space in which the geometric number system is isomorphic with the complex number system of analysis. Although this geometry does not have the same relation to the space of external nature as the real geometry, it is extremely important because of its relation to other branches of mathematics.

One way of founding this geometry is to replace Assumption K by another assumption of an equally summary character, namely,

J. *A geometric number system is isomorphic with the complex number system of analysis.*

Since this number system obeys the commutative law of multiplication, the corresponding geometry satisfies Assumption P, and all the theorems of Vol. I apply. Thus, a set of postulates for the complex geometry is A, E, J.

The problem of finding the double points of a one-dimensional projectivity is completely solvable in the complex geometry; for any such projectivity may be represented by the bilinear equation (§ 54, Vol. I)

$$cxx' + dx' - ax - b = 0,$$

and therefore its double points are given by the roots of

$$cx^2 + (d - a)x - b = 0,$$

which exist in the complex number system.

The analogous result holds good for an n-dimensional projectivity. In this case the problem reduces to that of finding the roots of an algebraic equation of the nth degree.

6. Imaginary elements adjoined to a real space. In this connection it is desirable to think of another point of view which we may adopt toward the complex space. Suppose we are working in a real geometry on the basis of A, E, K (or of A, E, H, C, R; see below). It is a theorem about the real number system* that it is contained in a number system (the complex number system) all of whose elements are of the form $ai + b$ where a and b are real and i satisfies the equation

$$i^2 + 1 = 0.$$

Hence it is a theorem about the real space that it is contained in another space which contains the double points of any given involution.

This may be seen in detail as follows: By the theory of homogeneous coördinates the points of a real projective space S are in a correspondence with the ordered tetrads of real numbers (x_0, x_1, x_2, x_3), except (0, 0, 0, 0), such that to each tetrad corresponds one point, and to each point a set of tetrads, given by the expression $(mx_0, mx_1,$

* This same question is discussed from the point of view of a general space and a general field in Chap. IX, Vol. I.

mx_2, mx_3) where x_0, x_1, x_2, x_3 are fixed and m takes on all real number values except zero. By the property of the real number system mentioned above, the set of all ordered tetrads of real numbers is contained in the set of all ordered tetrads (z_0, z_1, z_2, z_3) where z_0, z_1, z_2, z_3 are complex numbers.

Let us define a *complex point* as the class of all ordered tetrads of complex numbers of the form

$$(kz_0, kz_1, kz_2, kz_3)$$

where for a given class z_0, z_1, z_2, z_3 are fixed and not all zero and k takes on all complex values different from zero. Let the set of these classes satisfying two independent linear equations

$$\begin{aligned} a_0z_0 + a_1z_1 + a_2z_2 + a_3z_3 &= 0, \\ b_0z_0 + b_1z_1 + b_2z_2 + b_3z_3 &= 0 \end{aligned} \tag{3}$$

be called a *complex line.* With these conventions it is easy to see that the set of all complex points and complex lines satisfies the assumptions A, E, P, and thus the complex points constitute a proper projective space. Let us call this space S_c.

The space S_c contains the set of all complex points of the form

$$(kx_0, kx_1, kx_2, kx_3)$$

where x_0, x_1, x_2, x_3 are all real. Let us call this subset of complex points S_r. If any set of complex points of S_r which satisfy two equations of the form (3) with real coefficients be called a "real line," we have, by reference to the homogeneous coördinate system in S, that the complex points of S_r are in such a one-to-one correspondence with the points of S that to every line in S corresponds a "real line" in S_r, and conversely.

Thus, S_r is a real projective space and is contained in the complex projective space S_c. Obviously S may also be regarded as contained in a complex projective space S' where S' consists of the points of S together with the points of S_c which are not in S_r, and where each line of S' consists of the complex points of S' which satisfy two equations of the form (3) together with the points of S whose coördinates satisfy the same two equations.

DEFINITION. Points of the real space S are called *real* points, and points of the extended space S', *complex* points. Points in S' but not in S are called *imaginary* points.

This discussion of imaginary elements does not require a detailed knowledge or study of the complex number system as such. It is, in fact, a special case of the more general theory in Chap. IX, Vol. I (cf. particularly § 92), which applies to a general projective space. It serves in a large variety of cases where it is sufficient to know merely the *existence* of the complex space S′ containing S and satisfying Assumptions A, E, P. It is a logically exact way of stating the point of view of the geometers who used imaginary points before the advent of the modern function theory.

There are problems, however, which require a detailed study of the complex space, and this implies, of course, a study of the complex number system and such geometrical subjects as the theory of chains (see §§ 11, 12, below, and later chapters).

There is a very elegant and historically important method of introducing imaginaries in geometry without the use of coördinates, namely, that due to von Staudt.* It depends essentially on the properties of involutions which are developed in Chap. VIII, Vol. I, and §§ 74–75 of this volume. The reader will find it an excellent exercise to generalize the Von Staudt theory so as to obtain the result stated in Proposition K_2, Chap. IX, Vol. I.

7. Harmonic sequence. We shall now take up a more searching study of the assumptions of the geometry of reals. In Chap. IV, Vol. I, it was proved that every space satisfying Assumptions A, E contains a net of rationality R^3, and that this net is itself a three-space which satisfies not only Assumptions A and E but also Assumption P (Theorem 20). To this rational subspace, therefore, apply all the theorems in Vol. I which do not depend essentially on Assumption H_0. For example, every line of R^3 is a linear net of rationality and may be regarded (with the exception of one point chosen as ∞) as a commutative number system all of whose numbers are expressible as rational combinations of 0 and 1.

Throughout Vol. I we left the character of this net indeterminate. It might contain only a finite number of points or it might contain an infinite number. We propose now to introduce a new assumption which will fix definitely the structure of a net of rationality.

* Cf. K. G. C. von Staudt, Beiträge zur Geometrie der Lage, Nürnberg (1856 and 1857). J. Lüroth, Mathematische Annalen, Vol. VIII (1874), p. 145. Segre, Memorie della R. Accademia delle scienze di Torino (2), Vol. XXXVIII (1886).

DEFINITION. Let H_0, H_1, H_∞ be any three distinct points of a line h; let S and T be two distinct points collinear with H_∞ but not on h; and let K_0 be a point of intersection of SH_0 and TH_1. Denote the

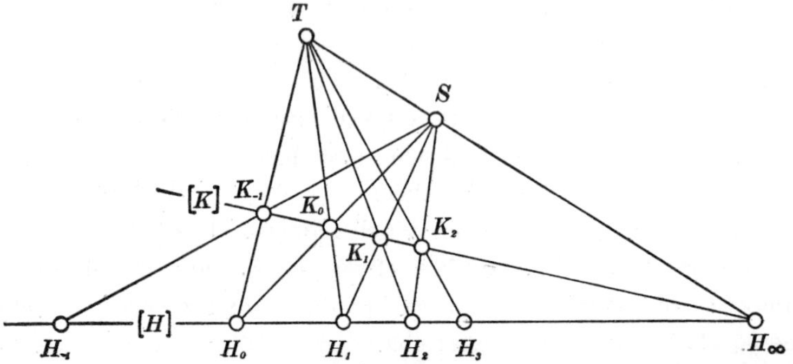

FIG. 3

points of the line h by $[H]$ and those of the line K_0H_∞ by $[K]$, and let Π be a projectivity defined by perspectivities as follows:

$$[H] \overset{S}{\underset{\wedge}{=}} [K] \overset{T}{\underset{\wedge}{=}} [\Pi(H)].$$

The set of points

$$H_0, \quad H_1, \quad H_2, \quad \cdots, \quad H_i, \quad H_{i+1}, \quad \cdots$$

such that $\Pi(H_i) = H_{i+1}$, together with the set

$$\cdots \quad H_{-i-1}, \quad H_{-i}, \quad \cdots, \quad H_{-2}, \quad H_{-1}$$

such that $\Pi(H_{-i-1}) = H_{-i}$, is called a *harmonic sequence.* The point H_∞ is not in the sequence but is called its *limit point.*

The projectivity Π is evidently parabolic and carries H_0 to H_1.

THEOREM 2. *The middle one of any three consecutive* points of a harmonic sequence is the harmonic conjugate of the limit point of the sequence with regard to the other two.*

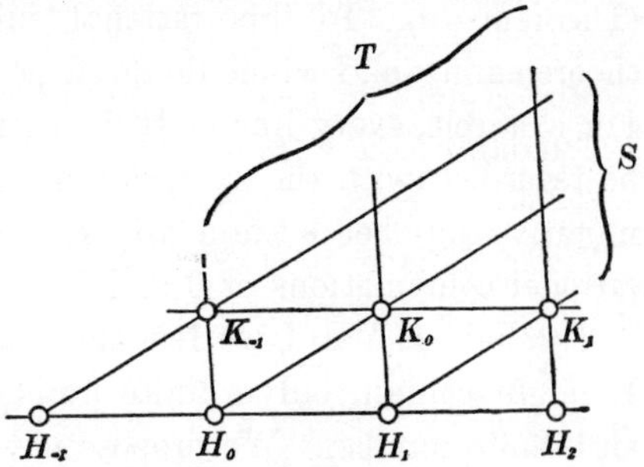

FIG. 4

Proof. By construction we have

$$\mathrm{Q}(H_\infty H_i H_{i+1}, \quad H_\infty H_{i+2} H_{i+1}).$$

* This term refers to the subscripts in the notation H_j.

Corollary. *All points of a harmonic sequence belong to the same net of rationality.*

Theorem 3. *Two harmonic sequences determined by* H_0, H_1, H_∞ *and by* M_0, M_1, M_∞ *are projective in any projectivity* Π *by which*

$$H_0H_1H_\infty \barwedge M_0M_1M_\infty.$$

Proof. By Theorem 3, Chap. IV, Vol. I, the projectivity Π transforms harmonic sets of points into harmonic sets.

8. Assumption H. By reference to fig. 3 it is intuitively evident to most observers that in any picture which can be drawn representing points by dots, and lines by marks drawn with the aid of a straightedge, no point H_i which can be accurately marked will ever coincide with $H_j (i \neq j)$. On the other hand, there is nothing in Assumptions A and E to prove that $H_i \neq H_j$, because (Introduction, § 2, Vol. I) these assumptions are all satisfied by the miniature spaces discussed in § 72, Chap. VII, Vol. I, and if the number of points on a line is finite, the sequence must surely repeat itself. Thus we are led to make a further assumption.

Assumption H.* *If any harmonic sequence exists, not every one contains only a finite number of points.*

The existence of a harmonic sequence determined by any three points follows directly from Assumptions A and E. That any two sequences are projective follows from Theorem 3. Hence Assumption H gives at once

Theorem 4. *Any three distinct collinear points* H_0, H_1, H_∞ *determine a harmonic sequence containing an infinite number of points and having* H_0 *and* H_1 *as consecutive points and* H_∞ *as the limit point.*

Theorem 5. *The principle of duality is valid for all theorems deducible from Assumptions* A, E, H.

Proof. This principle has been proved in Chap. I, Vol. I, for all theorems deducible from A and E. If $\eta_0, \eta_1, \eta_\infty$ are any three planes on a line l, let a line l' meet them in H_0, H_1, H_∞ respectively. The projection by l of the harmonic sequence determined on l' by H_0, H_1, H_∞ is the space dual of a harmonic sequence of points. Since the

* Cf. Gino Fano, Giornale di Matematiche, Vol. XXX (1892), p. 106. Obviously Assumption H_0 (Vol. I, p. 45) is a consequence of H. Hence, after introducing Assumption H, we have that a net of rationality satisfies not only A, E, P but also H_0, and thus every theorem in Vol. I can be applied to a net of rationality.

sequence of points is infinite, so is the sequence of planes. Hence the space dual of Assumption H is true. The principle of duality in a plane or a bundle follows as in § 11, Chap. I, Vol. I.

By reference to the definition of addition in Chap. VI, Vol. I, it is evident on the basis of Assumptions A and E alone that the transformation $x' = x + a$ is a parabolic projectivity. Denoting it by α, it is clear that if there is any integer n such that α^n is the identity, then $\alpha^{nk+m} = \alpha^m$, k and m being any integers. Hence, if α has a finite period, there is only a finite number of points in a harmonic sequence, contrary to Assumption H. Hence

THEOREM 6. *A parabolic projectivity never has a finite period. In other words, if of three points determining a harmonic sequence the limit point is taken as* ∞ *in a scale and two consecutive points as 0 and 1, then the sequence consists of*

$$\begin{array}{ll} 0 & \\ 1 & -1 \\ 1+1=2 & -1-1=-2 \\ 2+1=3 & -2-1=-3 \\ 3+1=4 & -3-1=-4 \\ \vdots & \vdots \end{array}$$

that is, of zero and all positive and negative integers.

COROLLARY 1. *The net of rationality determined by 0, 1,* ∞ *consists of zero and all numbers of the form* $\frac{m}{n}$ *where* m *and* n *are positive or negative integers.*

Proof. By Theorem 14, Chap. VI, Vol. I, the net of rationality determined by 0, 1, ∞ consists of all numbers obtainable from 0 and 1 by the operations of addition, multiplication, subtraction, and division (excluding division by zero).

COROLLARY 2. *The homogeneous coördinates of any point in a linear planar or spatial net of rationality may be taken as integers.*

Proof. If x_0, x_1, x_2, x_3 are the homogeneous coördinates of a point in the net, they are defined, according to Chap. VII, Vol. I, in terms of the coördinates in certain linear nets. Hence they may be taken in the form 0 or $\frac{m_1}{n_1}$ where m_1 and n_1 are integers. If m is the product of their denominators, mx_0, mx_1, mx_2, mx_3 are integers.

The first of these corollaries enables us to obtain the following simple result with regard to the construction of any point in a net of rationality. Let $H_{\frac{1}{n}}$ be the harmonic conjugate of H_n with regard to H_1 and H_{-1}. The sequence

$$\cdots,\ H_{-\frac{1}{3}},\ H_{-\frac{1}{2}},\ H_{-1},\ H_{\infty},\ H_1,\ H_{\frac{1}{2}},\ H_{\frac{1}{3}},\ \cdots$$

is projective (fig. 5) with

$$H_{-3},\ H_{-2},\ H_{-1},\ H_0,\ H_1,\ H_2,\ H_3,\ \cdots$$

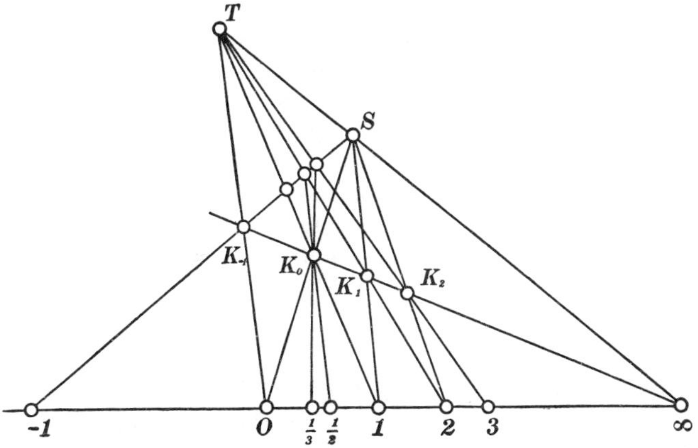

FIG. 5

and therefore must be harmonic. The points H_0, $H_{\frac{1}{n}}$, H_∞ determine a harmonic sequence

$$\cdots,\ H_{-\frac{3}{n}},\ H_{-\frac{2}{n}},\ H_{-\frac{1}{n}},\ H_0,\ H_{\frac{1}{n}},\ H_{\frac{2}{n}},\ H_{\frac{3}{n}},\ \cdots.$$

By Cor. 1, any point of the net of rationality is contained in a sequence of the last variety for some value of n.

9. Order in a net of rationality. DEFINITION. If A and B are points of $\mathsf{R}(H_0H_1H_\infty)$ different from H_∞, A is said to *precede* B with respect to the scale H_0, H_1, H_∞ if and only if the nonhomogeneous coördinate (cf. § 53, Vol. I) of A is less than the nonhomogeneous coördinate of B. If A precedes B, B is said to *follow* A.

From the corresponding properties of the rational numbers there follow at once the fundamental propositions: With respect to the scale H_0, H_1, H_∞, (1) if A precedes B, B does not precede A; (2) if A precedes B and B precedes C, then A precedes C; (3) if A and B are distinct points of $\mathsf{R}(H_0H_1H_\infty)$, then either A precedes B or B precedes A.

The use of the properties of numbers in the argument above and in analogous cases does not imply that our treatment of geometry is dependent on analytical foundations. Every theorem which we employ here is a logical consequence of the assumptions A, E, H alone.

The argument which is involved in the present case may be stated as follows: The coördinates relative to a scale H_0, H_1, H_∞ of the points

$$\cdots, H_{-2}, H_{-1}, H_0, H_1, H_2, \cdots$$

of a harmonic sequence, when combined according to the rules for addition and multiplication given in Chap. VI, Vol. I, satisfy the conditions which are known to characterize the system of positive and negative integers (including zero). From these conditions (the axioms of the system of positive and negative integers) follow theorems which state the order relations among these integers, and also theorems which state the order relations among the rational numbers, the latter being defined in terms of the integers. But by Theorem 6, Cor. 1, the rational numbers are the coördinates of points in $\mathsf{R}(H_0H_1H_\infty)$. Hence the points of $\mathsf{R}(H_0H_1H_\infty)$ satisfy the conditions given above.

It would of course be entirely feasible to make the discussion of order in a net of rationality without the use of coördinates.

***10. Cuts in a net of rationality.** DEFINITION. Two subsets, $[A]$ and $[B]$, of a net of rationality $\mathsf{R}(H_0H_1H_\infty)$ constitute a *cut* (A, B) *with respect to the scale* H_0, H_1, H_∞ if and only if they satisfy the following conditions: (1) Every point of the net except H_∞ is in $[A]$ or $[B]$; (2) with respect to the scale H_0, H_1, H_∞ every point of $[A]$ precedes every point of $[B]$. If there is a point O in $[A]$ or in $[B]$ such that every point of $[A]$ distinct from O precedes it and every point of $[B]$ distinct from O follows it, the cut is said to be *closed* and to have O as its *cut-point;* otherwise the cut is said to be *open.* The class $[A]$ is said to be the *lower side* and $[B]$ to be the *upper side* of the cut.

With respect to the scale H_0, H_1, H_∞ any point $O\,(O \neq H_\infty)$ of a net $\mathsf{R}(H_0H_1H_\infty)$ determines two sets of points $[A]$ and $[B]$ such that every A precedes or is identical with O and O precedes every B. These sets of points are therefore a closed cut having O as cut-point. Not every cut, however, is closed, for consider the set $[A]$, including all points whose coördinates in a system of nonhomogeneous coördinates having H_∞ as the point ∞ are negative or, if positive, such that their squares are less than 2; and the set $[B]$, including all points whose

* An asterisk at the left of a section number indicates that the section may be omitted on a first reading. We have marked in this manner most of the sections which are not essential to an understanding of the discussion of metric geometry in Chaps. III and IV.

coördinates are positive and have their squares greater than 2. Since no rational number can satisfy the equation

$$x^2 = 2,$$

this equation is not satisfied by the coördinates of any point in the net. The sets $[A]$ and $[B]$ constitute an open cut.

DEFINITION. With respect to the scale H_0, H_1, H_∞, an open cut *precedes* all the points of its upper side and *is preceded by* all points of its lower side. A closed cut *precedes* all the points which its cut-point precedes and *is preceded by* all points by which its cut-point is preceded. A cut (A, B) *precedes* a cut (C, D) if and only if there is a point B preceding a point C.

THEOREM 7. (1) *If a cut (A, B) precedes a cut (C, D), then (C, D) does not precede (A, B).*

(2) *If a cut (A, B) is not the same as the cut (C, D), then either (A, B) precedes (C, D) or (C, D) precedes (A, B), or both cuts are closed and have the same cut-point.*

(3) *If a cut (A, B) precedes a cut (C, D) and (C, D) precedes a cut (E, F), then (A, B) precedes (E, F).*

Proof. These propositions are direct consequences of the definition above and of the corresponding properties of the relation of precedence between points.

DEFINITION. With respect to the scale H_0, H_1, H_∞, a cut (A_1, A_2) is said to be *between* two cuts (B_1, B_2) and (C_1, C_2) in case (B_1, B_2) precedes (A_1, A_2) and (A_1, A_2) precedes (C_1, C_2) or in case (C_1, C_2) precedes (A_1, A_2) and (A_1, A_2) precedes (B_1, B_2). If any one of these cuts is closed, it may be replaced by its corresponding cut-point in this definition. (Thus, for example, any open cut is between any point of its upper side and any point of its lower side.)

An open cut (A, B) is said to be algebraic if there exists an equation,

$$a_0x^n + a_1x^{n-1} + \cdots + a_n = 0,$$

with integral coefficients, and two points A_0, B_0, such that the coördinates of all points of $[A]$ between A_0 and B_0 make the left-hand member of this equation greater than zero and all points of $[B]$ between A_0 and B_0 make it less than zero.* If it is assumed that this equation has a root between A_0 and B_0, this is equivalent to assuming that there exists a point corresponding to the cut (A, B) on the line A_0B_0 but not in the given net.

* It is perhaps needless to remark that not every algebraic equation with integral coefficients can be associated in this way with a cut. For example, $x^2 + 1 = 0$.

For the purposes of geometric constructions it would be sufficient to assume the existence of cut-points for all algebraic open cuts (see Chap. IX, Vol. I). For many purposes, indeed, it would be desirable to make the assumption referred to on p. 97, Chap. IV, Vol. I, and which we here put down for reference as Assumption Q.

ASSUMPTION Q. *There is not more than one net of rationality on a line.*

But it is customary in analysis to assume the existence of an irrational number corresponding to every open cut in the system of rationals, and it is convenient in geometry to have a one-to-one correspondence between the points of a line and the system of real numbers. Hence we make the assumption which follows in the next section.

It must not be supposed that in the assumption which follows we are introducing new points in any respect different from those already considered. What we are doing is to postulate that a space is a class of points having certain additional properties. The assumption limits the type of space which we consider; it does not extend the class of points. In this respect our procedure is not parallel to the genetic method of developing the theory of irrational numbers.

EXERCISE

The points of $\mathsf{R}(H_0H_1H_\infty)$, together with the open cuts with respect to the scale H_0, H_1, H_∞, constitute a set $[X]$ of things having the following property: If $[S]$ and $[T]$ are any two subclasses of $[X]$ including all X's and such that every S precedes every T, then there is either an S or a T which precedes all other T's and is preceded by all other S's.

***11. Assumption of continuity.** We shall denote the cut-point of a closed cut (M, N) by $P_{(M,N)}$. In the following assumption it is not stated whether the cuts (A_1, A_2), (B_1, B_2), and (D_1, D_2) are open or closed. If one of them is closed, therefore, the corresponding one of the symbols $P_{(A_1,A_2)}$, $P_{(B_1,B_2)}$, and $P_{(D_1,D_2)}$ must be understood in the sense just defined.

ASSUMPTION C. *If every net of rationality contains an infinity of points, then on one line l in one net $\mathsf{R}(H_0H_1H_\infty)$ there is associated with every open cut (A, B), with respect to the scale H_0, H_1, H_∞, a point $P_{(A,B)}$ which is on l and such that the following conditions are satisfied:*

(1) *If two open cuts (A, B) and (C, D) are distinct, the points $P_{(A,B)}$ and $P_{(C,D)}$ are distinct;*

(2) *If (A_1, A_2) and (B_1, B_2) are any two cuts and (C_1, C_2) any open cut between two points A and B of $\mathsf{R}(H_0H_1H_\infty)$, and if T is a projectivity such that*

$$\mathrm{T}(H_\infty AB) = H_\infty P_{(A_1,A_2)} P_{(B_1,B_2)},$$

then $\mathrm{T}(P_{(C_1,C_2)})$ is a point associated with some cut (D_1, D_2) between (A_1, A_2) and (B_1, B_2).

DEFINITION. The set of all points of $\mathsf{R}(H_0H_1H_\infty)$, together with all points associated with cuts in $\mathsf{R}(H_0H_1H_\infty)$, with respect to the scale H_0, H_1, H_∞, is called the *chain* $\mathsf{C}(H_0H_1H_\infty)$. The points of $\mathsf{R}(H_0H_1H_\infty)$ are called *rational*, and any other point of the chain is called *irrational* with respect to $\mathsf{R}(H_0H_1H_\infty)$. A point associated with a cut which follows H_0 is called *positive*, and one associated with a cut which precedes H_0 is called *negative*.

THEOREM 8. *The point $P_{(A,B)}$, associated, by Assumption* C, *with an open cut* (A, B) *of* $\mathsf{R}(H_0H_1H_\infty)$, *is not a point of* $\mathsf{R}(H_0H_1H_\infty)$.

Proof. The associated point could not be H_∞, because there are projectivities of $\mathsf{R}(H_0H_1H_\infty)$ which leave H_∞ invariant and change the given cut into different cuts, and therefore, by Assumption C, change the associated point. Now suppose a point D, distinct from H_∞ but in $\mathsf{R}(H_0H_1H_\infty)$, to be associated with some open cut. Since the given cut is open, there must be a point A between D and the cut. If B is a point on the opposite side of the cut from D, A and B both precede or both follow D with respect to the scale H_0, H_1, H_∞. The transformation which changes every point of l into its harmonic conjugate with regard to H_∞ and D has, when regarded as a transformation of the points of $\mathsf{R}(H_0H_1H_\infty)$ with respect to the scale H_0, H_1, H_∞, the equation

$$x' = 2d - x,$$

where d is the coördinate of D. It therefore transforms rational points which follow D into rational points which precede it, and vice versa. Hence A and B are transformed into two points, A' and B', which precede D if A and B follow D, or which follow D if A and B precede D. By Assumption C (2), the point D which is associated with an open cut between A and B is transformed into a point D' associated with a cut between A' and B'. By Assumption C (1), D' is distinct from D, contrary to the hypothesis that D is a fixed point of the transformation.

THEOREM 9. *The points of* $\mathsf{C}(H_0H_1H_\infty)$, *excluding* H_∞, *form, with reference to the scale in which* $H_0 = 0$, $H_1 = 1$, $H_\infty = \infty$, *a number system isomorphic with the real number system of analysis.*

Proof. The definitions of Chap. VI, Vol. I, give a meaning to the operations of addition and multiplication for all points of the line l. In that place we derived all the fundamental laws of operation, except the commutative law of multiplication, on the basis of Assumptions A and E. We have also seen in the present chapter (Theorem 6, Cor. 1) that the coördinates of points in $\mathsf{R}(H_0 H_1 H_\infty)$ are the ordinary rational numbers. Hence it remains to show that the geometric laws of combination as applied to the irrational points of $\mathsf{C}(H_0 H_1 H_\infty)$ are the same as for the ordinary irrational numbers.

The analytic definition of addition of irrational numbers* may be stated as follows: If a and b are two numbers defined by cuts (x_1, y_1) and (x_2, y_2), then $a + b$ is the number defined by the cut $(x_1 + x_2, y_1 + y_2)$.

To show that our geometric number system satisfies this condition in $\mathsf{C}(H_0 H_1 H_\infty)$, suppose first that a is a rational point of $\mathsf{C}(H_0 H_1 H_\infty)$ and b an irrational point. The projective transformation

$$(4) \qquad x' = x + a$$

changes the set of points $[x_2]$ into the set $[x_2 + a]$, which is the same as $[x_2 + x_1]$. Similarly, it changes $[y_2]$ into $[y_2 + y_1]$. Hence, it changes the cut (x_2, y_2) into $(x_1 + x_2, y_1 + y_2)$, and hence, by Assumption C (2), changes b into a point determined by a cut which lies between every pair $x_1 + x_2$ and $y_1 + y_2$. Therefore b is changed into the point associated with the cut $(x_1 + x_2, y_1 + y_2)$. But the transform of b is $a + b$. Hence the geometric sum $a + b$ is the number defined by the cut $(x_1 + x_2, y_1 + y_2)$.

Next, suppose both a and b irrational. The transformation (4) changes $[x_2]$ into the set of irrational points $[x_2 + a]$, b into $b + a$, and $[y_2]$ into $[y_2 + a]$. By the paragraph above, the cut which defines any $x_2 + a$ precedes the cut which defines any $y_2 + a$. Hence, by Assumption C (2), the cut which defines any point $x_2 + a$ precedes the cut which defines $b + a$, and this precedes the cut which defines $y_2 + a$. Any point $x_1 + x_2$ of the lower side of the cut $(x_1 + x_2, y_1 + y_2)$ precedes the cut defining one of the points $x_2 + a$, by the paragraph above, and hence precedes the cut defining $b + a$. Similarly, any point of the upper side of this cut follows the cut defining $b + a$. Hence $(x_1 + x_2, y_1 + y_2)$ is the cut defining $b + a$. Thus we have identified geometric addition of points in $\mathsf{C}(H_0 H_1 H_\infty)$ with the addition of ordinary real numbers.

* Cf. Fine, College Algebra, p. 50; or Veblen and Lennes, Infinitesimal Analysis, Chap. I.

The analytic definition of multiplication of irrational numbers may be stated as follows: If a and b are positive numbers defined by the cuts (x_1, y_1) and (x_2, y_2), let $[x_1']$ be the set of positive values of x_1. Then ab is the number defined by the cut $(x_1'x_2, y_1y_2)$. If a is negative and b positive, $ab = -(-a)b$. If a is positive and b negative, $ab = -(a(-b))$. If both a and b are negative, $ab = (-a)(-b)$. If $a = 0$ or $b = 0$, $ab = 0$.

Consider the transformation

$$x' = ax.$$

If a is positive and rational while b is positive and irrational, this transforms $[x_2]$ into $[ax_2]$, which is the same as $[x_1'x_2]$. It also transforms b into ab and $[y_2]$ into $[ay_2]$, which is the same as $[y_1y_2]$. Hence, by Assumption C (2), ab is the number associated with $(x_1'x_2, y_1y_2)$.

If both a and b are irrational and positive, we again have $[x_2]$, b, and $[y_2]$ transformed into $[ax_2]$, ab, and $[ay_2]$, where, as in the analogous case of addition, the cut defining ax_2 precedes the cut defining ab, which in turn precedes the cut defining ay_2. Moreover, any $x_1'x_2$ precedes some ax_2, and any y_1y_2 follows some ay_2. Hence, by the same argument as in the case of addition, $(x_1'x_2, y_1y_2)$ is the cut with which ab is associated.

The transformation

$$x' = (-1)x$$

changes the cut (x_1, x_2) defining the irrational number a into the open cut $(-x_2, -x_1)$, which therefore defines an irrational a'. But since $x_1 - x_2$ may be any negative rational and $x_2 - x_1$ may be any positive rational, the sum of a and a', which has been proved to be determined by the cut $(x_1 - x_2, x_2 - x_1)$, must be zero. Hence we have that $(-1)a$ is the irrational $-a$ such that $-a + a = 0$.

The transformation

$$x' = x(-1)$$

is the same as $x' = (-1)x$ for all rational points. Hence, by Assumption C (2), these transformations are the same for all points of $\mathsf{C}(H_0H_1H_\infty)$. Hence, for points of $\mathsf{C}(H_0H_1H_\infty)$, $(-1)x = x(-1)$.

By the associative law of multiplication (which, it is to be remembered, depends only on Assumptions A and E) we have, if a is negative and b positive,

$$ab = -(-a)b,$$

where $(-a)b$ is determined by the analytic (cut) rule. If a is positive and b is negative, it follows similarly, with the aid of the relation $(-1)a = a(-1)$, that

$$ab = a(-1)(-b) = -(a(-b));$$

and if both a and b are negative,

$$ab = (-1)(-a)(-1)(-b) = (-a)(-b).$$

COROLLARY. *With respect to a scale in which* $H_\infty = \infty$, $H_0 = 0$, $H_1 = 1$, *we have* $ab = ba$ *whenever* a *and* b *are in* $\mathsf{C}(H_0H_1H_\infty)$.

THEOREM 10. *Any projectivity which transforms* H_0, H_1, *and* H_∞ *into points of the chain* $\mathsf{C}(H_0H_1H_\infty)$ *transforms any point of the chain into a point of the chain.*

Proof. We have seen that $x' = ax$ and $x' = x + a$, for rational or irrational values of a, are projectivities which change H_∞ into itself and all other points of $\mathsf{C}(H_0H_1H_\infty)$ into points of the chain. The transformation $x' = 1/x$ is a projectivity which interchanges H_∞ and H_0 (see § 54, Chap. VI, Vol. I), and by Theorem 9 it changes every point of $\mathsf{C}(H_0H_1H_\infty)$, except H_∞ and H_0, into a point of $\mathsf{C}(H_0H_1H_\infty)$.

As in the proof of Theorem 11, Chap. VI, Vol. I, it follows that H_0, H_1, H_∞ can be transformed into any three points of the chain by a product of transformations of these three types. Moreover, any projectivity is fully determined as a transformation of $\mathsf{C}(H_0H_1H_\infty)$ by the three points B_0, B_1, B_∞ into which it transforms H_0, H_1, H_∞. For, suppose there were two such projectivities, Π and Π', the product $\Pi^{-1}\Pi'$ would transform H_0, H_1, H_∞ into themselves. Hence, by Theorem 16, Chap. IV, Vol. I, it would leave invariant every point of $\mathsf{R}(H_0H_1H_\infty)$. Hence, by Assumption C (2), it would leave invariant every point of $\mathsf{C}(H_0H_1H_\infty)$. Hence $\Pi^{-1}\Pi'$ would be the identity for all points of the chain, and Π would be the same as Π' for all points of the chain. Hence every projectivity changing H_0, H_1, H_∞ into points of the chain is expressible as a product of projectivities of the forms $x' = ax$, $x' = x + a$, $x' = 1/x$. As all these transform the chain into itself, the theorem follows.

COROLLARY 1. *Any projectivity leaving invariant three points of the chain* $\mathsf{C}(H_0H_1H_\infty)$ *leaves every point of the chain invariant.*

Proof. Let Π be the given projectivity leaving the given points, say B_0, B_1, B_∞, invariant. Let P be the projectivity such that $\mathrm{P}(B_0B_1B_\infty) = (H_0H_1H_\infty)$. Then $\mathrm{P}\Pi\mathrm{P}^{-1}$ leaves H_0, H_1, H_∞ invariant and hence leaves all points of the chain invariant, as shown in the proof of the theorem. Hence Π leaves all points of the chain invariant.

COROLLARY 2. *Any projectivity of the chain* $\mathsf{C}(H_0H_1H_\infty)$ *into itself is of the form*

$$\rho x_0' = ax_0 + bx_1, \qquad \rho x_1' = cx_0 + dx_1, \qquad \begin{vmatrix} a & b \\ c & d \end{vmatrix} \neq 0,$$

where the coefficients are real numbers.

***12. Chains in general.** DEFINITION. If (A, B) is an open cut in any net of rationality $\mathsf{R}(K_0K_1K_\infty)$ with respect to the scale K_0, K_1, K_∞, let Π be a projectivity transforming $\mathsf{R}(K_0K_1K_\infty)$ into $\mathsf{R}(H_0H_1H_\infty)$ and K_∞ into H_∞. This projectivity transforms (A, B) into a cut (C, D) in $\mathsf{R}(H_0H_1H_\infty)$ with respect to the scale H_0, H_1, H_∞. If X is the point associated by Assumption C with (C, D), the point $\Pi^{-1}(X)=X'$ is called *the irrational cut-point associated with* (A, B).

The point X' is independent of the particular projectivity Π. For let Π' be any projectivity changing (A, B) into a cut (E, F) in $\mathsf{R}(H_0H_1H_\infty)$ with respect to the scale H_0, H_1, H_∞, and let Y be the point associated with (E, F) and $Y'=\Pi'^{-1}(Y)$. Then $\Pi \cdot \Pi'^{-1}$ changes (E, F) into (C, D) and hence, by Assumption C (2), must change Y into X. This can take place only if $Y'=X'$, that is, only if the cut-point X' associated with (A, B) is unique.

By projecting any net of rationality into $\mathsf{R}(H_0H_1H_\infty)$ it is shown that the cut-points associated with it satisfy the conditions stated for the points associated with the cuts of $\mathsf{R}(H_0H_1H_\infty)$ in Assumption C. Hence the theorems of the last section also apply to any chain whatever, a chain being defined as follows:

DEFINITION. The totality of points of a net of rationality $\mathsf{R}(ABC)$, together with all the irrational cut-points defined by open cuts with respect to the scale A, B, C in $\mathsf{R}(ABC)$, is called the *chain* defined by A, B, C and is denoted by $\mathsf{C}(ABC)$. The irrational cut-points are said to be *irrational with respect to* $\mathsf{R}(ABC)$.

Thus we have

THEOREM 11. (1) *The projective transform of a chain is a chain.*

(2) *Every open cut in any net of rationality defines a unique irrational cut-point collinear with, but not in, the net.*

(3) *If two such cuts with respect to the same scale and in the same net are distinct, their cut-points are distinct.*

(4) *If two open cuts are homologous in a projectivity, their cut-points are homologous in the same projectivity.*

(5) *Any projectivity which transforms three points A, B, C into three points of the chain $\mathsf{C}(ABC)$ transforms any point of the chain into a point of the chain.*

THEOREM 12. *There is one and only one chain containing three distinct points of a line.*

Proof. Let A, B, C be the given points. They belong to the chain $\mathsf{C}(ABC)$ into which $\mathsf{C}(H_0H_1H_\infty)$ is transformed by a projectivity such that $H_0H_1H_\infty \barwedge ABC$. By Theorem 11 (5) any projectivity such that $ABC \barwedge BAC$ transforms all points of $\mathsf{C}(ABC)$ into points of $\mathsf{C}(ABC)$. But by definition such a projectivity transforms $\mathsf{C}(ABC)$ into $\mathsf{C}(BAC)$; hence $\mathsf{C}(BAC)$ is contained in $\mathsf{C}(ABC)$. In like manner $\mathsf{C}(ABC)$ is contained in $\mathsf{C}(BAC)$. Hence $\mathsf{C}(ABC) = \mathsf{C}(BAC) = \mathsf{C}(BCA)$, etc.

Now suppose A, B, C to be points of some other chain $\mathsf{C}(PQR)$. By Theorem 11 (5) a projectivity such that* $PQRA \barwedge QPAR$ changes all points of $\mathsf{C}(PQR)$ into points of $\mathsf{C}(PQR)$. But by definition it changes $\mathsf{C}(PQR)$ into $\mathsf{C}(QPA)$. Hence $\mathsf{C}(QPA)$ is contained in $\mathsf{C}(PQR)$. But the same projectivity changes $\mathsf{C}(QPA)$ into $\mathsf{C}(PQR)$. Hence $\mathsf{C}(PQR) = \mathsf{C}(QPA)$. In like manner $\mathsf{C}(QPA) = \mathsf{C}(PBA) = \mathsf{C}(CBA) = \mathsf{C}(ABC)$.

COROLLARY. *A chain contains the irrational cut-point of every open cut in any net of rationality in the chain.*

THEOREM 13. THE FUNDAMENTAL THEOREM OF PROJECTIVITY FOR A CHAIN. *If A, B, C, D are distinct points of a chain and A', B', C' any three distinct points of a line, then for any projectivities giving $(A, B, C, D) \barwedge (A', B', C', D')$ and $(A, B, C, D) \barwedge (A', B', C', D_1')$ we have $D' = D_1'$.*

Proof. Let Π, Π_1 be the two projectivities mentioned in the theorem. $\Pi_1^{-1}\Pi$ then leaves every point of $\mathsf{C}(ABC)$ fixed; for it leaves every point of $\mathsf{R}(ABC)$ fixed, and hence, by Theorem 11 (4), must leave every irrational cut-point of an open cut in $\mathsf{R}(ABC)$ fixed. But $\Pi_1^{-1}\Pi$ is then the identical transformation as far as the points of $\mathsf{C}(ABC)$ are concerned. Hence $D' = D_1'$.

* Cf. Theorem 2, Chap. III, Vol. I.

This theorem may also be stated as follows:

Any projective correspondence between the points of two chains is uniquely determined by three pairs of homologous points.

Our list of assumptions for the geometry of reals may now be completed by the following assumption of closure.

ASSUMPTION R. *On at least one line, if there is one there is not more than one chain.*

It follows at once, by Theorem 12, that every line is a chain. It also follows, by an argument strictly analogous to the proof of Theorem 5, that the dual propositions of Assumptions C and R are true. Hence we have

THEOREM 14. *The principle of duality is valid for all theorems deducible from Assumptions* A, E, H, C, R.

***13. Consistency, categoricalness, and independence of the assumptions.** Let us now apply the logical canons explained in the Introduction (Vol. I) to the foregoing set of assumptions.

THEOREM 15. *Assumptions* A, E, H, C, R *are consistent if the real number system of analysis is existent.*

Proof. Consider the class of all ordered tetrads of real numbers (x_0, x_1, x_2, x_3), with the exception of (0, 0, 0, 0). Any class of these ordered tetrads such that if one of its members is (a_0, a_1, a_2, a_3) all its other members are given by the formula (ma_0, ma_1, ma_2, ma_3), where m is any real number not zero, shall be called a point. Any class consisting of all points whose component tetrads satisfy two independent linear homogeneous equations

$$u_0x_0 + u_1x_1 + u_2x_2 + u_3x_3 = 0,$$
$$v_0x_0 + v_1x_1 + v_2x_2 + v_3x_3 = 0$$

shall be called a line. The class of all points and lines so defined satisfy the assumptions A, E, H, C, R (cf. § 4, Vol. I).

THEOREM 16. *Assumptions* A, E, H, C, R *form a categorical set.*

Proof. In Chap. VII, Vol. I, it has been proved that the points of a space satisfying Assumptions A, E, P can be denoted by homogeneous coördinates which are numbers of the geometric number system of Chap. VI, Vol. I. Since P is a logical consequence of A, E, H, C, R (cf. Theorem 13), this result applies here, and by Theorem 9 the number system in question is isomorphic with the real number system of analysis.

Now if two spaces S_1 and S_2 satisfy A, E, H, C, R, consider a homogeneous coördinate system in each space and let each point of S_1 correspond to that point of S_2 which has the same coördinates. This correspondence is evidently such that if three points of S_1 are collinear, their correspondents in S_2 are collinear.

It is worthy of remark that the above correspondence may be set up in as many ways as there are collineations of S_1 into itself.

THEOREM 17. *Assumptions* A 1, A 2, A 3, E 0, E 1, E 2, E 3, E 3′, H, C, R *are an independent set.*

Proof. The method of proving that a given assumption is not a logical consequence of the other assumptions was explained in the Introduction, p. 6, Vol. I. Suppose there is given a class of objects $[x]$ and a class of subclasses of $[x]$. If we call each x a point and each element of the class of subclasses a line, then each of our assumptions, when thus interpreted, will be either true or false* with respect to this interpretation. If all the assumptions but one are true and the one is false, it cannot be a logical consequence of the others; for a logical consequence of true statements must be true. In the sequel we shall call the objects, x, pseudo-points, and the subclasses of $[x]$ which play the rôle of lines, pseudo-lines.

A 1. The pseudo-points shall be the points of a real projective plane π together with one other point O. The pseudo-lines shall be the lines of π. A 1 is false because there is no pseudo-line containing O. A 2 is true because it is satisfied by the ordinary projective plane. A 3 is true because the only sets of points A, B, C, D, E which satisfy its hypothesis are in π. The only pseudo-plane is π, and there is no pseudo-space. Hence it is evident that E 0, E 1, E 2, E 3 are true and E 3′ is vacuously true. Assumptions H, C, R are evidently true.

* If the hypothesis of a statement is not verified, we regard the statement as true. Following the terminology of E. H. Moore (Transactions of the American Mathematical Society, Vol. III, p. 489), we shall describe statements which are true in this sense as "vacuously true" or "vacuous."

It is possible to put any or all of the assumptions into a form such that they are vacuous for the ordinary real space. For example, Professor Moore has pointed out that A 1 could be replaced by the following proposition, which is vacuous for ordinary space.

$\overline{\text{A}}$ 1. Let A be a point and B be a point. If there is no line which is on A and on B, then $A = B$

A 2. The pseudo-points shall be the points of a real projective three-space S_3 together with one other pseudo-point O. The pseudo-lines shall be the lines of S_3, each pseudo-line, however, containing O. Thus any two pseudo-points are collinear with O; a pseudo-plane is an ordinary plane together with O; a pseudo-space is S_3 together with O. Hence it is evident that A 2 is false and A 1, A 3, E 0, E 1, E 2, E 3, E 3′ are true. There exist harmonic sequences of pseudo-points, some of which are ordinary harmonic sequences. Hence Assumption H is true. By reference to the definition of a quadrangular set and harmonic conjugate it is clear (because every line contains O) that any pseudo-point P is harmonically conjugate to O with regard to any two pseudo-points which are collinear with P. Hence a linear net of rationality contains all the pseudo-points of a pseudo-line. The operations of addition and multiplication are not unique, however, and hence the definition of order does not apply; there are no open cuts, and Assumptions C and R are vacuously true.

A 3. The pseudo-points shall be the points of a real projective space S_3, with the exception of a single point O. The pseudo-lines shall be the lines of S_3, except that in case of those lines which pass through O the pseudo-lines do not contain O. Clearly A 3 is false whenever the pseudo-points A, B, C, D, E are chosen so that the lines AB and DE meet in O. A 1, A 2, E 0, E 1, E 2, E 3, E 3′ are obviously true. A harmonic sequence and a net of rationality of pseudo-points can be found identical with an ordinary harmonic sequence and net of rationality on any line not passing through O. Hence H, C, and R are also true.

E 0. The pseudo-points shall be the vertices of a tetrahedron, and the pseudo-lines the six pairs of pseudo-points. Thus the pseudo-planes are the trios of pseudo-points, and a pseudo-space consists of all four pseudo-points. A 1 and A 2 are obviously true. A 3 is true because we may have $E=A$ and $D=B$. E 1, E 2, E 3, E 3′ are true. H, C, R are vacuously true.

E 1. There shall be one pseudo-point and no pseudo-line. E 1 is false and all the other assumptions are vacuously true.

E 2. There shall be three pseudo-points and one pseudo-line containing all three pseudo-points. A 1, A 2, E 0, E 1 are true. A 3, E 3, E 3′, H, C, R are vacuously true.

E 3. The pseudo-points and pseudo-lines shall be the points and lines of a real projective plane. A 1, A 2, A 3, E 0, E 1, E 2, H, C, R are true and E 3′ is vacuous.

E 3′. The pseudo-points and pseudo-lines shall be the points and lines of a real four-dimensional projective space. E 3′ is false and all the other assumptions are true.

H. The pseudo-points and pseudo-lines shall be the points and lines of any modular projective three-space (cf. § 72, Vol. I, and § 16, below). All the assumptions A and E are true, H is false, and C and R are vacuously true.

C. The pseudo-points and pseudo-lines shall be the points and linear nets of rationality of a three-dimensional net of rationality in an ordinary real projective space. All the assumptions are true except C, which is false. R is vacuously true.

R. The pseudo-points and pseudo-lines shall be defined as the points and lines in Theorem 15, the coördinates, however, being elements of the system of ordinary complex numbers. All the assumptions are true except R, which is false.

Assumption C, which is more complicated in its statement than the others, is, however, such that neither of the two statements into which it is separated may be omitted. This result is established in the following theorem:

THEOREM 18. *Assumption* C (1) *is not a consequence of Assumption* C (2) *and all the other assumptions. Assumption* C (2) *is not a consequence of* C (1) *and of the other assumptions even if we add to* C (1) *the following: If a projectivity transforms* H_∞ *into itself and* H_0 *and* H_1 *into points of* $\mathsf{R}(H_0H_1H_\infty)$, *and transforms an open cut* (A, B) *into an open cut* (C, D), *it transforms the point associated with* (A, B) *into the point associated with* (C, D).

*Proof.** (1) Any real number x determines a class K_x of numbers of the form $ax + b$ where a and b are any rationals. K_x is the same as K_{ax+b} for all rational values of a and b. Hence, if x and y are two irrationals, K_x and K_y are either identical or mutually exclusive. Thus the class of all real numbers falls into a set of mutually exclusive

* This argument makes use of portions of the theory of classes which could not be treated adequately without a long digression. Hence we assume knowledge of the methods and terminology of this branch of mathematics without further explanation.

classes $[K]$. With each class K we associate a particular one of its numbers,* k, and thus obtain a set of numbers $[k]$ such that every real number can be written uniquely in the form $ak + b$.

Now consider the number system whose elements are the complex numbers of the form $ai + b$, where a and b are rational and $i = \sqrt{-1}$. If we take as pseudo-points and pseudo-lines the points and lines of a three-space based (as in the proof of Theorem 15) on this number system, it is clear that all the assumptions except C are satisfied. If we also take as the pseudo-points H_0, H_1, H_∞ those having the coördinates (0, 1, 0, 0), (1, 1, 0, 0), (1, 0, 0, 0), the net of rationality $\mathsf{R}(H_0H_1H_\infty)$ consists of H_∞ and the points whose coördinates are $(x, 1, 0, 0)$, where x is rational. Suppose now that we associate the pseudo-point $(ai + b, 1, 0, 0)$ with every cut in this net which in the ordinary geometry would determine an irrational point $(ak + b, 1, 0, 0)$. Every point is thus associated with an infinity of cuts, contrary to Assumption C (1). Moreover, the cuts with which any point is associated occur between every two pseudo-points and hence between every two cuts of $\mathsf{R}(H_0H_1H_\infty)$. Therefore Assumption C (2) remains true in this space.

(2) For the second half of the theorem the pseudo-points and pseudo-lines shall be the points and lines of a three-space based on a commutative number system whose elements are the ordinary rational numbers and all open cuts in the rational numbers. The laws of combination shall be such that addition is precisely the same as for the ordinary number system and multiplication is the same between rationals and rationals or rationals and irrationals, but different between irrationals and irrationals. Thus the product of the numbers associated with two open cuts will not, in general, be the number associated with the cut given by the usual rule. Hence the projective transformation $x' = ax$ will not preserve order relations, and Assumption C (2) must be false. On the other hand, C (1) and the other assumptions are obviously true.

* We do not show how to set up the correspondence. The assumption that this correspondence exists is a weaker form of the assumption used by Zermelo (Mathematische Annalen, Vol. LIX, p. 514) in his proof that any class can be well ordered. Our proof of the second part of the theorem is dependent on the validity of Zermelo's result that the continuum can be well ordered. The whole theorem is therefore subject to the doubts that attach to the Zermelo process because of the lack of explicit methods of setting up the correspondences in question.

The existence of the required new number system can be inferred from Hamel's theorem* that there exists a well-ordered set of real numbers

(5) $$a_1, a_2, a_3, \cdots, a_\omega, \cdots$$

such that every real number can be given uniquely by an expression of the form

(6) $$\alpha_0 + \alpha_1 a_{i_1} + \alpha_2 a_{i_2} + \cdots + \alpha_n a_{i_n},$$

containing only a finite number of terms, the α's all being rational. The ordinary rules of combination for cuts determine a multiplication table for the a's; that is, a set of rules of the form

(7) $$a_i a_j = \beta_0 + \beta_1 a_{k_1} + \beta_2 a_{k_2} + \cdots + \beta_m a_{k_m},$$

where the β's are rational. The laws of combination for the number system in general may now be stated as follows: Express the two numbers to be added or multiplied in the form (6); add or multiply by the rules for addition and multiplication of polynomials, reducing the result in the case of multiplication by means of the multiplication table for the a's.

Now suppose we denote by

(8) $$a'_1, a'_2, \cdots, a'_\omega, \cdots$$

the same set of numbers $[a]$ arranged in a different order of the same type as (5). Such an order would be obtained, for example, by interchanging a_1 and a_2 and leaving the other a's unaltered. There is therefore a one-to-one correspondence in which every a_i corresponds to the a'_i having the same subscript. Moreover, since the set of all a's includes the same elements as the set of all a''s, every real number is expressible in the form

(9) $$\alpha_0 + \alpha_1 a'_{i_1} + \alpha_2 a'_{i_2} + \cdots + \alpha_n a'_{i_n}.$$

A new law of multiplication, which we shall denote by $\times$, is now defined by setting up a multiplication table for the a''s according to the rule that

(10) $$a'_i \times a'_j = \alpha_0 + \alpha_1 a'_{i_1} + \cdots + \alpha_n a'_{i_n}$$

whenever

(11) $$a_i a_j = \alpha_0 + \alpha_1 a_{i_1} + \cdots + \alpha_n a_{i_n}.$$

* Mathematische Annalen, Vol. LX, p. 459.

The product, according to the new law of combination, of two real numbers is obtained by expressing each in the form (9), multiplying according to the rule for polynomials, and reducing by the multiplication table for the a''s.

Since the set of all expressions of the form

$$\alpha_0 + \alpha_1 a_{i_1} + \alpha_2 a_{i_2} + \cdots$$

forms a number system, the set of all expressions of the form

$$\alpha_0 + \alpha_1 a'_{i_1} + \alpha_2 a'_{i_2} + \cdots$$

forms a number system isomorphic with the first. For if we let each a_i correspond to the a'_i with the same subscript, the sum of any two elements of the first number system corresponds, by definition, to the sum of the corresponding two elements in the second number system. Similarly for the product of a rational by a rational or of a rational by an irrational. The product of two irrationals in the first system corresponds to the product of two irrationals in the second, because the two polynomials in the a's are multiplied by the same rules as the two in the a''s, and are also reduced by corresponding entries in the respective multiplication tables.

We may insure that the two number systems shall be distinct by selecting the a's, in the first place, so that $a_1 = \sqrt{2}$ and $a_2 = \sqrt{3}$, and then choosing the a''s so that $a'_1 = a_2$.

***14. Foundations of the complex geometry.** Let us add to Assumptions A, E, H, C the following assumption:

Assumption $\overline{\text{R}}$. *On some line, l, not all points belong to the same chain.*

Let P_0, P_1, P_∞ be three points of l. The geometric number system determined by the method of Chap. VI, Vol. I, by the scale P_0, P_1, P_∞ is commutative for all the points in the chain $\mathsf{C}(P_0P_1P_\infty)$ but not necessarily for other points. However, it is clear, without assuming the commutativity of multiplication, that

$$x' = x^{-1}, \; x' = x + a, \; x' = ax, \; x' = xa \quad (a = \text{constant})$$

define projectivities. For $x' = x^{-1}$ this follows from § 54, Vol. I; for $x' = x + a$ it reduces to Theorem 2, Chap. VI, Vol. I; and for the other two cases, to Theorem 4, Chap. VI, Vol. I.

Let J be any point of l not in $\mathsf{C}(P_0P_1P_\infty)$, and let $[X]$ be the set of all points in $\mathsf{C}(P_0P_1P_\infty)$. Then, by Theorem 11 (1), the set of points

$[X+J]$ is a chain. This chain has no point except P_∞ in common with $\mathsf{C}(P_0P_1P_\infty)$, because, if $X+J=X'\neq P_\infty$, it would follow that $X'-X=J$, and thus J would be a point of $\mathsf{C}(P_0P_1P_\infty)$. Let us denote the chain $[X+J]$ by C'.

In order to continue this argument we need the following assumption of closure:

ASSUMPTION I. *Through a point P of any chain C of the line l, and any point J on l but not in C, there is not more than one chain of l which has no other point than P in common with C.*

Now let P be any point of l not in $\mathsf{C}(P_0P_1P_\infty)$ or C'. Such points exist, because, for example, the chain $\mathsf{C}(P_0P_1J)$ does not coincide with $\mathsf{C}(P_0P_1P_\infty)$ or C'. The chain $\mathsf{C}(PJP_\infty)$ has, by Assumption I, a point different from P_∞ in common with $\mathsf{C}(P_0P_1P_\infty)$. Let X_1 be this point. In case $X_1\neq P_0$, the projectivity

$$X'=X+J(P_1-X_1^{-1}\cdot X) \tag{12}$$

transforms P_0 into J, X_1 into itself, and P_∞ into itself. Hence it transforms $\mathsf{C}(P_0P_1P_\infty)=\mathsf{C}(P_0X_1P_\infty)$ into $\mathsf{C}(JX_1P_\infty)$. Hence every point of $\mathsf{C}(JX_1P_\infty)$, and in particular P, is of the form $X+JX''$, where X and X'' are in $[X]$. If $X_1=P_0$, the projectivity

$$X'=JX \tag{13}$$

transforms $\mathsf{C}(P_0,P_1,P_\infty)$ into $\mathsf{C}(P_0JP_\infty)$, which contains P. Hence, in this case P is of the form JX. Thus we have

LEMMA 1. *Every point of the line l is expressible in the form $A+JB$, where A and B are in $\mathsf{C}(P_0P_1P_\infty)$.*

LEMMA 2. *Two points $A+JB$ and $A'+JB'$, where A, B, A', B' are in $\mathsf{C}(P_0P_1P_\infty)$, are identical if and only if $A=A'$ and $B=B'$.*

For if $B\neq B'$, $A+JB=A'+JB'$ implies $J=(A'-A)(B-B')^{-1}$, and thus J would be in $\mathsf{C}(P_0P_1P_\infty)$; and if $B=B'$, it implies directly that $A=A'$.

Each of the projectivities $X'=JX$ and $X'=XJ$ transforms the chain $\mathsf{C}(P_0P_1P_\infty)$ into $\mathsf{C}(P_0JP_\infty)$. Hence, if A be any point of $\mathsf{C}(P_0P_1P_\infty)$,

$$AJ=JA', \tag{14}$$

where A' is also in $\mathsf{C}(P_0P_1P_\infty)$.

Each of the projectivities $X' = (P_1 - J)X$ and $X' = X(P_1 - J)$ transforms $\mathsf{C}(P_0P_1P_\infty)$ into $\mathsf{C}(P_0(P_1 - J)P_\infty)$. Hence, if A be any point of $\mathsf{C}(P_0P_1P_\infty)$,

$$A(P_1 - J) = (P_1 - J)A'',$$

where A'' is also in $\mathsf{C}(P_0P_1P_\infty)$. By the distributive law (Theorem 5, Chap. VI, Vol. I) it follows that

$$A - AJ = A'' - JA''.$$

By (14), this reduces to

$$A - JA' = A'' - JA''.$$

By Lemma 2, it follows that $A = A'' = A'$. Hence $AJ = JA$. From this we can deduce, by the elementary laws of operation,

$$\begin{aligned}(A + JB)(C + JD) &= A(C + JD) + JB(C + JD)\\ &= AC + AJD + JBC + JBJD\\ &= CA + CJB + JDA + JDJB\\ &= C(A + JB) + JD(A + JB)\\ &= (C + JD)(A + JB).\end{aligned}$$

Hence the geometric number system determined by any scale on l is commutative. Since chains are transformed into chains by any projective transformation, it follows that the geometric number system determined by any scale on any line in a space satisfying A, E, H, C, $\overline{\text{R}}$, I satisfies the commutative law of multiplication. Hence, by Theorem 1,

THEOREM 19. *Assumption* P *is satisfied in any space satisfying Assumptions* A, E, H, C, $\overline{\text{R}}$, I.

Since every point in the geometric number system is expressible in the form $A + JB$, we have

$$(15) \qquad J^2 = A_0 + JB_0,$$

where A_0 and B_0 are in $\mathsf{C}(P_0P_1P_\infty)$. Thus J is one of the double points of the involution

$$(16) \qquad XX' - \tfrac{1}{2}B_0(X + X') - A_0 = 0,$$

which transforms $\mathsf{C}(P_0P_1P_\infty)$ into itself. Any two points of $\mathsf{C}(P_0P_1P_\infty)$ which are conjugate in this involution may be transformed projectively into P_0 and P_∞ by a transformation which carries $\mathsf{C}(P_0P_1P_\infty)$ into itself. This reduces the involution to

$$(17) \qquad XX' = A,$$

where A must be negative relatively to the scale $P_0P_1P_\infty$, since the double points are not in $C(P_0P_1P_\infty)$. The transformation $X=\sqrt{-A}X'$ now reduces (17) to

$$XX'=-P_1$$

and thus transforms J to a point satisfying the equation

$$J^2=-P.$$

Hence we have

THEOREM 20. *The geometric number system in any space satisfying Assumptions* A, E, H, C, $\overline{\text{R}}$, I *is isomorphic with the complex number system of analysis, i.e. with the system of numbers* $a+ib$, *where* $i^2=-1$ *and* a *and* b *are real.*

***15. Ordered projective spaces.** There is an important class of projective spaces which may be referred to as the *ordered projective spaces* and which are characterized by the Assumptions S given below. This class of spaces includes the rational and real projective spaces and many others. The set of assumptions, A, E, S, is not categorical, but it may be made so by adding a suitable continuity assumption or by some other assumption of closure.

These assumptions introduce a new class of undefined elements, called *senses*,* in addition to the points and lines which are the undefined elements of Assumptions A and E. The senses are denoted by symbols of the form $S(ABC)$, where A, B, C denote points.†

S 1. *For any three distinct collinear points* A, B, C *there is a sense* $S(ABC)$.

S 2. *For any three distinct collinear points there is not more than one sense* $S(ABC)$.

S 3. $S(ABC)=S(BCA)$.

S 4. $S(ABC)\neq S(ACB)$.

S 5. *If* $S(ABC)=S(A'B'C')$ *and* $S(A'B'C')=S(A''B''C'')$, *then* $S(ABC)=S(A''B''C'')$.

S 6. *If* $S(ABO)=S(BCO)$, *then* $S(ABO)=S(ACO)$.

S 7. *If* OA *and* OB *are distinct lines, and* $S(OAA_1)=S(OAA_2)$ *and* $OAA_1A_2 \overline{\wedge} OBB_1B_2$, *then* $S(OBB_1)=S(OBB_2)$.

* Sets of assumptions more or less related to these have been given by A. R. Schweitzer, American Journal of Mathematics, Vol. XXXI, p. 365, and A. N. Whitehead, The Axioms of Projective Geometry, Cambridge Tracts, Cambridge, 1906.

† With respect to the intuitional basis of these assumptions, cf. figs. 6–12, Chap. II.

If $S(ABC)$ be identified with the sense-class which is discussed below in § 19, Chap. II, it will be seen that S 1 and S 2 are immediately verified and S 3, · · ·, S 7 reduce to Theorems 2–6, Chap. II. This shows that the assumptions S are satisfied by a rational or a real projective space.

These assumptions are capable, as is shown in Chap. II, of serving as a basis for a very complete discussion of geometric order relations. Assumption P is not a consequence of A, E, S alone.

EXERCISES

1. Prove that Assumption H is a consequence of A, E, and S.

2. Prove that with a proper definition of the symbol < (less than) the geometric number system in an ordered projective space satisfies the following conditions:

(1) If a and b are distinct numbers, $a < b$ or $b < a$.

(2) If $a < b$, then $a \neq b$.

(3) If $a < b$ and $b < c$, then $a < c$.

(4) If $a < b$, there exists a number, x, such that $a < x$ and $x < b$.

(5) If $0 < a$, then $b < a + b$ for every b.

(6) If $0 < a$ and $0 < b$, then $0 < a \cdot b$.

(Cf. E. V. Huntington, Transactions of the American Mathematical Society, Vol. VI (1905), p. 17.)

3. Introduce an assumption of continuity and with this assumption and A, E, S prove Assumption P.

4. Prove that P is not a consequence of A, E, S alone.

***16. Modular projective spaces.** We have seen (§ 7) that, in any space satisfying Assumptions A and E, any two harmonic sequences are projective. Hence, if one harmonic sequence contains an infinity of points, every such sequence contains an infinity of points, and by § 8 these points are in one-to-one reciprocal correspondence with the ordinary rational numbers. On the other hand, if one harmonic sequence contains a finite number of points, every other harmonic sequence in the same space contains the same finite number of points. Hence the spaces satisfying Assumptions A and E fall into two classes — those satisfying Assumption H and those satisfying the following:

Assumption $\overline{\text{H}}$. *If any harmonic sequence exists, at least one contains only a finite number of points.*

The spaces satisfying $\overline{\text{H}}$ may be called *modular*, and those satisfying H *nonmodular*.

It follows, just as in Theorem 5, that the principle of duality is true for any modular space.

Let Π be any parabolic projectivity on a line, and let H_∞ be its invariant point. If H_0 be any other point of the line, the points

$$\cdots \Pi^{-2}(H_0),\ \Pi^{-1}(H_0),\ H_0,\ \Pi(H_0),\ \Pi^2(H_0)\cdots$$

form a harmonic sequence, by definition. If this is to contain only a finite number of points, there must be some positive integer n such that $\Pi^n(H_0) = \Pi^m(H_0)$, where m is zero or a positive integer less than n. If $n - m = k$, we have

$$\Pi^k(\Pi^m(H_0)) = \Pi^n(H_0),$$

and hence $$\Pi^k = 1.$$

Hence all the points of the harmonic sequence are contained in the set

$$H_0,\ \Pi(H_0),\ \cdots,\ \Pi^{k-1}(H_0).$$

In case k is not a prime number, that is, if there exist two positive integers, k_1, k_2, different from unity such that $k = k_1 \cdot k_2$, let us consider the parabolic projectivity Π^{k_2}. The points

$$H_0,\ \Pi^{k_2}(H_0),\ \Pi^{2k_2}(H_0),\ \cdots,\ \Pi^{(k_1-1)k_2}(H_0)$$

satisfy the definition of a harmonic sequence. Since any two harmonic sequences contain the same number of points, it follows that the given sequence could not have contained more than k_1 points. In case k_1 breaks up into two factors, the same argument shows that the given harmonic sequence could not contain a number of points larger than either factor. This process can be repeated only a finite number of times and can stop only when we arrive at a prime number. Hence we have

THEOREM 21. *The number of points in a harmonic sequence is prime. The points of a harmonic sequence may be denoted by*

$$H_0,\ \Pi(H_0),\ \cdots,\ \Pi^{p-1}(H_0),$$

where Π is a parabolic projectivity. The period, p, of any parabolic projectivity is a prime number.

With reference to a scale in which $H_0 = 0$, $\Pi(H_0) = 1$, and the limit point of the harmonic sequence is ∞, Π has the equation

$$x' = x + 1.$$

Hence the coördinates of the points in the harmonic sequence are

$$0,\ 1,\ 2,\ \cdots,\ p-1,$$

respectively, where 2 represents $1+1$, 3 represents $2+1$, etc. Since $\Pi^p = 1$, we must have that $p = 0$, $p+1 = 1$, $np+k = k$, etc. In other words, the coördinates of the points in a harmonic sequence are elements of the field obtained by reducing the integers modulo p, as explained in § 72, Vol. I.

By Theorem 14, Chap. VI, Vol. I, the net of rationality determined by the points whose coördinates are $0, 1, \infty$ consists of the point ∞ and all points whose coördinates are obtainable from 0 and 1 by the operations of addition, subtraction, multiplication, and division (except division by zero). Since all numbers of this sort are contained in the set

$$0,\ 1,\ \cdots,\ p-1,$$

we have

THEOREM 22. *The number of points in a net of rationality in a modular space is* $p+1$, *p being a prime number constant for the space in question.*

Obviously, if Assumption Q (§ 10) be added to the set A, E, $\overline{\text{H}}$, the number of points on any line must be $p+1$, p being prime. A space satisfying A, E, $\overline{\text{H}}$ shall be called a *rational modular space.* The problem of finding the double points of a projectivity in a rational modular space of one or more dimensions leads to the consideration of modular spaces bearing a relation to the rational ones analogous to the relation which the complex geometry bears to the real geometry. The existence of such spaces follows from the considerations in Chap. IX, Vol. I (Propositions K_2 and K_n). The geometric number systems for such spaces may be finite* (Galois fields) or infinite.†

* E. H. Moore, The Subgroups of the Generalized Finite Modular Group, Decennial publications of The University of Chicago, Vol. IX (1903), pp. 141–190; L. E. Dickson, Linear Groups, Chap. I.

† L. E. Dickson, Transactions of the American Mathematical Society, Vol. VIII (1907), p. 389. See also the article by E. Steinitz referred to in § 92, Vol. I

17. Recapitulation. The various groupings of assumptions which we have considered thus far may be resumed as follows: A space satisfying Assumptions

A, E	is a general projective space;
A, E, P	is a proper projective space;
A, E, H	is a nonmodular projective space;
A, E, $\bar{H}$	is a modular projective space;
A, E, S	is an ordered projective space;
A, E, $\bar{H}$, Q	is a rational modular projective space;
A, E, H, Q	is a rational nonmodular projective space;
A, E, H, C, R or A, E, K	is a real projective space;
A, E, H, C, $\bar{R}$, I or A, E, J	is a complex projective space.

The first six sets of assumptions are not, and the remaining ones are, categorical. The set of theorems deducible from any one of these sets of assumptions is called a projective geometry, and the various geometries may be distinguished by the adjectives applied above to the corresponding spaces.

CHAPTER II

ELEMENTARY THEOREMS ON ORDER

18. Direct and opposite projectivities on a line. In § 9 a point A was said to precede a point B relative to a scale P_0, P_1, P_∞ if the coördinate of A in this scale was less than the coördinate of B. Supposing the coördinate of A to be a and that of B to be b, the projectivity changing P_0 to A and P_1 to B and leaving P_∞ fixed has the equation

$$x' = (b - a)x + a. \tag{1}$$

In this transformation the coefficient of x is positive if and only if A precedes B. But the transformations of the form

$$x' = \alpha x + \beta, \tag{2}$$

where α is positive, evidently form a group. This group is a subgroup of the group of all projectivities leaving P_∞ invariant, for the latter group contains all transformations (2) for which $\alpha \neq 0$.

The group of transformations (2) for which α is positive is, by what we have just seen, such that whenever a pair of points A and B are transformed to A' and B' respectively, A precedes B if and only if A' precedes B'. The discussion of order relative to a scale could therefore be based on the theory of this group.

The order relations defined by means of this group have all, however, a special relation to the point P_∞, and they can all be derived by specialization from a more general relation defined by means of a more extensive group. We shall therefore enter first into the discussion of this larger group, and afterwards (§ 23) show how to derive the relations of "precede" and "follow" from the general notion of "sense." The definitions for the general case, like those for the special one, will be seen to depend simply on the distinction between positive and negative numbers.

A projective transformation of a line may be written in the form

$$\begin{aligned} x_0' &= a_{00}x_0 + a_{01}x_1, \\ x_1' &= a_{10}x_0 + a_{11}x_1, \end{aligned} \qquad \Delta = \begin{vmatrix} a_{00} & a_{01} \\ a_{10} & a_{11} \end{vmatrix} \neq 0, \tag{3}$$

where the a_{ij}'s are numbers of the geometric number system.

Under Assumptions A, E, H, C, R (or A, E, K) the a_{ij}'s are real. If attention be restricted to a single net of rationality satisfying Assumption H, the a_{ij}'s may be taken (Theorem 6, Cor. 2, Chap. I) as integers. The discussion which follows is valid on either hypothesis.*

DEFINITION. The projectivities of the form (3) for which $\Delta > 0$ are called *direct*, and those for which $\Delta < 0$ are called *opposite*.

Since the determinant of the product of two transformations (3) is the product of the determinants, the direct projectivities form a subgroup of the projective group. The same transformation (3) cannot be both direct and opposite, for two transformations (3) are identical only if the coefficients of one are obtainable from those of the other by multiplying them all by the same constant ρ; but this merely changes Δ into $\rho^2\Delta$.

In form, the definition is dependent on the choice of the coördinate system which is used in equations (3). Actually, however, the definition is independent of the coördinate system, for if a given projectivity has a positive Δ with respect to one scale, it has a positive Δ with respect to every scale. This may be proved as follows:

Let the fundamental points of the scale to which the coördinates in (3) refer be P_0, P_1, P_∞, and let Q_0, Q_1, Q_∞ be the fundamental points of any other scale. By § 56, Vol. I, the coördinates y_0, y_1 of any point R with respect to any scale Q_0, Q_1, Q_∞ are such that $y_1/y_0 = \text{R}(Q_\infty Q_0, Q_1 R)$. Suppose that, relative to the scale P_0, P_1, P_∞, the projectivity which transforms Q_0, Q_1, Q_∞ to P_0, P_1, P_∞ respectively has the equations

$$(4) \qquad \begin{aligned} y_0 &= b_{00}x_0 + b_{01}x_1, \\ y_1 &= b_{10}x_0 + b_{11}x_1, \end{aligned} \qquad \begin{vmatrix} b_{00} & b_{01} \\ b_{10} & b_{11} \end{vmatrix} = D \neq 0.$$

Thus any point R whose coördinates relative to the scale P_0, P_1, P_∞ are (x_0, x_1) is transformed by this projectivity to a point R' whose coördinates relative to the scale P_0, P_1, P_∞ are (y_0, y_1).

Since cross ratios are unaltered by projective transformations,

$$\text{R}(Q_\infty Q_0, Q_1 R) = \text{R}(P_\infty P_0, P_1 R') = \frac{y_1}{y_0}.$$

Hence it follows that *if x_0 and x_1 are the coördinates of any point R relative to the scale P_0, P_1, P_∞, the corresponding values of y_0 and y_1 given*

* It is, in fact, valid in any space satisfying Assumptions A, E, S, P. The purely ordinal theorems are indeed valid in any ordered projective space (§ 15), but those regarding involutions, conic sections, etc. necessarily involve Assumption P also. Cf. the fine print at the end of § 19.

by (4) *are the coördinates of R relative to the scale* Q_0, Q_1, Q_∞. Let us indicate (4) by $(y_0, y_1) = T(x_0, x_1)$, and (3) by $(x_0', x_1') = S(x_0, x_1)$.

Now a direct transformation (3) carries a point whose coördinates relative to the scale P_0, P_1, P_∞ are (x_0, x_1) into one whose coördinates relative to the same scale are (x_0', x_1'), where $(x_0', x_1') = S(x_0, x_1)$. The coördinates of these two points relative to the scale Q_0, Q_1, Q_∞ are $(y_0, y_1) = T(x_0, x_1)$ and $(y_0', y_1') = T(x_0', x_1')$ respectively. Hence, by substitution,

$$(y_0', y_1') = T(S(x_0, x_1)) = T(S(T^{-1}(y_0, y_1))),$$

or

$$(y_0', y_1') = TST^{-1}(y_0, y_1),$$

where T^{-1} indicates, as usual, the inverse of T. The determinant of the transformation TST^{-1} is

$$\Delta' = D\Delta \frac{K^2}{D},$$

where K is real (or rational), and Δ' therefore has the same sign as Δ. Thus the definition of a direct projectivity is independent of the choice of the coördinate system.

This result can be put in another form which is important in the sequel:

DEFINITION. Two figures are said to be *conjugate under* or *equivalent with respect to* a group of transformations if and only if there exists a transformation of the group carrying one of the figures into the other.

THEOREM 1. *If two sets of points are conjugate under the group of direct projectivities on a line, so are also the two sets of points into which they are transformed by any projectivity of the line.*

Proof. Let S be a direct projectivity changing a set of points $[A]$ into a set of points $[B]$, and let T be any other projectivity on the line, and let $T(A) = A'$ and $T(B) = B'$. Since $T^{-1}(A') = A$, $S(A) = B$, and $T(B) = B'$, it follows that $TST^{-1}(A') = B'$. But the discussion above shows that TST^{-1} is a direct projectivity. Hence $[A']$ and $[B']$ are conjugate under the group of direct projectivities, as was to be proved.

According to the definition in § 75, Vol. I (see also § 39, below), the group of direct projectivities is a self-conjugate subgroup of the group of all projectivities on a line. Since this is the only relation between the two groups which we have employed in the proof of the theorem above, this theorem can be generalized to any case in which we have one group of transformations appearing as a self-conjugate subgroup of another.

EXERCISES

1. Within the field of all real numbers the positive numbers may be defined as those numbers different from zero which possess square roots. Generalize this definition to other fields, and thus generalize the definitions of direct projectivities. In each case determine how far the theorems on sense and order in the following sections can be generalized (cf. § 72, Vol. I).

2. The group of projectivities which transform a net of rationality into itself has a self-conjugate subgroup consisting of those transformations which are products of pairs of involutions having their double points in the net of rationality. This group contains all projectivities for which the determinant is the square of a rational number.

***3.** Work out a definition and theory of the group of direct projectivities independent of the use of coördinates. This may be done by the aid of theorems in Chap. VIII, Vol. I (cf. §§ 69 and 70, below).

19. The two sense-classes on a line. DEFINITION. Let A_0, B_0, C_0 be any three distinct points of a line. The class of all ordered* triads of points ABC on the line, such that the projectivities

$$A_0B_0C_0 \barwedge ABC$$

are direct, is called a *sense-class* and is denoted by $S(A_0B_0C_0)$. Two ordered triads in the same sense-class are said *to have the same sense* or *to be in the same sense.* Two collinear ordered triads not in the same sense-class are said *to have opposite senses* or *to be in opposite senses.*

One sense-class chosen arbitrarily may be referred to by a particular name, as *right-handed, clockwise, positive,* etc.†

The term "sense," standing by itself, might have been defined as follows: "The senses are any set of objects in one-to-one and reciprocal correspondence with the sense classes." This is analogous to the definition of a vector given in § 42. When there is question only of one line, any two objects whatever may serve as the two senses — for example, the signs + and −. This agrees with the definition of sense as "the sign of a certain determinant." When dealing with more than one line, it is no longer correct to say that there are two senses; there are, in fact, two senses for each line.

* "Order," here, is a logical rather than a geometrical term, just as in the definition of "throw" (§ 23, Vol. I). It is a device for distinguishing the elements of a set. For example, when we say that ABC cannot be transformed into ACB by any transformation of a given group, it is a way of saying that the group contains no transformation changing A into A, B into C, and C into B.

† A partial list of references on the notion of sense in one and more dimensions would include: Möbius, Barycentrische Calcul, note in § 140; Gauss, Werke, Vol. VIII, p. 248; von Staudt, Beiträge zur Geometrie der Lage, §§ 3, 14; Study, Archiv der Mathematik und Physik, Vol. XXI (1913), p. 193; Encyclopädie der Math. Wiss. III AB 7, p. 618.

When one adopts, as we do, the symbol $S(ABC)$ to stand for a sense-class, there is no occasion for attaching a separate meaning to the word "sense." It may be regarded as an incomplete symbol,* like the $\frac{d}{dx}$ in the $\frac{dy}{dx}$ of the calculus.

THEOREM 2. *If the ordered triad ABC is in the sense-class $S(A_0B_0C_0)$, then $S(ABC) = S(A_0B_0C_0)$. If $S(ABC) = S(A'B'C')$ and $S(A'B'C') = S(A''B''C'')$, then $S(ABC) = S(A''B''C'')$.*

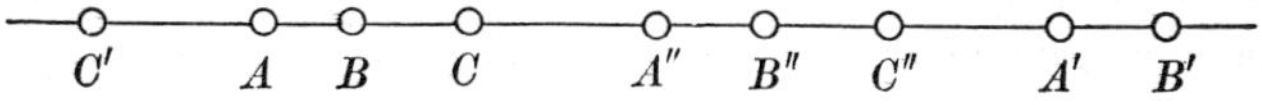

FIG. 6

Proof. Both statements are consequences of the fact that the direct projectivities form a group.

THEOREM 3. *If $S(ABC) \neq S(A'B'C')$ and $S(A'B'C') \neq S(A''B''C'')$, then $S(ABC) = S(A''B''C'')$.*

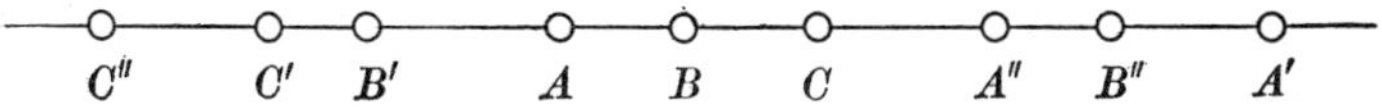

FIG. 7

Proof. If $S(ABC) \neq S(A'B'C')$, the projectivity $ABC \barwedge A'B'C'$ is opposite. Hence the theorem follows from the fact that the product of two opposite projectivities is direct.

COROLLARY. *There are two and only two sense-classes on a line.*

THEOREM 4. *If A, B, C are distinct collinear points, $S(ABC) = S(BCA)$ and $S(ABC) \neq S(ACB)$.*†

Proof. Let A, B, C be taken as (1, 1), (1, 0), (0, 1) respectively. Then

$$x_0' = x_1,$$
$$x_1' = x_0$$

is an opposite projectivity interchanging B and C and leaving A invariant. Hence $S(ABC) \neq S(ACB)$. In like manner, we can prove that $S(ACB) \neq S(BCA)$. It follows, by Theorem 3, that $S(ABC) = S(BCA)$.

* The term "incomplete symbol" appears in Whitehead and Russell's Principia Mathematica, Vol. I, Chap. III, of the Introduction, together with a discussion of its logical significance.

† This may be expressed by the phrase "Sense is preserved by even and altered by odd permutations." A *transposition* is a permutation in which two and only two elements are interchanged, and an *even* (*odd*) permutation is the resultant of an even (odd) number of transpositions. Cf. Burnside, Theory of Groups of Finite Order, Chap. I.

THEOREM 5. *If* $S(ABD)=S(BCD)$, *then* $S(ABD)=S(ACD)$.

Proof. Choose the coördinates so that $D=(0, 1)$, $A=(1, 0)$, $B=(1, 1)$. The transformation of ABD to BCD may be written in the form

$$x_0' = x_0,$$
$$x_1' = x_0 + a x_1,$$

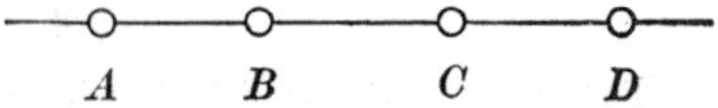

FIG. 8

because (0, 1) is invariant and (1, 0) goes to (1, 1). This transformation will be direct if and only if $a > 0$. The point C, being the transform of (1, 1), is $(1, 1+a)$. The transformation carrying ABD to ACD is

$$x' = x_0,$$
$$x_1' = (1+a)x_1,$$

which is direct because $(1+a) > 0$.

As an immediate consequence of Theorem 1 we have

THEOREM 6. *If* $S(ABC)=S(A_1B_1C_1)$ *and* $ABCA_1B_1C_1 \overline{\wedge} A'B'C'A_1'B_1'C_1'$, *then*

$$S(A'B'C') = S(A_1'B_1'C_1').$$

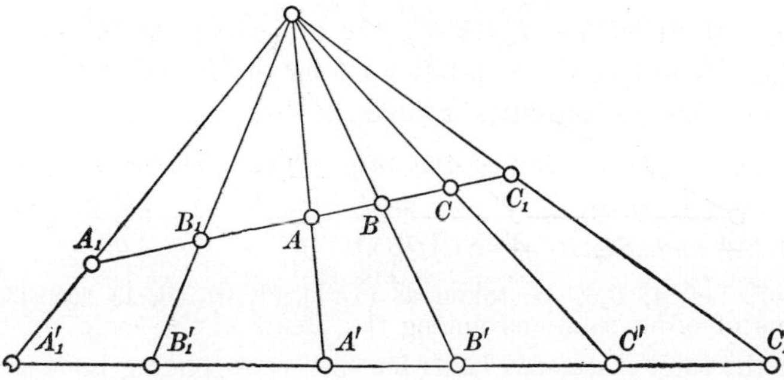

FIG. 9

Theorems 2–6 contain the propositions given in § 15, Chap. I, as Assumptions S. Theorem 6 is slightly more general than S 7 but is directly deducible from it. The developments of the following sections will be based entirely on these propositions, and hence belong to the theory of any ordered projective space, except where reference is made to figures whose existence depends on Assumption P Theorems of the latter sort hold in any space satisfying A, E, P, S.

These propositions have the advantage, as assumptions, of corresponding to some of our simplest intuitions with regard to the linear order relations. The reader may verify this by constructing the figures to which they correspond (cf. figs. 6–9). Each proposition will be found to correspond to a number of visually distinct figures.

20. Sense in any one-dimensional form. DEFINITION. If 1, 2, 3, 1′, 2′, 3′ are elements of the same one-dimensional form, and A, B, C, A', B', C' are collinear points such that

$$1231'2'3' \barwedge ABCA'B'C',$$

then the ordered triad 123 is said *to have the same sense as* 1′2′3′ if and only if $S(ABC) = S(A'B'C')$. The set of all ordered triads having the same sense as 123 is called a *sense-class* and denoted by $S(123)$.

In view of Theorem 6 this definition is independent of the choice of the points A, B, C, A', B', C'. It is an immediate corollary of the definition that the plane and space duals of Theorems 2–6 all hold good (cf. figs. 10 and 13).

By the definition of a point conic there is a one-to-one correspondence between the points $[P]$ of the conic and the lines joining them to a fixed point P_0 of the conic. We now define any statement in

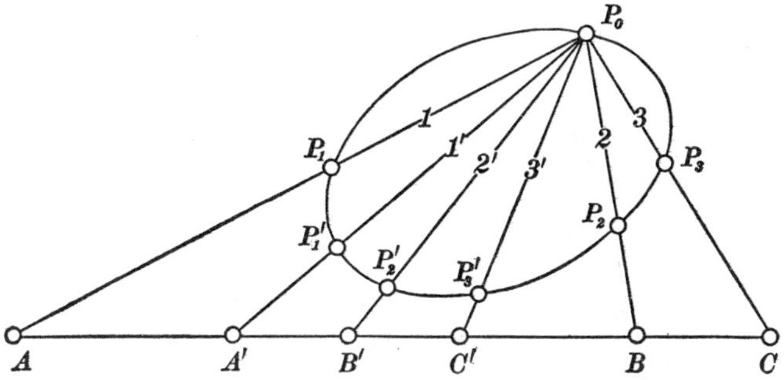

FIG. 10

terms of order relations among the points of the conic $[P]$ to mean that the same statement holds for the corresponding lines $[P_0P]$. By Theorem 6, above, together with Theorem 2, Chap. V, Vol. I, it follows that this definition is independent of the choice of the point P_0. The definitions of the order relations in the line conic, the cone of lines, and the cone of planes are made dually.*

The propositions with regard to sense are perhaps even more evident intuitionally when stated with regard to a conic or a flat pencil than with regard to the points of a line (cf. figs. 10 and 11).

* These definitions are in reality special cases of the definition given above for any one-dimensional form, since the cones and conic sections are one-dimensional forms of the second degree (§ 41, Vol. I) and since the notion of projectivity between one-dimensional forms of the first and second degrees has been defined in § 76, Vol. I. However, at present we do not need to avail ourselves of the theorems in Chap. VIII, Vol. I, on which the latter definition is based.

21. Separation of point pairs. DEFINITION. Two points A and B of a line are said to *separate* two points C and D of the same line if and only if $S(ABC) \neq S(ABD)$. This is indicated by the symbol $AB \parallel CD$.

THEOREM 7. (1) *The relation* $AB \parallel CD$ *implies the relations* $CD \parallel AB$ *and* $AB \parallel DC$, *and excludes the relation* $AC \parallel BD$. (2) *Given any four distinct points of a line, we have either* $AB \parallel CD$ *or* $AC \parallel BD$ or $AD \parallel BC$. (3) *From the relations* $AB \parallel CD$ *and* $AD \parallel BE$ *follows the relation* $AD \parallel CE$. (4) *If* $AB \parallel CD$ *and* $ABCD \,\overline{\wedge}\, A'B'C'D'$, *then* $A'B' \parallel C'D'$.*

Proof. (1) If $AB \parallel CD$, we have

$$S(ABC) \neq S(ABD), \tag{5}$$

which, by the definition of separation, implies $AB \parallel DC$. By Theorems 2–6 we obtain successively, from (5),

$$S(ABC) = S(ADB),$$
$$S(ABC) = S(ADC),$$
$$S(ACB) = S(DAB),$$
$$S(ACB) = S(DCB),$$
$$S(ABC) = S(CDB),$$
$$S(CDA) \neq S(CDB),$$

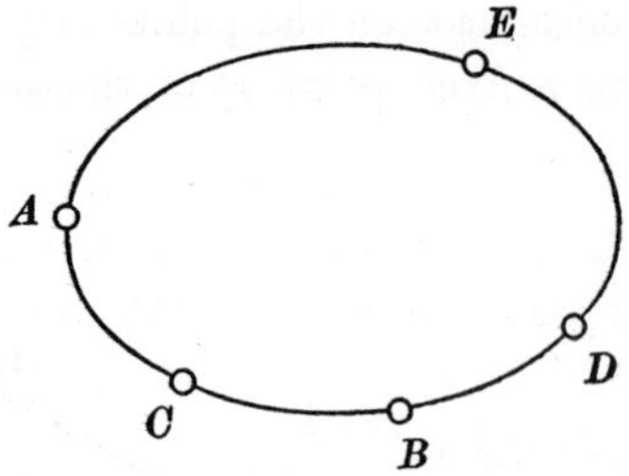

FIG. 11

the last of which implies $CD \parallel AB$. The relation $AC \parallel BD$ is excluded because it means $S(ACB) \neq S(ACD)$, which contradicts the second of the equations above.

(2) By the corollary of Theorem 3 we have either $S(ABC) \neq S(ABD)$ (in which case $AB \parallel CD$) or $S(ABC) = S(ABD)$. In the latter case either $S(ABC) \neq S(ADC)$ or $S(ABC) = S(ADC)$. The first of these alternatives is equivalent to $S(ACB) \neq S(ACD)$ and yields $AC \parallel BD$; the second implies $S(ADC) = S(ABC) = S(ABD) \neq S(ADB)$, and thus yields $AD \parallel BC$.

(3) The hypotheses give $S(ABC) \neq S(ABD)$ and $S(ADB) \neq S(ADE)$. The first of these gives $S(BCA) = S(DBA)$, which, by Theorem 5, implies $S(DBA) = S(DCA)$, and thus $S(ADB) = S(ADC)$. Hence, by the second hypothesis, $S(ADC) \neq S(ADE)$, and therefore $AD \parallel CE$.

(4) This is a direct consequence of Theorem 6.

* The properties expressed in this theorem are sufficient to define abstractly the relation of separation. Cf. Vailati, Revue de Mathématiques, Vol. V, pp. 76, 183; also Padoa, Revue de Mathématiques, Vol. VI, p. 35.

THEOREM 8. *If A and B are harmonically conjugate with regard to C and D, they separate C and D.*

Proof. By Theorem 7 (2) we have either $AB \parallel CD$ or $AC \parallel BD$ or $AD \parallel BC$. We also have $ABCD \barwedge BACD$. Hence $AC \parallel BD$ would imply $BC \parallel AD$, contrary to Theorem 7 (1); and $AD \parallel BC$ would imply $BD \parallel AC$, contrary to Theorem 7 (1). Hence we must have $AB \parallel CD$.

THEOREM 9. *An involution in which two pairs separate one another has no double points.*

Proof. Suppose that the given involution had the double points M, N, and that the two pairs which separate one another are A, A' and B, B' respectively. Since the involution would be determined by the projectivity

$$MNA \barwedge MNA',$$

in which, by Theorem 8,

$$S(MNA) \neq S(MNA'),$$

it would follow, by Theorem 6, that every ordered triad was carried into an ordered triad in the opposite sense. Since the involution carries $AA'B$ to $A'AB'$, we should have

$$S(AA'B) \neq S(A'AB');$$

and hence

$$S(AA'B) = S(AA'B'),$$

contrary to hypothesis.

This theorem can also be stated in the following form:

COROLLARY 1. *An involution with double points is such that no two pairs separate one another.*

COROLLARY 2. *If an involution is direct, each pair separates every other pair. If an involution is opposite, no pair separates any other pair.*

22. Segments and intervals. DEFINITION. Let A, B, C be any three distinct points of a line. The set of all points X such that

$$S(AXC) = S(ABC)$$

is called a *segment* and is denoted by $\overline{ABC}$. The points A and C are called the *ends* of the segment. The segment $\overline{ABC}$, together with its ends, is called the *interval* ABC. The points of $\overline{ABC}$ are said to be *interior* to the interval ABC, and A and C are called its *ends*.

COROLLARY 1. *A segment does not contain its ends.*

COROLLARY 2. *If D is in $\overline{ABC}$, then*

$$\overline{ABC} = \overline{ADC}.$$

COROLLARY 3. *If D is in* $\overline{ABC}$, *then B and D are not separated by A and C.*

THEOREM 10. *If A and B are any two distinct points of a line, there are two and only two segments, and also two and only two intervals, of which A and B are ends.*

Proof. Let C and D be two points which separate A and B harmonically. If X is any point of the line distinct from A and B, either

$$S(AXB) = S(ACB)$$

or

$$S(AXB) = S(ADB).$$

In one case X is in $\overline{ACB}$, and in the other case in $\overline{ADB}$.

DEFINITION. Either of the two segments (or of the two intervals) whose ends are two points A, B may be referred to as a *segment* $\overline{AB}$ (or an *interval* AB). The two segments or intervals AB are said to be *complementary* to one another.

COROLLARY. *If A, B, C are any three distinct points of a line, the line consists of the three segments complementary to* $\overline{ABC}$, $\overline{BCA}$, $\overline{CAB}$, *together with the points A, B, and C.*

Proof. Any point X distinct from A, B, C satisfies one of the relations $AC \parallel BX$ or $AB \parallel CX$ or $AX \parallel BC$.

THEOREM 11. *If* $A_1, A_2, \cdots, A_n$ *is any set of* $n\,(n > 1)$ *distinct points of a line, the remaining points of the line constitute n segments, each of which has two of the points* $A_1, A_2, \cdots, A_n$ *as end points and no two of which have a point in common.*

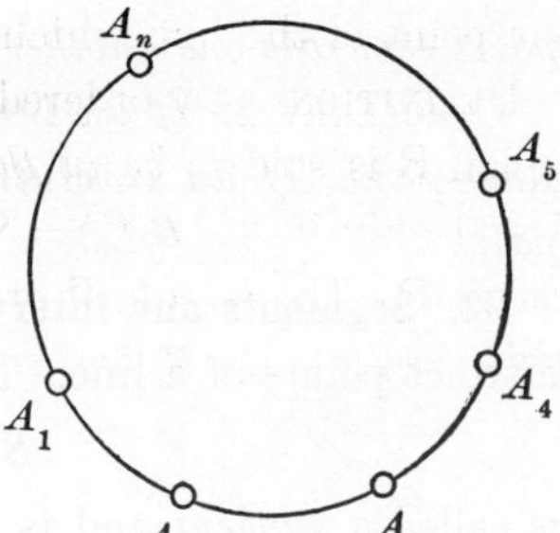

FIG. 12

Proof. The theorem is true for $n = 2$, by Theorem 10. Suppose it true for $n = k$. If $k+1$ points are given, the point A_{k+1} is, by the theorem for the case $n = k$, on one of the k segments determined by the other k points, say on the segment whose ends are A_i and A_j. By the corollary to Theorem 10, this segment consists of A_{k+1}, together with two segments whose ends are respectively A_{k+1}, A_i and A_{k+1}, A_j. Hence the theorem is valid for $n = k+1$ if valid for $n = k$. Hence the theorem is established by mathematical induction.

DEFINITION. A finite set of collinear points, $A_i\,(i = 1, \cdots, n)$, is in the *geometrical order* $\{A_1A_2A_3A_4 \cdots A_n\}$ if no two of its points are separated by any of the pairs A_1A_2, A_2A_3, $\cdots$, A_nA_1. As an obvious consequence of Theorem 11 we now have

THEOREM 12. *To any set* $[A]$ *of* n *points of a line the notation* A_1, A_2, $\cdots$, A_n *may be assigned so that they are in the order* $\{A_1A_2 \cdots A_n\}$. *A set of points in the order* $\{A_1A_2 \cdots A_n\}$ *is also in the orders* $\{A_2A_3 \cdots A_nA_1\}$ *and* $\{A_nA_{n-1} \cdots A_2A_1\}$.

EXERCISES

1. If $AB \parallel CD$ and $AC \parallel BE$, then $CD \parallel BE$.

2. The relations $AB \parallel CD$, $AB \parallel CE$, $AB \parallel DE$ are not possible simultaneously.

3. Any two points A, B are in the orders $\{AB\}$ and $\{BA\}$. Any three collinear points are in the orders $\{ABC\}$, $\{ACB\}$, $\{CAB\}$.

23. Linear regions. The set of all points on a line, the set of all points on a line with the exception of a single one, and the segment are examples (cf. Ex. 1 below) of what we shall define as linear regions on account of their analogy with the planar and spatial regions considered later.

DEFINITION. *A region* on a line is a set of collinear points such that (1) any two points of the set are joined by an interval consisting entirely of points of the set and (2) every point is interior to at least one segment consisting entirely of points of the set. A region is said to be *convex* if it satisfies also the condition that (3) there is at least one point of the line which is not in the set.

DEFINITION. An ordered pair of distinct points AB of a convex region R is said *to be in the same sense* as an ordered pair $A'B'$ of R if and only if $S(ABA_\infty) = S(A'B'A_\infty)$, where A_∞ is a point of the line not in R. The set of all ordered pairs of R in the same sense as AB is denoted by $S(AB)$ and is called a *sense-class*. The segment complementary to $\overline{AA_\infty B}$ is called *the segment* $\overline{AB}$. The corresponding interval is called *the interval* AB. A set of points of R is said to be in the *order* $\{A_1A_2 \cdots A_n\}$ if they are in the order $\{A_1A_2 \cdots A_nA_\infty\}$. If C is separated from A_∞ by A and B, C is *between* A and B with respect to R. If $S(AB) = S(CD)$, then C is said to *precede* D, and D to *follow* C, *in the sense* AB.

If there is a point B_∞, other than A_∞, which is not in the convex region R, the sense $S(ABA_\infty)$ is the same as the sense $S(ABB_\infty)$, and the segment $\overline{AA_\infty B}$ is the same as the segment $\overline{AB_\infty B}$. Hence

THEOREM 13. *For a given convex region* R *the above definition has the same meaning if any other point collinear with* R *but not in* R *be substituted for* A_∞.

COROLLARY 1. *If* $S(AB) = S(A'B')$ *and* $S(A'B') = S(A''B'')$, *then* $S(AB) = S(A''B'')$.

COROLLARY 2. *If* $S(AB) \neq S(A'B')$ *and* $S(A'B') \neq S(A''B'')$, *then* $S(AB) = S(A''B'')$.

COROLLARY 3. $S(AB) \neq S(BA)$.

COROLLARY 4. *If* $S(AB) = S(BC)$, *then* $S(AB) = S(AC)$.

These corollaries are direct translations of Theorems 2–5 into our present terminology. Theorem 7 translates into the following statements in terms of betweenness:

THEOREM 14. (1) *If C is between A and B, then B is not between A and C.* (2) *If three points A, B, C are distinct, C is between A and B or B is between A and C or A is between C and B.* (3) *If C is between A and B and A is between B and E, then C is between B and E.*

Theorem 7 translates into the following statements in terms of "precede" and "follows."

THEOREM 15. (1) *If C precedes B in the sense AC, then B does not precede C in this sense.* (2) *In the sense AC, either B precedes C or C precedes B.* (3) *If, in the sense AB, A precedes C and E precedes A, then E precedes C.*

DEFINITION. If A and B are any two points of a convex region R, the set consisting of all points which follow A in the sense AB is called the *ray AB*. The point A is called the *origin* of the ray. The ray consisting of all points which precede A in the sense AB is said to be *opposite* to the ray AB. The set of all points which precede A in the sense AB is sometimes called the *prolongation of the segment AB beyond A.*

EXERCISES

1. A convex region on a line is either a segment or the set of all points on the line with the exception of one point.*

2. If three points of a convex region are in the order $\{ABC\}$, they are in the order $\{CBA\}$ but not in the order $\{ACB\}$ or $\{CAB\}$.

3. In a convex region, if A is between B and C, it is between C and B.

4. Between any two points there is an infinity of points.

* This exercise requires the use of an assumption of continuity (C and R, or K).

5. If B is on $\overline{AC}$ and C is on $\overline{BD}$, then C is on $\overline{AD}$ and B is on $\overline{AD}$.

6. The relations B is on $\overline{AC}$, B is on $\overline{AD}$, B is on $\overline{CD}$ are not possible simultaneously.

7. If B and C are on $\overline{AD}$, then B is on $\overline{AC}$ or on $\overline{CD}$.

8. Choosing a system of nonhomogeneous coördinates in which A_∞ is ∞, show that the sense AB is the same as the sense $A'B'$ if and only if $B-A$ is of the same sign as $B'-A'$; also that two point pairs have the same sense if and only if they are conjugate under the group

$$x' = ax + b,$$

where $a > 0$.

24. Algebraic criteria of sense. If $A=(a_0, a_1)$, $B=(b_0, b_1)$, and $C=(c_0, c_1)$ are any three distinct points of the line, the transformation

$$\begin{aligned} x_0' &= \rho_0 a_0 x_0 + \rho_1 b_0 x_1, \\ x_1' &= \rho_0 a_1 x_0 + \rho_1 b_1 x_1 \end{aligned} \tag{6}$$

changes (1, 0), (0, 1), and (1, 1) into A, B, and C respectively if and only if ρ_0 and ρ_1 satisfy the equations

$$\begin{aligned} c_0 &= \rho_0 a_0 + \rho_1 b_0, \\ c_1 &= \rho_0 a_1 + \rho_1 b_1, \end{aligned}$$

that is, if

$$\frac{\rho_0}{\rho_1} = \frac{\begin{vmatrix} c_0 & b_0 \\ c_1 & b_1 \end{vmatrix}}{\begin{vmatrix} a_0 & c_0 \\ a_1 & c_1 \end{vmatrix}}.$$

With this choice of ρ_0/ρ_1 the determinant of the transformation (6) is of the same sign as

$$S = \begin{vmatrix} a_0 & b_0 \\ a_1 & b_1 \end{vmatrix} \cdot \begin{vmatrix} b_0 & c_0 \\ b_1 & c_1 \end{vmatrix} \cdot \begin{vmatrix} c_0 & a_0 \\ c_1 & a_1 \end{vmatrix}.$$

By definition the projectivity is direct if and only if S is positive. Now if $A' = (a_0', a_1')$, $B' = (b_0', b_1')$, $C' = (c_0', c_1')$ are any three points of the line, and

$$S' = \begin{vmatrix} a_0' & b_0' \\ a_1' & b_1' \end{vmatrix} \cdot \begin{vmatrix} b_0' & c_0' \\ b_1' & c_1' \end{vmatrix} \cdot \begin{vmatrix} c_0' & a_0' \\ c_1' & a_1' \end{vmatrix},$$

two cases are possible. If S' is of the same sign as S, the projectivities in which

$$(1, 0)\,(0, 1)\,(1, 1) \;\overline{\wedge}\; ABC, \tag{7}$$

$$(1, 0)\,(0, 1)\,(1, 1) \;\overline{\wedge}\; A'B'C' \tag{8}$$

are both direct or both opposite, and hence the projectivity in which

$$ABC \;\overline{\wedge}\; A'B'C' \tag{9}$$

is direct. If S' is opposite in sign to S, one of the projectivities (7) and (8) is direct and the other opposite, and hence (9) is opposite. Hence

THEOREM 16. *Let* $A=(a_0, a_1)$, $B=(b_0, b_1)$, $C=(c_0, c_1)$, $A'=(a'_0, a'_1)$, $B'=(b'_0, b'_1)$, $C'=(c'_0, c'_1)$ *be collinear points. Then* $S(ABC)=S(A'B'C')$ *if and only if the expressions*

$$\begin{vmatrix} a_0 & b_0 \\ a_1 & b_1 \end{vmatrix} \cdot \begin{vmatrix} b_0 & c_0 \\ b_1 & c_1 \end{vmatrix} \cdot \begin{vmatrix} c_0 & a_0 \\ c_1 & a_1 \end{vmatrix} \quad \textit{and} \quad \begin{vmatrix} a'_0 & b'_0 \\ a'_1 & b'_1 \end{vmatrix} \cdot \begin{vmatrix} b'_0 & c'_0 \\ b'_1 & c'_1 \end{vmatrix} \cdot \begin{vmatrix} c'_0 & a'_0 \\ c'_1 & a'_1 \end{vmatrix}$$

have the same sign.

COROLLARY 1. *Three points given by the finite nonhomogeneous coördinates* a, b, c *are conjugate under the group of all direct projectivities to three points given by the finite nonhomogeneous coördinates* a', b', c', *respectively, if and only if* $(a-b)(b-c)(c-a)$ *and* $(a'-b')(b'-c')(c'-a')$ *have the same sign.*

Proof. Set $a=a_1/a_0$, $b=b_1/b_0$, $c=c_1/c_0$, and apply the theorem.

COROLLARY 2. *Two points given by the finite nonhomogeneous coördinates* a *and* b *are conjugate under the group of all direct projectivities leaving the point* ∞ *of the nonhomogeneous coördinate system invariant to the two points given by the finite nonhomogeneous coördinates* a' *and* b' *respectively if and only if* $a-b$ *and* $a'-b'$ *have the same sign.*

Proof. Set $a=a_1/a_0$, $b=b_1/b_0$, $c_0=0$, $c_1=1$, and apply the theorem.

THEOREM 17. *A, B separate C, D if and only if the cross ratio* R(AB, CD) *is negative.*

Proof. By the last theorem, A, B separate C, D if and only if

$$\begin{vmatrix} a_0 & b_0 \\ a_1 & b_1 \end{vmatrix} \cdot \begin{vmatrix} b_0 & c_0 \\ b_1 & c_1 \end{vmatrix} \cdot \begin{vmatrix} c_0 & a_0 \\ c_1 & a_1 \end{vmatrix} \quad \text{and} \quad \begin{vmatrix} a_0 & b_0 \\ a_1 & b_1 \end{vmatrix} \cdot \begin{vmatrix} b_0 & d_0 \\ b_1 & d_1 \end{vmatrix} \cdot \begin{vmatrix} d_0 & a_0 \\ d_1 & a_1 \end{vmatrix}$$

are opposite in sign. But the quotient of these two expressions has the same sign as R(AB, CD) (cf. p. 165, Chap. VI, Vol. I).

With the aid of this theorem the proof of Theorem 7 can be made much more simply than in § 21.

25. Pairs of lines and of planes. THEOREM 18. *The points of space not on either of two planes* α *and* β *fall into two classes such that two points* O_1, O_2 *of the same class are not separated by the points in which the line* O_1O_2 *meets the planes* α *and* β, *while two points* O, P *of different classes are separated by the points in which the line* OP *meets* α *and* β.

Proof. By the space dual of Theorem 10 the planes of the pencil $\alpha\beta$ are separated by α and β into two segments. Let $[O]$ be the set of points on the planes of one of these segments but not on the line $\alpha\beta$, and let $[P]$ be the set of the points on the planes of the other segment but not on the line $\alpha\beta$.

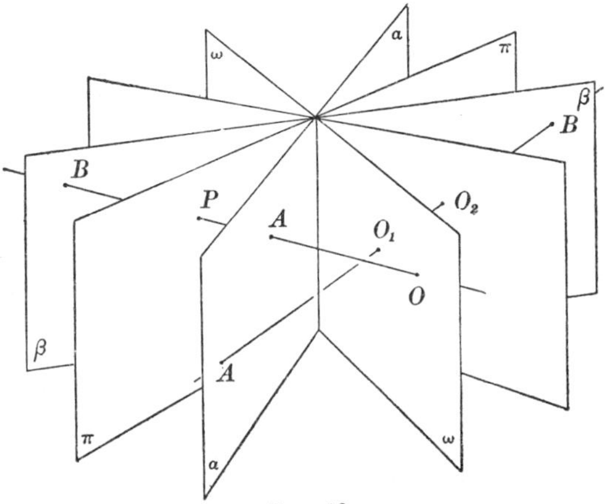

FIG. 13

The two planes ω and π of the pencil $\alpha\beta$ which are on any two points O and P are separated by α and β. Hence, by Theorem 7 and § 20, the points in which the line OP meets α and β are separated by O and P. In like manner, any two points O_1, O_2 determine with the line $\alpha\beta$ a pair of planes (or a single plane) not separated by α and β, and hence the line O_1O_2 meets α and β in points (or a single point) not separated by O_1 and O_2. By the same reasoning, any line P_1P_2 meets α and β in points (or a point) not separated by P_1 and P_2.

COROLLARY 1. *If l and m are two coplanar lines, the points of the plane which are not on l or m fall into two classes such that two points O_1, O_2 of the same class are not separated by the points in which the line O_1O_2 meets l and m, while two points O, P of different classes are separated by the points in which OP meets l and m.*

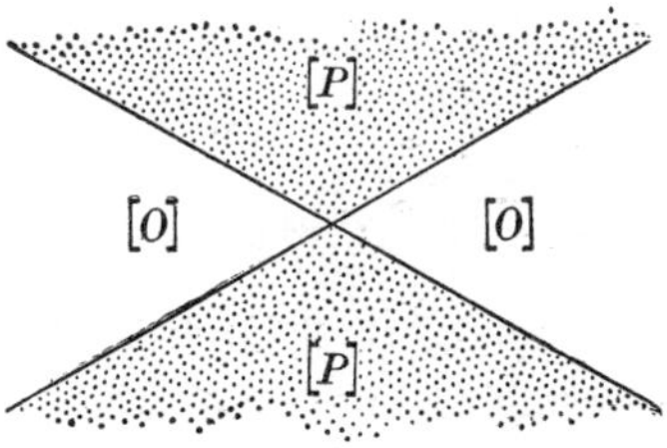

FIG. 14

COROLLARY 2. *There is only one pair of classes $[O]$ and $[P]$ satisfying the conditions of the above theorem (or its first corollary) determined by a given pair of planes (or lines).*

DEFINITION. Two points in different classes (according to Corollary 1) relative to two coplanar lines are said to be *separated* by the two lines; otherwise they are said not to be separated by the lines. Two points in different classes (according to Theorem 18) relative to two planes are said to be *separated* by the two planes; otherwise they are said not to be separated by the planes.

EXERCISES

1. If l_1 and l_2 are two coplanar lines and O any point of their common plane, all triads of points in a fixed sense-class S_1 on l_1 are projected from O into triads in a fixed sense-class S_2 on l_2 (Theorem 6). If P is any other point of the plane, it is separated from O by l_1 and l_2 if and only if triads in the sense S_1 are not projected from P into triads in the sense S_2.

This problem can be stated also in terms of the sense of pairs of points in the region obtained on l_1 or l_2 respectively by leaving out the common point. The theorem in this form is generalized in § 30. In the form stated in Ex. 1 it has the following generalization.

2. If l_1 and l_2 are two noncoplanar lines, and o is any line not intersecting them, all triads in a fixed sense S_1 on l_1 are axially projected from o into triads in a fixed sense S_2 on l_2 (Theorem 6). The lines not intersecting l_1 and l_2 fall into two classes: those by which triads in the sense S_1 are projected into triads in the sense S_2, and those by which triads in the sense S_1 are projected into triads in the sense opposite to S_2.

3. Obtain the definition of separation of two coplanar lines by two points as the plane dual of the definition of separation of two points by two coplanar lines. Prove that if two coplanar lines separate two points, then the points separate the lines. State and prove the corresponding result for pairs of points and of planes.

26. The triangle and the tetrahedron.

THEOREM 19. *If a line l not passing through any vertex of a triangle ABC meets the sides BC, CA, AB in A_1, B_1, C_1 respectively, then any other line m which meets the segments $\overline{BA_1C}$, $\overline{CB_1A}$ also meets the segment $\overline{AC_1B}$.*

Proof. Suppose first that m passes through A_1; then

$$ACB_1B_2 \stackrel{A_1}{\overline{\overline{\wedge}}} (ABC_1C_2),$$

and hence, if B_1 and B_2 do not separate A and C, C_1 and C_2 do not separate A and B. Similarly, the theorem is true if m passes through B_1.

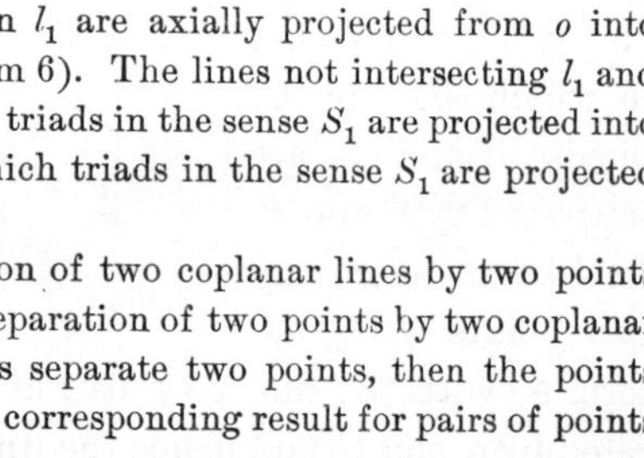

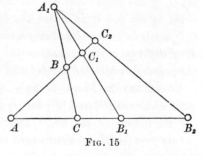

FIG. 15

If m does not pass through A_1 or B_1, let m' be a line joining A_1 to the point in which m meets CA. By the argument above we have first that m' meets all three segments $\overline{BA_1C}$, $\overline{CB_1A}$, and $\overline{AC_1B}$, and then that m meets them.

Let us denote the segment $\overline{AC_1B}$ by γ, $\overline{BA_1C}$ by α, and $\overline{CB_1A}$ by β, and the segments complementary to α, β, γ by $\bar{\alpha}, \bar{\beta}, \bar{\gamma}$ respectively. The above theorem then gives the information that every line which meets two of the segments α, β, γ meets the third. Any line which meets α and $\bar{\beta}$ meets $\bar{\gamma}$, for, as it does not pass through A or B, it meets either γ or $\bar{\gamma}$; but if it met γ, and by hypothesis meets α, it would meet β. Hence the theorem gives that $\alpha, \bar{\beta}, \bar{\gamma}$ are such that any line meeting two of these segments meets the third. By a repetition of this argument it follows that every line of the plane which does not pass through a vertex of the triangle meets all three segments of one of the trios $\alpha\beta\gamma$, $\bar{\alpha}\bar{\beta}\gamma$, $\bar{\alpha}\beta\bar{\gamma}$, $\alpha\bar{\beta}\bar{\gamma}$, and no line whatever meets all three segments in any of the trios $\alpha\beta\bar{\gamma}$, $\alpha\bar{\beta}\gamma$, $\bar{\alpha}\beta\gamma$, $\bar{\alpha}\bar{\beta}\bar{\gamma}$.

The lines of the plane, exclusive of those through the vertices, therefore fall into four classes:

(1) those which meet α, β, γ,
(2) those which meet $\bar{\alpha}, \bar{\beta}, \gamma$,
(3) those which meet $\alpha, \bar{\beta}, \bar{\gamma}$,
(4) those which meet $\bar{\alpha}, \beta, \bar{\gamma}$.

No two lines l_1, l_2 of the same class are separated by any pair of the lines joining the point l_1l_2 to the vertices of the triangle, while any two lines l_1, m_1 of different classes are separated by two of the lines joining the point l_1m_1 to the vertices. This result is perhaps more intuitively striking when put into the dual form, as follows:

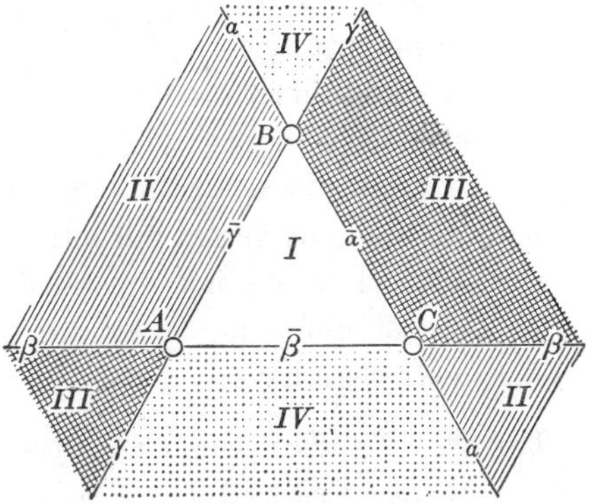

FIG. 16

THEOREM 20. *The points of a plane not on the sides of a triangle fall into four classes such that no two points L_1, L_2 of the same class are separated by any pair of the points in which the line L_1L_2 meets the sides of the triangle, while any two points L_1, M_1 of different classes are separated by two of the points in which the line L_1M_1 meets the sides of the triangle.*

DEFINITION. Any one of the four classes of points in Theorem 20 is called a *triangular region*. The vertices of the triangle are also called *vertices of the triangular region*.

The property of the triangle stated in Theorem 19 can also serve as a basis for a discussion of the ordinal theorems on the tetrahedron and for those of the $(n+1)$-point in n-space. Suppose we have a tetrahedron whose vertices are A_1, A_2, A_3, A_4. Let us denote its faces by $\alpha_1, \alpha_2, \alpha_3, \alpha_4$, the face α_1 being opposite to the vertex A_1, etc.; let us denote the edges by $a_{12}, a_{13}, a_{14}, a_{23}, a_{34}, a_{42}$, the edge a_{ij} being the line A_iA_j. Each edge a_{ij} is separated by the vertices A_i, A_j into two segments, which we shall denote by σ_{ij} and $\bar{\sigma}_{ij}$. Let π be a plane not passing through any vertex; the six segments which it meets may be denoted by $\sigma_{12}, \sigma_{13}, \cdots, \sigma_{42}$, and the complementary segments by $\bar{\sigma}_{12}, \bar{\sigma}_{13}, \cdots, \bar{\sigma}_{42}$. Then as a corollary of Theorem 19 we have that any plane which meets three noncoplanar segments of the set $\sigma_{12}, \sigma_{13}, \cdots, \sigma_{42}$ meets all the rest of them, and, moreover, no plane meets all the segments $\bar{\sigma}_{12}, \bar{\sigma}_{13}, \cdots, \bar{\sigma}_{42}$. If we observe that any plane not passing through a vertex must meet the edges a_{12}, a_{13}, a_{14} in three distinct points, it becomes clear that the planes not passing through any vertex fall into eight classes such that two planes of the same class are not separated by a pair of vertices, whereas two planes of different classes are separated by a pair of vertices. Under duality we have

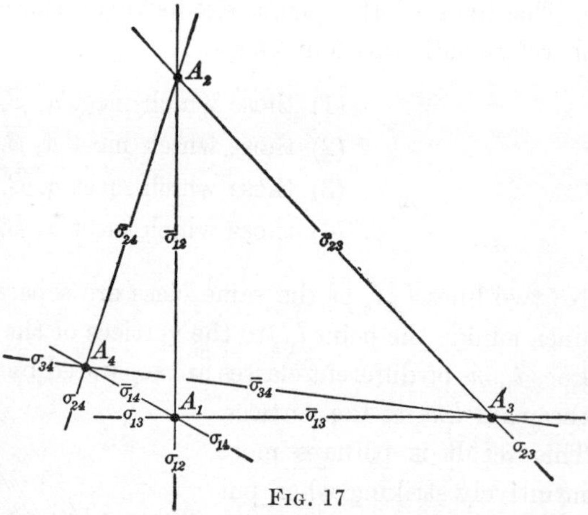

FIG. 17

THEOREM 21. *The points not upon the faces of a tetrahedron fall into eight classes such that two points of the same class are not separated by the points in which the line joining them meets the faces, whereas two points of different classes are separated by two of the points in which their line meets the faces of the tetrahedron.*

DEFINITION. Any one of the eight classes of points in Theorem 21 is called a *tetrahedral region.* The vertices of the tetrahedron are also called vertices of any one of the tetrahedral regions.

It would be easy to complete the discussion of the triangle and the tetrahedron at this point — for example, to define the term "boundary" and to prove that the boundary of any one of the classes of points in Theorem 20 is composed of A, B, C and three segments having the property that no line meets them all. We shall defer this discussion, however, to a later chapter, where the results will appear as special cases of more general theorems.

27. Algebraic criteria of separation. Cross ratios of points in space. The classes of points determined (Theorems 18–21) by a pair of intersecting lines, a triangle, a pair of planes or by a tetrahedron can be discussed by means of some very elementary algebraic considerations. As these are similar in the plane and in space, let us carry out the work only for the three-dimensional cases.

Suppose that the homogeneous coördinates of four noncoplanar points A_1, A_2, A_3, A_4 are given by the columns of the matrix,

$$(10)\qquad \begin{pmatrix} a_{01} & a_{02} & a_{03} & a_{04} \\ a_{11} & a_{12} & a_{13} & a_{14} \\ a_{21} & a_{22} & a_{23} & a_{24} \\ a_{31} & a_{32} & a_{33} & a_{34} \end{pmatrix},$$

and let (x_0, x_1, x_2, x_3) be the homogeneous coördinates of any other point X. Let us indicate by $|x, a_2, a_3, a_4|$ the determinant of the matrix obtained by substituting x_0, x_1, x_2, x_3 respectively for the elements of the first column in the matrix above; by $|a_1, x, a_3, a_4|$ the determinant obtained by performing the same operation on the second column, etc. The expressions $|y, a_2, a_3, a_4|$ etc. have similar meanings in terms of the coördinates of a point $(y_0, y_1, y_2, y_3) = Y$. The following expressions are formed analogously to the cross ratios of four points on a line (cf. § 58, Vol. I):

$$(11)\qquad \begin{aligned} k_{14} &= \frac{|x, a_2, a_3, a_4|}{|a_1, a_2, a_3, x|} \div \frac{|y, a_2, a_3, a_4|}{|a_1, a_2, a_3, y|}, \\ k_{24} &= \frac{|a_1, x, a_3, a_4|}{|a_1, a_2, a_3, x|} \div \frac{|a_1, y, a_3, a_4|}{|a_1, a_2, a_3, y|}, \\ k_{34} &= \frac{|a_1, a_2, x, a_4|}{|a_1, a_2, a_3, x|} \div \frac{|a_1, a_2, y, a_4|}{|a_1, a_2, a_3, y|}. \end{aligned}$$

Clearly there are twelve numbers k_{ij} which could be defined analogously to these; and if the notation A_1, A_2, A_3, A_4, X, Y be permuted among the six points, 720 such expressions are defined. Each number k_{ij}

is an absolute invariant of the six points, for it is unaltered if the coördinates of any point be multiplied by a constant or if all six points be subjected to the same linear transformation.

If Y be not upon any of the planes determined by the points A_1, A_2, A_3, A_4, there exists a projectivity which carries Y into $(1, 1, 1, 1)$ and the points A_1, A_2, A_3, A_4 into the points represented by the columns of

$$\begin{pmatrix} 1 & 0 & 0 & 0 \\ 0 & 1 & 0 & 0 \\ 0 & 0 & 1 & 0 \\ 0 & 0 & 0 & 1 \end{pmatrix}. \tag{12}$$

Let (X_0, X_1, X_2, X_3) be the point into which (x_0, x_1, x_2, x_3) is carried by this projectivity. By substituting in (11) we see that

$$k_{14} = \frac{X_0}{X_3}, \quad k_{24} = \frac{X_1}{X_3}, \quad k_{34} = \frac{X_2}{X_3}.$$

From this it follows that $|x, a_2, a_3, a_4|$, $|a_1, x, a_3, a_4|$, etc. *could be taken as the homogeneous coördinates with respect to the tetrahedron of reference whose vertices are* A_1, A_2, A_3, A_4.

The line $$(X_0, X_1, X_2, X_3) - \lambda(1, 1, 1, 1)$$
meets the planes determined by the four points represented by (12) in four points given by the values $\lambda = X_0$, $\lambda = X_1$, $\lambda = X_2$, $\lambda = X_3$. The cross ratios of pairs of these points with (X_0, X_1, X_2, X_3) and $(1, 1, 1, 1)$ are X_0/X_3, X_1/X_3, and X_2/X_3. Hence k_{14}, k_{24}, k_{34} *are cross ratios of* X *and* Y *with pairs of points in which the line joining them meets the faces of the tetrahedron* $A_1A_2A_3A_4$.

By Theorem 17, the points X and Y are separated by the planes $A_2A_3A_4$ and $A_2A_3A_1$ if and only if k_{14} is negative. They will be separated by $A_1A_3A_4$ and $A_1A_3A_2$ if and only if k_{24} is negative, and by $A_1A_2A_4$ and $A_1A_2A_3$ if and only if k_{34} is negative. Hence, by Theorem 21, we have

THEOREM 22. *The points* X *and* Y *will be in the same class with respect to the tetrahedron* $A_1A_2A_3A_4$ *if and only if* k_{14}, k_{24}, k_{34} *are all positive.*

COROLLARY. *The eight regions determined by the tetrahedron* $A_1A_2A_3A_4$ *are those for which the algebraic signs of* k_{14}, k_{24}, k_{34} *appear in the following combinations:* $(+, +, +)$, $(+, +, -)$, $(+, -, +)$, $(-, +, +)$, $(-, -, -)$, $(-, -, +)$, $(-, +, -)$, $(+, -, -)$.

Recalling that $|x, a_2, a_3, a_4| = 0$ is the equation of the plane $A_2A_3A_4$ (cf. § 70, Vol. I), we see that if

$$\alpha(x) \equiv \alpha_0 x_0 + \alpha_1 x_1 + \alpha_2 x_2 + \alpha_3 x_3 = 0$$

and

$$\beta(x) \equiv \beta_0 x_0 + \beta_1 x_1 + \beta_2 x_2 + \beta_3 x_3 = 0$$

are the equations of two planes, the formula given above for the cross ratio of two points X and Y with the points of intersection of the line XY with these planes becomes

$$\frac{\alpha(x)}{\alpha(y)} \div \frac{\beta(x)}{\beta(y)}. \tag{13}$$

Thus two points are in the same one of the two classes determined by the planes $\alpha(x)$ and $\beta(x)$ if and only if this expression is positive.

This result assumes an even simpler form when specialized somewhat with respect to a system of nonhomogeneous coördinates. Suppose that $x_0 = 0$ be chosen as the singular plane in a system of nonhomogeneous coördinates; then the same point is represented nonhomogeneously by (x, y, z) or homogeneously by $(1, x, y, z)$, and the plane represented above by $\alpha(x) = 0$ has the equation

$$\alpha_1 x + \alpha_2 y + \alpha_3 z + \alpha_0 = 0.$$

If $\beta(x) = 0$ be the plane $x_0 = 0$, the expression for the cross ratio written above becomes

$$\frac{\alpha(x)}{\alpha(y)} \div \frac{x_0}{y_0},$$

which reduces in nonhomogeneous coördinates, when (x_0, x_1, x_2, x_3) and (y_0, y_1, y_2, y_3) are replaced by $(1, x', y', z')$ and $(1, x'', y'', z'')$, to

$$\frac{\alpha_1 x' + \alpha_2 y' + \alpha_3 z' + \alpha_0}{\alpha_1 x'' + \alpha_2 y'' + \alpha_3 z'' + \alpha_0}. \tag{14}$$

Hence two points (x', y', z') and (x'', y'', z'') are separated by the singular plane, and $\alpha_1 x + \alpha_2 y + \alpha_3 z + \alpha_0 = 0$ if and only if the numerator and denominator of (14) are of opposite sign. For reference we shall state this as a theorem in the following form:

THEOREM 23. *The two classes of points determined, according to Theorem 18, by the singular plane of a nonhomogeneous coördinate system and a plane $ax + by + cz + d = 0$ are respectively the points (x, y, z) for which $ax + by + cz + d$ is positive and the points for which it is negative.*

EXERCISES

1. Carry out the discussion analogous to the above in the two-dimensional case. Generalize to n dimensions.

2. How many of the 720 numbers analogous to k_{14} are distinct?

28. Euclidean spaces. DEFINITION. The set of all points of a projective space* of n dimensions, with the exception of those on a single $(n-1)$-space S^∞ contained in the n-space, is called a *Euclidean space of n dimensions.* Thus, in particular, the set of all but one of the points of a projective line is called a *Euclidean line,* and the set of all the points of a projective plane, except those on a single line, is called a *Euclidean plane.*

DEFINITION. The projective $(n-1)$-space S^∞ is called the *singular* $(n-1)$*-space* or *the* $(n-1)$*-space at infinity* or the *ideal* $(n-1)$*-space associated with* the Euclidean space. Any figure in S^∞ is said to be *ideal* or to be *at infinity,* whereas any figure in the Euclidean n-space is said to be *ordinary.*

The ordinary points of any line in a Euclidean plane or space form a Euclidean line and thus satisfy the definition (§ 23) of a linear convex region. The definitions and theorems of that section may therefore be applied at once in discussing Euclidean spaces. Thus, if A and B are any two ordinary points, we shall speak of "the segment AB," "the ray AB," etc.

The first corollary of Theorem 18 yields a very simple and important theorem if the line m be taken as the line at infinity, namely:

THEOREM 24. *The points of a Euclidean plane which are not on a line l fall into two classes such that the segment joining two points of the same class does not meet l and the segment joining two points of different classes does meet l.*

COROLLARY. *If a is any ray whose origin is a point of l, all points of a are either on l or on the same side of l.*

In like manner Theorem 18 yields

THEOREM 25. *The points of a Euclidean three-space which are not on a plane π fall into two classes such that the segment joining two points of the same class does not meet π and the segment joining two points of different classes does meet π.*

* We shall refer to a line, plane, or n-space in the sense of Chap. I, Vol. I, as a projective line, plane, or n-space whenever there is possibility of confusion with other types of spaces.

DEFINITION. The two classes of points determined by a line l in a Euclidean plane, according to Theorem 24, are called the two *sides* of l. The two classes of points determined by a plane π in a Euclidean three-space, according to Theorem 25, are called the two *sides* of π.

The two sides of π are characterized algebraically in Theorem 23.

DEFINITION. An ordered pair of rays h, k having a common origin is called an *angle* and is denoted by $\measuredangle hk$. If the rays are AB and AC, the angle may also be denoted by $\measuredangle BAC$. If the rays are opposite, the angle is called a *straight* angle; if the rays coincide, it is called a *zero* angle. The rays h, k are called the *sides* of $\measuredangle hk$, and their common origin the *vertex* of $\measuredangle hk$.

EXERCISES

1. The points of a Euclidean plane not on the sides or vertex of a nonzero angle $\measuredangle hk$ fall into two classes such that the segment joining two points of different classes contains one point of h or k. In case $\measuredangle hk$ is not a straight angle, one of these two classes consists of every point which is between a point of h and a point of k.

2. Generalize Theorem 25 to n dimensions.

29. Assumptions for a Euclidean space. A Euclidean space can be characterized completely by means of a set of assumptions stated in terms of order relations. Such a set of assumptions is given below. It is a simple exercise, which we shall leave to the reader, to verify that these assumptions are all satisfied by a Euclidean space as defined in the last section.

The reverse process is also of considerable interest. This consists (1) in deriving the elementary theorems of alignment and order from Assumptions I–VIII below, and (2) in defining ideal elements and showing that these, together with the elements of the Euclidean space, form a projective space. For the details of (1) and an outline of (2) the reader may consult the article by the writer, in the Transactions of the American Mathematical Society, Vol. V (1904), pp. 343–384, and also a note by R. L. Moore, in the same journal, Vol. XIII (1912), p. 74. On (2) one may consult the article by R. Bonola, Giornale di Matematiche, Vol. XXXVIII (1900), p. 105, and also that by F. W. Owens, Transactions of the American Mathematical Society, Vol. XI (1910), p. 141. Compare also the Introduction to Vol. I.

This set of assumptions refers to an undefined class of elements called points and an undefined relation among points indicated by saying "the points A, B, C are in the order $\{ABC\}$."

The assumptions are as follows:

I. *If points A, B, C are in the order $\{ABC\}$, they are distinct.*

II. *If points A, B, C are in the order $\{ABC\}$, they are not in the order $\{BCA\}$.*

DEFINITION. If A and B are distinct points, the *segment* $\overline{AB}$ consists of all points X in the order $\{AXB\}$; all points of the segment $\overline{AB}$ are said to be *between* A and B; the segment together with A and B is called the *interval* AB; the *line* AB consists of A and B and all points X in one of the orders $\{ABX\}$, $\{AXB\}$, $\{XAB\}$; and the *ray* AB consists of B and all points X in one of the orders $\{AXB\}$ and $\{ABX\}$.

III. *If points C and D ($C \neq D$) are on the line AB, then A is on the line CD.*

IV. *If three distinct points A, B, and C do not lie on the same line, and D and E are two points in the orders $\{BCD\}$ and $\{CEA\}$, then a point F exists in the order $\{AFB\}$ and such that D, E, and F lie on the same line.*

V. *If A and B are two distinct points, there exists a point C such that A, B, and C are in the order $\{ABC\}$.*

VI. *There exist three distinct points A, B, C not in any of the orders $\{ABC\}$, $\{BCA\}$, $\{CAB\}$.*

DEFINITION. If A, B, C are three noncollinear points, the set of all points collinear with pairs of points on the intervals AB, BC, CA is called the *plane* ABC.

VII. *If A, B, C are three noncollinear points, there exists a point D not in the same plane with A, B, and C.*

VIII. *Two planes which have one point in common have two distinct points in common.*

IX. *If A is any point and a any line not containing A, there is not more than one line through A coplanar with a and not meeting a.*

XVII. *If there exists an infinitude of points, there exists a certain pair of points A, C such that if $[\sigma]$ is any infinite set of segments of the line AC, having the property that each point of the interval AC is a point of a segment σ, then there is a finite subset, $\sigma_1, \sigma_2, \cdots, \sigma_n$, with the same property.**

* The proposition here stated about the interval AC is commonly known as the Heine-Borel theorem. The continuity assumption is more usually stated in the form of the "Dedekind Cut Axiom." Cf. R. Dedekind, Stetigkeit und irrationalen Zahlen, Braunschweig, 1872.

Assumptions I to VIII are sufficient to define a three-space which is capable of being extended by means of ideal elements into a projective space satisfying A, E, S. This space will not, in general, satisfy Assumption P. If the continuity assumption, XVII, be added, the corresponding projective space is real and hence properly projective. Assumption IX is the assumption with regard to parallel lines. Assumption VIII limits the number of dimensions to three.

30. Sense in a Euclidean plane. Suppose that l_∞ is the line at infinity of a Euclidean plane. Every collineation transforming the Euclidean plane into itself effects a projectivity on l_∞ which is either direct or opposite (§ 18). Since the direct projectivities on l_∞ form a group, the planar collineations which effect these transformations on l_∞ also form a group.

DEFINITION. A collineation of a Euclidean plane which effects a direct projectivity on the line at infinity of this plane is said to be a *direct collineation* of the Euclidean plane. Any other collineation of the Euclidean plane is said to be *opposite*. Let A, B, C be three noncollinear points; the class of all ordered triads $A'B'C'$ such that the collineation carrying A, B, and C to A', B', and C' respectively is direct, is called a *sense-class* and is denoted by $S(ABC)$. Two ordered triads of noncollinear points in the same sense-class are said to *have the same sense* or to *be in the same sense.* Otherwise they are said to *have opposite senses* or to *be in opposite senses.*

Since the direct projectivities form a group, it follows that if a triad $A'B'C'$ is in $S(ABC)$, then $S(ABC) = S(A'B'C')$.

THEOREM 26. *There are two and only two sense-classes in a Euclidean plane. If A, B, and C are noncollinear points, $S(ABC) = S(BCA) \neq S(ACB)$.*

Proof. Let A, B, C be three noncollinear points. If A', B', C' are any three noncollinear points such that the projectivity carrying A, B, C to A', B', C' respectively is direct, $S(ABC)$ contains the triad $A'B'C'$. Because the direct projectivities form a group, $S(ABC) = S(A'B'C')$. The triads to which ABC is carried by collineations which are not direct all form a sense-class, because the product of two opposite collineations is direct. Thus there are two and only two sense-classes.

Suppose we denote the lines BC, CA, AB by a, b, c respectively and let A', B', C' be the points of intersection of a, b, c respectively with l_∞. The projectivity carrying ABC to BCA evidently carries a, b, and c to b, c, and a respectively, and thus carries $A'B'C'$ to $B'C'A'$, and thus is direct (§ 19). Hence

$$S(ABC) = S(BCA).$$

The projectivity carrying ABC to ACB carries $A'B'C'$ to $A'C'B'$, and hence is not direct; and hence

$$S(ABC) \neq S(ACB).$$

THEOREM 27. *Two points C and D are on opposite sides of a line AB if and only if*

$$S(ABC) \neq S(ABD).$$

This theorem can be derived as a consequence of Ex. 1, § 25. It can also be derived from the following algebraic considerations.

Let us choose a system of nonhomogeneous coördinates in such a way that the singular line of the coördinate system is the same as the singular line of the Euclidean plane. The group of all projective collineations transforming the Euclidean plane into itself then reduces (§ 67, Vol. I) to

$$\begin{aligned} x' &= a_1x + b_1y + c_1, \\ y' &= a_2x + b_2y + c_2, \end{aligned} \qquad \Delta = \begin{vmatrix} a_1 & b_1 \\ a_2 & b_2 \end{vmatrix} \neq 0. \tag{15}$$

If we change to the homogeneous coördinates for which $x = x_1/x_0$ and $y = x_2/x_0$, the line at infinity has the equation $x_0 = 0$, and the equations (15) reduce to

$$\begin{aligned} x_0' &= x_0, \\ x_1' &= c_1x_0 + a_1x_1 + b_1x_2, \\ x_2' &= c_2x_0 + a_2x_2 + b_2x_2. \end{aligned} \tag{16}$$

On the line at infinity this effects the transformation

$$\begin{aligned} x_1' &= a_1x_1 + b_1x_2, \\ x_2' &= a_2x_1 + b_2x_2, \end{aligned}$$

which is direct if and only if $\Delta > 0$.

Let the nonhomogeneous coördinates of three points A, B, C be (a_1, a_2), (b_1, b_2), (c_1, c_2) respectively. The determinant

$$S = \begin{vmatrix} a_1 & a_2 & 1 \\ b_1 & b_2 & 1 \\ c_1 & c_2 & 1 \end{vmatrix} \tag{17}$$

is multiplied by Δ whenever the points A, B, C are subjected to the transformation (15). This is verified by a direct substitution. Hence the algebraic sign of S is left invariant by all direct collineations and changed by all others. Hence we have

THEOREM 28. *An ordered triad of points* (a_1, a_2), (b_1, b_2), (c_1, c_2) *has the same sense as an ordered triad* (a_1', a_2'), (b_1', b_2'), (c_1', c_2') *if and only if the determinants*

$$\begin{vmatrix} a_1 & a_2 & 1 \\ b_1 & b_2 & 1 \\ c_1 & c_2 & 1 \end{vmatrix} \quad \textit{and} \quad \begin{vmatrix} a_1' & a_2' & 1 \\ b_1' & b_2' & 1 \\ c_1' & c_2' & 1 \end{vmatrix}$$

have the same sign.

Theorem 27 now follows as a corollary of Theorem 23, § 27.

EXERCISES

1. If $\measuredangle ABC = \measuredangle A'BC'$, $S(ABC) = S(A'BC')$.

2. Let $\measuredangle hk$ be said to have the same sense as $\measuredangle h'k'$ if $S(ABC) = S(A'B'C')$, where B is the vertex of $\measuredangle hk$, A a point of h, C a point of k, and A', B', C' points analogously defined for $\measuredangle h'k'$. Define positive and negative angles and develop a theory of the order relations of rays through a point.

3. Let ρ and σ be two planes of a projective space which meet in a line l_∞; let us denote the two Euclidean planes obtained by leaving l_∞ out of ρ and σ by ρ_1 and σ_1 respectively; and let S_ρ be an arbitrary sense-class in ρ_1. All ordered point triads of S_ρ are projected from a point O not on ρ or σ into triads of a fixed sense-class S_σ in σ_1. Any other point P not on ρ or σ is separated from O by ρ and σ if and only if triads in the sense-class S_ρ are not projected from P into triads of S_σ.

***31. Sense in Euclidean spaces.** The definition given above of direct transformations in a Euclidean plane, based on the concept of direct transformations on the singular line, cannot be generalized to three dimensions. This is because the plane at infinity is projective and, as will be proved in the next section, does not admit of a distinction between direct and opposite projectivities. Nevertheless, the algebraic criterion $\Delta > 0$ does generalize and is made the basis of the definition which follows.

With reference to a nonhomogeneous coördinate system, of which the singular $(n-1)$-space is the $(n-1)$-space at infinity, the equations of any projective collineation of a Euclidean n-space take the form*

$$x_i' = b_i + \sum_{j=1}^{n} a_{ij}x_j, \qquad (i = 1, \cdots, n) \tag{18}$$

where the determinant $|a_{ij}|$ is different from zero. The resultant of

* The reader may, if he wishes, limit attention to the case $n = 3$. We have not actually developed the theory of coördinate systems in n dimensions, but as there is no essential difference in this theory between the three-dimensional case and the n-dimensional, we do not intend to write out the details.

two transformations of this form has a determinant which is the product of the determinants of the two transformations. Since the coefficients appear nonhomogeneously in (18), it is clear that a self-conjugate subgroup of the group of all transformations (18) is defined by the condition $|a_{ij}|>0$. It follows by the same reasoning as used in § 18 that this subgroup is independent of the choice of the frame of reference, so long as the singular $(n-1)$-space coincides with the singular $(n-1)$-space of the corresponding Euclidean n-space.

DEFINITION. The group of all transformations (18) for which the determinant $|a_{ij}|>0$ is called the group of *direct* collineations. In a Euclidean n-space let $A_1, A_2, \cdots, A_{n+1}$ be $n+1$ linearly independent points; the class of all ordered $(n+1)$-ads* $A'_1A'_2\cdots A'_{n+1}$ such that the collineation transforming $A_1, A_2, \cdots, A_{n+1}$ into $A'_1, A'_2, \cdots, A'_{n+1}$ respectively is direct is called a *sense-class* and is denoted by $S(A_1A_2\cdots A_{n+1})$.

THEOREM 29. *There are two and only two sense-classes in a Euclidean n-space. The sense-class of an ordered n-ad is unaltered by even permutations and altered by odd permutations.*

Proof. The argument for the three-dimensional case is typical of the general case. Let the coördinates of four points A, B, C, D be $(a_1, a_2, a_3), (b_1, b_2, b_3), (c_1, c_2, c_3), (d_1, d_2, d_3)$ respectively. The determinant

$$\begin{vmatrix} a_1 & a_2 & a_3 & 1 \\ b_1 & b_2 & b_3 & 1 \\ c_1 & c_2 & c_3 & 1 \\ d_1 & d_2 & d_3 & 1 \end{vmatrix} \tag{19}$$

is multiplied by $|a_{ij}|$ whenever the points are simultaneously subjected to a transformation (18). Hence the algebraic sign of (19) is left invariant by all direct collineations.

Since an odd permutation of the rows of (19) would change the sign of (19), no such permutation can be effected by a direct collineation. The remaining statements in the theorem now follow directly from the theorem that any ordered tetrad of points can be transformed by a transformation of the form (18) into any other ordered tetrad.

***32. Sense in a projective space.** Let us consider the group of all linear transformations

$$x'_i=\sum_{j=0}^{n}a_{ij}x_j, \qquad (i=0,\cdots,n) \tag{20}$$

for which the determinant $|a_{ij}|$ is different from zero.

* An n-ad is a set of n objects (cf. § 19).

If $(x_0, \cdots, x_n)$ is a set of homogeneous coördinates, the equations (20) continue to represent the same transformation when all the a_{ij}'s are multiplied by the same constant ρ; and two sets of equations like (20) represent the same transformation only if the coefficients of one are proportional to those of the other.

If each a_{ij} be multiplied by ρ, $|a_{ij}|$ is multiplied by ρ^{n+1}. Hence, if $|a_{ij}|$ is negative *and n is even,* we may multiply each a_{ij} by -1 and thus obtain an equivalent expression of the form (20) for which $|a_{ij}|$ is positive. If, however, n is odd, $\rho^{n+1} = k < 0$ has no real root. Hence, if n is odd, a transformation (20) for which $|a_{ij}|$ is negative is not equivalent to one for which $|a_{ij}|$ is positive. Hence the condition $|a_{ij}| > 0$ determines a subset of the transformations (20) if and only if n is odd. This subset of transformations forms a group for the reason given in § 18 for the case $n = 1$.

DEFINITION. If n is odd, the group of transformations (20) for which $|a_{ij}| > 0$ is called the group of *direct* collineations in n-space.

This definition of the group of direct collineations is independent of the choice of the frame of reference, as follows by an argument precisely like that used to prove the corresponding proposition in § 18.

In a space of three dimensions, let us inquire into what sets of five points the set (1, 0, 0, 0), (0, 1, 0, 0), (0, 0, 1, 0), (0, 0, 0, 1), (1, 1, 1, 1) can be transformed by direct collineations. If the initial points are to be transformed respectively into the points whose coördinates are the columns of the matrix

$$\begin{pmatrix} a_{00} & a_{01} & a_{02} & a_{03} & a_{04} \\ a_{10} & a_{11} & a_{12} & a_{13} & a_{14} \\ a_{20} & a_{21} & a_{22} & a_{23} & a_{24} \\ a_{30} & a_{31} & a_{32} & a_{33} & a_{34} \end{pmatrix}, \tag{21}$$

the collineation must take the form

$$\begin{aligned} x_0' &= \rho_0 a_{00} x_0 + \rho_1 a_{01} x_1 + \rho_2 a_{02} x_2 + \rho_3 a_{03} x_3, \\ x_1' &= \rho_0 a_{10} x_0 + \rho_1 a_{11} x_1 + \rho_2 a_{12} x_2 + \rho_3 a_{13} x_3, \\ x_2' &= \rho_0 a_{20} x_0 + \rho_1 a_{21} x_1 + \rho_2 a_{22} x_2 + \rho_3 a_{23} x_3, \\ x_3' &= \rho_0 a_{30} x_0 + \rho_1 a_{31} x_1 + \rho_2 a_{32} x_2 + \rho_3 a_{33} x_3, \end{aligned} \tag{22}$$

where the ρ's satisfy the equations

$$\begin{aligned} \rho_0 a_{00} + \rho_1 a_{01} + \rho_2 a_{02} + \rho_3 a_{03} &= a_{04}, \\ \rho_0 a_{10} + \rho_1 a_{11} + \rho_2 a_{12} + \rho_3 a_{13} &= a_{14}, \\ \rho_0 a_{20} + \rho_1 a_{21} + \rho_2 a_{22} + \rho_3 a_{23} &= a_{24}, \\ \rho_0 a_{30} + \rho_1 a_{31} + \rho_2 a_{32} + \rho_3 a_{33} &= a_{34}. \end{aligned} \tag{23}$$

Substituting the values of ρ_i determined from these equations in the determinant of the transformation (22), we see that the value of this determinant is

$$(24) \qquad \frac{(a_{04}a_{11}a_{22}a_{33})(a_{00}a_{14}a_{22}a_{33})(a_{00}a_{11}a_{24}a_{33})(a_{00}a_{11}a_{22}a_{34})}{(a_{00}a_{11}a_{22}a_{33})^3},$$

where the expressions in parentheses are abbreviations for determinants formed from the matrix (21) having these expressions as their main diagonals. The number (24) has the same sign as

$$(25) \quad (a_{04}a_{11}a_{22}a_{33})(a_{00}a_{14}a_{22}a_{33})(a_{00}a_{11}a_{24}a_{33})(a_{00}a_{11}a_{22}a_{34})(a_{00}a_{11}a_{22}a_{33}),$$

which is entirely analogous to the expression found in Theorem 16. The initial set of points is transformable into the points whose coördinates are the columns of (21) by a direct transformation if and only if (25) is positive.

This result may be stated in the form of a theorem as follows:

THEOREM 30. *If a set of five points whose homogeneous coördinates are the columns of the matrix* (21) *be such that the product of the four-rowed determinants obtained by omitting columns of this matrix is positive, it can be transformed by a direct collineation into any other set of points having the same property, but not into a set for which the analogous product is zero or negative.*

COROLLARY. *Any even permutation but no odd permutation of the vertices of a complete five-point can be effected by a direct collineation.*

DEFINITION. Let A, B, C, D, E be five points no four of which are coplanar. The class of all ordered pentads obtainable from the pentad A, B, C, D, E by direct collineations is called a *sense-class* and is denoted by $S(ABCDE)$.

Theorem 30 and its corollary now give at once the following:

THEOREM 31. *There are two and only two sense-classes in a real projective three-space. The sense-class of a set of five points is unaltered by even permutations and altered by odd permutations.*

If an analogous definition of sense-class had been made in the plane, we should have had that all planar collineations are direct, and hence that there is only one sense-class in the plane. This remark, together with Theorem 31, expresses in part what is meant by the proposition:

The real projective plane is one-sided and the real projective three-space is two-sided.

Although we have grounded this discussion upon propositions regarding certain groups of collineations, the notion of sense is connected with a much more extensive group. We shall return to this study, which will give a deeper insight into the notions of sense and of one- and two-sidedness, in a later chapter.

33. Intuitional description of the projective plane. We may assist our intuitive conception* of the one-sidedness of the real projective plane by a further consideration of the regions into which a plane is separated by a triangle. These are represented in fig. 16. Since any triangular region is projectively transformable into any other, it follows that any triangular region may be represented like Region I in fig. 16. In fig. 18 the four regions are thus represented, together with a portion of the relations among them.

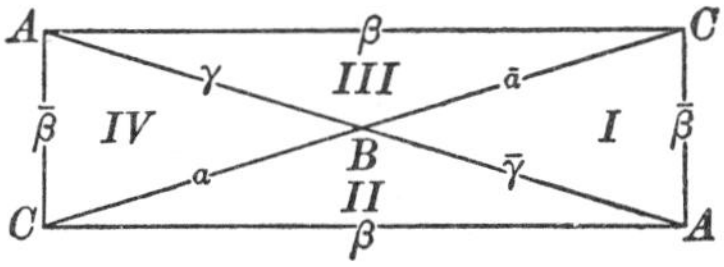

FIG. 18

The representation is more complete if the two segments labeled $\bar{\beta}$ are superposed in such a way that the end labeled A of one coincides with the end labeled A of the other. This is represented in fig. 19 and may be realized in a model by cutting out a rectangular strip of paper, giving it a half twist, and pasting together the two ends.

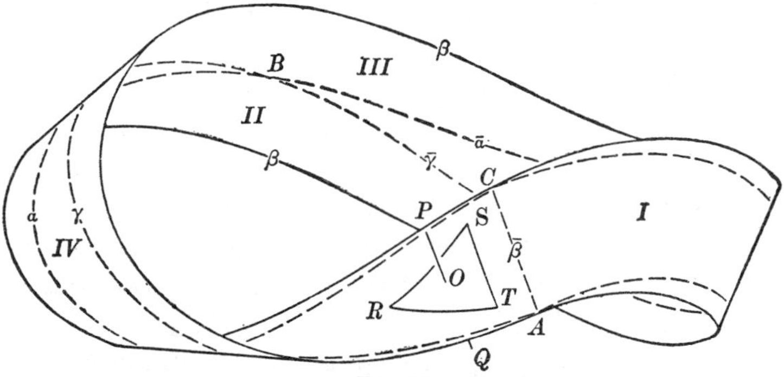

FIG. 19

To complete the model it would be necessary to bring the two edges labeled β in fig. 18 into coincidence. This, however, is not possible in a finite three-dimensional figure without letting the surface cut itself.†

The twisted strip as an example of a one-sided surface is due to Möbius.‡ It has only *one* boundary $A\beta C\beta A$. An imaginary man OP on the surface (fig. 19) could walk, without crossing the boundary, along a path which is the

* It would not be difficult to give a rigorous treatment of the propositions in this section, but it is thought better to postpone this to a later chapter.

† Plaster models showing this surface are manufactured by Martin Schilling of Leipzig. ‡ Gesammelte Werke, Vol. II, p. 519.

image of a straight line in the projective plane, till he arrived at the antipodal position OQ. If a small triangle RST were to be moved with the man without being lifted from the surface or being allowed to touch the man, it would be found, when the man arrived at the position OQ, that the triangle could be superposed upon itself, R coinciding with itself, *but S and T interchanged.* In other words, the boundary of the triangular region containing O would coincide with itself with sense reversed.

It is not essential that the triangular region RST be small, but merely that the figure $ORST$ move continuously so that the triangle RST remains a triangle and the point O is never on one of its sides. The possibility of making this transformation of the figure $ORST$ into $ORTS$ is not affected by joining the two β-edges together, because none of the paths need meet the boundary of the strip. Therefore a corresponding continuous deformation can be made in the projective plane.

If we think of the figure $ORST$ in the projective plane, the four points enter symmetrically. Thus, since S and T can be interchanged by continuously moving the complete quadrangle, any two vertices can be interchanged by such a motion, and hence any permutation of the four vertices can be effected by such a motion. This is intimately associated with the fact that all projectivities in the plane are direct (§ 32), as will be proved in a later chapter, where the notion of continuous deformation of a complete quadrangle in a projective plane is given a precise formulation.

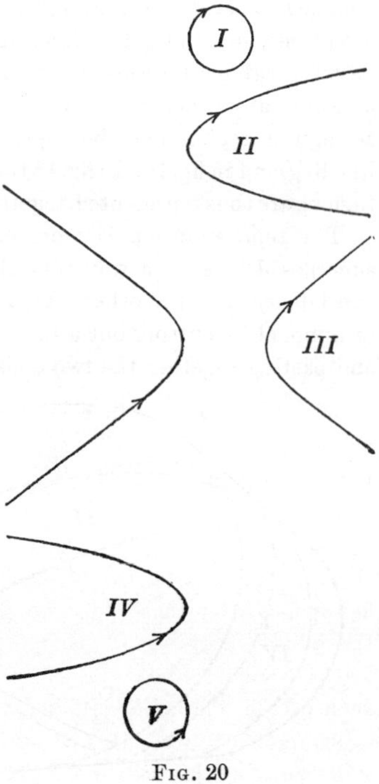

FIG. 20

The triangle RST may be replaced by any small circuit containing O, and it still remains true that O and the circuit may be continuously deformed till O coincides with itself and the circuit coincides with itself reversed. For example, the circuit may be taken as a conic section, and the projective plane imaged as the plane of elementary geometry plus "a line at infinity" (see the introduction to Vol. I, §§ 3, 4, 5, and also § 28 above). The ellipse I (fig. 20) may be deformed into the parabola II, this into the hyperbola III, this into the parabola IV, and this into the ellipse V. The reader can easily verify that the sense indicated by the arrow on I goes continuously to that indicated on V. The figures may be regarded as the projections from a variable center of an ellipse in a plane at right angles to the plane of the paper.

This deformation of an ellipse and also the corresponding one of the quadrangle $ORST$ depend on internal properties of the surface; i.e. they are independent of the situation of the surface in a three-dimensional space. They are sharply to be distinguished from the property expressed by saying that the man OP comes back to the position OQ, for the latter is a property of the space in which the surface lies.* In fact, the closely related proposition, that if the man OP walk along a straight line in a projective plane till he comes back to the position OQ, the triangle RST comes back to RTS, implies that if a tetrahedron (e.g. $PQRS$) be deformed into coincidence with itself so that two vertices are interchanged, the other two vertices will also be interchanged. And the last statement is a manifestation of the theorem (§ 32) that although the projective plane is one-sided, the projective three-space is two-sided.

A sort of model of the projective three-space may be obtained by generalizing the discussion of the plane given above. Any one of the eight regions determined by a tetrahedron is projectively equivalent to any other. Hence we pass from fig. 17 to fig. 21, which represents in full only the relations among the segments, triangular regions, and tetrahedral regions having A_1 as an end, or vertex. Each of the triangles having A_2, A_3, A_4 as vertices is represented by two triangles in fig. 21. Thus, in order to represent the projective space completely we should have to bring each of the triangular regions $A_2A_3A_4$ into coincidence with the one which is symmetrical with it with respect to A_1. In other words, fig. 21 would represent a projective three-space completely if each point on the octahedral surface formed by the triangular regions $A_2A_3A_4$ were brought into coincidence with the opposite point.

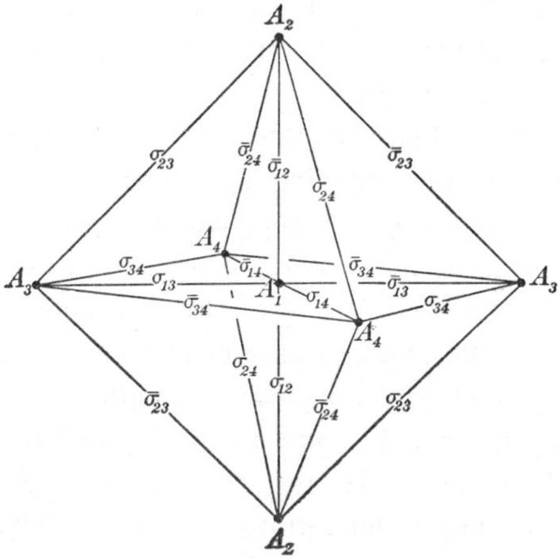

Fig. 21

EXERCISE

Show that the octahedron in fig. 21 may be distorted into a cube so that the projective three-space is represented by a cube in which each point coincides with its symmetric point with respect to the center of the cube.

* E. Steinitz, Sitzungsberichte der Berliner Mathematischen Gesellschaft, Vol. VII (1908), p. 35.

CHAPTER III

THE AFFINE GROUP IN THE PLANE

34. The geometry corresponding to a given group of transformations. The theorems which we have hitherto considered, whether in general projective geometry or in the particular geometry of reals, state properties of figures which are unchanged when the figures are subjected to collineations. For example, we have had no theorems about individual triangles, because any two triangles are equivalent under the general projective group, and thus are not to be distinguished from one another. On the other hand, there does not, in general, exist a collineation carrying a given pair of coplanar triangles into another given pair of coplanar triangles; and thus we have the theorem of Desargues, and other theorems, stating projective properties of pairs of triangles. We have thus considered only very general properties of figures, and so have dealt hardly at all with the familiar relations, such as perpendicularity, parallelism, congruence of angles and segments, which make up the bulk of elementary Euclidean geometry. These properties are not invariant under the general projective group, but only under certain subgroups. We shall therefore approach their study by a consideration of the properties of these subgroups.

There are, in general, at least two groups of transformations to consider in connection with a given geometrical relation: (1) a group by means of which the relation may be defined, and (2) a group under which the relation is left invariant. These two groups may or may not be the same.*

We have already had one example of a definition of a geometrical relation by means of a group of transformations. In § 19 two collinear triads of points are defined as being in the same sense-class if they are conjugate under the group of direct projectivities on the line. The relation between pairs of triads which is thus defined is invariant under the group of all projectivities (§ 18).

* The group (1) will always be a self-conjugate subgroup of (2), as follows directly from the definition of a self-conjugate subgroup. See § 39, below, where the rôle of self-conjugate subgroups is explained and illustrated.

The system of definitions and theorems which express properties invariant under a given group of transformations may be called, in agreement with the point of view expounded in Klein's Erlangen Programm,* *a geometry.* Obviously, all the theorems of the geometry corresponding to a given group continue to be theorems in the geometry corresponding to any subgroup of the given group; and the more restricted the group, the more figures will be distinct relatively to it, and the more theorems will appear in the geometry. The extreme case is the group corresponding to the identity, the geometry of which is too large to be of consequence.

For our purposes we restrict attention to groups of projective collineations,† and in order to get a more exact classification of theorems we narrow the Kleinian definition by assigning to the geometry corresponding to a given group only the theory of those properties which, while invariant under this group, are *not invariant under any other group of projective collineations containing it.* This will render the question definite as to whether a given theorem belongs to a given geometry.

Perhaps the simplest example of a subgroup of the projective group in a plane is the set of all projective collineations which leave a line of the plane invariant. The present chapter is concerned chiefly with the geometry belonging to this group.

The chapter is based entirely on Assumptions A, E, P, H_0. In fact, the theorems of §§ 36, 38, 39, 40, 42, 45, 46, 48 depend only on A, E, H_0. The class of theorems which depend on assumptions with regard to order relations has already been touched on in §§ 28–30.

35. Euclidean plane and the affine group. Let l_∞ be an arbitrary but fixed line of a projective plane π. In accordance with the definition in § 28 we shall refer to l_∞ as the *line at infinity.* The points of l_∞ shall be called *ideal*‡ *points* or *points at infinity,* whereas the remaining points and lines of π shall be called *ordinary* points and lines. The set of all ordinary points is a *Euclidean plane.* In the rest of this chapter the term "point," when unmodified, will refer to an ordinary point.

* Cf. F. Klein, Vergleichende Betrachtungen über neuere geometrische Forschungen, Erlangen 1872; also in Mathematische Annalen, Vol. XLIII (1893), p. 63.

† From some points of view it would have been desirable to include also all projective groups containing correlations.

‡ There is some divergence in the literature with respect to the use of this word and the word "improper." On the latter term see § 85, Vol. I.

DEFINITION. Any projective collineation transforming a Euclidean plane into itself is said to be *affine*; the group of all such collineations is called the *affine group*, and the corresponding geometry the *affine geometry*.

THEOREM 1. *There is one and only one affine collineation transforming three vertices A, B, C of a triangle to three vertices A', B', C' respectively of a triangle.*

Proof. Since l_∞ is transformed into itself, this is a corollary of Theorem 18, § 35, Vol. I.

With respect to any system of nonhomogeneous coördinates of which l_∞ is the singular line, any affine collineation may be written in the form (§ 67, Vol. I)

$$(1)\qquad \begin{aligned} x' &= a_1x + b_1y + c_1, \\ y' &= a_2x + b_2y + c_2, \end{aligned}$$

where

$$\Delta = \begin{vmatrix} a_1 & b_1 \\ a_2 & b_2 \end{vmatrix} \neq 0.$$

36. Parallel lines. DEFINITION. Two ordinary lines not meeting in an ordinary point are said to be *parallel* to each other, and the pair of lines is said to be *parallel.* A line is also said to be *parallel* to itself.

Hence, in a Euclidean plane we have the following theorem as a consequence of the theorems in Chap. I, Vol. I:

THEOREM 2. *In a Euclidean plane, two points determine one and only one line; two lines meet in a point or are parallel; two lines parallel to a third line are parallel to each other; through a given point there is one and only one line parallel to a given line l.*

DEFINITION. A simple quadrangle $ABCD$ such that the side AB is parallel to CD and BC to DA is called a *parallelogram.*

DEFINITION. The lines AC and BD are called the *diagonals* of the simple quadrangle $ABCD$.

In terms of parallelism, most projective theorems lead to a considerable number of special cases. Moreover, since the affine geometry is not self-dual, theorems which are dual in projective geometry may have essentially different affine special cases. A few affine theorems which are obtainable by direct specialization are given in the following list of exercises, and a larger number in the next section.

EXERCISES

1. If the sides of two triangles are parallel by pairs, the lines joining corresponding vertices meet in a point or are parallel.

2. If in two projective flat pencils three pairs of corresponding lines are parallel, then each line is parallel to its homologous line.

3. With respect to any system of nonhomogeneous coördinates in which l_∞ is the singular line, the equation of a line parallel to $ax + by + c = 0$ is $ax + by + c' = 0$.

4. A homology (or an elation) whose center and axis are ordinary transforms l_∞ into a line parallel to the axis.

5. If the number of points on a projective line is $p + 1$, the number of points in a Euclidean plane is p^2, the number of triangles in a Euclidean plane is $p^3(p-1)^2(p+1)/6$, and the latter is also the number of projective collineations transforming a Euclidean plane into itself.

37. Ellipse, hyperbola, parabola. DEFINITION. A conic meeting l_∞ in two distinct points is called a *hyperbola*, one meeting it in only one point a *parabola*, and one meeting it in no point an *ellipse*. The

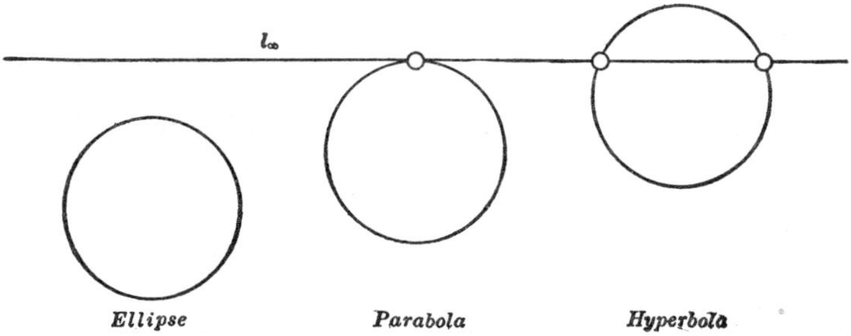

FIG. 22

pole of l_∞ is called the *center* of the conic. Any line through the center is called a *diameter*. The tangents to a hyperbola at its points of intersection with l_∞ are called its *asymptotes*. A conic having an ordinary point as center is called a *central conic*.

EXERCISES

1. An ellipse or a hyperbola is a central conic, but a parabola is not.

2. The center of a parabola is its point of contact with l_∞.

3. No two tangents to a parabola are parallel.

4. The asymptotes of a hyperbola meet at its center.

5. Two conjugate diameters (cf. § 44, Vol. I) of a hyperbola are harmonically conjugate with respect to the asymptotes.

6. If a simple hexagon be inscribed in a conic in such a way that two of its pairs of opposite sides are parallel, the third pair of opposite sides is parallel.

7. If a parallelogram be inscribed in a conic, the tangents at a pair of opposite vertices are parallel.

8. If the vertices of a triangle are on a conic and two of the tangents at the vertices are parallel to the respectively opposite sides, the third tangent is parallel to the third side.

9. If a parallelogram be circumscribed to a conic, its diagonals meet in the center and are conjugate diameters.

10. If a parallelogram be inscribed in a conic, any pair of adjacent sides are parallel to conjugate diameters. Its diagonals meet at the center of the conic.

11. Let P and P' be two points which are conjugate with respect to a conic, let p be the diameter parallel to PP', and let Q and Q' be points of intersection with the conic of the diameter conjugate to p. The lines PQ and $P'Q'$ meet on the conic.

12. If a parallelogram $OAPB$ is such that the sides OA and OB are conjugate diameters of a hyperbola and the diagonal OP is an asymptote, then the other diagonal AB is parallel to the other asymptote.

13. If two lines OA and OB are conjugate diameters of a conic which they meet in A and B, then any two parallel lines through A and B respectively meet the conic in two points A' and B' such that OA' and OB' are conjugate diameters.

14. Any two parabolas are conjugate under a collineation transforming l_∞ into itself.*

15. Any two hyperbolas are conjugate under a collineation transforming l_∞ into itself.*

16. Derive the equation of a parabola referred to a nonhomogeneous coördinate system with a tangent and a diameter as axes.

17. Derive the equation of a hyperbola referred to a nonhomogeneous coördinate system with the asymptotes as axes.

18. Derive the equation of an ellipse or a hyperbola referred to a nonhomogeneous coördinate system with a pair of conjugate diameters as axes.

38. The group of translations. DEFINITION. Any elation having l_∞ as an axis is called a *translation.* If l is any ordinary line through the center of a translation, the translation is said to be *parallel* to l.

COROLLARY. *A translation carries every proper line into a parallel line and leaves invariant every line of a certain system of parallel lines.*

THEOREM 3. *There is one and only one translation carrying a point A to a point B.*

Proof. Any translation carrying A to B must be an elation with l_∞ as axis and the point of intersection of the line AB with l_∞ as center. Hence the theorem follows from Theorem 9, Chap. III, Vol. I.

* On the corresponding theorem for ellipses, see § 76, Ex. 7.

THEOREM 4. *An ordered point pair AB can be carried by a translation to an ordered point pair A′B′ such that A′ is not on the line AB, if and only if ABB′A′ is a parallelogram.*

Proof. Let L_∞ and M_∞ be the points at infinity on the lines AA' and AB respectively. The translation carrying A to A' must carry the line AM_∞ to $A'M_\infty$ and leave the line BL_∞ invariant. Hence the point B, which is the intersection of AM_∞ with BL_∞, is carried to B', which is the intersection of $A'M_\infty$ with BL_∞. Hence the points A' and B' to which A and B respectively are carried by a translation are such that $ABB'A'$ is a parallelogram. Since there is one and only one translation carrying A to A', the same reasoning shows that whenever $ABB'A'$ is a parallelogram there exists a translation carrying A and B to A' and B' respectively.

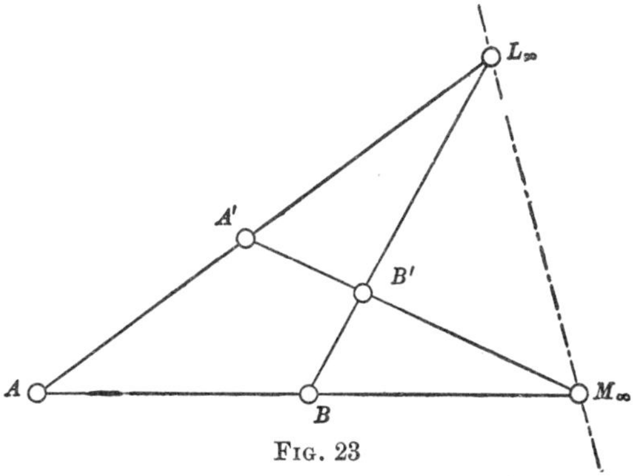

FIG. 23

THEOREM 5. *An ordered point pair AB is carried by a translation to an ordered point pair A′B′, where A′ is on the line AB, if and only if* $Q(L_\infty AA', L_\infty B'B)$, *$L_\infty$ being the point at infinity of AB.*

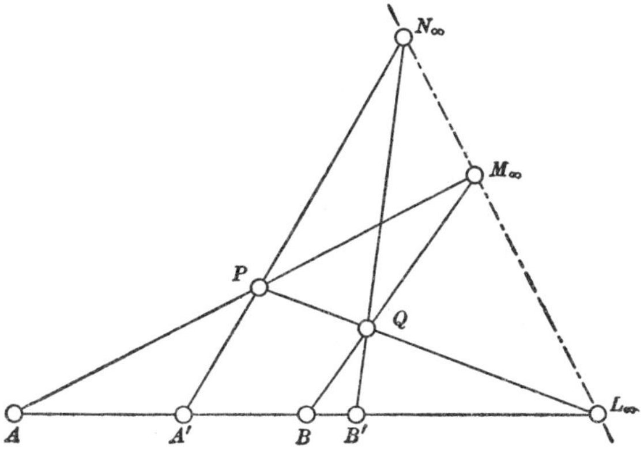

FIG. 24

Proof. Let P be any point not on the line AB, and let M_∞ and N_∞ respectively be the points of intersection of PA and PA' with l_∞. Let Q be the point of intersection of BM_∞ with PL_∞. Then, by the last theorem, the translation carrying

A to B carries P to Q, and hence carries A' to the point of intersection of QN_∞ with AB. Hence N_∞, Q, and B' are collinear, and hence we have $Q(L_\infty AA', L_\infty B'B)$.

THEOREM 6. *If A, B, C are any three points, the resultant of the translations carrying A to B and B to C is the translation carrying A to C.*

Proof. Let A_∞, B_∞, C_∞ be the points of intersection of the lines BC, CA, AB respectively with l_∞. Suppose first that the three points A_∞, B_∞, C_∞ are all distinct. The translation carrying A to B changes the line AB_∞ into the line BB_∞, and the translation carrying B to C changes the line BB_∞ into CB_∞. Hence the line AB_∞ is invariant under the resultant of these two translations.

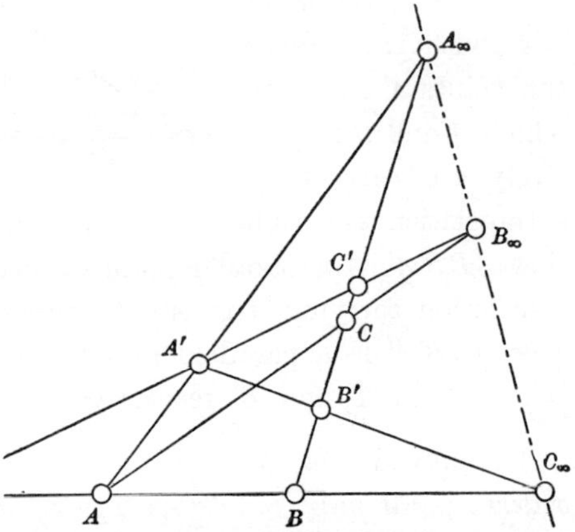

FIG. 25

Consider now any other line through B_∞, and let it meet AA_∞ in A' and BC in C'; also let B' be the point of intersection of $A'C_\infty$ with BC (fig. 25). We then have that the translation carrying A to B carries A' to B' (Theorem 4), and on account of $Q(A_\infty BB', A_\infty C'C)$ (Theorem 5) the translation carrying B to C carries B' to C'. Hence the resultant of the two translations carries A' to C' and thus leaves the line $A'B_\infty$ invariant; that is, it leaves all the lines through B_∞ invariant. Since it obviously leaves all points on l_∞ invariant, it is a translation (Cor. 3, Theorem 9, Chap. III, Vol. I).

If two of the three points A_∞, B_∞, C_∞ coincide, they all coincide, and in this case the theorem is obvious.

By definition, the identity is a translation. Hence we have

COROLLARY. *The set of all translations form a group.*

THEOREM 7. *The group of translations is commutative.*

Proof. Given two translations T_1 and T_2 and let A be any point, $T_1(A) = A'$ and $T_2(A') = B'$. If $B' = A$, T_2 is the inverse of T_1, and hence T_1 and T_2 are obviously commutative. If $B' \neq A$ and B' is not on the line AA', let B (fig. 23) be the point of intersection of the line through A parallel to $A'B'$ with the line through B' parallel to AA', then $ABB'A'$ is a parallelogram, and it is obvious that $T_1(B)=B'$ and $T_2(A)=B$. Hence $T_1T_2(A)=B'$. But, by the definition of A' and B', $T_2T_1(A)=B'$. Hence, in this case also, T_1 and T_2 are commutative.

In case B' is on the line AA', let P and Q (fig. 24) be two points such that $A'B'QP$ is a parallelogram, let B be the point of intersection of AA' with the line through Q parallel to AP, and let L_∞, M_∞, N_∞ be the points at infinity of PQ, PA, and PA' respectively. Then, since $T_2(A')=B'$, it is obvious that $T_2(P)=Q$, and hence that $T_2(A)=B$. Moreover, on account of $\mathsf{Q}(L_\infty AB, L_\infty B'A')$, $T_1(A)=A'$ implies that $T_1(B)=B'$. Hence $T_1T_2(A)=B'$, and thus, in this case also, T_1 and T_2 are commutative.

THEOREM 8. *If OX and OY are two nonparallel lines and* T *is any translation, there is a unique pair of translations* T_1, T_2 *such that* T_1 *is parallel to OX,* T_2 *parallel to OY, and* $T_1T_2=T$.

Proof. In case T is parallel to OX or OY the theorem is trivial. If T is parallel to neither of them, let $P=T(O)$ and let X_1 and Y_1 be the points in which the lines through P parallel to OY and OX respectively meet OX and OY respectively. Then OX_1PY_1 is a parallelogram, and if T_1 be the translation carrying O to X_1, and T_2 the translation carrying O to Y_1, it follows, by Theorems 4 and 6, that $T_1T_2=T$.

On the other hand, if T_1' is any translation parallel to OX, and T_2' any translation parallel to OY, and $T_1'(O)=X_1'$ and $T_2'(O)=Y_1'$, the product $T_1'T_2'$ carries O to a point P' such that $OX_1'P'Y_1'$ is a parallelogram. But $P'=P$ if and only if $X_1'=X_1$ and $Y_1'=Y_1$. Hence T determines T_1 and T_2 uniquely.

THEOREM. 9. *With respect to a nonhomogeneous coördinate system in which l_∞ is the singular line a translation parallel to the x-axis has the equations*

$$x'=x+a,\qquad y'=y. \tag{2}$$

Proof. The point into which (0, 0) is transformed by a given translation parallel to the x-axis may be denoted by $(a, 0)$. By Theorem 5 and § 48, Vol. I, it then follows that any point $(x, 0)$ of the x-axis is transformed into $(x+a, 0)$. Since lines parallel to the y-axis are transformed into lines parallel to the y-axis, and since lines parallel to the x-axis are invariant, it follows that the given translation takes the given form (2).

Conversely, any transformation of the type (2) leaves all lines parallel to the x-axis invariant and transforms any other line into a line parallel to itself. Hence it is a translation parallel to the x-axis.

THEOREM 10. *With respect to a nonhomogeneous coördinate system in which l_∞ is the singular line, any translation can be expressed in the form*

$$(3)\qquad \begin{aligned} x' &= x + a, \\ y' &= y + b. \end{aligned}$$

Proof. By Theorem 8 any translation is the product of a translation parallel to the x-axis by one parallel to the y-axis. Hence it is the product of a transformation of the form

$$x' = x + a,$$
$$y' = y,$$

by a transformation of the form

$$x' = x,$$
$$y' = y + b.$$

EXERCISE

Investigate the subgroups of the group of translations.

39. Self-conjugate subgroups. Congruence. DEFINITION. Any subgroup G' of a group G is said to be *self-conjugate* or *invariant** under G if and only if $\Sigma \mathrm{T} \Sigma^{-1}$ is an operation of G' whenever Σ is an operation of G and T of G'.

The geometric significance of this notion is as follows: Suppose that two figures F_1 and F_2 are conjugate under G', and T is a transformation of G' such that $F_2 = \mathrm{T}(F_1)$. If F_1 and F_2 are changed into F_1' and F_2' by any transformation Σ of G, then $\Sigma^{-1}(F_1') = F_1$. Hence† $\mathrm{T}\Sigma^{-1}(F_1') = F_2$,

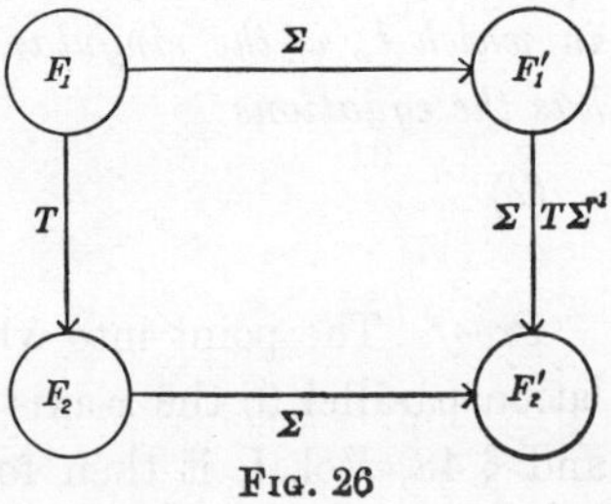

FIG. 26

* These terms have already been defined in § 75, Vol. I.

† These relations may be illustrated by the accompanying diagram (probably due to S. Lie).

and $\Sigma T \Sigma^{-1}(F_1') = F_2'$. Therefore, if G' is self-conjugate under G, the figures F_1' and F_2' are conjugate under G'. Hence *the property of being conjugate under the self-conjugate subgroup G' is a property left invariant by the group G.* Thus the theory of figures conjugate under G' belongs to the geometry corresponding to G, provided that G is not a self-conjugate subgroup of any other group of projective collineations.

THEOREM 11. *The group of translations is self-conjugate under the affine group.*

Proof. Let T be an arbitrary translation and Σ an arbitrary affine transformation. We have to show that $\Sigma T \Sigma^{-1}$ is a translation. If P be any point of l_∞, $\Sigma(P)$ is also on l_∞. Therefore, since T leaves all points of l_∞ invariant, so does $\Sigma T \Sigma^{-1}$. The system of lines through the center of T is a system of parallel lines; Σ transforms this system of parallel lines into a system of parallel lines; and hence the latter system of parallel lines is invariant under $\Sigma T \Sigma^{-1}$. Hence (cf. Cor. 3, Theorem 9, Chap. III, Vol. I) $\Sigma T \Sigma^{-1}$ is a translation.

COROLLARY 1. *The group of translations is self-conjugate under any subgroup of the affine group which contains it.*

COROLLARY 2. *For any affine collineation Σ, and any translation* T, *there exists a translation* T′ *such that* $\Sigma T = T' \Sigma$ *and a translation* T″ *such that* $T\Sigma = \Sigma T''$.

Proof. Let $\Sigma T \Sigma^{-1} = T'$ and $\Sigma^{-1} T \Sigma = T''$. By the theorem, T′ and T″ are translations. But

$$\Sigma T \Sigma^{-1} = T' \quad \text{and} \quad \Sigma^{-1} T \Sigma = T''$$

imply

$$\Sigma T = T' \Sigma \quad \text{and} \quad T\Sigma = \Sigma T'' \text{ respectively.}$$

DEFINITION. Two figures are said to be *congruent* if they are conjugate under the group of translations.

This definition will presently be extended by giving other conditions under which two figures are said to be congruent.* In view of Theorem 11, the theory of congruence as thus far defined belongs to the affine geometry.

* A complete definition would be of the form, "Two figures are said to be congruent if *and only if* . . ."

40. Congruence of parallel point pairs. The figure consisting of two distinct points A, B may be looked at in two ways with respect to congruence. We consider either the two ordered* point pairs AB and BA or the point pair AB without regard to order. In the second case AB and BA mean the same thing and AB is congruent to BA because the identity belongs to the group of translations. On the other hand, the ordered pair AB is not conjugate to the ordered pair BA under the group of translations, because the translation carrying A to B does not carry B to A (this is under Assumptions A, E, H_0).

THEOREM 12. *If $ABDC$ is a parallelogram, the ordered point pair AB is congruent to the ordered point pair CD. If the condition $Q(P_\infty AC, P_\infty DB)$ is satisfied where P_∞ is an ideal point, the ordered point pair AB is congruent to the ordered point pair CD.*

Proof. This is a corollary of Theorems 4 and 5.

COROLLARY 1. *Let A and B be any two distinct points and O the harmonic conjugate of the point at infinity of the line AB with respect to A and B. Then the pair AO is congruent to the pair OB.*

DEFINITION. The point O in the last corollary is called the *mid-point* of the pair AB. In case $B=A$, A is called the *mid-point* of the pair AB.

COROLLARY 2. *The line joining the mid-points of the pairs of vertices AB and AC of a triangle ABC is parallel to the line BC.*

Proof. Let B_∞ and C_∞ be the points at infinity of the lines AB and AC respectively, and let B_1 and C_1 be the mid-points of the pairs AB and AC respectively. Then, by the definition of "mid-point,"

$$AB_1BB_\infty \overline{\wedge} AC_1CC_\infty.$$

Hence the lines B_1C_1, BC, and $B_\infty C_\infty$ concur, which means that B_1C_1 and BC are parallel.

DEFINITION. The line joining a vertex, say A, of a triangle ABC to the mid-point of BC is called a *median* of the triangle.

THEOREM 13. *The three medians of a triangle meet in a point.*

* Cf. footnote on page 40.

Proof. Let the triangle be ABC; let A_∞, B_∞, C_∞ be the points at infinity of the sides BC, CA, AB respectively; and let A_1, B_1, C_1 be the points of intersection of the pairs of lines BB_∞ and CC_∞, CC_∞ and AA_∞,

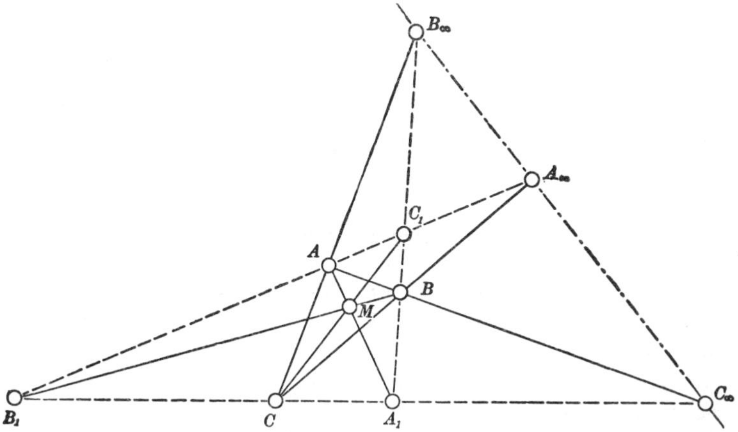

FIG. 27

AA_∞ and BB_∞ respectively (fig. 27). Then, by well-known theorems on harmonic sets (§ 31, Vol. I), the medians of the triangle ABC are AA_1, BB_1, and CC_1, and these three lines concur.

EXERCISES

1. The diagonals of a parallelogram bisect one another; that is, if $ABCD$ is a parallelogram, the mid-points of the pairs AC and BD coincide.

2. Let a and b be two parallel lines. The mid-points of all the pairs AB where A is on a and B on b are on a line parallel to a and b.

3. If the sides AB, BC, CA of a triangle ABC are respectively parallel to the sides $A'B'$, $B'C'$, $C'A'$ of a triangle $A'B'C'$, and the ordered point pair AB is congruent to the ordered point pair $A'B'$, then the two triangles are congruent.

4. The mid-points of the pairs of opposite vertices of a complete quadrilateral are collinear. Let us call this line the *diameter* of the quadrilateral.

5. A line through a diagonal point O of a complete quadrangle, parallel to the opposite side of the diagonal triangle, is met by either pair of opposite sides of the quadrangle which do not pass through O in a pair of points having O as mid-point.

41. Metric properties of conics. The following list of exercises contains a number of theorems on conics which involve the congruence of parallel point pairs and can be derived by aid of the theorems in the last sections.

EXERCISES

1. The mid-points of a system of pairs of points of a conic AA', BB', CC', etc. are collinear if the lines AA', BB', CC' are parallel. The line containing the mid-points is a diameter conjugate to the diameter parallel to AA'.

2. Let A and B be two points of a parabola. If the line joining the mid-point C of the pair AB to the pole P of the line AB meets the conic in O, then O is the mid-point of the pair CP.

3. If a line meets a hyperbola in a pair of points H_1H_2, and its asymptotes in a pair A_1A_2, the two pairs have the same mid-point. The pair H_1A_1 is congruent to the pair H_2A_2.

4. The point of contact of a tangent to a hyperbola is the mid-point of the pair in which the tangent meets the asymptotes.

5. Let A_1 and A_2 be each a fixed and X a variable point of a hyperbola, and let X_1 and X_2 be the points in which the lines XA_1 and XA_2 meet one of the asymptotes. The point pairs X_1X_2 determined by different values of X are all congruent.

6. The centers of all conics inscribed in* a simple quadrilateral $ABCD$ are on the line joining the mid-points of the point pairs CA and BD.

7. The centers of all conics which pass through the vertices of a complete quadrangle $ABCD$ are on a conic C^2, which contains the six mid-points of the pairs of vertices of the quadrangle, the three vertices of its diagonal triangle, and the double points (if existent) of the involution in which l_∞ is met by the pencil of conics through A, B, C, D. From the projective point of view, according to which l_∞ is any line whatever, C^2 is called the *nine-point* (or the *eleven-point*) *conic* of the complete quadrangle $ABCD$ and the line l_∞. Derive the analogous theorems for the pencils of conics of Types II–V (cf. § 47, Vol. I).

8. The five diameters† of the complete quadrilaterals formed by leaving out one line at a time from a five-line meet in a point A, which is the center of the conic tangent to the five lines.

9. The six points A determined, according to the last exercise, by the six complete five-lines formed by leaving out one line at a time from a six-line are on a conic C^2.

10. The seven conics C^2 determined, according to the last exercise, by the seven complete six-lines formed by leaving out one line at a time from a seven-line, all pass through three points.

42. Vectors. Any ordered pair of points determines a set of pairs all of which are equivalent to it under the group of translations. In order to study the relations between such sets of pairs we introduce the notion of a vector. The term "vector" appears in the literature

* A conic is said to be inscribed in a given figure if the figure is circumscribed to the conic (cf. § 43, Vol. I).

† Cf. Ex. 4, § 40. This and the following exercises are taken from an article by W. W. Taylor, Messenger of Mathematics, Vol. XXXVI (1907), p. 118.

under a multitude of guises, none of which, however, is in serious contradiction with the following abstract definition. In this definition the term "ordered pair of points" is to be understood to include the case of a single point counted twice.

DEFINITION. *A planar field of vectors* (or *vector field*) is any set of objects, the individuals of which are called *vectors*, such that (1) there is one vector for each ordered pair of points in a Euclidean plane, and (2) there is only one vector for any two ordered pairs AB and $A'B'$ which are equivalent under the group of translations. A vector corresponding to a coincident pair of points is called a *null* vector or a *zero* vector, and denoted by the symbol 0.

For example, a properly chosen set of matrices would be a vector field according to this definition. So would also the set of all translations including the identity; also a set of classes of ordered point pairs such that two point pairs are in the same class if and only if equivalent under the group of translations. However a vector field be defined, it will be found that, in most applications, only those properties which follow from the definition as stated above are actually used.

A precisely similar state of affairs exists in the definition of a number system. The objects in the particular number system determined for a given space by the methods of Chap. VI, Vol. I, are points, but a number system in general is any set of objects in a proper one-to-one correspondence with this set of points.

In the following discussion we shall suppose that one field of vectors has been selected, and all statements will refer to this one field. Thus, the vector corresponding to the point pair AB is a definite object, and we shall denote it as "the vector AB," or, in symbols, Vect (AB).

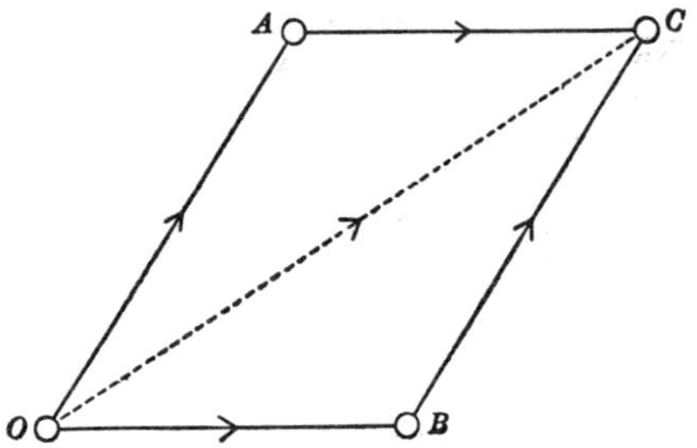

FIG. 28

Since any point of a Euclidean plane can be carried by a translation to any other point, the set of all vectors is the same as the set of vectors OA, where O is a fixed and A a variable point. Consequently, the following definition gives a meaning to the operation of "adding" any two vectors.

DEFINITION. If O, A, C are points of a Euclidean plane, the vector OC is called the *sum* of the vectors OA and AC. In symbols this is indicated by Vect (OC) = Vect (OA) + Vect (AC). The operation of obtaining the sum of two vectors is called *addition* of vectors.

An obvious corollary of this definition is that

$$\text{Vect}\,(AB) + \text{Vect}\,(BA) = 0.$$

Hence we define:

DEFINITION. The vector Vect (BA) is called the *negative* of the vector Vect (AB), and denoted by − Vect (AB).

THEOREM 14. *The operation of addition of vectors is associative; that is, if a, b, c are vectors, $(a + b) + c = a + (b + c)$.*

Proof. Let the three vectors be OA, AB, BC respectively; then, by definition, both (Vect (OA) + Vect (AB)) + Vect (BC) and Vect (OA) + (Vect (AB) + Vect (BC)) are the same as Vect (OC).

DEFINITION. Two vectors are said to be *collinear* if and only if they can be expressed as Vect (OA) and Vect (OB) respectively, where O, A, B are collinear points.

THEOREM 15. *The sum of two noncollinear vectors OA and OB is the vector OC, where C is such that $OACB$ is a parallelogram.*

Proof. By Theorem 4, the vector OB is the same as the vector AC. Hence, by definition, the sum of OA and OB is OC.

THEOREM 16. *The sum of two collinear vectors OA and OB is a vector OC such that Q$(P_\infty AO, P_\infty BC)$, where P_∞ is the point at infinity of the line AB.*

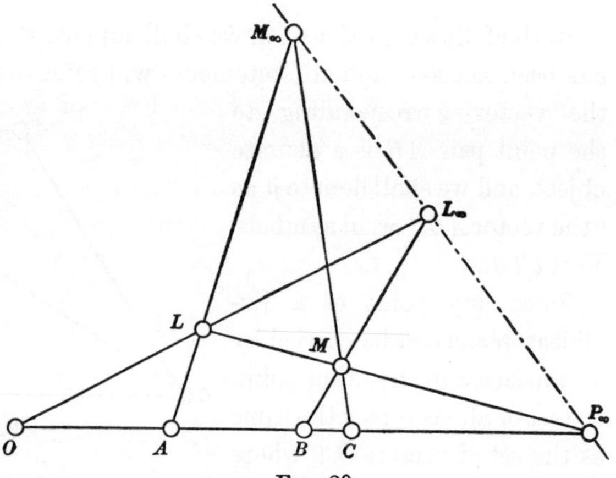

FIG. 29

Proof. Let L and M be two points such that $OBML$ is a parallelogram. Hence Vect (OB) = Vect (LM). Then, by definition, C must be such that Vect (LM) = Vect (AC), that is, such that $ACML$ is a parallelogram. Let L_∞ be the ideal point of intersection of the lines OL and BM, and let M_∞ be the ideal point of intersection of the lines AL and MC. The complete quadrangle $LML_\infty M_\infty$ determines Q$(P_\infty AO, P_\infty BC)$.

Corollary. *If O, A, B are three collinear points, and C a point such that Vect (OA) + Vect (OB) = Vect (OC), then, with respect to any scale* (cf. § 48, Vol. I) *in which P_0 is O and P_∞ the point at infinity of the line OA,*

$$A + B = C.$$

Proof. Cf. Cor. 1, Theorem 1, Chap. VI, Vol. I.

Theorem 17. *The operation of adding vectors is commutative; that is, if a and b are vectors, $a + b = b + a$.*

Proof. Let the vectors a and b be Vect (OA) and Vect (OB) respectively. If O, A, B are noncollinear, the result follows from Theorem 15, and if they are collinear, from Theorem 16.

43. Ratios of collinear vectors. By analogy with the case of addition we should be led to base a definition of multiplication of collinear vectors upon the multiplication of points in § 49, Vol. I. There are, however, a great many ways of defining the product of two vectors, which would not reduce to this sort of multiplication in the case of collinear vectors. Hence, in order to avoid possible confusion we shall not introduce a definition of the multiplication of vectors at present, but only of what we shall call the ratio of two collinear vectors.

Definition. The *ratio* of two collinear vectors OA and OB is the number which corresponds to A in the scale in which P_0 is O, P_1 is B, and P_∞ is the point at infinity of the line OA. It is denoted by

$$\frac{\text{Vect}\,(OA)}{\text{Vect}\,(OB)} \text{ or by } \frac{OA}{OB}.$$

It is to be emphasized that the ratio of two collinear vectors as here defined is a number. By comparison with the definition in § 56, Vol. I, we have at once

Theorem 18. *If A, B, C, D_∞ are collinear points, D_∞ being ideal,*

$$\text{R}\,(D_\infty A, BC) = \frac{AC}{AB}.$$

Theorem 13, Chap. VI, Vol. I now gives

Theorem 19. *If A_1, A_2, A_3, A_4 are any four collinear ordinary points,*

$$\text{R}\,(A_1A_2, A_3A_4) = \frac{A_1A_3}{A_1A_4} : \frac{A_2A_3}{A_2A_4}.$$

Theorem 20. *If two triangles ABC and $A'B'C'$ are such that the sides AB, BC, CA are parallel to $A'B'$, $B'C'$, $C'A'$ respectively,*

$$\frac{AB}{A'B'} = \frac{BC}{B'C'} = \frac{CA}{C'A'}.$$

Proof. Suppose that the translation which carries A' to A carries B' to B_1 and C' to C_1. Then B_1 is on the line AB and C_1 on the line AC, and the line B_1C_1 is parallel to BC. Thus, if B_∞ be the point at infinity of the line AB, and C_∞ the point at infinity of the line AC,

$$B_\infty ABB_1 \overline{\wedge} C_\infty ACC_1.$$

Hence, by Theorem 18, $$\frac{AB}{AB_1} = \frac{AC}{AC_1} = \frac{CA}{C_1A},$$

which is, by definition, the same as

$$\frac{AB}{A'B'} = \frac{CA}{C'A'}.$$

In like manner, it follows that

$$\frac{AB}{A'B'} = \frac{BC}{B'C'}.$$

Since we have not defined the product of two vectors, it is necessary to resort to a device in order to compute conveniently with them. This we do as follows:

DEFINITION. With respect to an arbitrary vector OA, which is called a unit vector, the ratio
$$\frac{OB}{OA},$$
where OB is any vector collinear with OA, is called the *magnitude* of OB.

Observe that the magnitude of OB is the negative of the magnitude of BO. Since the magnitude of a vector is a number, there is no difficulty about algebraic computations with magnitudes. In the rest of this section we shall use the symbol AB to denote the magnitude of the vector AB. No confusion is introduced by this double use of the symbol, because the ratio of two vectors is precisely the same as the quotient of their magnitudes.

DEFINITION. If Γ is any collineation not leaving l_∞ invariant, the lines $\Gamma(l_\infty)$ and $\Gamma^{-1}(l_\infty)$ are called the *vanishing lines* of Γ. If Π is any projectivity transforming a line l to a line l' (which may coincide with l), the ordinary points of l and l' which are homologous with points at infinity are (if existent) called the *vanishing points* of Π. If Π is an involution transforming l into itself but not leaving the point at infinity invariant, the vanishing point is called the *center* of the involution.

THEOREM 21. DEFINITION. *If O and O' are the vanishing points, on l and l' respectively, of a projectivity transforming a line l to a* *parallel* line l', and X is a variable point of l, and X' the point of l' to which X is transformed, the product $OX \cdot O'X'$ is a constant, called the* power *of the transformation.*

Proof. Let P_∞ be the point at infinity of l and l'; and let X_1 and X_2 be two values of X, and X_1' and X_2' the points to which they are transformed by the given projectivity. Then, by the fundamental property of a cross ratio,

$$R(P_\infty O, X_1X_2) = R(O'P_\infty, X_1'X_2') = R(P_\infty O', X_2'X_1'),$$

and hence, by Theorem 18, $\dfrac{OX_2}{OX_1} = \dfrac{O'X_1'}{O'X_2'}.$

Hence, by the definition of magnitude of vectors,

$$OX_2 \cdot O'X_2' = OX_1 \cdot O'X_1'.$$

COROLLARY 1. *The power of an involution having a center O and a conjugate pair AA_1 is $OA \cdot OA_1$.*

COROLLARY 2. *Let Π be a homology whose center is an ordinary point F and whose axis is an ordinary line, and let D be any point of the vanishing line $\Pi^{-1}(l_\infty)$. If P is a variable point, $P' = \Pi(P)$, and D' is the point in which the line through P' parallel to FD meets the vanishing line $\Pi(l_\infty)$, then* $\dfrac{FP}{FP'} = \dfrac{DF}{P'D'}.$

Proof. Let Q and Q' be the points in which the line FP meets the vanishing lines $\Pi^{-1}(l_\infty)$ and $\Pi(l_\infty)$ respectively. By the theorem,

$$PQ \cdot P'Q' = FQ \cdot FQ';$$

from which we derive successively

$$\frac{PF + FQ}{FQ} = \frac{FP' + P'Q'}{P'Q'},$$

$$\frac{PF}{FQ} = \frac{FP'}{P'Q'},$$

$$\frac{FP}{FP'} = \frac{QF}{P'Q'}.$$

Since Π is a homology, the two vanishing lines are parallel. Hence

$$\frac{QF}{P'Q'} = \frac{DF}{P'D'}.$$

Hence $$\frac{FP}{FP'} = \frac{DF}{P'D'}$$

* With the extension of the definition of congruence in the next chapter the restriction to parallel lines may be removed.

EXERCISES

1. If a projectivity $ABCD \overline{\wedge} A'B'C'D'$ is such that the point at infinity of the line AB corresponds to the point at infinity of the line $A'B'$,

$$\frac{AB}{CD} = \frac{A'B'}{C'D'}.$$

2. If three parallel lines a, b, c are met by one line in the points A', B', C' respectively and by another line in $A''B''C''$ respectively, then

$$\frac{A'B'}{A'C'} = \frac{A''B''}{A''C''}.$$

3. If $ABCD$ are any four collinear points,

$$AB \cdot CD + AC \cdot DB + AD \cdot BC = 0.$$

4. Six points form a quadrangular set $Q\,(A_2B_2C_2, A_1B_1C_1)$ if and only if

$$R\,(A_1A_2, B_1C_1) \cdot R\,(B_1B_2, C_1A_1) \cdot R\,(C_1C_2, A_1B_1) = -1.$$

5. The condition for a quadrangular set may also be written

$$\frac{A_1B_2}{A_2B_1} \cdot \frac{B_1C_2}{B_2C_1} \cdot \frac{C_1A_2}{C_2A_1} = -1.$$

6. If three tangents to a parabola meet two other tangents in P_1, P_2, P_3 and Q_1, Q_2, Q_3 respectively, then

$$\frac{P_1P_2}{P_1P_3} = \frac{Q_1Q_2}{Q_1Q_3}.$$

Conversely, if five lines are such that the points in which two of them meet the other three satisfy this condition, the conic to which the five lines are tangent is a parabola.

7. Let O be the center of a hyperbola, and A_1 and A_2 the points in which the asymptotes are met by an arbitrary tangent; if another tangent meets the asymptotes OA_1, OA_2 in B_1 and B_2 respectively,

$$\frac{OA_1}{OB_1} = \frac{OB_2}{OA_2}.$$

8. If a fixed tangent p to a conic at a point P meets two variable conjugate diameters in Q and Q', then $PQ \cdot PQ'$ is a constant. Let O be the center of the conic. If the diameter parallel to p meets the conic in S, then

$$PQ \cdot PQ' = -(OS)^2.$$

9. Let O_1 and O_2 be the points of contact of two fixed parallel tangents to a conic. If a variable tangent meets the two fixed tangents in X_1 and X_2 respectively, $O_1X_1 \cdot O_2X_2$ is constant. If O is the center of the conic and B is a point of intersection of the diameter through O parallel to the fixed tangents,

$$O_1X_1 \cdot O_2X_2 = (OB)^2.$$

44. Theorems of Menelaus, Ceva, and Carnot.

THEOREM 22 (MENELAUS). *Three points A', B', C' of the sides BC, CA, AB, respectively, of a triangle are collinear if and only if*

$$\frac{A'B}{A'C}\cdot\frac{B'C}{B'A}\cdot\frac{C'A}{C'B}=1.$$

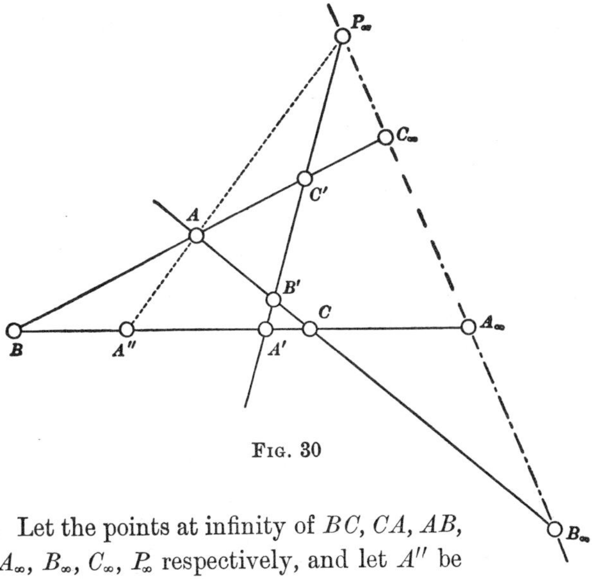

FIG. 30

Proof. Let the points at infinity of BC, CA, AB, $A'B'$ be A_∞, B_∞, C_∞, P_∞ respectively, and let A'' be the intersection of AP_∞ with BC. Then, supposing A', B', C' collinear,

$$(B_\infty B'AC)\overset{P_\infty}{\underset{\wedge}{=}}(A_\infty A'A''C) \text{ and } (C_\infty C'BA)\overset{P_\infty}{\underset{\wedge}{=}}(A_\infty A'BA'').$$

Hence $$\frac{B'C}{B'A}=\text{R}(B_\infty B',\, AC)=\text{R}(A_\infty A',\, A''C)=\frac{A'C}{A'A''},$$

and $$\frac{C'A}{C'B}=\text{R}(C_\infty C',\, BA)=\text{R}(A_\infty A',\, BA'')=\frac{A'A''}{A'B}.$$

Hence $$\frac{A'B}{A'C}\cdot\frac{B'C}{B'A}\cdot\frac{C'A}{C'B}=\frac{A'B}{A'C}\cdot\frac{A'C}{A'A''}\cdot\frac{A'A''}{A'B}=1.$$

The converse argument is now obvious.

THEOREM 23 (CEVA). *The necessary and sufficient condition for the concurrence of the lines joining the vertices A, B, C of a triangle to the points A', B', C' of the opposite sides is*

$$\frac{A'B}{A'C}\cdot\frac{B'C}{B'A}\cdot\frac{C'A}{C'B}=-1. \tag{4}$$

Proof. Let C'' be the point of intersection of the lines $A'B'$ and AB. Suppose first that C'' is an ordinary point. Then, by the theorem of Menelaus,

$$\frac{A'B}{A'C}\cdot\frac{B'C}{B'A}\cdot\frac{C''A}{C''B}=1. \tag{5}$$

The point C'' is harmonically conjugate to C' with respect to A and B if and only if the lines AA', BB', CC' meet in a point. Thus,

$$\frac{C'A}{C'B}\div\frac{C''A}{C''B}=-1 \tag{6}$$

is a necessary and sufficient condition that AA', BB', CC' concur. But on multiplying (5) by (6) we obtain (4).

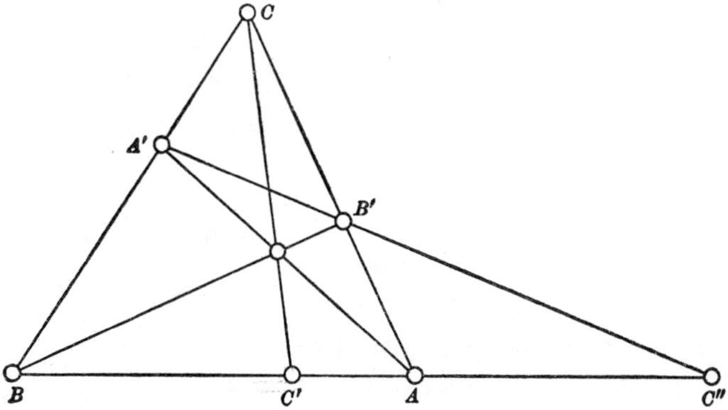

FIG. 31

In case C'' is an ideal point, the line $A'B'$ is parallel to AB and, by Theorem 20,

$$\frac{A'B}{A'C}\cdot\frac{B'C}{B'A}=1. \tag{7}$$

The condition that C'' be harmonically conjugate to C' with regard to A and B now takes the form

$$\frac{C'A}{C'B}=-1.$$

On multiplying this into (7) we again obtain (4).

THEOREM 24 (CARNOT). *Three pairs of points, A_1A_2, B_1B_2, C_1C_2, respectively, on the sides BC, CA, AB, respectively, of a triangle are on the same conic if and only if*

$$\frac{A_1B}{A_1C}\cdot\frac{B_1C}{B_1A}\cdot\frac{C_1A}{C_1B}\cdot\frac{A_2B}{A_2C}\cdot\frac{B_2C}{B_2A}\cdot\frac{C_2A}{C_2B}=1. \tag{8}$$

Proof. Suppose first that the conic reduces to two lines containing A_1, B_1, C_1 and A_2, B_2, C_2 respectively. The formula (8) in this case follows directly from Theorem 22 when we multiply together the conditions that A_1, B_1, C_1 and A_2, B_2, C_2 be respectively collinear.

Now consider any proper conic through A_1, A_2, B_1, B_2 meeting the line AB in $C_1'C_2'$. By the theorem of Desargues (Theorem 19, Chap. V, Vol. I) the pairs AB, C_1C_2, and $C_1'C_2'$ are in involution. Hence

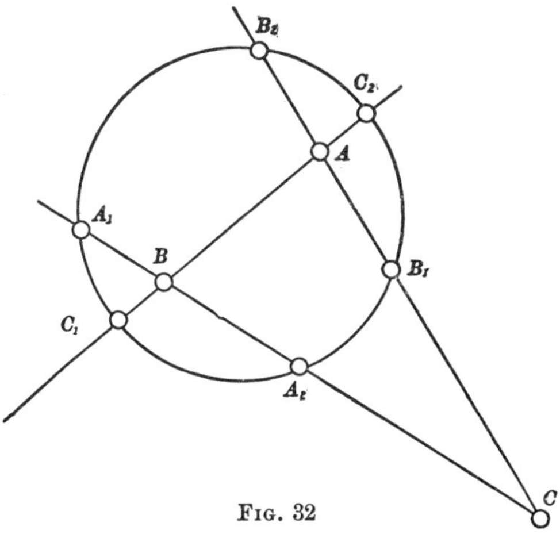

FIG. 32

$$C_1C_2'AB \barwedge C_2C_1'BA \barwedge C_1'C_2AB,$$

and hence
$$\frac{C_1A}{C_1B} : \frac{C_2'A}{C_2'B} = \frac{C_1'A}{C_1'B} : \frac{C_2A}{C_2B},$$

or
$$\frac{C_1A}{C_1B} \cdot \frac{C_2A}{C_2B} = \frac{C_1'A}{C_1'B} \cdot \frac{C_2'A}{C_2'B}.$$

Hence the formula (8) is equivalent to the formula obtained from it by substituting C_1', C_2' for C_1, C_2 respectively. Hence the formula holds for any conic. The converse argument is now obvious.

The last three theorems are the most important special cases of the "theory of transversals." A few further theorems of this class and some other propositions which can readily be derived from them are stated in the exercises below. Further theorems and references will be found in the Encyclopädie der Math. Wiss. III AB 5, § 2, and III C 1, § 23.

EXERCISES

1. The six lines joining the vertices A, B, C of a triangle to pairs of points A_1A_2, B_1B_2, C_1C_2 on the respectively opposite sides are tangents to a conic if and only if the relation (8) is satisfied.

2. If the sides BC, CA, AB of a triangle are tangent to a conic in A_1, B_1, C_1 respectively,
$$\frac{CA_1}{BA_1} \cdot \frac{AB_1}{CB_1} \cdot \frac{BC_1}{AC_1} = -1.$$

3. If a line BC meets a conic in A_1 and A_2, and two parallel lines through B and C, respectively, meet it in the pairs C_1, C_2 and B_1, B_2 respectively,

$$\frac{A_1B}{A_1C} \cdot \frac{A_2B}{A_2C} \cdot \frac{B_1C}{C_1B} \cdot \frac{B_2C}{C_2B} = 1.$$

4. Let two lines a and b through a point O meet a conic in the pairs A_1, A_2 and B_1, B_2 respectively. If O, a, b are variable in such a way that a and b remain respectively parallel to two fixed lines,

$$\frac{OA_1 \cdot OA_2}{OB_1 \cdot OB_2}$$

is a constant.

5. If the sides of a triangle meet a conic in three pairs of points, the three pairs of lines joining the pairs of points to the opposite vertices of the triangle are tangents to a second conic. State the dual and converse of this theorem.

6. If two points are joined to the vertices of a triangle by six lines, these lines meet the sides in six points (other than the vertices) which are on a conic. Dualize.

7. If a line meets the sides A_0A_1, A_1A_2, $\cdots$, A_nA_0, respectively, of a simple polygon $A_0A_1A_2 \cdots A_n$ in points B_0, B_1, $\cdots$, B_n respectively,

$$\frac{A_0B_0}{A_1B_0} \cdot \frac{A_1B_1}{A_2B_1} \cdots \frac{A_nB_n}{A_0B_n} = 1.$$

8. If a conic meets the lines A_0A_1, A_1A_2, $\cdots$, A_nA_0, respectively, in the pairs of points B_0C_0, B_1C_1, $\cdots$, B_nC_n respectively,

$$\frac{A_0B_0}{A_1B_0} \cdot \frac{A_0C_0}{A_1C_1} \cdot \frac{A_1B_1}{A_2B_1} \cdot \frac{A_1C_1}{A_2C_1} \cdots \frac{A_nB_n}{A_0B_n} \cdot \frac{A_nC_n}{A_0C_n} = 1.$$

9. If a conic is tangent to the lines A_0A_1, A_1A_2, $\cdots$, A_nA_0, respectively, in the points B_0, B_1, $\cdots$, B_n respectively,

$$\frac{A_0B_0}{A_1B_0} \cdot \frac{A_1B_1}{A_2B_1} \cdots \frac{A_nB_n}{A_0B_n} = (-1)^{n-1}.$$

45. Point reflections. DEFINITION. A homology of period two whose axis is l_∞ is called a *point reflection.*

From this definition there follows at once:

THEOREM 25. *A point reflection is fully determined by its center. The center is the mid-point of every pair of homologous points. Every two homologous lines are parallel.*

THEOREM 26. *The product of two point reflections whose centers are distinct is a translation parallel to the line joining their centers.*

Proof. The product obviously leaves fixed all points of l_∞ and also the line joining the two centers. Let C_1 and C_2 be the two centers, and let P be any point not on the line C_1C_2. Also let P' be the transform of P by the point reflection with C_1 as center, and let Q be the transform of P' by the point reflection with C_2 as center. Since C_1 is the mid-point of the pair PP', and C_2 of the pair $P'Q$, the line PQ is parallel to C_1C_2 (Theorem 12, Cor. 2). Thus the product of the two point reflections leaves invariant all lines parallel to C_1C_2, and hence is a translation.

COROLLARY. *The product of any even number of point reflections is a translation.*

THEOREM 27. *Any translation is the product of two point reflections one of which is arbitrary.*

Proof. Let T be any translation, C_1 the center of any point reflection, $C_3 = \mathrm{T}(C_1)$, and C_2 the mid-point of the pair C_1C_3. The product of the reflections in C_1 and C_2 is a translation, by Theorem 26, and since it carries C_1 to C_3, it is the translation T, by Theorem 3.

COROLLARY 1. *The product of any odd number of point reflections is a point reflection.*

Proof. Let the given point reflections be $\mathrm{P}_1, \mathrm{P}_2, \cdots, \mathrm{P}_{2n+1}$. By Theorem 26 the product $\mathrm{P}_1\mathrm{P}_2 \cdots \mathrm{P}_{2n}$ reduces to a translation, which, by Theorem 27, is the product of two point reflections one of which is P_{2n+1}. Hence there exists a point reflection P such that

$$\mathrm{P}_1\mathrm{P}_2 \cdots \mathrm{P}_{2n+1} = \mathrm{P}\mathrm{P}_{2n+1}\mathrm{P}_{2n+1} = \mathrm{P}.$$

COROLLARY 2. *The product of a translation and a point reflection is a point reflection.*

COROLLARY 3. *The set of all point reflections and translations form a group.*

THEOREM 28. *The group of point reflections and translations is a self-conjugate subgroup of the affine group.*

Proof. It has been proved, in Theorem 11, that if T is a translation and Σ an affine collineation, $\Sigma\mathrm{T}\Sigma^{-1}$ is a translation. Precisely similar reasoning shows that if T is a point reflection, $\Sigma\mathrm{T}\Sigma^{-1}$ is a point reflection.

COROLLARY. *The group G of point reflections and translations is self-conjugate under any subgroup of the affine group which contains G.*

Theorem 29. *With respect to any system of nonhomogeneous coördinates in which l_∞ is the singular line, the equations of a point reflection have the form*

$$x' = -x + a,$$
(9)
$$y' = -y + b.$$

Proof. The point reflection whose center is the origin is of the form

$$x' = -x,$$
$$y' = -y,$$

because this transformation evidently leaves (0, 0) and l_∞ pointwise invariant and is of period two. Since any other point reflection is the resultant of this one and a translation, it must be of the form (9).

EXERCISES

1. An ellipse or a hyperbola is transformed into itself by a point reflection whose center is the center of the conic.

2. Let $[C^2]$ be a system of conics conjugate under the group of translations to a single conic. Under what circumstances is $[C^2]$ invariant under the group of translations and point reflections?

3. Investigate the subgroups of the group of translations and point reflections.

4. Any odd number of point reflections $P_1, P_2, \cdots, P_n$ satisfy the condition,

$$(P_1 P_2 \cdots P_n)^2 = 1.$$

5. Let T be the point reflection whose center is the pole of l_∞ with respect to the n-point whose vertices are the centers of n point reflections $P_1, P_2, \cdots, P_n$. Then*

$$P_1 T P_2 T P_3 T \cdots P_n T = 1.$$

46. Extension of the definition of congruence. Definition. Two figures are said to be *congruent* if they are conjugate under the group of translations and point reflections.

This definition is obviously in agreement with that given in § 39. It will be completed in § 57, Chap. IV. The main significance of the present extension of the definition is that it removes any necessity of distinguishing between ordered and nonordered point pairs in statements about congruence.

* Cf. pp. 46, 84, Vol. I. The center of T is the "center of gravity" of the centers of $P_1, \cdots, P_n$. Cf. H. Wiener, Berichte der Gesellschaft der Wissenschaften zu Leipzig, Vol. XLV (1893), p. 568.

THEOREM 30. *Any ordered point pair AB is congruent to the ordered point pair BA.*

Proof. Let O be the mid-point of the ordered point pair AB. The point reflection with O as center interchanges A and B.

COROLLARY. *If a point reflection transforms an ordered point pair AB to A′B′,*

$$\text{Vect}\,(AB) = -\,\text{Vect}\,(A'B').$$

Proof. By Theorem 26 the given point reflection is the product of the point reflection in the mid-point of AB and a translation. The point reflection in the mid-point of AB interchanges A and B, and the translation leaves all vectors unchanged.

47. The homothetic group. DEFINITION. A homology whose axis is l_∞ is called a *dilation.* Dilations and translations are both called *homothetic transformations.* Two figures conjugate under a homothetic transformation are said to be *homothetic.*

Homothetic figures are also called, in conformity with definitions introduced later, "similar and similarly placed."

The point reflections are evidently special cases of dilations. Since the product of two perspective collineations (§ 28, Vol. I) having a common axis is a perspective collineation, the set of all homothetic transformations form a group; and by an argument like that used for Theorem 11 this group is self-conjugate under the affine group. Hence we have

THEOREM 31. *The set of all homothetic transformations form a group which is a self-conjugate subgroup of the affine group.*

Further theorems on the homothetic group are stated in the exercises below.

EXERCISES

1. The ratios of parallel vectors are left invariant by the homothetic group.

2. If two point pairs AB and CD are transformed by a dilation into $A'B'$ and $C'D'$ respectively,

$$\frac{AB}{A'B'} = \frac{CD}{C'D'}.$$

3. If two triangles are homothetic, the lines joining corresponding vertices meet in a point or are parallel.

4. The equations of the homothetic group with respect to any nonhomogeneous coördinate system of which l_∞ is the singular line are

$$x' = ax + b,\qquad y' = ay + d. \qquad (a \neq 0)$$

48. Equivalence of ordered point triads. Although the theory of congruence as based on the group of translations and point reflections does not yield metric relations between pairs of points unless they are on parallel lines, yet when applied to point triads it yields a complete theory of the equivalence (in area) of triangles.*

In this section we shall give the definitions and the more important sufficient conditions for equivalence, using methods somewhat analogous to those in the first book of Euclid's Elements. Instead of triangles, however, we shall work with ordered triads of points. This permits the introduction of algebraic signs of areas, though, as we do not need to refer to the interior and exterior of a triangle, we shall not actually employ the word "area." The triads of points which are referred to are all triads of *noncollinear points*.

Our definitions have their origin in the intuitional notions: that any triangle ABC is equivalent in area to the triangle BCA, that two triangles are equivalent in area if one can be transformed into the other by a translation or point reflection, and that two triangles which can be obtained by adding equivalent triangles are equivalent.

DEFINITION. If ABC and ACD are two ordered point triads, and B, C, and D are collinear, and $B \neq D$ (fig. 33), the point triad ABD is called the *sum* of ABC and ACD and is denoted by $ABC + ACD$ or by $ACD + ABC$.

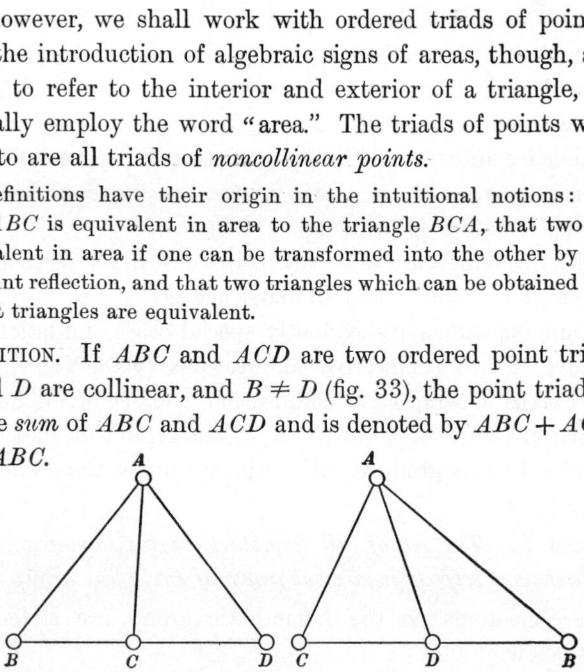

FIG. 33

DEFINITION. An ordered point triad t is said to be *equivalent* to an ordered point triad t' (in symbols, $t \backsimeq t'$) (1) if t can be carried to t' by a point reflection, or (2) if t and t' can be denoted by ABC and

* The idea of building up the theory of areas without the aid of a full theory of congruence is due to E. B. Wilson, Annals of Mathematics, Vol. V (2d series) (1903), p. 29. His method is quite different from ours, being based on the observation (cf. § 52, below) that an equiaffine collineation is expressible as a product of simple shears. Still another treatment of areas based on the group of translations and employing continuity considerations is outlined by Wilson and Lewis, "The Space-time Manifold of Relativity," Proceedings of the American Academy of Arts and Sciences. Vol. XLVIII (1912). We shall return to the subject in later sections.

BCA respectively, or (3) if there exists an ordered point triad $\bar{t}$ such that $t \backsimeq \bar{t}$ and $\bar{t} \backsimeq t'$, or (4) if there exist ordered point triads t_1, t_2, t_1', t_2' such that $t_1 \backsimeq t_1'$, $t_2 \backsimeq t_2'$ and $t = t_1 + t_2$ and $t' = t_1' + t_2'$. An ordered point triad t is not said to be equivalent to an ordered point triad t' unless it follows, by a finite number of applications of the criteria (1), (2), (3), (4), that $t \backsimeq t'$.

Since any translation is a product of two point reflections, Criteria (1) and (3) give

THEOREM 32. *Two ordered point triads are equivalent if they are conjugate under the group of translations and point reflections.*

THEOREM 33. *If A, B, and C are noncollinear points, $ABC \backsimeq ABC$, $ABC \backsimeq BCA$, $ABC \backsimeq CAB$.*

Proof. From (2) of the definition it follows that $ABC \backsimeq BCA$ and $BCA \backsimeq CAB$. Hence, by (3), $ABC \backsimeq CAB$. But, by (2), $CAB \backsimeq ABC$. Hence, by (3), $ABC \backsimeq ABC$.

From the last two theorems and from the form of the definition we now have at once

THEOREM 34. *If $t_1 \backsimeq t_2$, then $t_2 \backsimeq t_1$.*

THEOREM 35. *If A, B, C are any three noncollinear points and O the mid-point of the pair AB, then $AOC \backsimeq OBC$.*

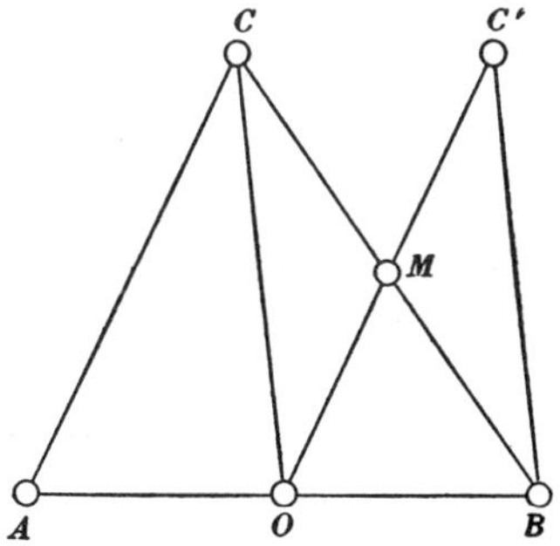

FIG. 34

Proof. Let C' be the point to which C is changed by the translation shifting A to O, and let M be the point of intersection of the nonparallel lines BC and OC'. Since $COBC'$ is a parallelogram, M is the mid-point of the pairs CB and $C'O$. Thus we have

$$AOC \backsimeq OBC' \backsimeq BC'O = BC'M + BMO$$

and

$$OBC = OBM + OMC.$$

But the point reflection with M as center carries OMC into $C'MB$. Thus

$$OMC \backsimeq C'MB \backsimeq BC'M,$$

and

$$OBM \backsimeq BMO,$$

and hence, by comparison with the equivalences and equations above,

$$AOC \backsimeq OBC.$$

THEOREM 36. *Two ordered point triads* ABC_1 *and* ABC_2, *where* $C_1 \neq C_2$, *are equivalent if the line* C_1C_2 *is parallel to the line* AB.

Proof. Let C_3 be such that B is the mid-point of C_1C_3, and let the line C_2C_3 meet the line AB in O, which is an ordinary point because C_3 is not on the line C_1C_2. It follows (§ 40) that O is the mid-point of the pair C_2C_3.

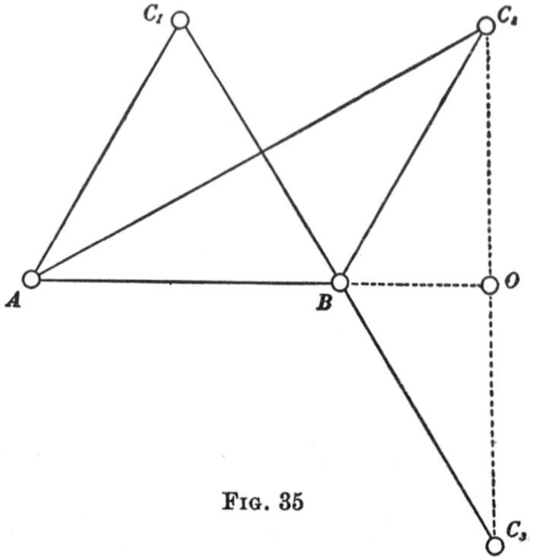

FIG. 35

By Theorems 34 and 35, $ABC_1 \backsimeq BAC_3 \backsimeq C_3BA$. By definition, $C_3BA = C_3BO + C_3OA$. By Theorem 35, $C_3BO \backsimeq C_2OB$ and $C_3OA \backsimeq C_2AO$. Hence $C_3BA \backsimeq C_2AO + C_2OB = C_2AB \backsimeq ABC_2$. Hence $ABC_1 \backsimeq ABC_2$.

COROLLARY. *If a point* B' *is on a line* OB *and a point* C' *on a different line* OC, *and the lines* BC' *and* $B'C$ *are parallel,* $BOC \backsimeq B'OC'$.

Proof. By hypothesis,

$$BOC = BOC' + BC'C$$

and $C'B'O = C'B'B + C'BO$.

But $C'B'B \backsimeq C'CB \backsimeq BC'C$, by Theorems 36 and 34, and $C'BO \backsimeq BOC'$, by Theorem 34. Hence $BOC \backsimeq C'B'O \backsimeq B'OC'$.

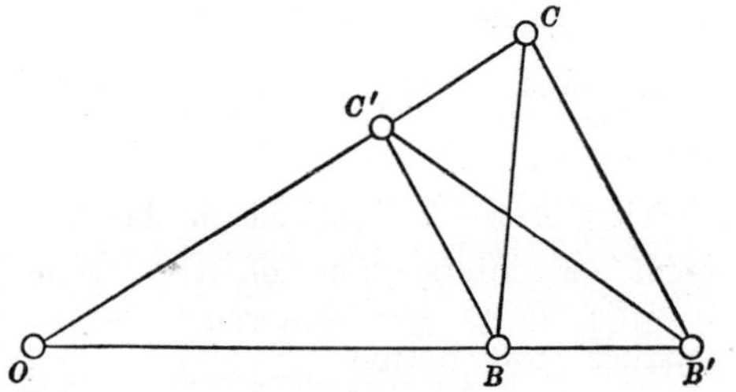

FIG. 36

THEOREM 37. *If* A, B, *and* C *are any three noncollinear points, and* P *and* Q *are any two distinct points, there exists a line* r *parallel to* PQ *such that if* R *is any point of* r, $ABC \backsimeq PQR$.

Proof. Let T be the translation such that $\mathrm{T}(A) = P$, and let $\mathrm{T}(B) = B'$ and $\mathrm{T}(C) = C'$. If B' is not on the line PQ, let R' be the intersection (fig. 37) of the line through C' parallel to PB' with the line through P parallel to QB'. If B' is on the line PQ, let R' be the point of intersection with PC' of the line through B' parallel to QC'.

In both cases the lines which intersect in R' are by hypothesis non-parallel, so that R' is always an ordinary point. By Theorem 32. $ABC \backsimeq PB'C'$. In case B' is not on PQ, it follows, by Theorem 36, that $PB'C' \backsimeq PB'R' \backsimeq PQR'$. In case B' is on PQ, it follows, by the corollary of Theorem 36, that $PB'C' \backsimeq PQR'$. By Theorem 36 the line r through R' parallel to PQ is such that for every point R on r, $ABC \backsimeq PQR$.

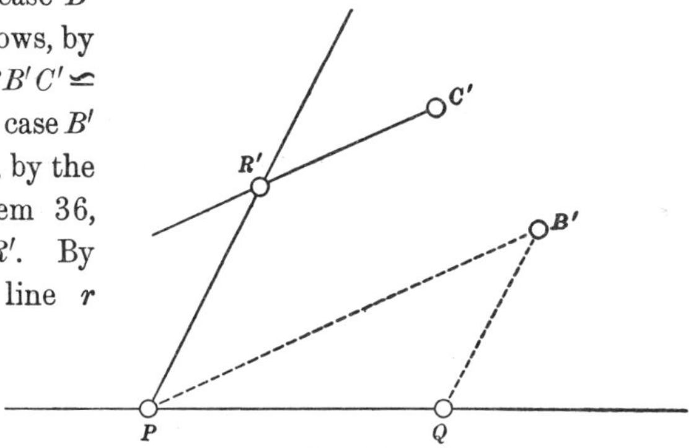

FIG. 37

EXERCISES

1. Two ordered point triads ABC and $AB'C'$ are equivalent if the points B, C, B', C' are collinear and $\text{Vect}(BC) = \text{Vect}(B'C')$.

2. Let O be the point of intersection of the asymptotes l and m of a hyperbola, and let L and M be the intersections with l and m respectively of a variable tangent to the hyperbola. Then the ordered point triads OLM are all equivalent.

49. Measure of ordered point triads. The theorems of the last section state sufficient conditions for the equivalence of ordered point triads. In order to obtain necessary conditions, we shall introduce the notion of *measure*, analogous to the magnitude of a vector.

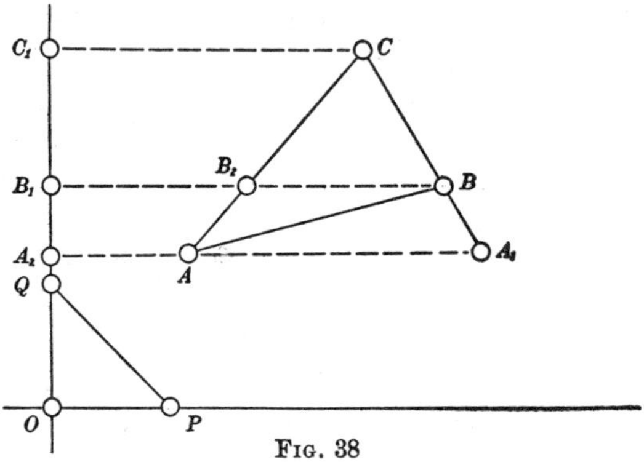

FIG. 38

DEFINITION. Let O, P, Q be three non-collinear points. The *measure* of an ordered point triad ABC *relative to the ordered triad OPQ as a unit* is a number $m(ABC)$ determined as follows: If the line BC is not parallel to OP, let B_1 and C_1 be the points in which the lines through B and C respectively, parallel to OP, meet the line OQ, and let A_1 be the point in which the line through A, parallel to OP, meets the line BC. Let AA_1 denote the magnitude of the vector AA_1 relative to the unit OP (§ 43), and B_1C_1 the magnitude of the vector B_1C_1 relative to the unit OQ. The measure of the ordered triad ABC is *

$$AA_1 \cdot B_1C_1$$

and is denoted by $m\,(ABC)$. If the line BC is parallel to OP, CA is not parallel to OP, and the measure of ABC is defined to be $m\,(BCA)$.

If this definition be allowed to apply to any ordered point triad whatever (instead of only to noncollinear triads, cf. § 48), we have $m\,(ABC) = 0$ whenever the points A, B, C are collinear.

THEOREM 38. *If* $ABC \backsimeq A'B'C'$, *then* $m\,(ABC) = m\,(A'B'C')$.

Proof. Let us examine the four criteria in the definition of equivalence in § 48.

(1) In case ABC is carried to $A'B'C'$ by a point reflection, each of the vectors AA_1 and B_1C_1 is transformed into its negative (Theorem 30, corollary), and hence the product of their magnitudes is unchanged.

(2) According to the second criterion, $ABC \backsimeq BCA$. Suppose, first, that neither BC nor CA is parallel to OP, and let A_1, B_1, C_1 have the meaning given them in the definition above. Then

$$m\,(ABC) = AA_1 \cdot B_1C_1.$$

Let B_2 (fig. 38) be the point in which the line through B, parallel to OP, meets the line CA, and let A_2 be the point in which OQ is met by the parallel to OP through A. Then if BB_2 and C_1A_2 represent the magnitudes of the corresponding vectors relative to OP and OQ as units,

$$m\,(BCA) = BB_2 \cdot C_1A_2.$$

By Theorem 20,
$$\frac{AA_1}{B_2B} = \frac{A_1C}{BC}.$$

But since the lines CC_1, A_1A_2, BB_1 are parallel, it follows from § 43 that

$$\frac{A_1C}{BC} = \frac{A_2C_1}{B_1C_1}.$$

Hence
$$\frac{AA_1}{B_2B} = \frac{A_2C_1}{B_1C_1},$$

or
$$m\,(ABC) = AA_1 \cdot B_1C_1 = BB_2 \cdot C_1A_2 = m\,(BCA).$$

* The factor $\frac{1}{2}$ is lacking in this expression, because we are taking a triangle rather than a parallelogram as the unit.

In case BC is parallel to OP, the last clause of the definition states that

$$m(ABC) = m(BCA).$$

In case CA is parallel to OP, AB and BC are not parallel to OP, and hence the argument above shows that

$$m(CAB) = m(ABC).$$

But, by definition, $m(BCA) = m(CAB)$.

Hence $m(ABC) = m(BCA)$.

(3) Corresponding to the fact that if $t_1 \backsimeq t_2$ and $t_2 \backsimeq t_3$, then $t_1 \backsimeq t_3$, we have that, since $m(t)$ is a uniquely defined number, if $m(t_1) = m(t_2)$, and $m(t_2) = m(t_3)$, then $m(t_1) = m(t_3)$.

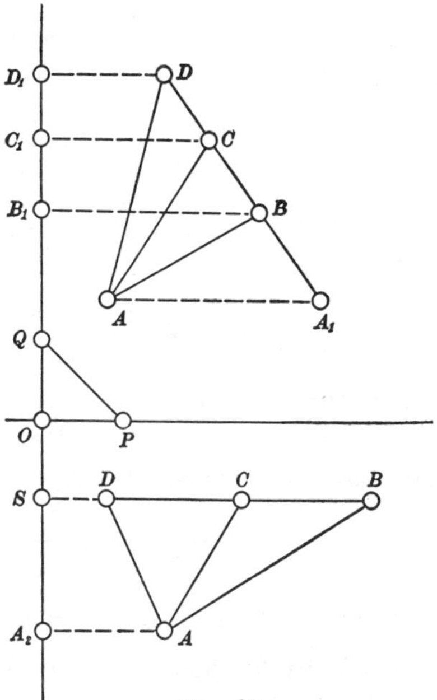

Fig. 39

(4) Let B, C, D be three collinear points and A any point not on the line BC (fig. 39). In case the line BC is not parallel to OP, let A_1 be the point in which the line through A, parallel to OP, meets BC, and let B_1, C_1, D_1 be the points in which the lines through B, C, D respectively, parallel to OP, meet OQ. Then

$$\begin{aligned} m(ABD) &= AA_1 \cdot B_1D_1 \\ &= AA_1 \cdot B_1C_1 + AA_1 \cdot C_1D_1 \\ &= m(ABC) + m(ACD). \end{aligned}$$

In case the line BC is parallel to OP, let S be the point in which BC meets OQ, and A_2 be the point in which the line through A, parallel to OP, meets OQ. Then

$$\begin{aligned} m(ABD) = m(BDA) = BD \cdot SA_2 &= BC \cdot SA_2 + CD \cdot SA_2 \\ = m(BCA) + m(CDA) &= m(ABC) + m(ACD). \end{aligned}$$

Thus, in every case, if $t_1 + t_2 = t_3$, $m(t_1) + m(t_2) = m(t_3)$.

Comparing the results proved in these four cases with the definition of equivalence, we have at once that whenever $t_1 \backsimeq t_2$, $m(t_1) = m(t_2)$.

THEOREM 39. *If B, C, and D are collinear points, and the point A is not on the line BC,*

$$\frac{m(ABC)}{m(ABD)}=\frac{BC}{BD}.$$

Proof. In case the line BC is not parallel to OP, let A_1, B_1, C_1 have the meaning given them in the definition of measure, and let D_1 be the point in which the line through D, parallel to OP, meets OQ (fig. 39). Then

$$\frac{m(ABC)}{m(ABD)}=\frac{AA_1\cdot B_1C_1}{AA_1\cdot B_1D_1}=\frac{B_1C_1}{B_1D_1}.$$

But, by § 43,

$$\frac{B_1C_1}{B_1D_1}=\frac{BC}{BD}.$$

In case BC is parallel to OP, let A_2 be the point in which the line through A, parallel to OP, meets OQ, and S the point in which BC meets OQ. Then

$$\frac{m(ABC)}{m(ABD)}=\frac{m(BCA)}{m(BDA)}=\frac{BC\cdot SA_2}{BD\cdot SA_2}=\frac{BC}{BD}.$$

COROLLARY 1. *If B, C, D, E are points no two of which are collinear with a point A,*

$$\text{R}(AB, AC, AD, AE)=\frac{m(ABD)}{m(ABE)}\div\frac{m(ACD)}{m(ACE)}.$$

COROLLARY 2. *If B, C, D are points no two of which are collinear with a point A, and if P_∞ is the point at infinity of the line CD (the latter not being parallel to AB),*

$$\text{R}(AP_\infty, AB, AC, AD)=\frac{m(ABD)}{m(ABC)}.$$

THEOREM 40. *If $m(ABC)=m(A'B'C')\neq 0$, then $ABC\backsimeq A'B'C'$.*

Proof. By Theorem 37 there exists a point C'' on the line $A'C'$ such that $ABC\backsimeq A'B'C''$. Hence $A'B'C'\backsimeq A'B'C''$, and by the last theorem, $C'=C''$.

In consequence of the last two theorems the unit point triad may be replaced by any equivalent triad without changing the measure of any triad.

THEOREM 41. *If $ABC\backsimeq ABC'$, and $C\neq C'$, the line CC' is parallel to the line AB.*

Proof. The unit triad OPQ may be chosen so that OP is parallel to AB. Then if C_1 is the point in which the line through C, parallel to OP, meets OQ, and B_1 the point in which AB meets OQ,

$$m(ABC) = AB \cdot B_1C_1.$$

If C_1' is the point in which the line through C', parallel to OP, meets OQ,

$$m(ABC') = AB \cdot B_1C_1'.$$

By Theorem 38, $m(ABC) = m(ABC')$, and hence $C_1 = C_1'$. Hence the line CC' is parallel to AB.

THEOREM 42. *If $ABC \backsimeq AB'C'$, and B' is on the line AB, and C' on the line AC, then the line BC' is parallel to the line $B'C$.*

Proof. By the corollary of Theorem 36, if C'' is a point of AC' such that BC'' is parallel to $B'C$, then

$$ABC \backsimeq AB'C''.$$

By Theorem 41 the only points $\overline{C}$ such that $ABC \backsimeq AB'\overline{C}$ are on the line through C'', parallel to AB'. Hence $C' = C''$.

It is notable that although the sufficient conditions for equivalence given in § 48 are all proved on the basis of Assumptions A, E, H_0, the discussion of the ratios of vectors, and hence all the necessary conditions for equivalence, involve Assumption P in their proofs. This is essential,* as we can show by proving that Assumption P is a logical consequence of these theorems, together with the previous theorems on equivalence. As was pointed out in § 3, Assumption P is a logical consequence of the theorem of Pappus, Theorem 21, § 36, Vol. I. When one of the lines of the configuration is taken as l_∞, this theorem assumes the form:

If a simple hexagon $AB'CA'BC'$ is such that A, B, C are on one line and A', B', C' on another line, and if AB' is parallel to $A'B$ and BC' parallel to $B'C$, then CA' is parallel to $C'A$.

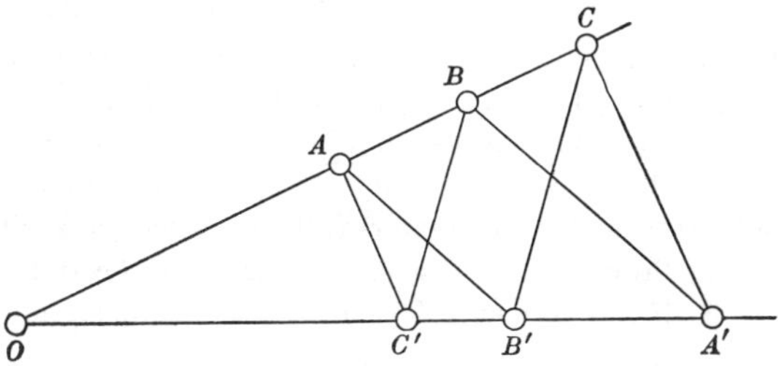

FIG. 40

In case the lines containing ABC and $A'B'C'$, respectively, are parallel, this can be proved from the Desargues theorem on perspective triangles; so that we are interested only in the

* The rôle of Assumption P (or rather of the equivalent theorem of Pappus) in the theory of areas was first determined in a definite way by D. Hilbert, Grundlagen der Geometrie, Chap. IV.

case when AB and $A'B'$ intersect in a point O. By Theorem 36, since AB' is parallel to $A'B$, $OAA' \backsimeq OBB'$; and since BC' is parallel to $B'C$, $OBB' \backsimeq OCC'$. By the definition (3) of equivalence it follows that $OAA' \backsimeq OCC'$. But by Theorem 42 this implies that AC' is parallel to $A'C$.

This is perhaps the simplest way of proving the fundamental theorem of projective geometry if it be desired to base projective geometry upon elementary Euclidean geometry (cf. Ex. 3, § 54).

The notion of measure can be extended to any ordered set of n points, i.e. (cf. § 14, Vol. I) to any *simple n-point*. The details of this discussion are left to the reader. An outline is furnished by the problems below. The principal references are to A. F. Möbius, Der barycentrische Calcul, §§ 1, 17, 18, 165; Werke, Vol. I, pp. 23, 39, 200; Vol. II, p. 485. See also the Encyclopädie der Math. Wiss., III AB 9, § 12. It is to be borne in mind in using these references that our hypotheses are narrower than those used by the previous writers.

EXERCISES

1. For any three points A, B, C,

$$m(ABC) + m(ACB) = 0.$$

2. For any four points O, A, B, C,

$$m(ABC) = m(OAB) + m(OBC) + m(OCA).$$

3. For any n points $A_1, A_2, \cdots, A_n$ the number

$$m(OA_1A_2) + m(OA_2A_3) + \cdots + m(OA_{n-1}A_n) + m(OA_nA_1)$$

is the same for all choices of the point O. We define it to be the *measure* of the simple n-point $A_1A_2 \cdots A_n$ and denote it by $m(A_1A_2 \cdots A_n)$.

4. $m(A_1A_2 \cdots A_{n-1}A_n) = m(A_2A_3 \cdots A_nA_1)$.

5. $m(A_1A_2 \cdots A_n) + m(A_1A_nA_{n+1} \cdots A_{n+k}) = m(A_1A_2 \cdots A_{n+k})$.

6. Derive a formula for $m(A_1A_2 \cdots A_n)$ analogous to the definition of $m(ABC)$ in terms of vectors collinear with two arbitrary vectors OP and OQ.

7. Prove the converse propositions to those stated in the exercises in § 48.

8. If $ABCD$ and $A'B'C'D'$ are two parallelograms whose sides are respectively parallel,

$$\frac{m(ABCD)}{m(A'B'C'D')} = \frac{AB}{A'B'} \cdot \frac{BC}{B'C'}.$$

9. The variable parallelogram two of whose sides are the asymptotes of a hyperbola and one vertex of which is on the hyperbola has a constant measure.

10. If a variable pair of conjugate diameters meets a conic in point pairs AA', BB', the parallelogram whose sides are the tangents at A, A', B, B' has a constant measure. The parallelogram $ABA'B'$ also has a constant measure.

50. The equiaffine group. THEOREM 43. *If two equivalent ordered point triads* t_1 *and* t_2 *are transformed by an affine collineation into* t_1' *and* t_2', then $t_1' \backsimeq t_2'$.

Proof. It is necessary merely to verify that the relation used in each of the criteria (1), · · ·, (4) in the definition of equivalence (§ 48) is unaffected by an affine collineation. For Criterion (1) this reduces to Theorem 28. For Criteria (2), (3), (4) it is a consequence of the fact that an affine collineation transforms ordered triads into ordered triads and collinear points into collinear points.

THEOREM 44. *If an affine collineation transforms one ordered point triad into an equivalent point triad, it transforms every ordered point triad into an equivalent point triad.*

Proof. It follows from Theorem 43 that if ABC is transformed by a given collineation into an equivalent ordered point triad $A'B'C'$, then every point triad equivalent to ABC is transformed into a point triad equivalent to $A'B'C'$ and thus into one equivalent to ABC. By Theorem 37 any ordered point triad whatever is equivalent to some point triad ADC, where D is on the line AB. Hence the present theorem will be proved if we can show that ADC is transformed into an equivalent point triad.

Denote the point to which D is transformed by the given collineation by D'. By Theorem 39,

$$\frac{m(ADC)}{m(ABC)} = \frac{AD}{AB} \text{ and } \frac{m(A'D'C')}{m(A'B'C')} = \frac{A'D'}{A'B'}.$$

By § 43,
$$\frac{AD}{AB} = \text{R}(P_\infty A, BD),$$

where P_∞ is the point at infinity of the line AB. But since the given collineation is affine, P_∞ is transformed to the point at infinity P_∞' of the line $A'B'$, and

$$\text{R}(P_\infty A, BD) = \text{R}(P_\infty' A', B'D') = \frac{A'D'}{A'B'} = \frac{m(A'D'C')}{m(A'B'C')}.$$

Since $m(ABC) = m(A'B'C')$, it follows that $m(ADC) = m(A'D'C')$. Hence

$$ADC \backsimeq A'D'C'.$$

DEFINITION. Any affine collineation which transforms an ordered point triad into an equivalent point triad is said to be *equiaffine.*

THEOREM 45. *The equiaffine collineations form a self-conjugate subgroup of the affine group.*

Proof. By the last theorem an equiaffine collineation transforms every ordered point triad into an equivalent point triad. Hence, by Condition (3) in the definition of equivalence, the product of two equiaffine collineations is equiaffine. By Theorem 43, $\Sigma T \Sigma^{-1}$ is equiaffine whenever T is equiaffine and Σ affine.

THEOREM 46. *Let A, B, A', B' be points such that $A \neq B$ and $A' \neq B'$; let a be a line on A but not on B, and let a' be a line on A' but not on B'. There is one and only one equiaffine collineation transforming A to A', B to B', and a to a'.*

Proof. Let C be any point distinct from A on a. By Theorem 37, there is a point C' on the line a' such that

$$ABC \backsimeq A'B'C'.$$

By Theorem 1 there is one and only one affine transformation carrying A, B, C to A', B', C' respectively, and by definition this transformation is equiaffine. By Theorem 41, C' is the only point on a' such that $ABC \backsimeq A'B'C'$. Hence (Theorem 44) there is only one equiaffine transformation carrying A, B, a into A', B', a' respectively.

EXERCISE

Any affine collineation leaves invariant the ratio of the measures of any two point triads.

***51. Algebraic formula for measure. Barycentric coördinates.** Consider a nonhomogeneous coördinate system in which l_∞ is the singular line. Let the unit of measure for ordered triads be OPQ, where $O = (0, 0)$, $P = (1, 0)$, $Q = (0, 1)$. Let $A = (a_1, a_2)$, $B = (b_1, b_2)$, $C = (c_1, c_2)$; the line through A, parallel to OP, consists of the points $(a_1 + \lambda, a_2)$, where λ is arbitrary, and the line BC has the equation (§ 64, Vol. I),

$$\begin{vmatrix} x & y & 1 \\ b_1 & b_2 & 1 \\ c_1 & c_2 & 1 \end{vmatrix} = 0.$$

In case the line BC is not parallel to OP, and therefore $b_2 \neq c_2$, the point A_1 which appears in the definition of measure (§ 49) is $(a_1 + \lambda, a_2)$, where λ satisfies

$$\begin{vmatrix} \lambda & 0 & 0 \\ b_1 & b_2 & 1 \\ c_1 & c_2 & 1 \end{vmatrix} + \begin{vmatrix} a_1 & a_2 & 1 \\ b_1 & b_2 & 1 \\ c_1 & c_2 & 1 \end{vmatrix} = 0.$$

Hence
$$AA_1 = \frac{-1}{(b_2 - c_2)} \cdot \begin{vmatrix} a_1 & a_2 & 1 \\ b_1 & b_2 & 1 \\ c_1 & c_2 & 1 \end{vmatrix}.$$

The points B_1 and C_1 of the definition of measure are $(0, b_2)$ and $(0, c_2)$, respectively, so that
$$B_1C_1 = c_2 - b_2.$$

Hence

(10)
$$m(ABC) = \begin{vmatrix} a_1 & a_2 & 1 \\ b_1 & b_2 & 1 \\ c_1 & c_2 & 1 \end{vmatrix}.$$

That the same result holds good in case BC is parallel to OP is readily verified.

Now if A, B, C are transformed to A', B', C' respectively by a transformation

(11)
$$\begin{aligned} x' &= \alpha_1 x + \beta_1 y + \gamma_1, \\ y' &= \alpha_2 x + \beta_2 y + \gamma_2, \end{aligned} \qquad \Delta = \begin{vmatrix} \alpha_1 & \beta_1 \\ \alpha_2 & \beta_2 \end{vmatrix} \neq 0$$

of the affine group,

(12)
$$m(A'B'C') = \begin{vmatrix} \alpha_1 a_1 + \beta_1 a_2 + \gamma_1, & \alpha_2 a_1 + \beta_2 a_2 + \gamma_2, & 1 \\ \alpha_1 b_1 + \beta_1 b_2 + \gamma_1, & \alpha_2 b_1 + \beta_2 b_2 + \gamma_2, & 1 \\ \alpha_1 c_1 + \beta_1 c_2 + \gamma_1, & \alpha_2 c_1 + \beta_2 c_2 + \gamma_2, & 1 \end{vmatrix}$$
$$= \begin{vmatrix} a_1 & a_2 & 1 \\ b_1 & b_2 & 1 \\ c_1 & c_2 & 1 \end{vmatrix} \cdot \begin{vmatrix} \alpha_1 & \beta_1 \\ \alpha_2 & \beta_2 \end{vmatrix}.$$

Hence we have

THEOREM 47. *A transformation* (11) *of the affine group is equiaffine if and only if**
$$\begin{vmatrix} \alpha_1 & \beta_1 \\ \alpha_2 & \beta_2 \end{vmatrix} = 1.$$

Let $A = (a_1, a_2)$, $B = (b_1, b_2)$, $C = (c_1, c_2)$ be the vertices of any triangle, and $P = (x, y)$ any point. In the homogeneous coördinates for which $x_1/x_0 = x$, $x_2/x_0 = y$, these points may be written $A = (1, a_1, a_2)$, etc. Hence by the result established in § 27 for the three-dimensional case, the numbers proportional to
$$\xi_0 = \begin{vmatrix} 1 & x & y \\ 1 & b_1 & b_2 \\ 1 & c_1 & c_2 \end{vmatrix}, \quad \xi_1 = \begin{vmatrix} 1 & a_1 & a_2 \\ 1 & x & y \\ 1 & c_1 & c_2 \end{vmatrix}, \quad \xi_2 = \begin{vmatrix} 1 & a_1 & a_2 \\ 1 & b_1 & b_2 \\ 1 & x & y \end{vmatrix}$$
may be regarded as homogeneous coördinates of P in a system for which ABC is the triangle of reference.

* By comparison with § 30 this condition yields the result that, in an ordered space, the equiaffine collineations are all direct.

This is a particular one of the homogeneous coördinate systems for which ABC is the triangle of reference, and of course corresponds to a particular choice of the point (1, 1, 1). Other particular systems may be obtained by replacing $(1, a_1, a_2)$ by (k, ka_1, ka_2) and like changes. The coördinates written down, however, have (in view of (10)) the remarkable property that

$$\xi_0 = m(PBC), \quad \xi_1 = m(APC), \quad \xi_2 = m(ABP).$$

Also, in view of Ex. 2, § 49, they satisfy the condition

$$\xi_0 + \xi_1 + \xi_2 = m(ABC)$$

for all ordinary points P. If ABC be taken as the unit of measure, this condition assumes the form

$$\xi_0 + \xi_1 + \xi_2 = 1.$$

Since all ordinary points satisfy this condition, the equation

$$\xi_0 + \xi_1 + \xi_2 = 0,$$

which can always be satisfied by properly chosen homogeneous coördinates, must represent l_∞. Therefore the point $(\frac{1}{3}, \frac{1}{3}, \frac{1}{3})$, which is polar to l_∞ relatively to the triangle ABC, must be the point of intersection of the medians of this triangle.

DEFINITION. Given a homogeneous coördinate system with respect to which the line at infinity has the equation

$$x_0 + x_1 + x_2 = 0,$$

the three numbers x_0, x_1, x_2, which are homogeneous coördinates of an ordinary point P and satisfy the condition

$$x_0 + x_1 + x_2 = 1,$$

are called the *barycentric coördinates* of P, relative to the triangle $x_0 = 0$, $x_1 = 0$, $x_2 = 0$.

EXERCISES

1. Defining the barycentric coördinates of a point P, relative to a triangle ABC, as

$$\xi_0 = \frac{m(ABP)}{m(ABC)}, \quad \xi_1 = \frac{m(BCP)}{m(ABC)}, \quad \xi_2 = \frac{m(CAP)}{m(ABC)},$$

prove that a line is represented by a linear equation.

2. If A, B, C, D are four fixed points of a conic, and P a variable point, the ratio

$$\frac{m(ABP) \cdot m(CDP)}{m(ADP) \cdot m(CBP)}$$

is constant (cf. Cor. 1. Theorem 39).

3. Show that the equation of a conic through five points A, B, C, D, E may be written in the form

$$(ADE)(BCE)(ABX)(CDX) - (ABE)(CDE)(ADX)(BCX) = 0,$$

where (ADE) stands for
$$\begin{vmatrix} a_1 & a_2 & a_3 \\ d_1 & d_2 & d_3 \\ e_1 & e_2 & e_3 \end{vmatrix},$$

and the other parenthetical triads have analogous meanings.

***52. Line reflections.** Definition. A homology of period two whose center is on l_∞ is called a *line reflection*; if its center is L and its axis l, we shall denote the line reflection by $\{Ll\}$.

This definition could also be expressed by saying that a line reflection is a transformation having an axis such that (1) if P' be the transform of a point P and $P \neq P'$, the mid-point of the pair PP' is on the axis of the reflection; and (2) if P_1 and P_1' are any other pair of homologous points, the line P_1P_1' is parallel to PP'.

Theorem 48. *A product of two line reflections is an equiaffine collineation.*

Proof. Let the given line reflections be $\{L_1l_1\}$ and $\{L_2l_2\}$. Let l be any line meeting both l_1 and l_2, and let L be any point at infinity not on l. Then
$$\{L_2l_2\} \cdot \{L_1l_1\} = \{L_2l_2\} \cdot \{Ll\} \cdot \{Ll\} \cdot \{L_1l_1\}.$$

Let A be the point of intersection of l and l_1, B any other point of l_1, C any other point of l, C_1 the point to which C is transformed by $\{L_1l_1\}$, and O the point in which the line CC_1 meets l_1. Since O is the mid-point of CC_1, Theorem 35 gives in case $A \neq O \neq B$,

$$COB \backsimeq C_1BO,$$
$$CAO \backsimeq C_1OA.$$

Since $CAO + COB = CAB$,

and $C_1BO + C_1OA = C_1BA$,

it follows that

$$CAB \backsimeq C_1BA.$$

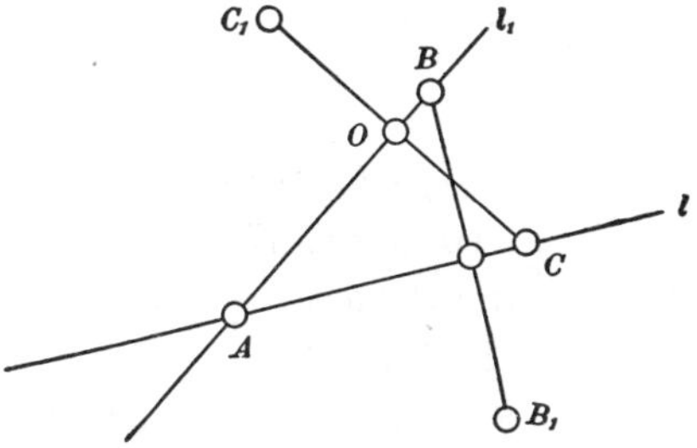

Fig. 41

In case $A=O$ or $O=B$ the same result follows directly from Theorem 35.

In like manner, if B_1 be the point to which B is transformed by $\{Ll\}$,
$$CAB \backsimeq CB_1A.$$

Hence
$$C_1BA \backsimeq CB_1A.$$

The product $\{Ll\} \cdot \{L_1l_1\}$ transforms C_1BA to CB_1A and is therefore an equiaffine collineation. In like manner, $\{L_2l_2\} \cdot \{Ll\}$ is also equiaffine. Hence the product $\{L_2l_2\} \cdot \{L_1l_1\}$ is equiaffine.

THEOREM 49. *An equiaffine collineation is a product of two line reflections.*

Proof. Let Γ be any equiaffine collineation. If there be any point which is not on an invariant line of Γ, let A_1 be such a point. Let A_0, A_2, A_3 be defined by the conditions

$$\Gamma(A_0)=A_1,\ \Gamma(A_1)=A_2,\ \Gamma(A_2)=A_3.$$

By the hypothesis on A_1 the points A_0, A_1, A_2 are noncollinear, and by the hypothesis that Γ is equiaffine

$$A_0A_1A_2 \simeq A_1A_2A_3 \simeq A_3A_1A_2.$$

Hence, by Theorem 41, the line A_0A_3 is parallel to A_1A_2, or else $A_0=A_3$.

Let M_1 be the mid-point of the pair A_0A_2, and M_2 of the pair A_1A_3. Let L_1 be the point at infinity of the line A_0A_2, L_2 of the line A_1A_2, and K of the line A_1A_3. Since A_0A_3 is parallel to A_1A_2, it follows that

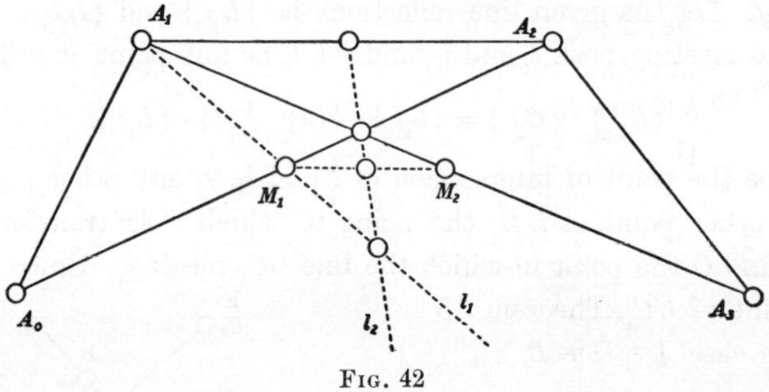

FIG. 42

$A_0A_2L_1 \overset{L_2}{\underset{\wedge}{=}} A_3A_1K$, and hence, by the definition of mid-point, that M_1, M_2, and L_2 are collinear. Since A_0, A_2, and the point at infinity of the line A_0A_2 are transformed by Γ to A_1, A_3, and the point at infinity of the line A_1A_3, $\Gamma(M_1)=M_2$.

Let l_1 be the line A_1M_1, and l_2 the line joining the mid-point of A_1A_2 to the mid-point of M_1M_2. By the above,

$$\{L_1l_1\}(A_0A_1M_1)=A_2A_1M_1,$$

and $$\{L_2l_2\}(A_2A_1M_1)=A_1A_2M_2.$$

Hence $$\{L_2l_2\} \cdot \{L_1l_1\}(A_0A_1M_1)=A_1A_2M_2.$$

But since $\Gamma(A_0A_1M_1)=A_1A_2M_2$, it follows, by Theorem 1, that

$$\Gamma=\{L_2l_2\} \cdot \{L_1l_1\}.$$

In case there is no point not on an invariant line of Γ, the invariant lines all meet in a point O. For the point of intersection of any two of them is invariant, and any three nonconcurrent ordinary lines have at least two ordinary points in common. Thus we should be led to a contradiction with Theorem 46 if the invariant lines were not concurrent.

Let A_1 be a point which is not invariant, and let $A_2 = \Gamma(A_1)$. Also let B_1 be another point which is not invariant and not on the line A_1A_2, and let $\Gamma(B_1) = B_2$. The lines A_1A_2 and B_1B_2 necessarily meet in O.

If O is ordinary, then since any line through it is invariant, all points of l_∞ are invariant, and hence A_1B_1 is parallel to A_2B_2. Since Γ is equiaffine,

$$A_1B_1O \backsimeq A_2B_2O.$$

Hence, by Theorem 42, A_1B_2 and A_2B_1 are parallel, and $A_1B_1A_2B_2$ is a parallelogram. Hence O is the mid-point of A_1A_2 and B_1B_2, and Γ is a point reflection.

Let a be the line A_1A_2 and A the point at infinity of a, and let b be the line B_1B_2 and B the point at infinity of b. The product $\{Ab\} \cdot \{Ba\}$ transforms A_1, B_1, O into A_2, B_2, O respectively, and hence is Γ.

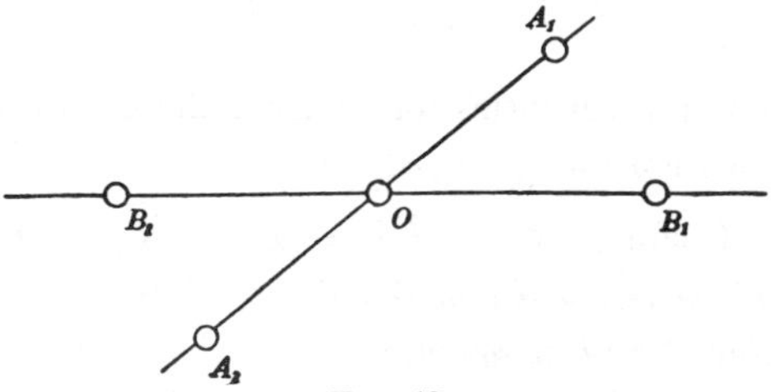

FIG. 43

If O is an ideal point, let l be the line A_1B_1, and let m be the line joining the mid-points of A_1A_2 and B_1B_2. Then $\{Om\} \cdot \{Ol\}$ transforms O, A_1, B_1 into O, A_2, B_2 respectively, and hence, by Theorem 46, is Γ.

COROLLARY 1. *An equiaffine collineation Γ such that A, $\Gamma(A)$ and $\Gamma^2(A)$ are collinear for all choices of A is either a point reflection or a translation or an elation whose center is at infinity and whose axis is an ordinary line.*

Proof. In the argument above it was proved that if the point O is ordinary, Γ is a point reflection; and that if O is ideal, $\Gamma = \{Om\} \cdot \{Ol\}$. If m and l are parallel, Γ is evidently a translation; and if m and l are not parallel, it is an elation with O as center and the line joining O to the point lm as axis.

DEFINITION. An elation whose center is at infinity and whose axis is an ordinary line is called a *simple shear.*

COROLLARY 2. *If* $\Gamma = \{L_2 l_2\} \cdot \{L_1 l_1\}$, *then for every line* l *concurrent with* l_1 *and* l_2 *which is not a double line of* Γ *there exist points* L *and* M *and a line* m *such that*

$$\Gamma = \{Mm\} \cdot \{Ll\}.$$

There also exist a point M' *and a line* m' *such that*

$$\Gamma = \{Ll\} \cdot \{M'm'\}.$$

If l *be taken as variable,*

$$[l] \barwedge [L] \barwedge [m] \barwedge [M] \barwedge [M'] \barwedge [m'].$$

Proof. The first conclusion follows from the arbitrariness in the choice of A_1 in the proof of the theorem above. The second conclusion follows from the first, combined with the fact that

$$\Gamma^{-1} = \{L_1 l_1\} \cdot \{L_2 l_2\}.$$

The projectivities follow from the constructions given in the proof of theorem for A_0, A_2, M_1, etc.

COROLLARY 3. *If* $\Gamma = \{L_2 l_2\} \cdot \{L_1 l_1\}$, *then for every point* L *of* l_∞ *which is not a double point of* Γ, *there exists a point* M *of* l_∞ *and two lines* l *and* m *concurrent with* l_1 *and* l_2 *such that*

$$\Gamma = \{Mm\} \cdot \{Ll\}.$$

There also exist a point M' *and a line* m' *such that*

$$\Gamma = \{Ll\} \cdot \{M'm'\}.$$

THEOREM 50. *The set of all affine collineations which are products of line reflections form a group. Every transformation of this group is either an equiaffine transformation or the product of an equiaffine transformation by a line reflection.*

Proof. By Theorems 48 and 49 the product of an even number of line reflections is equiaffine and reduces to a product of two line reflections. Hence the product of an odd number of line reflections reduces to a product of three line reflections. The statements above follow in an obvious way from this.

EXERCISES

1. Let the points at infinity of l_1, l_2, l respectively in Theorem 49, Cor. 2, be denoted by L_1', L_2', L'. If the points L_1, L_1', L_2, L_2' are distinct, the pairs L_1L_1', L_2L_2', LL' are in involution.

2. In case L_1 is on l_2 and L_2 is not on l_1, $\{L_2l_2\}\cdot\{L_1l_1\} = \mathrm{T}$ is a collineation of Type *II* (cf. § 40, Vol. I), parabolic on l_∞ and of period two on the line joining L_1 to the point of intersection of l_1 and l_2. If l be any line, except l_2, through the point l_1l_2, P the point in which l meets l_∞, and L the harmonic conjugate of L_1 with respect to P and $\mathrm{T}(P)$,

$$\mathrm{T} = \{Ll_2\}\cdot\{L_1l\}.$$

If M be the harmonic conjugate of L_1 with respect to P and $\mathrm{T}^{-1}(P)$, $\mathrm{T} = \{L_1l\}\cdot\{Ml_2\}$.

3. The product $\{L_2l_2\}\cdot\{L_1l_1\}$ is a point reflection if and only if L_1 is on l_2 and L_2 on l_1. A point reflection with O as center is the product of any two line reflections $\{L_1l_1\}$ and $\{L_2l_2\}$ for which l_1 is on O, l_2 on O, L_1 on l_2, and L_2 on l_1.

4. The product $\{L_2l_2\}\cdot\{L_1l_1\}$ is a translation if and only if $L_1 = L_2$ and l_1 is parallel to l_2. The ideal point L_1 is the center of the translation. If T is any translation, T_∞ its center, P_1 any ordinary point, $P = \mathrm{T}(P_1)$, P_2 the mid-point of the pair PP_1, and p_1 and p_2 two parallel lines through P_1 and P_2 respectively, $\mathrm{T} = \{T_\infty, p_2\}\cdot\{T_\infty, p_1\}$.

5. The product $\{L_2l_2\}\cdot\{L_1l_1\}$ is a simple shear if $L_1 \neq L_2$ and $l_1 = l_2$, or if $L_1 = L_2$ and l_1 intersects l_2 in an ordinary point, but not in any other case.

6. Let Σ be a simple shear whose axis is l and whose center is L. Let P_1 be any point of l_∞, $P = \Sigma(P_1)$, and P_2 the harmonic conjugate of L with respect to P and P_2. Then $\Sigma = \{P_2l\}\cdot\{P_1l\}$. If p_1 be any line meeting l in an ordinary point, $p = \Sigma(p_1)$, and p_2 the harmonic conjugate of l with respect to p and p_1,

$$\Sigma = \{Lp_2\}\cdot\{Lp_1\}.$$

7. Let $PP_1P_2P_3P_4$ be a simple pentagon. Let C_1, C_2, C_3, C_4, C_5 be the mid-points of the pairs PP_1, P_1P_2, P_2P_3, P_3P_4, P_4P respectively. If the line PP_1 is parallel to P_3P_4, and PP_4 is parallel to P_1P_2, the three lines C_1C_4, C_2C_5, PC_3 are concurrent or parallel. Discuss the degenerate cases.

8. Every equiaffine transformation is either the identity or a point reflection or an elation whose center is at infinity (i.e. a translation or a simple shear) or expressible as a product of two elations whose centers are at infinity.

9. Prove Cors. 2 and 3 of Theorem 49 directly, without using the theory of equivalence.

10. A necessary and sufficient condition that a planar collineation be the product of two harmonic homologies is that it transform ordered point triads into equivalent point triads relative to a fixed line of the collineation regarded as l_∞ (E. B. Wilson, Annals of Mathematics, Vol. V, 2d series (1903), p. 45)

11. Let us denote an involution whose double points are L and M by $\{LM\}$. If $I_1 = \{L_1M_1\}$ and $I_2 = \{L_2M_2\}$ are two distinct involutions on the same line, then for every point L_3 of this line, L_3 not being a double point of $I_1 \cdot I_2$, there exists a unique point M_3 and involution $\{L_4M_4\}$ such that if we denote $\{L_3M_3\}$ by I_3 and $\{L_4M_4\}$ by I_4,

$$I_3I_2I_1 = I_4, \quad \text{and} \quad I_2I_1 = I_3I_4.$$

The pairs L_1M_1, L_2M_2, L_3M_3, L_4M_4 are all pairs of the same involution, unless the pairs L_1M_1 and L_2M_2 have a point in common, in which case all four pairs have this point in common.

12. The projectivities on a line which are expressible in the form $\{L_1M_1\} \cdot \{L_2M_2\}$ form a group.

The last two exercises connect with the following algebraic considerations. An involution in a net of rationality is always of the form (§ 54, Vol. I)

$$x' = \frac{ax+b}{cx-a},$$

where a, b, c, d are rational. The double points are the roots of

$$cx^2 - 2\,ax - b = 0,$$

and both will be rational if k is rational in

$$a^2 + bc = k^2.$$

Now any projectivity is the product of two involutions, a double point of one of which may be chosen arbitrarily. The projectivity may therefore be written

$$x'' = \frac{a'\dfrac{ax+b}{cx-a} + b'}{c'\dfrac{ax+b}{cx-a} - a'} = \frac{(aa'+b'c)x + (a'b - ab')}{(ac' - a'c)x + (bc' + aa')},$$

and so has the determinant

$$\begin{aligned} aa'bc' + a^2a'^2 + bb'cc' + b'caa' - (aa'bc' - a^2b'c' - a'^2bc + aa'b'c) \\ = a^2(a'^2 + b'c') + bc\,(b'c' + a'^2) = k^2k'^2, \end{aligned}$$

where $k'^2 = a'^2 + b'c'$. Hence (1) the product of two involutions whose double points have rational coördinates is a projectivity whose determinant is a perfect square; and (2) if the determinant of a projectivity is a perfect square, and one of two involutions of which it is a product has rational double points, then the other has rational double points. Hence there is a subgroup of the group of collineations of a linear net of rationality generated by the involutions with rational double points. This is the group of transformations whose determinants are perfect squares.

***53. Algebraic formulas for line reflections.** Let us employ the nonhomogeneous coördinates for which l_∞ is the singular line and the corresponding homogeneous coördinates for which

$$\frac{x_1}{x_0} = x, \qquad \frac{x_2}{x_0} = y.$$

The line l_∞ now has the equation $x_0 = 0$, and the equations (1) of the affine group become

$$(13) \qquad \begin{aligned} x_0' &= x_0, \\ x_1' &= c_1 x_0 + a_1 x_1 + b_1 x_2, \\ x_2' &= c_2 x_0 + a_2 x_1 + b_2 x_2, \end{aligned} \qquad \Delta = \begin{vmatrix} a_1 & b_1 \\ a_2 & b_2 \end{vmatrix} \neq 0.$$

On the line l_∞ this effects the transformation

$$\begin{aligned} x_1' &= a_1 x_1 + b_1 x_2, \\ x_2' &= a_2 x_1 + b_2 x_2. \end{aligned}$$

According to § 54, Vol. I, this is an involution if and only if $a_1 = -b_2$. Thus $a_1 = -b_2$ is a necessary condition that (13) represent a line reflection.

The ordinary double points of (13) are given by the following equations, in which we have put $a = a_1 = -b_2$.

$$(14) \qquad \begin{aligned} (a-1)x + b_1 y + c_1 &= 0, \\ a_2 x - (a+1) y + c_2 &= 0. \end{aligned}$$

If (13) is to be a line reflection, it must have a line of fixed points. Hence the two equations (14) must represent a single ordinary line, which requires

$$(15) \qquad 0 = \begin{vmatrix} a-1 & b_1 \\ a_2 & -(a+1) \end{vmatrix} = \begin{vmatrix} a-1 & c_1 \\ a_2 & c_2 \end{vmatrix} = \begin{vmatrix} b_1 & c_1 \\ -(a+1) & c_2 \end{vmatrix}.$$

The first of these conditions is equivalent to $\Delta = -1$.

Since the coefficients of x and y in (14) cannot all vanish, the conditions (15) are also sufficient that (14) represent a single ordinary line. Hence

THEOREM 51. *A transformation of the form*

$$(16) \qquad \begin{aligned} x' &= ax + b_1 y + c_1, \\ y' &= a_2 x - ay + c_2, \end{aligned}$$

is a line reflection if and only if

$$\Delta = \begin{vmatrix} a & b_1 \\ a_2 & -a \end{vmatrix} = -1, \qquad \begin{vmatrix} a-1 & c_1 \\ a_2 & c_2 \end{vmatrix} = \begin{vmatrix} b_1 & c_1 \\ -(a+1) & c_2 \end{vmatrix} = 0.$$

From this it follows that a product of two line reflections is such that $\Delta = 1$, and a product of three line reflections is such that $\Delta = -1$. By Theorems 47 and 49 any transformation for which $\Delta = 1$ is a product of two line reflections. Any transformation T for which $\Delta = -1$, when multiplied by a line reflection Λ yields a transformation Σ for which $\Delta = 1$, i.e. an equiaffine transformation. From $T\Lambda = \Sigma$ follows $T = \Sigma\Lambda$. Hence T is a product of three line reflections. Thus we have (cf. Theorem 47)

THEOREM 52. *The group of affine transformations which are products of line reflections has the equations*

$$x' = a_1x + b_1y + c_1, \qquad y' = a_2x + b_2y + c_2, \qquad \begin{vmatrix} a_1 & b_1 \\ a_2 & b_2 \end{vmatrix}^2 = 1.$$

EXERCISES

1. The set of all affine transformations which are products of equiaffine transformations by dilations form a group which is a self-conjugate subgroup of the affine group. Its equations are

$$x' = a_1x + b_1y + c_1, \qquad y' = a_2x + b_2y + c_2, \qquad \begin{vmatrix} a_1 & b_1 \\ a_2 & b_2 \end{vmatrix} = k^2,$$

where k is any number in the geometric number system.

2. The set of all affine transformations which are products of line reflections and dilations form a group which is self-conjugate under the affine group. Its equations are

$$x' = a_1x + b_1y + c_1, \qquad y' = a_2x + b_2y + c_2, \qquad \begin{vmatrix} a_1 & b_1 \\ a_2 & b_2 \end{vmatrix} = \pm k^2,$$

where k is any number in the geometric number system.

54. Subgroups of the affine group. We give below a list of the principal subgroups of the affine group which we have considered in this chapter and in § 30 of Chap. II. These are all self-conjugate subgroups. We also include the groups which will be considered in the next chapter in connection with the Euclidean geometry.

The groups are all described by means of the conditions which must be imposed on the coefficients of the equations of the affine group to reduce it to each of the other groups. In some spaces, i.e. when the variables and coefficients are in certain number systems, these groups are not all distinct. However, they are all distinct in case the variables and coefficients are ordinary rational numbers.

With respect to a system of nonhomogeneous coördinates of which l_∞ is the singular line, the equations of the affine group are

$$(1)\qquad \begin{aligned} x' &= a_1x + b_1y + c_1 \\ y' &= a_2x + b_2y + c_2, \end{aligned}$$

where
$$\Delta = \begin{vmatrix} a_1 & b_1 \\ a_2 & b_2 \end{vmatrix} \neq 0.$$

The principal subgroups connected with the affine geometry are:

$$(2)\qquad \Delta > 0;$$

the transformations satisfying this condition are direct (§ 30).

$$(3)\qquad \Delta = k^2,$$

where k is in the geometric number system (§ 53, Ex. 1).

$$(4)\qquad \Delta = \pm k^2,$$

where k is in the geometric number system (§ 53, Ex. 2).

$$(5)\qquad \Delta^2 = 1;$$

these are products of two or of three line reflections (Theorem 52).

$$(6)\qquad \Delta = 1,$$

the equiaffine group (§ 51).

$$(7)\qquad a_2 = b_1 = 0, \quad a_1 = b_2,$$

the homothetic group (§ 47).

$$(8)\qquad a_2 = b_1 = 0, \quad a_1 = b_2, \quad a_1^2 = 1,$$

the group of translations and point reflections (§ 45).

$$(9)\qquad a_2 = b_1 = 0, \quad a_1 = b_2 = 1,$$

the group of translations (§ 38).

The principal groups connected with the Euclidean geometry are:

$$(10)\qquad a_1^2 + a_2^2 = b_1^2 + b_2^2 \neq 0, \quad a_1b_1 + a_2b_2 = 0,$$

the Euclidean group (§§ 55 and 62). Its transformations are called similarity transformations.

$$(11)\qquad a_1^2 + a_2^2 = b_1^2 + b_2^2 \neq 0, \quad a_1b_1 + a_2b_2 = 0, \quad \Delta > 0,$$

the direct similarity transformations.

$$(12)\qquad a_1^2 + a_2^2 = b_1^2 + b_2^2 \neq 0, \quad a_1b_1 + a_2b_2 = 0, \quad \Delta = k^2,$$

where k is in the geometric number system.

$$(13)\qquad a_1^2 + a_2^2 = b_1^2 + b_2^2 \neq 0, \quad a_1b_1 + a_2b_2 = 0, \quad \Delta = \pm k^2,$$

where k is in the geometric number system.

(14) $$a_1^2 + a_2^2 = 1, \quad a_1 = \pm b_2, \quad a_2 = \mp b_1,$$

the group of displacements and symmetries (§ 62).

(15) $$a_1^2 + a_2^2 = 1, \quad a_1 = b_2, \quad a_2 = -b_1,$$

the group of displacements.

The relations among these groups may be indicated by the following diagram, in which we have included only those groups which are distinct in case of the real geometry. A dotted line indicates that the lower of the two groups joined is a subgroup of the upper, and a solid line that it is a self-conjugate subgroup.

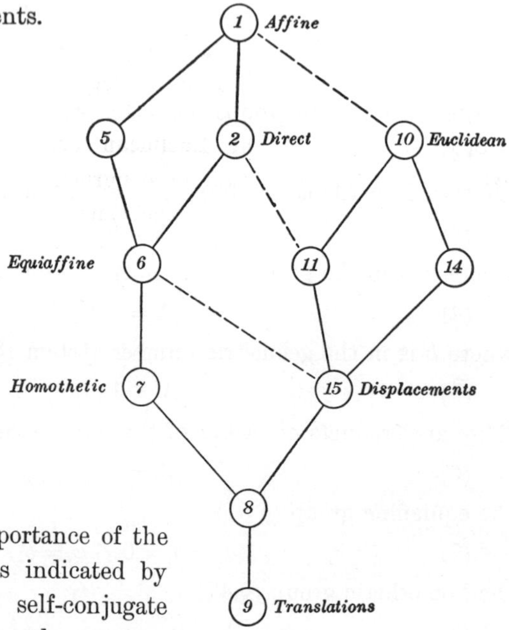

FIG. 44

The fundamental importance of the group of translations is indicated by the fact that it is a self-conjugate subgroup of each of the other groups.

EXERCISES

1. Supposing the number of points on a line to be $p + 1$, what is the number of transformations in each of the groups listed above?

2. Supposing the geometric number system to be (*a*) the ordinary real, or (*b*) the ordinary complex number system, how many parameters are there in the equations for each of the groups listed above?

3. Prove that the plane affine geometry as a separate science could be based on the following assumptions with regard to undefined elements, called points, and undefined classes of points, called lines:

I. Two points are contained in one and only one line.

II. For any line l and any point P, not on l, there is one and only one line containing P and not containing any point of l.

III. Every line contains at least two points.

IV. There exist at least three noncollinear points.

V. The special case of the Pappus theorem given in the fine print in § 49; or Theorem 41.

CHAPTER IV

EUCLIDEAN PLANE GEOMETRY

55. Geometries of the Euclidean type. We come now to the extension of the definition of congruence which was promised in §§ 39 and 46. This requires the consideration of groups which are not self-conjugate under the affine group. Not being self-conjugate, these groups are not determined uniquely by the affine group, and hence our definitions will contain a further arbitrary element.

DEFINITION. Let I be an arbitrary but fixed involution on l_∞. This involution shall be called the *absolute* or *orthogonal involution.* The group of all projective collineations leaving I invariant shall be called a *parabolic * metric group.* The transformations of the group shall be called *similarity transformations.* Two figures conjugate under the group shall be said to be *similar.* The geometry corresponding to the group shall be called the *parabolic metric geometry.*

The absolute involution is supposed to be fixed throughout the rest of the discussion, but of course there are as many parabolic metric groups as there are choices of I. We nevertheless speak of *the* parabolic metric group in order to emphasize the fact that we are fixing attention on one group.

In case the plane in which we are working is a real plane and the absolute involution is without double points, the parabolic metric geometry is the Euclidean geometry. It is for this reason that we refer to the parabolic metric geometries as geometries of the Euclidean type.

The investigations in the following sections are arranged in order of increasing specialization. First we consider a perfectly general involution, I, in a projective plane satisfying A, E, P, H_0. Then we consider a particular type of involution in an ordered plane, and finally limit the plane to be the real plane.

* The reason for the term "parabolic" in this connection is explained in a later chapter, where the elliptic and hyperbolic metric groups are defined.

When the plane and the involution are fully specialized, it is a theorem (§ 70) that the real plane is contained in a complex plane in which the absolute involution has double points. Thus the theorems on the general type of involution (where the possible existence of double points is taken into account) come to have a new application.

56. Orthogonal lines. DEFINITION. Two lines are said to be *orthogonal* or *perpendicular* to each other if and only if they meet l_∞ in conjugate points of the absolute involution.

The following consequences of this definition are obvious:

THEOREM 1. *The pairs of perpendicular lines through any point, O, are the pairs of an involution. Through any point there is one and but one line perpendicular to a given line. A line perpendicular to one of two parallel lines is perpendicular to the other. Two lines perpendicular to the same line are parallel.*

DEFINITION. In case the absolute involution I has two double points, I_1 and I_2, they are called the *circular points.* Any line through I_1 or I_2 is called an *isotropic line* or a *minimal line.*

Any isotropic line has the property of being perpendicular to itself. The circular points are so called because all ordinary points of any circle (cf. § 60) are on a conic through I_1 and I_2. The ordinary points of the conic section referred to in the following lemma will later be proved to be on a circle.

DEFINITION. A homology of period two whose center L is on l_∞, and whose axis l meets l_∞ in the point conjugate to the center with regard to the absolute involution, is called an *orthogonal line reflection,* and is denoted by $\{Ll\}$.

Since the center of a homology is not a point of the axis, the center cannot be a double point of the orthogonal involution, nor can the axis pass through such a point. An orthogonal line reflection is of course a special case of a line reflection as defined in § 52.

LEMMA. *Let O and P_1 be two points not collinear with either double point of the absolute involution. There is one and only one conic, C^2, having O as center, passing through P_1, and having the pairs of the absolute involution as pairs of conjugate points.*

Proof. Let P_2 be the harmonic conjugate of P_1 with respect to O and the point at infinity, P_∞, of the line OP_1. Any conic containing P_1

and having O as center must contain P_2, by the definition of center. Let X be a variable point of l_∞, and Y the conjugate of X in the absolute involution. Any of the triangles OXY must be self-polar to any conic satisfying the required conditions. But if P is the point of intersection of the lines P_1X and P_2Y, and Q the point of intersection of P_1X and OY,

$$P_2OP_1P_\infty \overset{Y}{\underset{\wedge}{=}} PQP_1X,$$

and hence the points P_1 and P are harmonically conjugate with respect to X and Q. Hence P must be on any conic through P_1 with regard to which X is the pole of QY. Hence P must be on any conic satisfying the hypotheses of the lemma.

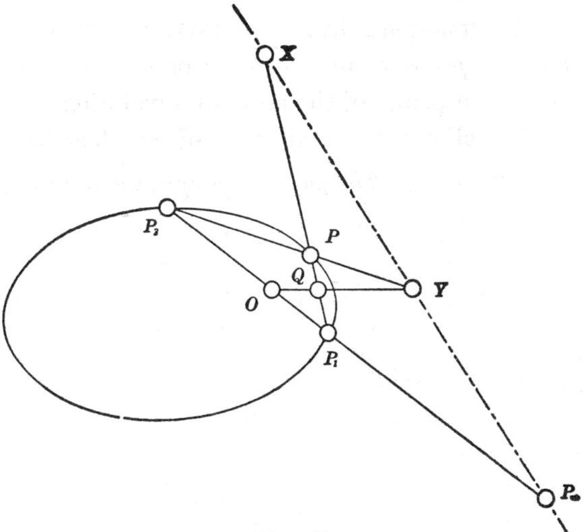

FIG. 45

Since $P_1[X] \overline{\wedge} P_2[Y]$, the points P, together with P_1 and P_2, constitute a unique conic (§ 41, Vol. I); and this conic, by its construction, satisfies the condition required by the lemma.

COROLLARY. *In case the absolute involution has double points the conic C^2 passes through them.*

THEOREM 2. *An orthogonal line reflection leaves the absolute involution invariant.*

Proof. If l is the axis of an orthogonal line reflection and L its center, let O be any point on l and P_1 any point not on l. The conic C^2 (cf. Lemma), which contains P_1, has O as center, and has the absolute involution as an involution of conjugate points, must have L and l as pole and polar. Hence, by the definition of pole and polar (§ 44, Vol. I) C^2 is transformed into itself by the harmonic homology having L and l as center and axis. Hence the absolute involution is transformed into itself by the orthogonal line reflection $\{Ll\}$.

THEOREM 3. *The product of two orthogonal line reflections whose axes are parallel is a translation parallel to any line perpendicular to the axes.*

Proof. Let the given line reflections be $\{L_1 l_1\}$ and $\{L_2 l_2\}$. Their axes meet in a point L' of l_∞, and L_1 and L_2 must be conjugate to L' with respect to the absolute involution. Hence $L_1 = L_2$. The product therefore leaves all points on l_∞ invariant and also all lines through L_1. Hence it is a translation parallel to any line through L_1.

THEOREM 4. *A translation,* T, *whose center is not a double point of the absolute involution, is a product of two orthogonal line reflections,* $\{Ll_2\}$, $\{Ll_1\}$, *where* L *is the center of the translation. If* O *is an arbitrary ordinary point and* P *the mid-point of the pair* O *and* T(O), l_1 *may be chosen as* OL' *and* l_2 *as* PL', *where* L' *is the conjugate of* L *with respect to the absolute involution. Or* l_1 *may be chosen as* PL' *and* l_2 *as the line joining* T(O) *to* L'. *A translation whose center is a double point of the absolute involution is a product of four orthogonal line reflections.*

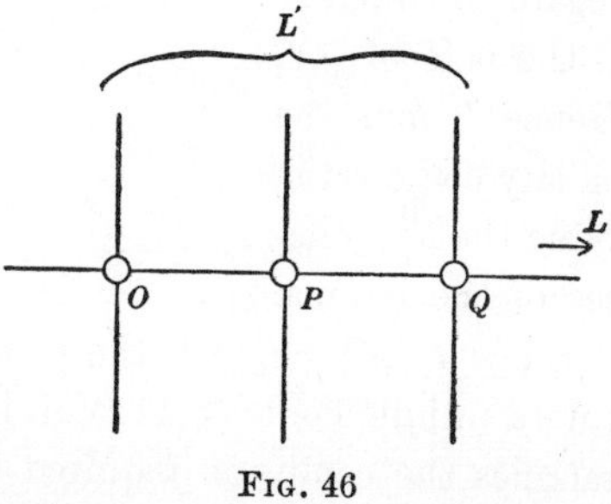

FIG. 46

Proof. If $l_1 = OL'$ and $l_2 = PL'$, the reflection $\{Ll_1\}$ leaves O invariant and $\{Ll_2\}$ carries O to T(O). Hence the translation $\{Ll_2\} \cdot \{Ll_1\}$ carries O to T(O), and, by Theorem 3, Chap. III, is identical with T.

If $l_1 = PL'$ and $l_2 = QL'$, where $Q =$ T(O), the reflection $\{Ll_1\}$ carries O to Q and $\{Ll_2\}$ leaves Q invariant. Hence, as before, $\{Ll_2\} \cdot \{Ll_1\} =$ T.

A translation whose center is a double point of the absolute involution can be expressed as a product of two translations with arbitrary points of l_∞ as centers (Theorem 8, Chap. III), and hence is expressible as a product of four orthogonal line reflections.

DEFINITION. If the axes of two orthogonal line reflections intersect in an ordinary point, O, the product is called a *rotation about* O, and the point O is called its *center*.

THEOREM 5. *A rotation which is the product of two orthogonal line reflections whose axes are orthogonal is a point reflection.*

Proof. Let the two line reflections be $\{L_1 l_1\}$ and $\{L_2 l_2\}$ and let O be the point of intersection of l_1 and l_2. Since l_1 and l_2 are orthogonal, L_1 is on l_2 and L_2 on l_1. The product $\{L_2 l_2\} \cdot \{L_1 l_1\}$ therefore leaves O and every point of l_∞ invariant. Moreover, it is of period two on the axis of either of the line reflections. Hence it is a homology of period two with O as center and l_∞ as axis, i.e. a point reflection.

DEFINITION. If a line l is perpendicular to a line m, the point of intersection of the two lines is called the *foot* of the perpendicular l. A line l is said to be the *perpendicular bisector* of a pair of points A and B if it is perpendicular to the line AB and its foot is the mid-point of the pair AB.

DEFINITION. A simple quadrangle $ABCD$ is said to be a *rectangle* if and only if the lines AB and CD are perpendicular to AD and BC.

EXERCISES

1. A parallelogram $ABCD$ is a rectangle if and only if the lines AB and AD are perpendicular.

2. The perpendicular bisectors of the point pairs AB, BC, CA of a triangle ABC meet in a point.

3. The perpendiculars from the vertices of a triangle to the opposite sides meet in a point.

4. The lines through the vertices of a triangle parallel to the transforms of the opposite sides by a fixed orthogonal line reflection are concurrent.

57. Displacements and symmetries. Congruence. DEFINITION. The product of an even number of orthogonal line reflections is called a *displacement*. The product of an odd number of orthogonal line reflections is called a *symmetry*.

THEOREM 6. *The set of all displacements form a self-conjugate subgroup of the parabolic metric group.*

Proof. That the displacements form a group is evident because (cf. § 26, Vol. I): (1) the identity is a displacement, being the product of any orthogonal line reflection by itself; (2) the inverse of a product of orthogonal line reflections is the product of the same set of line reflections taken in the reverse order; (3) the product of an even number of orthogonal line reflections by an even number of orthogonal line reflections is, by definition, a displacement.

The group of displacements is contained in the parabolic metric group by Theorem 2.

If $\{Ll\}$ is an orthogonal line reflection, Σ a similarity transformation, and $L' = \Sigma(L)$, $l' = \Sigma(l)$, then $\Sigma \cdot \{Ll\} \cdot \Sigma^{-1}$ is a harmonic homology with L' as center and l' as axis. But since L and the point at infinity of l are paired in the absolute involution, so are L' and the point at infinity of l'. Hence $\Sigma \cdot \{Ll\} \cdot \Sigma^{-1} = \{L'l'\}$ is an orthogonal line reflection.

If Λ_1 and Λ_2 are any two line reflections $\Sigma\Lambda_1\Lambda_2\Sigma^{-1} = \Sigma\Lambda_1\Sigma^{-1}\Sigma\Lambda_2\Sigma^{-1}$. A similar argument shows that $\Sigma\Lambda_1\Lambda_2 \cdots \Lambda_n \cdot \Sigma^{-1}$ is a product of n orthogonal line reflections whenever $\Lambda_1, \cdots, \Lambda_n$ are orthogonal line reflections and Σ is in the parabolic metric group. Hence the group of displacements is a self-conjugate subgroup of the parabolic metric group.

COROLLARY 1. *The set of all displacements and symmetries form a self-conjugate subgroup of the parabolic metric group.*

DEFINITION. Two figures such that one can be transformed into the other by a displacement are said to be *congruent.* Two figures such that one can be transformed into the other by a symmetry are said to be *symmetric.*

COROLLARY 2. *If a figure F_1 is congruent to a figure F_2, and F_2 to a figure F_3, then F_1 is congruent to F_3.*

COROLLARY 3. *If a figure F_1 is symmetric with a figure F_2, and F_2 is symmetric with a figure F_3, then F_1 is congruent to F_3.*

COROLLARY 4. *If a figure F_1 is symmetric with a figure F_2, and F_2 is congruent to a figure F_3, then F_1 is symmetric with F_3.*

Since translations and point reflections leave the absolute involution invariant, the definition of congruence given in this section includes the definitions in §§ 39 and 46 as special cases. Theorem 6 shows that the theory of congruence and symmetry in general belongs to the geometry of the parabolic metric group. It must be remembered, however, that the theory of congruence of point pairs on parallel lines belongs to the affine group. In other words, the part of the theory of congruence developed in Chap. III is independent of the choice of the absolute involution.

In case the absolute involution has double points, the theory of congruence of point pairs on the minimal lines (§ 56) is different from that on other lines. As will appear in the following sections the theory on any line which is not minimal is essentially the same as that developed in Chap. III on the basis afforded by the group of translations and point reflections. On a minimal line, however, the set of points $[P]$ such that OP_0 is congruent to OP consists of all points on this line except the point O. For let I_1 and I_2 denote the double points of the absolute involution, I_1 being the one on the line OP_0. Let Q be a point of the line OI_2 distinct from O and from I_2, and let P be any point of OI_1 distinct from O and from I_1. If Λ_1 be the orthogonal line reflection whose center is the point at infinity of the line P_0Q and whose axis passes through O, and Λ_2 be the orthogonal line reflection whose center is the point at infinity of the line QP and whose axis passes through O, we have $\Lambda_1(P_0) = Q$ and $\Lambda_2(Q) = P$. Hence the rotation $\Lambda_2\Lambda_1$ transforms P_0 to P. Combining transformations of the form $\Lambda_2\Lambda_1$ with translations it is clear that we have

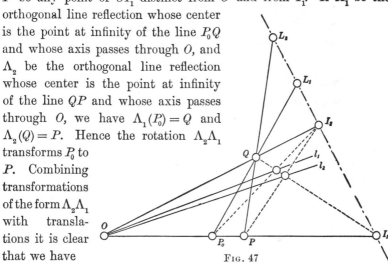

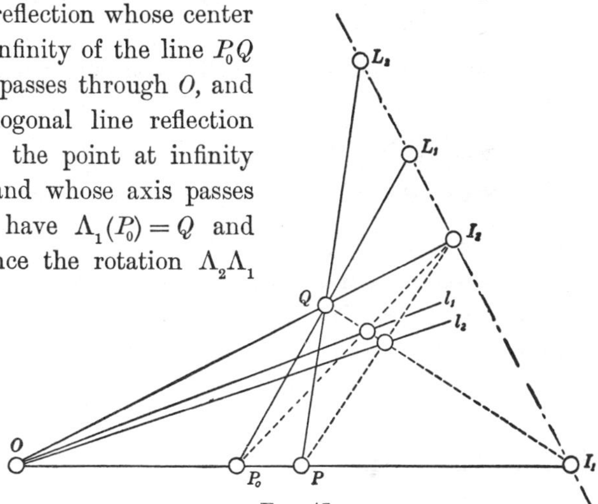

FIG. 47

THEOREM 7. *Any pair of points on a minimal line is congruent to any other pair of points on the same line.*

For example, if a mid-point of a pair AB were defined to be a point C such that AC is congruent to CB, we should have that whenever the line AB is minimal, the point C may be any point on this line different from A and B. The theorems on mid-points in Chap. III would in general have exceptional cases. It is to avoid this difficulty that we have adopted the definition of mid-point given in § 40, Chap. III. A similar remark applies to the definition of ratio of collinear point pairs in § 43, Chap. III.

DEFINITION. A parallelogram $ABCD$ whose sides do not pass through double points of the absolute involution and in which the point pair AB is congruent to the point pair AD is called a *rhombus.* A rhombus which is also a rectangle is called a *square.*

EXERCISES

1. Prove that the group of displacements and symmetries could be defined as the group of all collineations leaving invariant the set of all conics obtainable by translations from a fixed central conic.

2. The parabolic metric group consists of all projective collineations transforming the group of displacements into itself.

3. Two point pairs on nonminimal lines are symmetric if and only if they are congruent.

4. The perpendicular bisector of a point pair AB contains all points P such that AP is congruent to BP.

5. The simple quadrangle $ABCD$ is a rhombus if and only if the lines AC and BD are the perpendicular bisectors of the point pairs BD and AC respectively.

6. A parallelogram $ABCD$ is a rectangle if and only if the point pair AC is congruent to the point pair BD.

7. Specialize the quadrangle-quadrilateral configuration (§ 18, Vol. I) to the case where the vertices of the quadrangle are the vertices of a square.

58. Pairs of orthogonal line reflections. THEOREM 8. *If $\Lambda_1, \Lambda_2, \Lambda_3$ are three orthogonal line reflections whose axes pass through a point O (ordinary or ideal), the product $\Lambda_3\Lambda_2\Lambda_1$ is an orthogonal line reflection whose axis passes through O.*

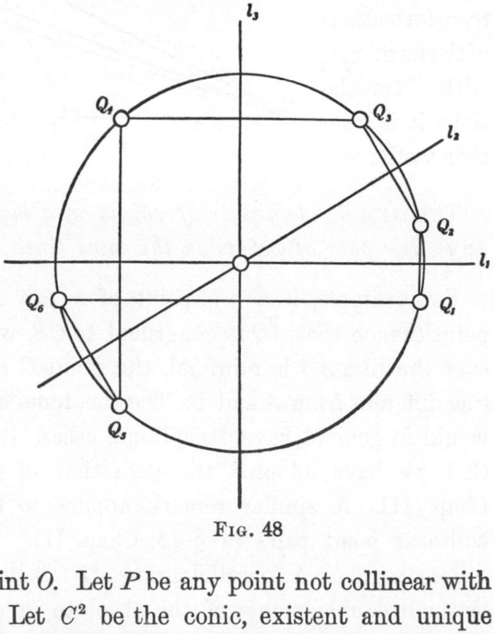

FIG. 48

Proof. In case the three axes are parallel, the product $\Lambda_3\Lambda_2$ is a translation, and so by Theorem 4 is expressible in the form $\Lambda_4\Lambda_1$, where Λ_4 is an orthogonal line reflection whose axis is parallel to the other axes. Hence

$$\Lambda_3\Lambda_2\Lambda_1 = \Lambda_4\Lambda_1\Lambda_1 = \Lambda_4.$$

In case two of the axes are not parallel, the third axis must pass through their common point O. Let P be any point not collinear with O and a circular point. Let C^2 be the conic, existent and unique according to the lemma of § 56, which passes through P, has O as center, and has the absolute involution as an involution of conjugate points. If Q_1 be any point of C^2, let $\Lambda_1(Q_1) = Q_2$, $\Lambda_2(Q_2) = Q_3$, $\Lambda_3(Q_3) = Q_4$, $\Lambda_1(Q_4) = Q_5$, $\Lambda_2(Q_5) = Q_6$.

According to this construction the line Q_1Q_2 is parallel to Q_4Q_5 and Q_2Q_3 to Q_5Q_6, where in case $Q_i = Q_j$, the line Q_iQ_j is taken to mean the tangent to C^2 at Q_i. Hence, by Pascal's theorem (Chap. V, Vol. I) or one of its degenerate cases, it follows that Q_3Q_4 is parallel to Q_6Q_1. Hence

$$\Lambda_3(Q_6) = Q_1$$

and

$$(\Lambda_3\Lambda_2\Lambda_1)^2(Q_1) = Q_1.$$

Since Q_1 is an arbitrary point of C^2,

$$(\Lambda_3\Lambda_2\Lambda_1)^2 = 1.$$

The transformation $\Lambda_3\Lambda_2\Lambda_1$ is not the identity, because it cannot leave invariant a point, different from O, of the axis of Λ_1 unless $\Lambda_2 = \Lambda_3$, and in the latter case the product is equal to Λ_1. Since $\Lambda_3\Lambda_2\Lambda_1$ leaves invariant the line Q_1Q_4 (or the tangent at Q_1, if $Q_1 = Q_4$), it leaves invariant the point at infinity of this line and also the line through O perpendicular to it. As $\Lambda_3\Lambda_2\Lambda_1$ is of period two, it follows that it is an orthogonal line reflection.

COROLLARY 1. *If Λ_1, Λ_2, and Λ_3 are any three orthogonal line reflections whose axes meet in a point or are parallel, there exists an orthogonal line reflection Λ_4 such that $\Lambda_2\Lambda_1 = \Lambda_3\Lambda_4$, and an orthogonal line reflection Λ_5 such that $\Lambda_2\Lambda_1 = \Lambda_5\Lambda_3$.*

Proof. By the theorem, Λ_4 exists such that

$$\Lambda_3\Lambda_2\Lambda_1 = \Lambda_4.$$

Hence

$$\Lambda_2\Lambda_1 = \Lambda_3\Lambda_4.$$

In like manner, Λ_5 exists such that

$$\Lambda_2\Lambda_1\Lambda_3 = \Lambda_5.$$

Hence

$$\Lambda_2\Lambda_1 = \Lambda_5\Lambda_3.$$

COROLLARY 2. *The product of any odd number of orthogonal line reflections whose axes meet in a point or are parallel is an orthogonal line reflection.*

Proof. By the theorem, whenever $n \geqq 3$, the product of n orthogonal line reflections whose axes are concurrent reduces to a product of $n-2$. Thus, if n is odd, the number of line reflections can be reduced by successive steps to one.

If n is even, this process reduces the number of line reflections in the product to two. Thus we have

COROLLARY 3. *The product of any even number of orthogonal line reflections is a rotation in case their axes meet in a point, and is a translation in case the axes are parallel.*

COROLLARY 4. *An orthogonal line reflection is not a displacement.*

COROLLARY 5. *The set of all rotations having a common center is a commutative group.*

Proof. A rotation is defined as a product of two orthogonal line reflections whose axes meet in an ordinary point. So, by definition, the identity is a rotation, and the inverse of a rotation $\Lambda_2\Lambda_1$ is the rotation $\Lambda_1\Lambda_2$. The product of two rotations is a rotation by Cor. 3. Hence the rotations having a given point as center form a group. To show that any two of these rotations are commutative amounts to showing that

$$(1) \qquad \Lambda_4\Lambda_3\Lambda_2\Lambda_1 = \Lambda_2\Lambda_1\Lambda_4\Lambda_3$$

whenever the Λ's are orthogonal line reflections whose axes concur. By the theorem we have

$$\Lambda_4\Lambda_3\Lambda_2 = \Lambda_2\Lambda_3\Lambda_4,$$

and hence

$$(2) \qquad \Lambda_4\Lambda_3\Lambda_2\Lambda_1 = \Lambda_2\Lambda_3\Lambda_4\Lambda_1.$$

But since

$$\Lambda_3\Lambda_4\Lambda_1 = \Lambda_1\Lambda_4\Lambda_3,$$

$$\Lambda_2\Lambda_3\Lambda_4\Lambda_1 = \Lambda_2\Lambda_1\Lambda_4\Lambda_3,$$

which combined with (2) gives (1).

THEOREM 9. *Any displacement leaving a point O invariant is a rotation about O.*

Proof. The given displacement is a product of an even number, n, of orthogonal line reflections, $\Lambda_n \cdots \Lambda_1$. Let Λ_i' be the line reflection whose axis is the line through O parallel to the axis of Λ_i. Then the product $T_i = \Lambda_i\Lambda_i'$ is a translation (Theorem 3) and

$$\Lambda_i = T_i\Lambda_i'.$$

Thus

$$\Lambda_n \cdots \Lambda_1 = T_n\Lambda_n' \cdots T_1\Lambda_1',$$

where each T_i is a translation. But by Cor. 2, Theorem 11, Chap. III, if Σ is any affine collineation, $T_i\Sigma = \Sigma T_i'$, where T_i' is a translation or the identity. Hence

$$\Lambda_n \cdots \Lambda_1 = \Lambda_n' \cdots \Lambda_1' T_n' \cdots T_1'.$$

But since $\Lambda_n \cdots \Lambda_1$ and $\Lambda'_n \cdots \Lambda'_1$ leave O invariant, the product $T'_n \cdots T'_1$ leaves O invariant, and hence, by Theorem 3, Chap. III, is the identity. Hence

$$\Lambda_n \cdots \Lambda_1 = \Lambda'_n \cdots \Lambda'_1,$$

where $\Lambda'_1, \cdots, \Lambda'_n$ are orthogonal line reflections whose axes pass through O. By Cor. 3, Theorem 8, $\Lambda'_n \cdots \Lambda'_1$ is a rotation about O.

59. The group of displacements. THEOREM 10. *Let O be an arbitrary point. Any displacement can be expressed in the form* PT, *where* P *is a rotation about O and* T *a translation.*

Proof. By precisely the argument used in the last theorem the given displacement can be expressed in the form

$$\Lambda'_{2n} \cdots \Lambda'_1 T'_{2n} \cdots T'_1,$$

where $\Lambda'_i\ (i = 1, \cdots, 2n)$ is an orthogonal line reflection whose axis passes through O, and $T'_i\ (i = 1, \cdots, 2n)$ is a translation or the identity. The product $T'_{2n} \cdots T'_1$ is, by Theorem 6, Chap. III, a translation. By Cor. 3, Theorem 8, $\Lambda'_{2n} \cdots \Lambda'_1$ is a rotation or a translation. Since it leaves O invariant, it is a rotation.

COROLLARY 1. *Any displacement can also be expressed in the form* T′P′, *where* T′ *is a translation and* P′ *a rotation with O as center.*

COROLLARY 2. *Any symmetry is a product of a line reflection whose axis contains an arbitrary point and a translation.*

THEOREM 11. *Any displacement, except a translation having a double point of the absolute involution as center, is a product of two orthogonal line reflections.*

Proof. Let O be an arbitrary point. By the last theorem the given displacement reduces to PT, where T is a translation and P a rotation about O. If the center, L, of T is not a double point of the absolute involution, by Theorem 4,

$$T = \{Ll_2\} \cdot \{Ll_1\},$$

where l_1 and l_2 meet l_∞ in the conjugate of L relative to the absolute involution and where l_2 passes through O. By Cor. 1, Theorem 8, there exists an orthogonal line reflection $\{Mm\}$ such that

$$P = \{Mm\} \cdot \{Ll_2\}.$$

Hence
$$PT = \{Mm\} \cdot \{Ll_2\} \cdot \{Ll_2\} \cdot \{Ll_1\}$$
$$= \{Mm\} \cdot \{Ll_1\}.$$

If P is not the identity, it is clear that m and l_1 cannot be parallel, and hence PT is a rotation.

In case T is a translation whose center is a double point of the absolute involution, it can be expressed (Theorem 8, Chap. III) as a product of two translations T_1, T_2 whose centers are not double points of the absolute involution. Hence, if P is not the identity, PT_2 is a rotation, and thus PT_2T_1 is also a rotation. In case P is the identity, we have the exceptional case noted in the theorem.

COROLLARY. *A displacement is either a rotation or a translation.*

The following two theorems have the same relation to the parabolic metric group and the group of displacements, respectively, that the fundamental theorem of projective geometry (Assumption P) has to the projective group on a line.

THEOREM 12. *A transformation of the parabolic metric group leaving invariant two ordinary points not collinear with a double point of the absolute involution is either an orthogonal line reflection or the identity.*

Proof. Denote the given fixed points by O and P, and let C^2 be the conic through P having O as center and the absolute involution as an involution of conjugate points. Since C^2 is uniquely determined by these conditions (cf. the lemma in § 56), it is left invariant by the given transformation Γ. Now Γ leaves O, P, and the point at infinity of the line OP invariant. Hence the line OP is point-wise invariant, and every line l perpendicular to it is transformed into itself. Since C^2 is also invariant and each of the lines perpendicular to OP meets C^2 in at most two points, Γ is either the identity or of period two. If of period two, it is evidently an orthogonal line reflection.

THEOREM 13. *A displacement leaving invariant a point O and a line l containing O but not containing a double point of the absolute involution is either the identity or a point reflection with O as center.*

Proof. Let P be any ordinary point of l distinct from O, and let C^2 be the conic through P having O as center and the absolute involution as an involution of conjugate points. A displacement leaving O invariant, being a product of two orthogonal line reflections whose axes meet in O, must leave C^2 invariant. Hence it either leaves P invariant or transforms it into the other point in which the line OP meets C^2. In the first case the transformation must, by Theorem 12 and Cor. 4, Theorem 8, reduce to the identity. In the second case the given displacement, which we shall denote by Δ, multiplied by the orthogonal line reflection Λ whose axis is the line through O perpendicular to OP, leaves P invariant. Hence, by Theorem 12,

$$\Delta\Lambda = \Lambda',$$

where Λ' is a line reflection having OP as axis or the identity. Hence

$$\Delta = \Lambda'\Lambda.$$

Since Δ cannot be a line reflection, Λ' cannot be the identity. Since the axes of Λ and Λ' are perpendicular, Δ is a point reflection.

EXERCISES

1. A displacement which carries a point A to a point B and has a point O (ordinary or not) as center is, if the line OA is not minimal, the product of an orthogonal line reflection whose axis is OA followed by one whose axis is the line joining O to the mid-point of the pair AB.

2. If three of the perpendicular bisectors of the point pairs AB, BC, CD, DA of a simple quadrangle meet in a point, the fourth perpendicular bisector passes through this point.

***3.** Any affine transformation which leaves a central conic invariant is a line reflection whose center and axis are pole and polar with regard to the conic or a product of two such line reflections.

***4.** In case the absolute involution is without double points, the group of displacements can be defined as the group of transformations common to the parabolic metric group and the equiaffine group. Thus two ordered point triads are congruent if they are both equivalent and similar. Develop the theory of congruence on this basis, and show what difficulties arise in case the absolute involution has double points.

60. Circles. DEFINITION. A *circle* is the set of all points $[P]$ such that the point pairs OP, where O is a fixed point, are all congruent to a fixed point pair OP_0, provided that the line OP_0 does not contain a double point of the absolute involution. The point O is called the *center* of the circle.

Since the displacements form a group, it is clear that P_0 may be any one of the points P. It has already been proved (§ 57) that if the line OP_0 contained an invariant point of the absolute involution, the set $[P]$ would consist of all ordinary points, except O, of the line OP_0.

THEOREM 14. *A circle consists of the ordinary points of a conic section having the pairs of the absolute involution as pairs of conjugate points. The center of the circle is the pole of* l_∞ *with respect to the circle.*

Proof. Let O be the center of the circle and P_0 any point of the circle. The circle consists of all points obtainable from P_0 by displacements which leave O invariant. If one of the line reflections of which each of these displacements is a product be taken to have OP_0 as axis (Cor. 1, Theorem 8), it follows that the circle consists of the points obtainable from P_0 by orthogonal line reflections whose axes pass through O. But the system of points so obtained is identical by construction with the ordinary points of the conic referred to in the lemma of § 56.

COROLLARY. *In case the absolute involution has no double points, every circle is a conic section. In case the circular points exist, they and the points of any circle form a conic section.*

THEOREM 15. *The ordinary points of any proper conic, with regard to which the pairs of the absolute involution are pairs of conjugate points, form a circle.*

Proof. A conic C^2 with regard to which the pairs of the absolute involution are conjugate points cannot be a parabola, since all points of l_∞ are conjugate to the point of contact of a parabola. Hence C^2 has an ordinary point O as center. Let P be any point of C^2. By definition there is one and only one circle through P which has O as a center. By Theorem 14, this circle is a conic through P having O as center and the pairs of the absolute involution as pairs of conjugate points. By the lemma of § 56 there is only one such conic. Hence the circle through P with O as center contains the ordinary points of C^2.

THEOREM 16. *Three noncollinear points, no two of which are on a minimal line, are contained in one and only one circle.*

Proof. Let the three points be P_0, P_1, and P_2. Let L_∞ be the point at infinity of the line P_0P_1 and l the perpendicular bisector of the point pair P_0P_1. The polar of L_∞ with regard to any circle through P_0 and P_1 must, by Theorem 14, pass through the mid-point of P_0P_1 and the conjugate of L_∞ in the absolute involution. Hence the polar of L_∞ with regard to any circle through P_0 and P_1 must be l. In like manner, the polar of the point at infinity M_∞ of the line P_1P_2 with regard to any circle containing P_1 and P_2 must be the perpendicular bisector m of P_1P_2. Since the points P_0, P_1, P_2 are not collinear, l and m intersect in an ordinary point O, which must be the pole of

$L_\infty M_\infty = l_\infty$ with regard to any circle through P_0, P_1, and P_2. Since, by definition, there is one and only one circle through P with O as center, there cannot be more than one circle through P_0, P_1, and P_2.

Since the product of the orthogonal line reflection with OP_0 as axis by that with l as axis transforms the point pair OP_0 into the point pair OP_1, the circle through P_0 with O as center contains P_1. A like argument shows that it contains P_2. Hence there is one circle containing P_0, P_1, and P_2.

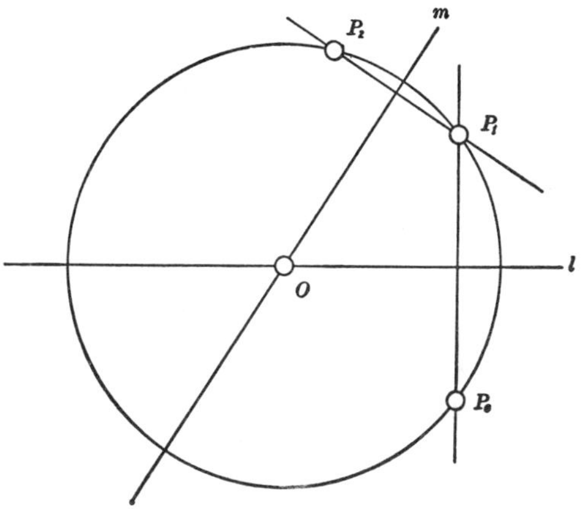

FIG. 49

Observe that we do not prove at this stage that a circle has a point on every line through its center. This could not be done without further hypotheses on the nature of the plane than we are making at present.

EXERCISES

1. The locus of the points of intersection of the lines through a point A with the perpendicular lines through a point B, not on a minimal line through A, is a circle whose center is the mid-point of the pair AB.

2. A tangent to a circle is perpendicular to the diameter through the point of contact.

3. Any two conjugate diameters of a circle are orthogonal.

4. If the tangents at two points A and B of a circle meet in a point O, the pairs OA and OB are congruent.

5. If l is the perpendicular bisector of a point pair AB, then the circles through A and B meet l in pairs of an involution whose center (§ 43) is the mid-point of AB.

6. The system of all circles having a common center meet any line in the pairs of an involution.

7. A parallelogram which circumscribes a circle must be a rhombus.

8. A parallelogram inscribed in a circle is a rectangle.

9. If two circles have two points in common, the pair of tangents at one common point is symmetric to the pair of tangents at the other.

10. The feet of the perpendiculars from any point of a circle to the sides of an inscribed triangle are collinear.

61. Congruent and similar triangles. Two of the three fundamental criteria for the congruence of triangles can be derived at the present stage. The third criterion, that in terms of "two sides and the included angle," essentially involves order relations and is given in § 63.

In the following theorems we shall restrict attention to triangles none of whose sides pass through double points of the absolute involution. The sides of a triangle ABC which are opposite to the vertices A, B, C are denoted by a, b, c respectively. It will be observed that instead of angles we refer to ordered line pairs.

THEOREM 17. *Two triangles ABC and $A'B'C'$ are congruent in such a way that A corresponds to A' and B to B' if the point pair AB is congruent to the point pair $A'B'$ and the ordered line pairs ca and cb are congruent to the ordered line pairs $c'a'$ and $c'b'$ respectively.*

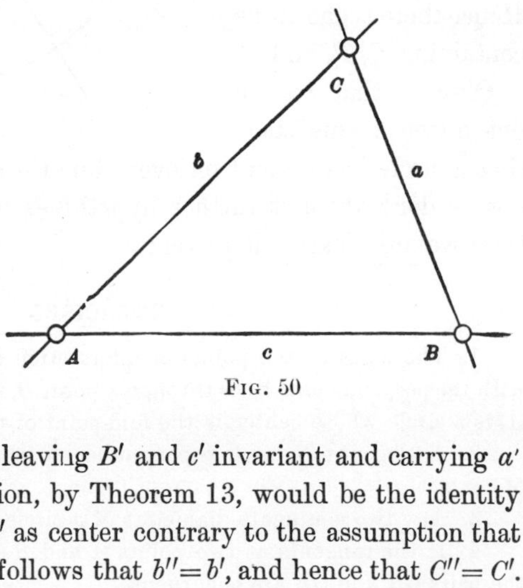

FIG. 50

Proof. By hypothesis, there is a displacement Γ carrying A and B to A' and B' respectively. Let $\Gamma(a)=a''$, $\Gamma(b)=b''$, and $\Gamma(C)=C''$. If $a''\neq a'$, we should have the ordered line pair $c'a'$ congruent to $c'a''$, and hence there would be a transformation leaving B' and c' invariant and carrying a' to a'', but this transformation, by Theorem 13, would be the identity or a point reflection with B' as center contrary to the assumption that $a''\neq a'$. In like manner it follows that $b''=b'$, and hence that $C''=C'$.

THEOREM 18. *If in two triangles ABC and $A'B'C'$ the point pairs AB, BC, CA are congruent, respectively, to $A'B', B'C', C'A'$, the pair of lines bc is congruent to the pair of lines $b'c'$. The two triangles are either congruent or symmetric.*

Proof. By hypothesis, there is a displacement which carries $A'B'$ to AB. Let C'' be the point into which C is carried by this displacement. Let C''' be the point to which C'' is carried by the orthogonal line reflection of which AB is axis. Now if C were not identical with C'' or C''' we should have three congruent point pairs AC, AC'', AC''' and three other congruent point pairs BC, BC'', BC'''. That is, there would be two circles, one with A as center and one with B as center, having three points in common. If C, C'', C''' were collinear, or if two of them were on a minimal line, this would contradict Theorem 14; otherwise it would contradict Theorem 16.

The conclusions of the theorem are now obvious.

The theorems converse to the above are not difficult and are stated in the exercises below. The theorems on similar triangles (Exs. 3, 4, 5) are proved in an analogous way, using Theorem 12 instead of Theorem 13. For these theorems we used the following definition:

DEFINITION. Two figures are said to be *directly similar* if and only if one can be transformed into the other by a similarity transformation which effects on l_∞ the same transformation as some displacement. A transformation of this sort is called a *direct similarity transformation.*

EXERCISES

1. If two ordered point triads are congruent, the corresponding ordered point pairs and line pairs are congruent.

2. If two ordered point triads are symmetric, the corresponding point pairs are congruent and the corresponding ordered line pairs are symmetric.

3. If the ordered line pairs ab, bc, ca are congruent, respectively, to the ordered line pairs $a'b'$, $b'c'$, $c'a'$, the ordered triad abc is directly similar to the ordered triad $a'b'c'$.

4. If the ordered line pairs ab, bc, ca are symmetric, respectively, to the ordered line pairs $a'b'$, $b'c'$, $c'a'$, the ordered triad abc is similar to the ordered triad $a'b'c'$.

5. If two ordered triads abc and $a'b'c'$ are directly similar, the ordered pairs ab, bc, ca are congruent to $a'b'$, $b'c'$, $c'a'$ respectively. If the ordered triads are similar but not directly similar, the ordered pairs ab, bc, ca are symmetric to $a'b'$, $b'c'$, $c'a'$ respectively.

6. A direct similarity transformation is a product of a displacement and a homology.

62. Algebraic formulas for certain parabolic metric groups. Adopting a system of nonhomogeneous coördinates (x, y) for which l_∞ is the singular line, and a system of homogeneous coördinates for which

$$\frac{x_1}{x_0} = x, \qquad \frac{x_2}{x_0} = y,$$

the line l_∞ has the equation $x_0 = 0$, and any involution on it can be written in the form (§§ 54, 58, Vol. I),

$$x_0 = 0, \quad ax_1\bar{x}_1 + bx_1\bar{x}_2 + bx_2\bar{x}_1 + cx_2\bar{x}_2 = 0.$$

If the coördinate system be chosen so that (0, 1, 0) and (0, 0, 1) are conjugate points in this involution, the bilinear equation reduces to

$$(3) \qquad a x_1 \bar{x}_1 + c x_2 \bar{x}_2 = 0.$$

Here the point (0, 1, 1) is paired with the point (0, c, $-a$). In case the involution contains two pairs of points which are harmonically conjugate, one pair may be chosen as (0, 1, 0) and (0, 0, 1) and the other pair as (0, 1, 1) and (0, 1, -1). In that case (3) reduces to

$$(4) \qquad x_1 \bar{x}_1 + x_2 \bar{x}_2 = 0.$$

For the rest of this section we assume that the absolute involution contains two pairs of points which are harmonically conjugate with respect to each other. Such involutions exist in every plane satisfying Assumption H_0, since any two distinct collinear pairs of points determine an involution. Hence this assumption is no restriction on the nature of the plane in which we are working. It is, moreover, easy to replace the formulas which we shall obtain from (4) by the more general but more cumbersome formulas based on (3).

The equations of the transformation required to change (3) into (4) are

$$x_0' = x_0, \quad x_1' = \sqrt{c}\, x_1, \quad x_2' = \sqrt{a}\, x_2.$$

Hence it is clear that in the complex geometry (§ 5) every involution may be reduced to the form (4), and in the real geometry only those involutions can be reduced to this form which are such that $a/c > 0$. The involutions of the latter type are direct (§ 18).

The equations of the affine group are

$$(5) \qquad \begin{aligned} x_0' &= x_0, \\ x_1' &= c_1 x_0 + a_1 x_1 + b_1 x_2, \\ x_2' &= c_2 x_0 + a_2 x_1 + b_2 x_2, \end{aligned}$$

and if the involution (4) is to be transformed into itself, all pairs x_1, x_2 and $\bar{x}_1$, $\bar{x}_2$ which satisfy

$$x_1 \bar{x}_1 + x_2 \bar{x}_2 = 0$$

must also satisfy

$$(a_1 x_1 + b_1 x_2)(a_1 \bar{x}_1 + b_1 \bar{x}_2) + (a_2 x_1 + b_2 x_2)(a_2 \bar{x}_1 + b_2 \bar{x}_2) = 0,$$

which is the same as

$$(a_1^2 + a_2^2) x_1 \bar{x}_1 + (a_1 b_1 + a_2 b_2)(x_1 \bar{x}_2 + x_2 \bar{x}_1) + (b_1^2 + b_2^2) x_2 \bar{x}_2 = 0.$$

Hence

$$\begin{cases} a_1^2 + a_2^2 = b_1^2 + b_2^2 \neq 0, \\ a_1 b_1 + a_2 b_2 = 0, \end{cases}$$

are the necessary and sufficient conditions that (5) leave (4) invariant. Combining these two equations, we obtain

$$a_1^2a_2^2 + a_2^4 - b_1^2a_2^2 - a_1^2b_1^2 = 0$$

or

$$(a_1^2 + a_2^2)(a_2^2 - b_1^2) = 0.$$

Thus we infer $a_2 = \pm b_1$ and $a_1 = \mp b_2$. Hence

THEOREM 19. *The equations of the parabolic metric group are*

$$(6) \qquad \begin{aligned} x' &= \alpha x + \beta y + \gamma_1, \\ y' &= \epsilon(-\beta x + \alpha y) + \gamma_2, \end{aligned}$$

where $\epsilon^2 = 1$.

Any conic section has an equation of the form (§ 66, Vol. I)

$$(7) \quad a_{00}x_0^2 + a_{11}x_1^2 + a_{22}x_2^2 + 2\,a_{01}x_0x_1 + 2\,a_{02}x_0x_2 + 2\,a_{12}x_1x_2 = 0,$$

which determines on the line $x_0 = 0$ an involution whose double elements satisfy

$$a_{11}x_1^2 + a_{22}x_2^2 + 2\,a_{12}x_1x_2 = 0.$$

Comparing with (4), we have that a circle must satisfy the condition

$$a_{11} = a_{22} \neq 0, \qquad a_{12} = 0.$$

If this circle is to have (1, 0, 0) as center, i.e. as pole of $x_0 = 0$, the equation (7) must also satisfy the condition

$$a_{01} = 0 = a_{02}.$$

Thus, returning to nonhomogeneous coördinates, the equation of a circle with the origin as center must be of the form*

$$(8) \qquad x^2 + y^2 = k.$$

According to § 59, the transformations of the parabolic metric group leaving such a circle invariant are all displacements or symmetries, and, moreover, all displacements and symmetries leaving the origin invariant leave this circle invariant. Substituting (6) in (8), we see that a displacement or symmetry leaving the origin invariant is of the form

$$\begin{aligned} x' &= \alpha x + \beta y, \\ y' &= \epsilon(-\beta x + \alpha y), \end{aligned} \qquad \alpha^2 + \beta^2 = 1.$$

* This argument does not prove that every equation of this form represents a circle. The answer to this question depends on the value of k.

Since any displacement or symmetry is expressible as the resultant of one leaving the origin invariant and a translation (Theorem 10, Cor. 1), we have

THEOREM 20. *The equations of the group of displacements and symmetries are*

$$(9) \qquad \begin{aligned} x' &= \alpha x + \beta y + \gamma_1, \\ y' &= \epsilon(-\beta x + \alpha y) + \gamma_2, \end{aligned}$$

where $\alpha^2 + \beta^2 = 1$ *and* $\epsilon^2 = 1$.

By § 54, Vol. I, a transformation of the form (9) effects an involution on l_∞ if and only if $\epsilon = -1$. By Theorem 10, Cor. 2, any symmetry leaving the origin invariant is a line reflection. Hence

THEOREM 21. *The displacements are the transformations of the type* (9) *for which* $\epsilon = 1$ *and the symmetries those for which* $\epsilon = -1$.

EXERCISES

1. The equation of a circle containing the point (a_2b_2) and having the point (a_1b_1) as center is

$$(x - a_1)^2 + (y - b_1)^2 = (a_2 - a_1)^2 + (b_2 - b_1)^2.$$

2. Two lines $ax + by + c = 0$ and $a'x + b'y + c' = 0$ are orthogonal if and only if $aa' + bb' = 0$.

3. In case the absolute involution has double points, the equiaffine transformations of the parabolic metric group are of the form (9), where $\alpha^2 + \beta^2 = \epsilon$ and $\epsilon = \pm 1$.

63. Introduction of order relations. Let us now assume that the plane which we are considering is an ordered plane in the sense of § 15. We may therefore apply the results of Chap. II, particularly of §§ 28–30. Let us also assume that the absolute involution satisfies the condition referred to in § 62, that there exist two pairs of points conjugate with regard to the absolute involution which separate each other harmonically. By Theorem 9, Chap. II, and its corollaries, it follows that any two pairs of the absolute involution separate each other, and that the absolute involution has no double points.* This result may conveniently be put in the following form:

THEOREM 22. *Two pairs of perpendicular lines intersecting in the same point separate each other. No line is perpendicular to itself.*

* The geometry arising from the hyperbolic case has been studied by Wilson and Lewis in the article referred to in § 48.

The restrictions which we have just introduced enable us to state the fundamental theorem (Theorem 13) about the group of displacements in the following more precise form:

THEOREM 23. *The only displacement leaving a ray invariant is the identity.*

Proof. Let A be the origin and B any point of the ray. Since any collineation preserves order relations, A is transformed into itself. Since the line AB is invariant, the displacement is a point reflection or the identity (Theorem 13). But a point reflection would change B into a point of the ray opposite to the ray AB, and thus not leave the ray AB invariant.

With the aid of this theorem we can complete the set of fundamental theorems on congruent triangles, the first two of which were given in § 61.

THEOREM 24. *Two triangles ABC and $A'B'C'$ are congruent if the point pairs AB, AC and the angle $\measuredangle CAB$ are congruent respectively to the point pairs $A'B'$, $A'C'$ and the angle $\measuredangle C'A'B'$.*

Proof. Since the angle* $\measuredangle CAB$ is congruent to the angle $\measuredangle C'A'B'$, there exists a displacement Δ_1 carrying A to A' and the rays AC and AB to $A'C'$ and $A'B'$ respectively. Since the point pair AB is congruent to $A'B'$, there is also a displacement Δ_2 carrying A to A' and B to B', and since AC is congruent to $A'C'$, there is a displacement Δ_3 carrying A to A' and C to C'. By Theorem 23, $\Delta_1 = \Delta_2$ and $\Delta_1 = \Delta_3$. Hence the displacement Δ_1 carries the triangle ABC to $A'B'C'$.

EXERCISES

1. Two triangles ABC and $A'B'C'$ are congruent if the point pair AB is congruent to the point pair $A'B'$ and the angles $\measuredangle CAB$ and $\measuredangle CBA$ are congruent respectively to the angles $\measuredangle C'A'B'$ and $\measuredangle C'B'A'$.

2. If two triangles ABC and $A'B'C'$ are congruent in such a way that A corresponds to A' and B to B', the angles $\measuredangle ABC$, $\measuredangle BCA$, $\measuredangle CAB$ are congruent to the angles $\measuredangle A'B'C'$, $\measuredangle B'C'A'$, $\measuredangle C'A'B'$ respectively.

3. If two triangles ABC and $A'B'C'$ are symmetric in such a way that A corresponds to A' and B to B', the angles $\measuredangle ABC$, $\measuredangle BCA$, $\measuredangle CAB$ are congruent to the angles $\measuredangle C'B'A'$, $\measuredangle A'C'B'$, $\measuredangle B'A'C'$ respectively.

4. Let A, B, C be three collinear points and P_∞ the point at infinity of the line joining them; B is between A and C if and only if

$$0 < \text{R}(P_\infty A, CB) < 1.$$

5. An orthogonal line reflection interchanges the two sides of its axis.

* Note that an angle is an *ordered* pair of rays (§ 28).

64. The real plane. Let us finally assume that we are dealing with the geometry of reals. In consequence, we have the theorem (§ 4) that any one-dimensional projectivity which alters sense (i.e. for which $\Delta < 0$) has two double elements. This may be put into the following form as a theorem of the affine geometry.

THEOREM 25. *If* A_1 and A_2 *are any two points of an ellipse, any line* l*, meeting the line* A_1A_2 *in a point between* A_1 *and* A_2*, meets the ellipse in two points.*

*Proof.** Let us denote the given ellipse by E^2, and let A be a variable point on it. Let L_1 and L_2 be the points in which l is met by A_1A and A_2A respectively, and let Q_1 and Q_2 be the points in which l_∞ is met by A_1A and A_2A respectively. Also let Q_3 be the point in which A_1L_2 meets l_∞. By construction, and by the definition of a conic,

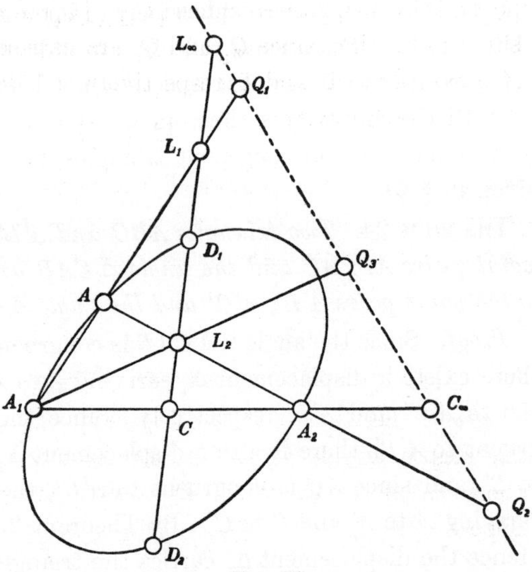

FIG. 51

$$(10) \qquad [L_1] \overset{A_1}{\barwedge} [Q_1] \barwedge A_1[A] \barwedge A_2[A] \barwedge [Q_2] \overset{A_2}{\barwedge} [L_2] \overset{A_1}{\barwedge} [Q_3].$$

The projectivity $[Q_1] \barwedge [Q_2]$ is direct, because, by the remark at the beginning of this section, if the projectivity altered sense it would have two double points, and these, by the definition of the projectivity, would be points of intersection of l_∞ with E^2, contrary to the hypothesis that E^2 is an ellipse.

Let C and C_∞ be the points of intersection of A_1A_2 with l and l_∞ respectively. Also let L_∞ be the point at infinity of l. Then, by the hypothesis that C is between A_1 and A_2,

$$S(C_\infty CA_2) \neq S(C_\infty CA_1).$$

*A simpler proof of this theorem, which, however, involves more preliminary theorems, is given in the next chapter (§ 76).

But, by construction, $A_1CA_2C_\infty \overset{L_2}{\overline{\wedge}} Q_3L_\infty Q_2C_\infty.$

Hence, by Theorem 6, Chap. II,

$$S(C_\infty L_\infty Q_2) \neq S(C_\infty L_\infty Q_3).$$

But the points C_∞, L_∞, Q_2 are carried to C_∞, L_∞, Q_3, respectively, by the projectivity $[Q_2]\overline{\wedge}[Q_3]$, indicated in (10). Hence the projectivity $[Q_2]\overline{\wedge}[Q_3]$ is opposite. Since $[Q_1]\overline{\wedge}[Q_2]$ is direct, $[Q_1]\overline{\wedge}[Q_3]$ is opposite. From this, since Q_1 and Q_3 are carried by a perspectivity with A_1 as center to L_1 and L_2 respectively, it follows (Theorem 6, Chap. II) that the projectivity

$$[L_1]\overline{\wedge}[L_2]$$

is opposite. By the remark at the beginning of the section this projectivity must therefore have two double points, and by the definition of the projectivity these double points must be points of intersection of l with E^2.

COROLLARY 1. *The points in which l meets the ellipse are separated by A_1 and A_2 relative to the order relations on the ellipse.*

Proof. Let D_1 and D_2 (fig. 51) be the two points in which l meets the ellipse, and let A, A_1, A_2, etc. have the meanings given them in the proof of the theorem. Then since the projectivity $[L_1]\overline{\wedge}[L_2]$ is opposite,

$$S(D_1D_2L_1) \neq S(D_1D_2L_2).$$

Hence the lines AD_1 and AD_2 separate the lines AA_1 and AA_2, which, according to the definition in § 20, implies that the pair of points D_1D_2 separates the pair A_1A_2 on the ellipse.

COROLLARY 2. *The points in which l meets the ellipse are on opposite sides of the line A_1A_2.*

Proof. Let a be the tangent at A_1. By the first corollary the lines a and A_1A_2 separate the lines A_1D_1 and A_1D_2. Hence, if A' denote the point in which a meets D_1D_2, D_1 and D_2 separate A' and C. Now A' is not between D_1 and D_2, because if it were, the line a would meet the ellipse in two points instead of only in one. Hence C is between D_1 and D_2, and hence D_1 and D_2 are on opposite sides of l.

THEOREM 26. *A rotation which transforms a given circle into itself transforms any triad of points on the circle into a triad of points in the same sense relatively to the order relations on the circle.*

Proof. Let the given triad of points be A, B, C, let O be any other point of the circle, and let A_∞, B_∞, C_∞ be the points at infinity of the lines OA, OB, OC respectively; let O', A', B', C', A'_∞, B'_∞, C'_∞ be the points to which O, A, B, C, A_∞, B_∞, C_∞, respectively, are carried by the given rotation; let A''_∞, B''_∞, C''_∞ be the points at infinity of the lines OA', OB', OC' respectively.

The given rotation effects on l_∞ a transformation which is the product of two hyperbolic involutions. Hence $S(A_\infty B_\infty C_\infty) = S(A'_\infty B'_\infty C'_\infty)$. As in the proof of Theorem 25, the projectivity $A'_\infty B'_\infty C'_\infty \barwedge A''_\infty B''_\infty C''_\infty$ is direct because otherwise it would have double points and these would be common to the circle and l_∞. Hence $S(A'_\infty B'_\infty C'_\infty) = S(A''_\infty B''_\infty C''_\infty)$ and, therefore, $S(A_\infty B_\infty C_\infty) = S(A''_\infty B''_\infty C''_\infty)$. Projecting from O, we have, by the definition of sense on a conic (§ 20), that

$$S(ABC) = S(A'B'C').$$

Theorem 26, which is here proved only for a real space, can be proved for any ordered space by the methods of the next chapter. This theorem states one of the most intuitionally immediate properties of a rotation. In fact, most of the older discussions of the notions of sense describe sense, without further explanation, as "sense of rotation."

EXERCISES

1. If $\measuredangle AOB$ is any angle, and PQ any ray, there is one and only one ray PR on a given side of the line PQ such that $\measuredangle AOB$ is congruent or symmetric to $\measuredangle QPR$.

*2. Prove that Theorem 25 is not true in a space satisfying Assumptions A, E, H, Q.

65. Intersectional properties of circles. THEOREM 27. *If A and B are any two distinct points, then on any ray having a point O as origin there is one and only one point P such that the pair AB is congruent to the pair OP.*

Proof. Let B_1 be the point to which B is carried by the translation which carries A to O. The circle through B_1 with O as center contains all points Q such that OQ is congruent to AB. Let B_2 be the point to which B_1 is transformed by a point reflection with O as center. Then since O is between B_1 and B_2, any line l through O (and distinct from OB_1) must meet the circle in two points, according to Theorem 25. But by Theorem 23 neither of the rays on l which have O as origin can contain more than one point of the circle. Hence each of these rays contains just one point of the circle. Hence each ray with O as origin contains a single point P such that AB is congruent to OP.

Combining this theorem with Theorem 23, we have

THEOREM 28. *There is one and only one displacement carrying a given ray to a given ray.*

This result characterizes the group of displacements in the same way that the proposition that there is a unique projectivity of a one-dimensional form carrying any ordered triad of elements to any ordered triad characterizes the one-dimensional projective group.

THEOREM 29. *If two circles are such that the line joining their centers meets them in two point pairs which separate each other, the circles have two points in common, one on each side of the line joining the centers.*

Proof. Let the two circles be C_1^2 and C_2^2, and let them meet the line joining the centers in the pairs P_1Q_1 and P_2Q_2 respectively. Let A be the center (§ 43) of the involution Γ in which P_1Q_1 and P_2Q_2 are pairs, and let a be the perpendicular to the line P_1P_2 at A.

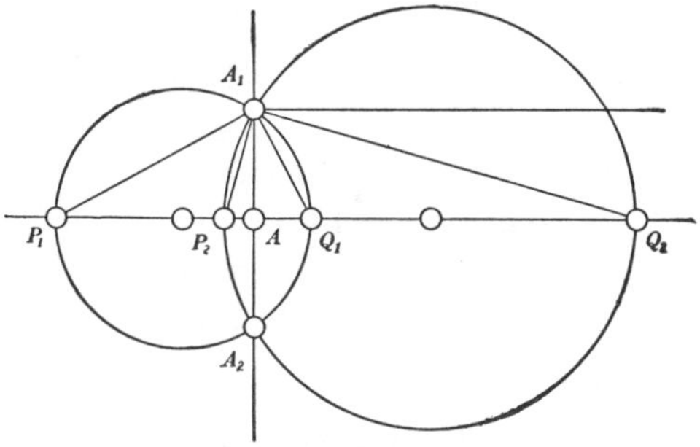

FIG. 52

Since P_1 and Q_1 separate P_2 and Q_2, the ordered triads $P_1Q_1P_2$ and $Q_1P_1Q_2$ are in the same sense. The involution Γ interchanges these two triads and hence transforms any triad into a triad in the same sense. Hence A is between P_1 and Q_1. Hence, by Theorem 25, the line meets the circle C_1^2 in two points A_1 and A_2; and by the second corollary of this theorem, A_1 and A_2 are on opposite sides of the line P_1Q_1.

The lines A_1P_1 and A_1Q_1 are orthogonal since P_1 and Q_1 are the ends of the diameter of a circle through A_1. The line A_1A is orthogonal to the line through A_1 parallel to P_1Q_1. Hence the involution Γ is perspective with the involution of pairs of orthogonal lines through A_1. Hence A_1, P_2, and Q_2 are on a circle whose center is on the line P_1Q_1. By Theorem 16 this circle must be C_2^2. Hence C_1^2 and C_2^2 have A_1 in common. A similar argument shows that A_2 is on C_1^2 and C_2^2.

66. The Euclidean geometry. A set of assumptions. In the geometry of reals the coefficients of the formulas derived in § 62 are real numbers. The formulas given for displacements in that section are the well-known equations for the "rigid motions" of elementary Euclidean geometry. Hence *the geometry of the parabolic metric group in a real plane is the Euclidean geometry.*

This result can also be established by considering a set of postulates from which the theorems of Euclidean geometry are deducible and proving that these postulates are theorems of the parabolic metric geometry. It then follows that all the theorems of Euclidean geometry are true in the parabolic metric geometry.

As a set of assumptions for Euclidean geometry of three dimensions we may choose the ordinal assumptions I–IX which are stated in § 29, together with the assumptions of congruence (X–XVI) stated below. For our immediate purpose, however, a set of assumptions for Euclidean plane geometry is needed. To obtain such a set we merely replace VII and VIII by the following:

$\overline{\text{VII}}$. *All points are in the same plane.*

Thus our set of postulates for Euclidean plane geometry is I–VI, $\overline{\text{VII}}$, IX–XVI.

Assumptions X–XVI make use of a new undefined relation between ordered point pairs which is indicated by saying "AB is congruent to CD." It must be verified that the new assumptions are valid when this relation is identified with the relation of congruence defined above.

X. *If $A \neq B$, then on any ray whose origin is a point C there is one and only one point D such that AB is congruent to CD.*

Proof. This is the same as Theorem 27.

XI. *If AB is congruent to CD and CD is congruent to EF, then AB is congruent to EF.*

Proof. This is a consequence of the fact that the displacements form a group.

XII. *If AB is congruent to $A'B'$, and BC is congruent to $B'C'$ and $\{ABC\}$ and $\{A'B'C'\}$, then AC is congruent to $A'C'$.*

Proof. By Theorem 28, there is a unique displacement which carries A and B to A' and B' respectively. This displacement carries

C to a point C' such that $\{A'B'C'\}$, because a collineation preserves order relations. Moreover, the point C' so obtained is such that BC is congruent to $B'C'$ and AC to $A'C'$; and, by Theorem 27, there is only one point C' in the order $\{A'B'C'\}$ such that BC is congruent to $B'C'$.

XIII. *AB is congruent to BA.*

Proof. AB is transformed into BA by the point reflection whose center is the mid-point of AB.

XIV. *If A, B, C are three noncollinear points and D is a point in the order $\{BCD\}$, and if $A'B'C'$ are three noncollinear points and D' is a point in the order $\{B'C'D'\}$ such that the point pairs AB, BC, CA, BD are respectively congruent to $A'B', B'C', C'A', B'D'$, then AD is congruent to $A'D'$.*

Proof. Since AB is congruent to $A'B'$, there exists a displacement Δ which carries AB to $A'B'$. Let $\Delta(C) = C_1$, $\Delta(D) = D_1$. Also let C_2 and D_2 be the points to which C_1 and D_1 are transformed by the orthogonal line reflection having $A'B'$ as axis.

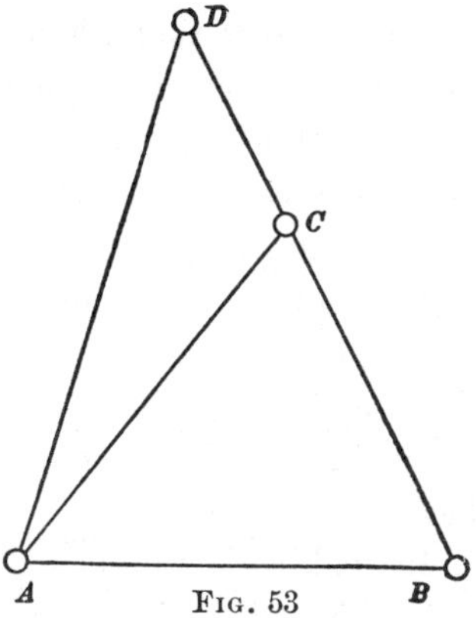

FIG. 53

According to § 57, the pair BC is congruent to $B'C_1$ and to $B'C_2$; CA to C_1A' and C_2A'; BD to $B'D_1$ and $B'D_2$; and AD to $A'D_1$ and $A'D_2$. It follows that C' must coincide with C_1 or C_2, for otherwise there would be two circles, one with A' as center and the other with B' as center, containing the three points C_1, C_2, C'.

If $C' = C_1$, it follows, by Theorem 23, that $D' = D_1$, and hence that AD is congruent to $A'D'$. If $C' = C_2$, it follows, similarly, that $D' = D_2$, and hence that AD is congruent to $A'D'$.

DEFINITION. If O and X_0 are two points of a plane α, then the set of points $[X]$ of α such that OX is congruent to OX_0 is called a *circle*.

XV. *If the line joining the centers of two coplanar circles meets them in pairs of points, P_1Q_1 and P_2Q_2 respectively, such that $\{P_1P_2Q_1\}$ and $\{P_1Q_1Q_2\}$, the circles have two points in common, one on each side of the line joining the centers.*

Proof. This is the same as Theorem 29.

XVI. *If A, B, C are three points in the order $\{ABC\}$ and B_1, B_2, B_3, $\cdots$ are points in the order $\{ABB_1\}$, $\{AB_1B_2\}$, $\cdots$ such that AB is congruent to each of the point pairs BB_1, B_1B_2, $\cdots$, then there are not more than a finite number of the points B_1, B_2, $\cdots$ between A and C.*

Proof. Let B_∞ be the point at infinity of the line AB. Then B_1 is the harmonic conjugate of A with respect to B and B_∞, B_2 is the harmonic conjugate of B with respect to B_1 and B_∞; and so on. Thus $A, B, B_1, B_2, \cdots$ form a harmonic sequence of which B_∞ is the limit-point. Since C has a finite coördinate, the result follows from § 8, Chap. I.

The set of assumptions I–XVI is not categorical. It provides merely for the existence of such irrational points as are needed in constructions involving circles and lines (see § 77, below). It can be made categorical by adding Assumption XVII, § 29. It must be noted, however, that when XVII is added, X–XVI become redundant in the sense that it is possible to introduce ideal elements and then bring in the congruence relations by means of the definitions in this and the preceding chapters.

In order to convince himself that the assumptions given above are a sufficient basis for the theorems of Euclid, the reader should carry out the deduction from these assumptions of some of the fundamental theorems in Euclid's Elements. An outline of this process will be found in the monograph on the subject from which the assumptions have been quoted.*

In making a rigorous deduction of the theorems of elementary geometry, either from the assumptions above or from the general projective basis, it is necessary to derive a number of theorems which are not mentioned in Euclid or in most elementary texts. These are mainly theorems on order and continuity. They involve such matters as the subdivision of the plane into regions by means of curves, the areas of curvilinear figures, etc., all of which are fundamental in the applications of geometry to analysis, and vice versa. In so far as these theorems relate to circles, they have been partially treated in §§ 64–65 and will be further discussed in the next chapter. The methods used for the more general theorems on order and continuity, however, are less closely related to the elementary part of projective geometry and will therefore be postponed to a later chapter.

* Foundations of Geometry, by Oswald Veblen, in Monographs on Modern Mathematics, edited by J. W. A. Young, New York, 1911.

67. Distance. In § 43 we have defined the magnitude of a vector OB as its ratio to a unit vector OA collinear with it; but in the affine geometry the magnitudes of noncollinear vectors are absolutely unrelated. In the parabolic metric geometry we introduce the additional requirement that any two unit vectors OA and $O'A'$ shall be such that the point pair OA is congruent to the point pair $O'A'$.

Thus, if a given unit vector OA is fixed and C^2 is the circle through A with O as center, any other unit vector must be expressible in the form Vect (OP), where P is a point of the circle. This gives two choices for the unit vector of any system of collinear vectors, and each of the two possible unit vectors is the negative of the other. Therefore, while it is possible under our convention to compare the absolute values of the magnitudes of noncollinear vectors, there is no relation at all between their algebraic signs. This corresponds to the fact that there is no unique relation between particular sense classes on two nonparallel lines.

Formulas in which the magnitudes of noncollinear vectors appear must, if they state theorems of the Euclidean geometry, be such that their meaning is unchanged when the unit vector on any line is replaced by its negative. This condition is satisfied, for example, in Exs. 2 and 4, § 71.

The ratio of two collinear vectors is invariant under the affine group; the magnitude of a vector is invariant under the group of translations; but the absolute value of the magnitude of a vector, according to our last convention, is invariant under the group of displacements. The last invariant may be defined directly in terms of point pairs as follows:

Definition. Let AB be an arbitrary pair of distinct points which shall be referred to as the *unit of distance*. If P and Q are any two points, let C be a point of the ray AB such that the pair AC is congruent to the pair PQ. The ratio

$$\frac{AC}{AB}$$

is called the *distance from P to Q*, and denoted by Dist (PQ). If L is any point and l any line, the distance from L to the foot of the perpendicular to l through L is called the *distance from L to l*.

It follows directly from the theorem above that Dist (PQ) is uniquely defined and positive whenever $P \neq Q$, and zero whenever $P = Q$. From the corresponding theorems on the magnitudes of vectors there follows the theorem that if $\{ABC\}$, then

$$\text{Dist}(AB) + \text{Dist}(BC) = \text{Dist}(AC).$$

Other properties of the distance-function are stated in the exercises.

The notion of the length (or circumference) of a circle may be defined as follows: Let $P_1, P_2, \cdots, P_n$ be n points in the order $\{P_1P_2 \cdots P_n\}$ on a circle, and let

$$p = \text{Dist}(P_1P_2) + \text{Dist}(P_2P_3) + \cdots + \text{Dist}(P_nP_1).$$

It can easily be proved that for a given circle C^2, the numbers p obtained from all possible ordered sets of points $P_1, P_2, \cdots, P_n$, for all values of n, do not exceed a certain number.

DEFINITION. The number c, which is the smallest number larger than all values of p, is called the *length* or *circumference* of the circle C^2.

The proof of the existence of the number c will be omitted for the reasons explained below. The existence of c having been established, it follows without difficulty that if c and c' are the lengths of two circles with centers O and O', respectively, and passing through points P and P', respectively,

$$\frac{c}{c'} = \frac{\text{Dist}(OP)}{\text{Dist}(O'P')}.$$

Choosing the point pair $O'P'$ as the unit of distance and denoting the constant c' by 2π, this gives the formula

$$c = 2\pi \cdot \text{Dist}(OP). \tag{11}$$

The theory of the lengths of curves in general could be developed at the present stage without any essential difficulty. This subject, however, is very different (in respect to method, at least) from the other matters which we are considering, and therefore will be passed over with the remark that, starting with the theory of distance here developed, all the results of this branch of geometry may be obtained as applications of the integral calculus. Even the theory of the length of circles which we have summarized in the paragraphs above involves the ideas, if not the methods, of the calculus.

EXERCISES

1. Two point pairs AB and CD are congruent if and only if Dist $(AB) =$ Dist (CD).

2. If A, B, C are noncollinear points, Dist (AB) + Dist $(BC) >$ Dist (AC).

3. Two triangles ABC and $A'B'C'$ are similar in such a way that A corresponds to A', B to B', and C to C' if and only if

$$\frac{\text{Dist}(AB)}{\text{Dist}(A'B')} = \frac{\text{Dist}(AC)}{\text{Dist}(A'C')} = \frac{\text{Dist}(BC)}{\text{Dist}(B'C')}.$$

4. Relative to a coördinate system in which the axes are at right angles, the distance between two points (x_1, y_1), (x_2, y_2) is

$$\sqrt{(x_1 - x_2)^2 + (y_1 - y_2)^2},$$

the positive determination of the radical being taken. The distance from a point $(x_1 y_1)$ to a line $ax + by + c = 0$ is the numerical value of

$$\frac{ax_1 + by_1 + c}{\sqrt{a^2 + b^2}}.$$

68. Area. The area of a triangle, as distinguished from the measure of an ordered point triad, may be defined as follows:

DEFINITION. Relative to a unit triad OPQ (§ 49) such that the lines OP and OQ are orthogonal and the point pairs OP and OQ are congruent to the unit of distance, the positive number

$$\tfrac{1}{2} \mid m\,(ABC) \mid$$

is called the *area of the triangle* ABC, and denoted by $a\,(ABC)$.

As was brought out in Chap. III, the theory of measure of polygons belongs properly to the affine geometry. But the standard formula for the area of a triangle in terms of base and altitude (Ex. 1, below) involves the ideas of distance and perpendicularity and hence belongs to the parabolic metric geometry. It should be noticed that this formula assumes that the side of the triangle which is regarded as the base does not pass through a double point of the absolute involution. This condition is satisfied under the hypotheses of §§ 63, 64, but is not always satisfied in a complex plane; whereas the definitions of equivalence and measure as given in Chap. III are entirely free of such restrictions.

The theory of areas in general depends on considerations of order and continuity which we have not yet developed, and which, like the theory of lengths of curves, belongs essentially to another branch of geometry than that with which we are concerned in this chapter. We shall, however, outline the definition of the area of an ellipse from the point of view of elementary geometry, because the derivation of the area of an ellipse from that of the circle affords rather an interesting application of one of the theorems about the affine group.

Let $P_1, P_2, \cdots, P_n$ be any finite number of points in the order $\{P_1 P_2 \cdots P_n\}$ on an ellipse E^2 with a point O as center, and let

$$A = a(OP_1P_2) + a(OP_2P_3) + \cdots + a(OP_nP_1).$$

It can easily be proved that there exists a finite number, $a(E^2)$, which is the smallest number which is greater than all values of A formed according to the rule above.

DEFINITION. The number $a(E^2)$ is called the *area* of the ellipse.

In case E^2 is a circle, C^2, it is easy to prove that

$$a(C^2) = \pi r^2,$$

where π is the constant defined above and $r = \text{Dist}(OP_1)$.

Now suppose E^2 is an ellipse with two perpendicular conjugate diameters OA and OB which meet E^2 in A and B respectively, and let C^2 be the circle through A with O as center, and let C be the point in which the ray OB meets C^2. The homology Γ with OA as axis and the point at infinity of OB as center, which transforms B to C, is an affine transformation carrying the ellipse E^2 to the circle C^2. This homology transforms the triangle OAB to the triangle OAC; and the areas of these triangles satisfy the relation

$$\frac{a(OAC)}{a(OAB)} = \frac{\text{Dist}(OC)}{\text{Dist}(OB)} = k.$$

It follows, by § 50, that the homology transforms any triangle into one whose area is k times as large. By the definition of the area of an ellipse, therefore,

$$\frac{a(C^2)}{a(E^2)} = \frac{\text{Dist}(OC)}{\text{Dist}(OB)}.$$

Denoting Dist (OA) by a and Dist (OB) by b, this gives

$$a(E^2) = \frac{\pi a^2 b}{a} = \pi ab.$$

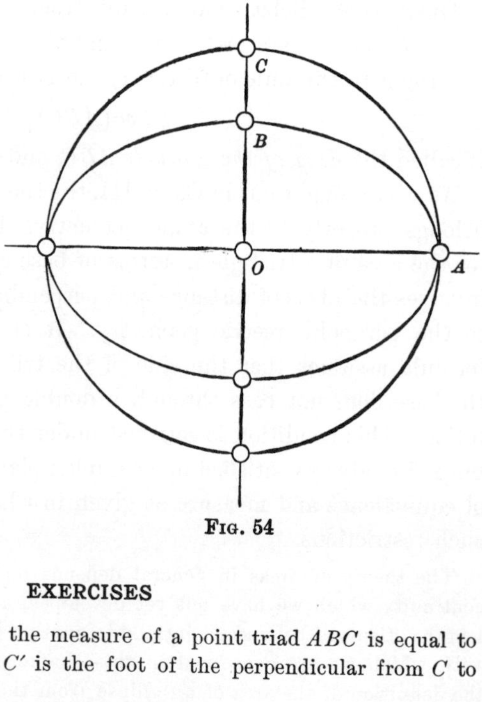

FIG. 54

EXERCISES

1. The numerical value of the measure of a point triad ABC is equal to $\text{Dist}(AB) \cdot \text{Dist}(CC')$, where C' is the foot of the perpendicular from C to the line AB.

2. If $abcd$ is a simple quadrilateral whose vertices are on a conic and P is a variable point of the conic,

$$\frac{\text{Dist}(Pa) \cdot \text{Dist}(Pc)}{\text{Dist}(Pb) \cdot \text{Dist}(Pd)}$$

is a constant (cf. Ex. 2, § 51).

3. If a projective collineation carries a variable point M and two fixed lines a, b to M', a', b' respectively, the number

$$\frac{\text{Dist}(Ma)}{\text{Dist}(Mb)} \div \frac{\text{Dist}(M'a')}{\text{Dist}(M'b')}$$

is a constant.

4. Let F be the center of a homology Γ and l the vanishing line, $\Gamma^{-1}(l_\infty)$. If P is a variable point and $Q = \Gamma(P)$,

$$\frac{\text{Dist}(FP)}{\text{Dist}(Pl)} = k \cdot \text{Dist}(FQ),$$

where k is a constant.

5. The area of an ellipse is $\pi a/2$, where a is the area of any inscribed parallelogram whose diagonals are conjugate diameters.

6. Among all simple quadrilaterals circumscribed to an ellipse, the ones whose sides are tangent at the ends* of conjugate diameters have the least area.

7. Among all simple quadrilaterals inscribed in an ellipse, the ones whose vertices are the ends of conjugate diameters have the greatest area.

8. Of all ellipses inscribed in a parallelogram, the one which has the lines joining the mid-points of opposite sides as a pair of conjugate diameters has the greatest area.

9. Of all ellipses circumscribed to a parallelogram, the smallest is the one having the diagonals as conjugate diameters.

69. The measure of angles. The unit of distance may be chosen arbitrarily, because any point pair can be transformed under the parabolic metric group into any other point pair. It is otherwise with angles or line pairs, because, for example, an orthogonal line pair cannot be transformed into a nonorthogonal pair. Therefore the systems of measurement for angles obtained by choosing different units are, in general, essentially different. We shall give an outline of the generally adopted system of measurement, basing it upon properties of the group of rotations leaving a point O invariant.

Let P_0 be an arbitrary point different from O, and C^2 the circle through P_0 with O as center. Let P_1 (fig. 55) be the point different from P_0 in which the line P_0O meets C^2, and let $P_{\frac{1}{2}}$ and $P_{\frac{3}{2}}$ be the points in which the perpendicular to P_0O at O meets C^2. By Cor. 1, Theorem 25, these points are in the order $\{P_0P_{\frac{1}{2}}P_1P_{\frac{3}{2}}\}$ on the circle. Let σ denote the segment $\overline{P_0P_{\frac{1}{2}}P_1}$. Any line through O meets C^2 in two points which are separated by P_0 and P_1, and hence meets σ in a unique point. Let $P_{\frac{1}{4}}$ be the point in which the line through O perpendicular to $P_0P_{\frac{1}{2}}$ meets σ. And, in general, let $[P_{\frac{1}{2^n}}]$, $n = 1, 2, \cdots$ be the set such that $P_{\frac{1}{2^n}}$ is the point in which the line through O perpendicular to $P_0P_{\frac{1}{2^{n-1}}}$ meets σ.

*The *ends* of a diameter are the points in which it meets the conic.

The line $OP_{\frac{1}{4}}$ obviously meets the line $P_0P_{\frac{1}{2}}$ in the mid-point of the pair $P_0P_{\frac{1}{2}}$, and the mid-point is between P_0 and $P_{\frac{1}{2}}$. Hence, by Cor. 1, Theorem 25, we have the order relation $\{P'P_0P_{\frac{1}{4}}P_{\frac{1}{2}}\}$, where P' denotes, for the moment, the point not on σ in which the line $OP_{\frac{1}{4}}$ meets the circle. Since O is between $P_{\frac{1}{4}}$ and P', the same corollary gives $\{P_0P_{\frac{1}{4}}P_1P'\}$.

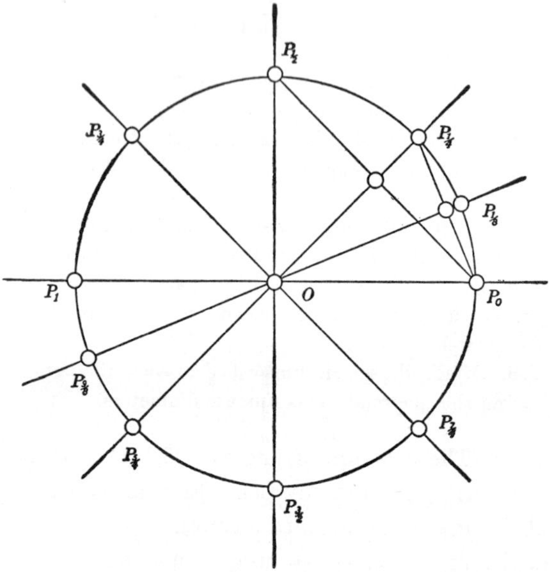

FIG. 55

Since $P_{\frac{1}{4}}$ is on the segment σ, we have either $\{P_0P_{\frac{1}{4}}P_{\frac{1}{2}}P_1\}$ or $\{P_0P_{\frac{1}{2}}P_{\frac{1}{4}}P_1\}$. The second of these alternatives, however, when combined with $\{P'P_0P_{\frac{1}{4}}P_{\frac{1}{2}}\}$, would imply $\{P'P_0P_1P_{\frac{1}{4}}P_{\frac{1}{2}}\}$, contrary to $\{P_0P_{\frac{1}{4}}P_1P'\}$. Hence $\{P_0P_{\frac{1}{2}}P_{\frac{1}{4}}P_1\}$ is impossible, and we must have $\{P_0P_{\frac{1}{4}}P_{\frac{1}{2}}P_1\}$. In like manner it is proved that $\{P_0P_{\frac{1}{8}}P_{\frac{1}{4}}P_1\}$ and, in general, that

$$\{P_0 \cdots P_{\frac{1}{2^n}}P_{\frac{1}{2^{n-1}}} \cdots P_{\frac{1}{2}}P_1\}.$$

Let Π denote the rotation (a point reflection in this case) which leaves O fixed and transforms P_0 to P_1, and let $\Pi^{\frac{1}{2^n}}$ denote the rotation transforming P_0 to $P_{\frac{1}{2^n}}$. The rotation $\Pi^{\frac{1}{2}}$, being the product of the orthogonal line reflection with $OP_{\frac{1}{4}}$ as axis followed by that with $OP_{\frac{1}{2}}$ as axis, carries the point pair $OP_{\frac{1}{2}}$ to the point pair OP_1. Hence*

$$(\Pi^{\frac{1}{2}})^2 = \Pi.$$

In like manner it follows that

$$(\Pi^{\frac{1}{2^n}})^2 = \Pi^{\frac{1}{2^{n-1}}}.$$

* The symbol A^n, where A is any transformation and n a positive integer, has been defined in § 24, Vol. I.

Let us denote $(\Pi^{\frac{1}{2^n}})^m$ by $\Pi^{\frac{m}{2^n}}$, where m is any positive or negative integer, and $\Pi^{\frac{m}{2^n}}(P_0)$ by $P_{\frac{m}{2^n}}$.

Now all rotations are direct (Theorem 26). Hence $S(P_0P_{\frac{1}{4}}P_{\frac{1}{2}}) = S(P_{\frac{1}{4}}P_{\frac{1}{2}}P_{\frac{3}{4}}) = S(P_{\frac{1}{2}}P_{\frac{3}{4}}P_1)$. Combining these relations with $\{P_0P_{\frac{1}{4}}P_{\frac{1}{2}}P_1\}$, we have the order relation $\{P_0P_{\frac{1}{4}}P_{\frac{1}{2}}P_{\frac{3}{4}}P_1\}$, and in general, by a like argument,

$$\{P_0P_{\frac{1}{2^n}}P_{\frac{2}{2^n}}P_{\frac{3}{2^n}} \cdots P_1\}.$$

Hence we have $\{P_0P_{\frac{m}{2^n}}P_{\frac{m'}{2^{n'}}}P_1\}$, whenever $0 < \dfrac{m}{2^n} < \dfrac{m'}{2^{n'}} < 1$, as can easily be seen on reducing the two fractions to a common denominator.

Since $\Pi^2 = 1$, it follows that whenever $m/2^n$ is expressible in the form $2k + \alpha$, k being an integer,

$$\text{(12)} \qquad \Pi^{2k+\alpha} = \Pi^{\alpha} \quad \text{and} \quad P_{2k+\alpha} = P_{\alpha}.$$

DEFINITION. Let π be the constant defined in § 67, (11). The number $\alpha \cdot \pi$, where $\alpha = m/2^n$, is called the *measure* of any angle congruent to $\measuredangle P_0OP_{\alpha}$. An angle whose measure is $\alpha\pi$ is also said *to be equal to* 2α *right angles.*

The measure of an angle is indeterminate according to this definition. In fact, according to (12), whenever the measure of an angle is β, it is also $2k\pi + \beta$, where k is any positive or negative integer. This indetermination can be removed by requiring that the measure β chosen for any angle shall always satisfy a condition of the form $0 \leqq \beta < 2\pi$, or $-\pi < \beta \leqq \pi$.

Since the rays $OP_{\frac{m}{2^n}}$ do not include all rays with O as center, the definition just given does not determine the measures of all angles. The required extension may be made by means of elementary continuity considerations, the details of which we shall omit. The essential steps required are: (1) to prove that if $\bar{P}$ be any point in the order $\{P_0\bar{P}P_{\frac{1}{2}}P_1\}$, there exists a positive integral value of n such that $\{P_0P_{\frac{1}{2^n}}\bar{P}P_{\frac{1}{2}}P_1\}$; (2) hence to prove that if P be any point on the circle not of the form $P_{\frac{m}{2^n}}$, the points of the form $P_{\frac{m}{2^n}}$ fall into two classes, $[P_{\alpha}]$ and $[P_{\beta}]$, such that $\{P_0P_{\alpha}PP_{\beta}\}$, and there is no point, except P, on every segment $\overline{P_{\alpha}PP_{\beta}}$ of the circle; (3) having required that $0 < \alpha < \beta < 2$, to define Π^{2k+x} (where k is an integer, positive, negative, or zero, and x is the number such that $\alpha < x < \beta$ for all α's and β's) as the rotation about O carrying P_0 to P; (4) to show that if x is a rational number m/n, $(\Pi^x)^n = \Pi^m$; (5) to define measure of angle as above, but with the restriction that $\alpha = m/2^n$ removed; (6) to prove that the measure of the sum of two angles differs from the sum of the measures by $2k\pi$, the sum being defined as below.

DEFINITION. If a, b, c are any three rays having a common origin, but not necessarily distinct, any angle $\measuredangle a_1c_1$ congruent to $\measuredangle ac$ is said to be the *sum* of any two angles $\measuredangle a_2b_2$ and $\measuredangle b_3c_3$ such that $\measuredangle a_2b_2$ is congruent to $\measuredangle ab$ and $\measuredangle b_3c_3$ is congruent to $\measuredangle bc$. The sum $\measuredangle a_1c_1$ is denoted by $\measuredangle a_2b_2 + \measuredangle b_2c_2$.

For some purposes it is desirable to have a conception of angle according to which any two numbers are the measures of distinct angles. This may be obtained as follows:

DEFINITION. A ray associated with an integer, positive, negative, or zero, is called a *numbered ray*. An ordered pair of numbered rays having the same origin is called a *numbered angle*. If the measure of an angle $\measuredangle hk$ in the earlier sense is a, where $0 \leqq a < 2\pi$, the measure of a numbered angle in which h is associated with m, and k with n, is

$$2(n-m)\pi + a.$$

Defining the sum of two numbered angles in an obvious way, it is clear that the sum of two numbered angles has a measure which is the sum of their measures.

The trigonometric functions can now be defined, following the elementary textbooks, as the ratios of certain distances multiplied by ± 1 according to appropriate conventions. This we shall take for granted in the future as having been carried out.

70. The complex plane. Instead of the assumption in § 64, we could assume that the Euclidean plane is obtained by leaving out one line from the complex projective plane (A, E, J, or A, E, H, C, $\overline{\text{R}}$, I). All the results of Chap. III and of the present chapter up to § 63 are applicable to this case. The rest of the theory, however, is essentially different from that of the real plane, because the absolute involution necessarily has two double points and because a line does not satisfy the one-dimensional order relations. Thus the minimal lines play a principal rôle and must be regarded as exceptional in the statement of a large class of theorems; and another large class of theorems of elementary geometry (those involving order relations) disappears entirely.

For the present, therefore, we shall confine attention to the geometry of reals, but shall make use, whenever we find it convenient to do so, of the fact (§ 6) that a real space S may be regarded as immersed in a complex space, S′, in such a way that every line l of S is contained in a unique line l' of S′. As a direct consequence it follows that any conic C^2 of S is a subset of the points of a unique conic of S′. For any five points of C^2, regarded as points of S′, determine a unique conic of S′ which, by construction (§ 41, Vol. I), contains all points of C^2 and is uniquely determined by any five of its points. Similar reasoning will show that any plane π of S is contained in a unique plane π' of S′; and like remarks may be made with regard to any one-, two-, or three-dimensional form.

A like situation arises with respect to transformations. A projective transformation Π of a form in S is fully determined, according to the fundamental theorem of projective geometry, by its effect on a finite set* of elements of S. Since the fundamental theorem is also valid in S′, there is a unique projective transformation Π′ which has the same effect on this set of elements as Π.

Specializing these remarks somewhat we have: A Euclidean plane π of S is a subset of the points of a certain Euclidean plane π' of S′. The line at infinity l_∞ associated with π is a subset of the line at infinity l'_∞ associated with π'. The absolute involution I on l_∞ determines an involution I′ on l'_∞ in which all the pairs of I are paired. The involution I′ has two imaginary double points, the circular points (§ 56), which shall be denoted by I_1 and I_2. Since a circle in π is a conic having I as an involution of conjugate points, every circle in π is a subset of the points on a conic in π' which passes through I_1 and I_2.

The problem of the intersection of a line and a circle, or indeed of a line and any ellipse, can now be discussed completely. In the proof of Theorem 25 the intersection of a line l and an ellipse E^2 was seen to depend on finding the double points of a certain projectivity $[L_1] \barwedge [L_2]$ on l. Any three points L_1', L_1'', L_1''', and their correspondents L_2', L_2'', L_2''', determine a projectivity on the complex line l' containing l, and, by the fundamental theorem of projective geometry, this projectivity is identical with $[L_1] \barwedge [L_2]$ so far as real points are concerned. The double points of this projectivity are common to the complex

*For example, in case of a one-dimensional form any three elements of the form are such a set.

line containing l and the complex conic containing E^2. These points are real if the hypothesis of Theorem 25 is satisfied; they are real and coincident if l is tangent to E^2; otherwise they are imaginary.

A similar discussion will be made in the next section of the problem of the intersection of two circles, but first let us make certain definitions and conventions which will simplify our terminology.

According to the definitions in § 6, any point of S' is said to be *complex*, and a complex point is *real* or *imaginary* according as it is contained in S or not. In the case of lines, however, we have three things to distinguish: a line of the space S, a line of S' which contains a line of S as a subset, and a line of S' which contains no such subset. In current usage a line of the last sort is called *imaginary*, a line of either of the first two sorts is called *real*, and a line of either of the last two sorts is called *complex*. The current terminology therefore permits a confusion between a real line as a locus in S and a real line as a particular kind of a complex line.

In most cases, however, no misunderstanding need be caused by this ambiguity of language, and we shall in future usually employ the same notation for the real line l of S and the line l' of S' which contains l. The same remarks apply to conic sections and, indeed, to all one-dimensional forms.

DEFINITION. Any element (point, line, or plane) or set of elements of S' is said to be *complex*. Any element or set of elements of S is said to be *real*. A line or plane of S' which contains a line or plane, respectively, of S is said to be a *real line* or *real plane of* S'. A one-dimensional form of S', a subset of whose elements are real elements of S' and contain all the elements of a one-dimensional form of S, is called a *real one-dimensional form of* S'. An element or one-dimensional form of S' which is not a real element or real one-dimensional form of S' is said to be *imaginary*.

DEFINITION. A projective transformation of a real form of S' is said to be *real* if it transforms each real element of S' into a real element of S'.

Strictly speaking, these definitions distinguish between the two senses of the word "real" by phrases such as "real line of S'." But in practice we shall drop the "of S'." The one-dimensional forms as thus far defined are all of the first or second degrees, but the definition can be extended without essential modification to forms of higher degree and also to forms of more than one dimension. We shall take this extension for granted whenever we have occasion to use it.

In accordance with these conventions, the points I_1 and I_2 which are really the double points of I′ will be referred to in future as the double points of the absolute involution I. In like manner, any line l and circle C^2 which have no real points in common will be said to have in common the two points common to the complex line and the complex conic which contain l and C^2 respectively.

The utility of these conventions will be understood by the reader if he will write out in full the discussion of pencils of circles in the following section, putting in explicitly, in notation and language, the distinction between elements of S and S′.

It is also convenient in many cases to extend the formulas for distance, area, etc. given in §§ 67–69 to imaginary elements. Thus, for example, in case (x_1, y_1) and (x_2, y_2) are imaginary points such that $(x_1 - x_2)^2 + (y_1 - y_2)^2$ is a positive real number, $\sqrt{(x_1 - x_2)^2 + (y_1 - y_2)^2}$ will be referred to as the distance from (x_1, y_1) to (x_2, y_2). Extensions of terminology of this self-evident sort will be made when needed, without further explanation.

71. Pencils of circles. Consider two circles C_1^2 and C_2^2 in a real Euclidean plane. Let their centers be denoted by C_1 and C_2, and in case $C_1 \neq C_2$, let b denote the line C_1C_2. By Theorem 25, b meets each circle in a pair of real points which we shall denote by P_1Q_1 and P_2Q_2 respectively. The two pairs may be entirely distinct, in which case let Γ denote the involution on b transforming each pair into itself; or they may have one point in common, in which case the line through this point perpendicular to b is a common tangent of the two circles. The two pairs cannot coincide, because the circles would then coincide. Thus four cases may be distinguished:

(1) The circles have the same center.
(2) The circles have a common tangent and point of contact.
(3) The involution Γ is direct.
(4) The involution Γ is opposite.

A circle is, by § 60, a real conic which, according to the terminology of the last section, contains the double points of the absolute involution. Let us denote these points (the circular points) by I_1 and I_2 and apply the results of § 47, Vol. I, on pencils of conics.

In the first case let O denote the common center of the two circles. The lines OI_1 and OI_2 are then tangent to both circles at I_1 and I_2 respectively. Hence, by reference to § 47, Vol. I, it is evident that the two circles belong to a pencil of circles of Type IV.

In the second case C_1^2 and C_2^2 have in common the points I_1 and I_2 as well as a common tangent and point of contact. Hence they belong to a pencil of Type II which contains all circles touching* the given line at the given point.

In the third case, since the involution Γ is direct, the pairs P_1Q_1 and P_2Q_2 separate each other. Hence, by Theorem 29, the circles have two real points, A_1 and A_2, in common. Hence they belong to a pencil of Type I consisting of all conics through A_1, A_2, I_1, and I_2. This may also be seen as follows:

Since the involution Γ has no double points (§ 21), it has a center (§ 43) which we shall call O. Let a be the line perpendicular to b at O. Then by the argument used in the proof of Theorem 29, O is between P_1 and Q_1. Hence a meets C_1^2 in two real points A_1 and A_2 (fig. 52). The pencil of conics through A_1, A_2, I_1, I_2 meets b in the pairs of an involution among which are P_1Q_1 and O and the point at infinity of b. Hence C_2^2 is a conic of the pencil, and hence a meets C_2^2 in A_1 and A_2. In this case, therefore, the two circles belong to a pencil of Type I.

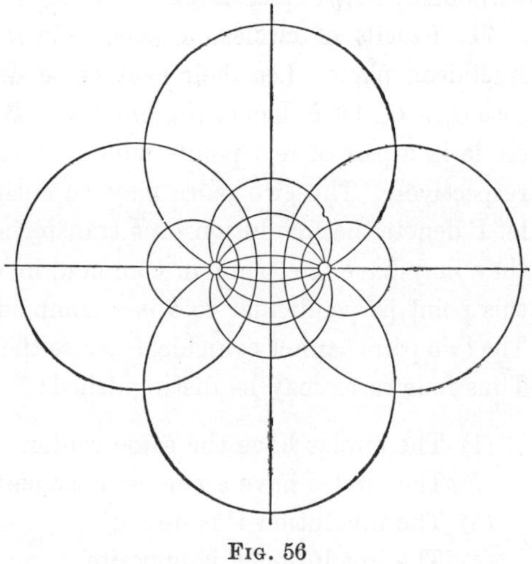
FIG. 56

In the fourth case the involution Γ cannot have a double point at infinity, because then the other double point would have to be the mid-point of P_1Q_1 and also of P_2Q_2, and thus C_1^2 and C_2^2 would have a common center. Hence in this case also the center O of the involution Γ is an ordinary point. Let a denote

*A conic and one of its tangent lines are said to *touch* each other at the point of contact. Two conics touching a line at the same point are said to *touch* each other.

the perpendicular to b at O, and let A_1 and A_2 be the points in which a meets C_1^2. These points are imaginary; for otherwise, since they are interchanged by the orthogonal line reflection with b as axis, O would be between them, and hence, by Cor. 1, Theorem 25, O would be between P_1 and Q_1, contrary to the hypothesis that Γ is opposite. Precisely as in the third case it follows that A_1 and A_2 are also on C_2^2. Hence in this case also C_1^2 and C_2^2 belong to a pencil of Type I.

In each case the facts established make it clear that the two circles could not both be members of more than one pencil of conics. Since any two circles fall under one of the four cases, we have

THEOREM 30. DEFINITION. *Any circle contains the real points of a certain conic in the complex plane. Two conics determined by circles are contained in a unique pencil of conics, which is of Type I, II, or IV. The set of circles which the conics of such a pencil have in common with the real plane is called a* pencil of circles. *If the pencil of conics is of Type IV, the pencil of circles is the set of all circles having a fixed point as center; if the pencil of conics is of Type II, the pencil of circles is the set of all circles tangent to a given line at a given point; if the pencil of conics is of Type I, the pencil of circles is the set of all circles having a given pair of distinct real points in common, or else the set of all circles with centers on a given line and meeting this line in the pairs of an involution with two ordinary double points.*

DEFINITION. The line a joining the centers of two nonconcentric circles is called *the line of centers* of the two circles or of the pencil of circles which contains them. If the circles have a common tangent and point of contact, this tangent is called the *radical axis* of the two circles or of the pencil of circles; if not, the line perpendicular to a at the center of the involution in which the circles of the pencil meet a is called the *radical axis.* The double points of this involution are called the *limiting points* of the pencil of circles. Any circle of the pencil is said to be *about* either one, or both, of the limiting points.

The discussion above has established

THEOREM 31. *The radical axis of two circles passes through all points common to them which are not on the line at infinity. The limiting points of the pencil which they determine are real if the circles meet only in imaginary points and imaginary if they meet in two real points.*

THEOREM 32. *The circular points, the limiting points of a pencil of circles of Type I, and the two points not at infinity in which the circles of the pencil intersect are the pairs of opposite vertices of a complete quadrilateral. The sides of the diagonal triangle of this quadrilateral are l_∞, the radical axis, and the line of centers of the pencil.*

Proof. Let A_1 and A_2 (fig. 57*) be the points other than I_1 and I_2 common to the circles of the pencil, and let B_1 and B_2 be the points of intersection of the pairs of lines I_1A_1, I_2A_2 and I_1A_2, I_2A_1 respectively. Whether A_1 and A_2 are real or imaginary, the line $A_1A_2 = a$, which is the radical axis, is real. Hence its point at infinity A_∞ is real; and hence the line B_1B_2, the polar of A_∞ with regard to any circle of the pencil, is real.

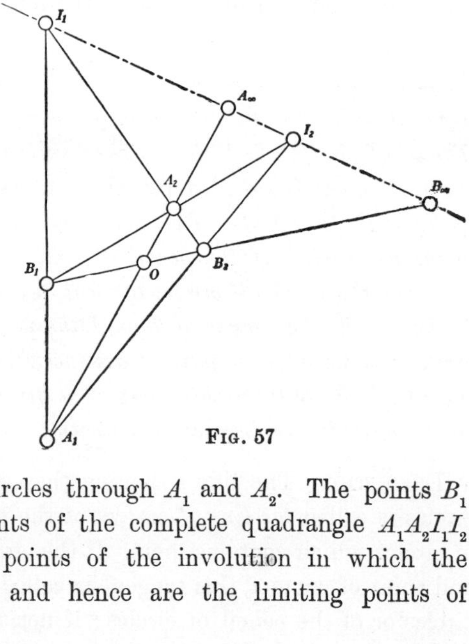

FIG. 57

Since the line $b = B_1B_2$ is the polar of A_∞, it contains the centers of all conics through A_1, A_2, I_1, I_2. Hence b is the line of centers of the pencil of circles through A_1 and A_2. The points B_1 and B_2 being diagonal points of the complete quadrangle $A_1A_2I_1I_2$ are evidently the double points of the involution in which the pencil of circles meets b, and hence are the limiting points of the pencil.

Taking Theorems 31 and 32 together, we see that any pair of real points A_1, A_2 determines a pair of imaginary points B_1, B_2 such that either pair is the pair of limiting points of the pencil of circles through the other pair; that, conversely, any pair of imaginary points B_1, B_2, which are common to two circles, determines two real points A_1, A_2 which are in the above relation to B_1, B_2; and that the three pairs A_1A_2, B_1B_2, I_1I_2 are pairs of opposite vertices of a complete quadrilateral. The relation between the two pencils of circles, the one

* Fig. 57 is, of course, a diagram in which certain imaginary elements are represented by real ones. On the use of figures in general, cf. p. 16, Vol. I.

through A_1 and A_2 and the other about A_1 and A_2, is thus extremely symmetrical. It can be described in purely real terms by means of the following theorems and definition:

THEOREM 33. DEFINITION. *If two circles have a point in common such that the tangents to the two circles at this point are orthogonal, the two circles have another such point in common. Two circles so related are said to be* orthogonal *to each other.*

Proof. An orthogonal line reflection whose axis is the line of centers transforms each circle into itself and transforms the given point of intersection into another point of intersection. Since orthogonal lines are transformed to orthogonal lines, the tangents at the second point are also orthogonal.

THEOREM 34. *If a line through the center of a circle C^2 meets the circle in a pair of points P_1Q_1 and meets any orthogonal circle K^2 in a pair of points P_2Q_2, the pairs P_1Q_1 and P_2Q_2 separate each other harmonically. Conversely, if P_1Q_1 and P_2Q_2 separate each other harmonically, any circle through P_2 and Q_2 is orthogonal to C^2.*

Proof. Let T be one of the points common to the two circles, and let t be the tangent to the circle TP_2Q_2 at T. The pencil of circles tangent to t at T meets the line P_1P_2 in the pairs of an involution Γ, and hence the first statement of the theorem will follow if we can prove that P_1 and Q_1 are the double points of this involution. The line perpendicular to t at T and the line perpendicular to P_1P_2 at P_1

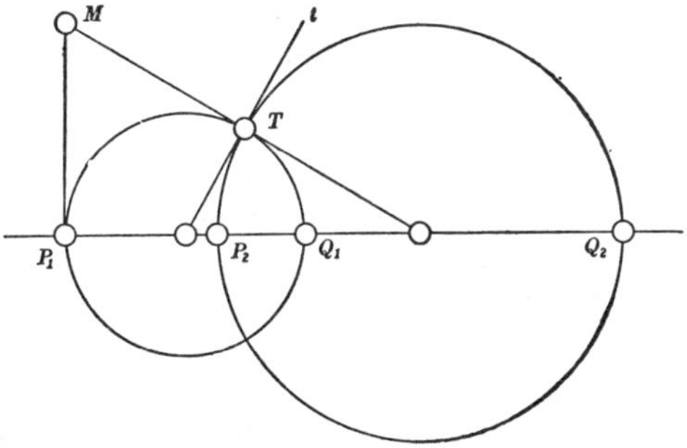

FIG. 58

are tangents to the circle TP_1Q_1 at T and P_1 respectively, and hence (Ex. 4, § 60) meet in a point M such that the pairs MP_1 and MT are congruent. Hence the circle through T with M as center is tangent to t at T and to P_1P_2 at P_1. Hence P_1 is a double point of Γ. A similar argument shows that Q_1 is also a double point.

To prove the converse proposition we observe that there is only one circle through P_2 and T and orthogonal to C^2. One such circle, by the argument above, passes through the point Q_2, which is harmonically separated from P_2 by P_1 and Q_1. Hence the circle P_2Q_2T is orthogonal to C^2.

As a corollary we have

COROLLARY 1. *The set of all circles orthogonal to a pencil of Type I is the pencil of circles through the limiting points of the first pencil.*

Another form in which this result may be stated is the following:

COROLLARY 2. *Let C^2 be a circle, A_1 any point not its center, and A_2 the point on the line joining A_1 to the center of C^2 which is conjugate to A_1 with regard to the conic C^2. Then all circles through A_1 and orthogonal to C^2 meet in A_2.*

DEFINITION. Two points are said to be *inverse* with respect to a circle if and only if they are conjugate with regard to the circle and collinear with its center. The transformation by which every point corresponds to its inverse is called an *inversion* or a *transformation by reciprocal radii.*

Thus the center of the circle is inverse to every real point at infinity. We shall return to the study of inversions in a later chapter.

EXERCISES

1. In case the limiting points of a pencil of circles are real, the radical axis is their perpendicular bisector.

2. If O is any point of the plane of a circle, and a variable line through O meets the circle in two points X, Y, the product $OX \cdot OY$ is constant, and equal to $(OT)^2$ in case there is a line OT tangent to the circle at T. The product $OX \cdot OY$ is called the *power* of O with respect to the circle.

3. The power of any point of the radical axis of a pencil of circles with respect to all circles of the pencil is a constant, and this constant is the same for all points of the radical axis.

4. If O is the center of a circle, C any point of the circle, and A_1 and A_2 any two points inverse with respect to it,

$$OA_1 \cdot OA_2 = (OC)^2.$$

5. Through two points not inverse relative to a given circle, there is one and but one circle orthogonal to it.

6. By a *center of similitude* of two circles is meant the center of a dilation (§ 47) or translation which transforms one of the circles into the other. If the circles are concentric, they have one center of similitude; if they are not concentric, they have two. The centers of similitude harmonically separate the centers of the two circles. The one which is between the centers of the two circles is called the *interior*, and the other is called the *exterior*, center of similitude. The common tangents of two circles meet in the centers of similitude.

7. Three circles whose centers are not collinear determine by pairs six centers of similitude which are the vertices of a complete quadrilateral having the centers of the circles as vertices of its diagonal triangle. Generalize to the case of n circles.

8. If a circle K^2 meets two circles C_1^2 and C_2^2 in four points at which the pairs of tangents are congruent or symmetric, the four points are collinear by pairs with the centers of similitude of C_1^2 and C_2^2. Prove the converse proposition.

72. Measure of line pairs. The circular points I_1, I_2 figure in a very important formula for the measure of a pair of lines.* With the exception of these two points, and two lines i_1, i_2 which pass through them, all the points and lines to which we shall refer in this section are real.

The center and the point at infinity of the axis of an orthogonal line reflection are harmonically conjugate with regard to I_1 and I_2. Hence any orthogonal line reflection, regarded as a transformation of the complex space, interchanges I_1 and I_2, and any displacement leaves I_1 and I_2 separately invariant. Moreover, there exists a displacement transforming any (real) point of l_∞ to any other (real) point of l_∞. Hence a necessary and sufficient condition that a pair of points P, P' of l_∞ be transformable by a displacement to a pair Q, Q' of l_∞ is

$$\text{(13)} \qquad \mathrm{R}(PP', I_1I_2) = \mathrm{R}(QQ', I_1I_2).$$

Now any pair of lines meeting l_∞ in P and P' can be transformed by a translation into any other pair of lines meeting it in P and P', and any pair of lines meeting l_∞ in Q and Q' can be transformed by a translation into any other pair of lines meeting it in Q and Q'. Hence the necessary and sufficient condition that a pair of lines meeting l_∞ in P and P' be congruent to a pair of lines meeting it in Q and Q' is (13).

This suggests as a possible definition of the measure of a pair of nonparallel lines l_1, l_2,

$$\mathrm{R}(l_1l_2, i_1i_2),$$

where i_1 and i_2 are the lines joining the point of intersection of l_1 and l_2 to I_1 and I_2 respectively. It would satisfy the requirement of

*This formula is due to A. Cayley. Cf. Encyclopädie der Math. Wiss. III *AB* 9, p. 901, footnotes 98 and 99.

being unaltered by displacements. In the case of measure of point pairs, however, we have

$$\text{Dist}(AB) + \text{Dist}(BC) = \text{Dist}(AC)$$

whenever $\{ABC\}$, and this condition is not satisfied by the cross ratio given above. We have, in fact,

$$(14) \qquad R(l_1l_2, i_1i_2) \cdot R(l_2l_3, i_1i_2) = R(l_1l_3, i_1i_2)$$

whenever l_1, l_2, l_3 are concurrent. This is easily verified by substituting in the formula for cross ratio (§ 56, Vol. I).

From (14) it is obvious that if we define

$$(15) \qquad m(l_1l_2) = c \log R(l_1l_2, i_1i_2),$$

the measure of line pairs will satisfy the condition

$$m(l_1l_2) + m(l_2l_3) = m(l_1l_3)$$

whenever l_1, l_2, l_3 are concurrent. Since the logarithm is a multiple-valued function, we must specify which value is chosen; and we must also determine the constant c conveniently.

Making use of the same coördinate system as in § 62, any point on l_∞ may be denoted by $(0, \alpha, \beta)$. In case α/β is real, $(\alpha/\beta)^2 > 0$, and hence α and β may be multiplied by a factor of proportionality so that

$$(16) \qquad \alpha^2 + \beta^2 = 1.$$

Throughout the rest of this section we shall suppose α and β subjected to this condition. This is equivalent to supposing that

$$\alpha = \cos(\theta + 2n\pi), \quad \beta = \sin(\theta + 2n\pi),$$

where $0 \leqq \theta \leqq 2\pi$, and n is an integer, positive, negative, or zero.

The double points of the absolute involution satisfy the condition (§ 62)

$$\alpha^2 + \beta^2 = 0,$$

and so may be written

$$I_1 = (0, 1, i) \quad \text{and} \quad I_2 = (0, 1, -i),$$

where $i = \sqrt{-1}$. Now if l_1 and l_2 meet l_∞ in $(0, \alpha_1, \beta_1)$ and $(0, \alpha_2, \beta_2)$ respectively, it follows that (§ 58, Vol. I)

$$\begin{aligned} R(l_1l_2, i_1i_2) &= \frac{\alpha_1 - i\beta_1}{\alpha_1 + i\beta_1} \div \frac{\alpha_2 - i\beta_2}{\alpha_2 + i\beta_2} \\ &= \frac{(\alpha_1\alpha_2 + \beta_1\beta_2) + i(\alpha_1\beta_2 - \alpha_2\beta_1)}{\alpha_1\alpha_2 + \beta_1\beta_2 - i(\alpha_1\beta_2 - \alpha_2\beta_1)} \end{aligned}$$

The numbers $\alpha = \alpha_1\alpha_2 + \beta_1\beta_2$ and $\beta = \alpha_1\beta_2 - \alpha_2\beta_1$ satisfy the condition $\alpha^2 + \beta^2 = 1$. In fact, if $\alpha_1 = \cos\theta_1$ and $\alpha_2 = \cos\theta_2$, then $\alpha = \cos\theta$ and $\beta = \sin\theta$, where $\theta = \theta_1 - \theta_2 + 2n\pi$. Hence

$$\text{R}(l_1l_2, i_1i_2) = \alpha^2 - \beta^2 + 2i\alpha\beta.$$

Here again, $\bar{\alpha} = \alpha^2 - \beta^2$ and $\bar{\beta} = 2\alpha\beta$ satisfy the condition

$$\bar{\alpha}^2 + \bar{\beta}^2 = 1.$$

In fact, $\bar{\alpha} = \cos 2\theta$. Thus

$$(17) \qquad \begin{aligned} \text{R}(l_1l_2, i_1i_2) &= \bar{\alpha} + i\bar{\beta} \\ &= \cos 2\theta + i \sin 2\theta \\ &= e^{2i\theta}. \end{aligned}$$

Hence

$$(18) \qquad \log \text{R}(l_1l_2, i_1i_2) = 2i\theta,$$

where 2θ is real and may be chosen so that $0 \leqq 2\theta < 2\pi$. Hence, choosing the constant c in (15) as $\frac{-i}{2}$, we have

$$(19) \qquad m(l_1l_2) = \frac{-i}{2}\log \text{R}(l_1l_2, i_1i_2) = \theta,$$

where θ may be chosen so that $0 \leqq \theta < \pi$.

The formula (19) is interesting in connection with the theorem that the sum of the angles of a triangle is equal to two right angles. This proposition can easily be established without the consideration of imaginaries, on the basis of the definitions in the last section. From our present point of view, however, it appears as follows: Let the three sides of a triangle be a, b, c, and let them meet the line at infinity in A_∞, B_∞, C_∞ respectively. It is easily verifiable that

$$\text{R}(A_\infty B_\infty, I_1I_2) \cdot \text{R}(B_\infty C_\infty, I_1I_2) \cdot \text{R}(C_\infty A_\infty, I_1I_2) = 1,$$

from which it follows by (19) that

$$m(ab) + m(bc) + m(ca) = \pi.$$

Here we have a theorem on the line pairs rather than on the angles of a triangle. Indeed, (19) is necessarily a formula for the measure of a pair of lines and not of an angle, because of the fact that two opposite rays determine the same point at infinity.

The number $m(ab)$ may also be defined as the smallest value between 0 and 2π, inclusive, of the measures of the four angles $\measuredangle a_1b_1$ which may be formed by a ray a_1 of a and a ray b_1 of b.

Following the common usage, we shall say that two pairs of lines which are congruent *make equal angles*, etc.

EXERCISES

1. If A and B are any two points, the locus of a point P such that the rays PA and PB make a constant angle is a circle.

2. If in two projective flat pencils three lines of one make equal angles with the corresponding three lines of the other, the angle between any two lines of the one is the same as the angle between the corresponding lines of the other.

3. If OA, OB, OC, OD are four lines of a flat pencil,

$$\text{R}(OA, OB;\ OC, OD) = \frac{\sin \measuredangle AOC}{\sin \measuredangle AOD} \div \frac{\sin \measuredangle BOC}{\sin \measuredangle BOD}.$$

In case the four lines form a harmonic set,

$$2 \cot \measuredangle AOB = \cot \measuredangle AOC + \cot \measuredangle AOD.$$

4. If A_1, A_2, A_3, A_4 are four points of a circle,

$$A_1A_3 \cdot A_2A_4 = A_1A_2 \cdot A_3A_4 + A_1A_4 \cdot A_2A_3,$$

where A_iA_j represents Dist (A_iA_j) or $-$ Dist (A_iA_j) according as $S(OA_iA_j) = S(OA_1A_2)$ or not, O being an arbitrary point of the circle and $S(OA_iA_j)$ being a sense-class on the circle.

5. If a, b, c are the sides of a triangle and a_1a_2, b_1b_2, c_1c_2 are pairs of lines through the vertices bc, ca, ab respectively, the six lines a_1, a_2, b_1, b_2, c_1, c_2 are tangents of a conic if and only if

$$\frac{\sin(a_1b)}{\sin(a_1c)} \cdot \frac{\sin(a_2b)}{\sin(a_2c)} \cdot \frac{\sin(b_1c)}{\sin(b_1a)} \cdot \frac{\sin(b_2c)}{\sin(b_2a)} \cdot \frac{\sin(c_1a)}{\sin(c_1b)} \cdot \frac{\sin(c_2a)}{\sin(c_2b)} = 1.$$

6. The points of a ray having (x, y) as origin may be represented in the form

$$(x + \lambda\alpha,\ y + \lambda\beta),$$

where α and β are fixed and $\lambda > 0$. There is a one-to-one reciprocal correspondence between the rays having (x, y) as origin and the ordered pairs of values of α and β which satisfy the condition

$$\alpha^2 + \beta^2 = 1.$$

When α and β satisfy this condition, the numerical value of λ is the distance between (x, y) and $(x + \lambda\alpha, y + \lambda\beta)$.

7. Two angles formed by the pairs of rays

$$\begin{aligned}(x_0 + \lambda\alpha,\ y_0 + \lambda\beta) &\text{ and } (x_0 + \lambda\alpha',\ y_0 + \lambda\beta'),\\ (\bar{x}_0 + \lambda\bar{\alpha},\ y_0 + \lambda\bar{\beta}) &\text{ and } (\bar{x}_0 + \lambda\bar{\alpha}',\ \bar{y}_0 + \lambda\bar{\beta}')\end{aligned} \qquad \lambda > 0$$

respectively are congruent if and only if

$$\alpha\alpha' + \beta\beta' = \bar{\alpha}\bar{\alpha}' + \bar{\beta}\bar{\beta}'.$$

8. Relative to the homogeneous coördinates employed above, the formula for the distance between (x_0, x_1, x_2) and (y_0, y_1, y_2) may be written

$$\frac{\sqrt{(x_1y_0 - x_0y_1)^2 + (x_2y_0 - x_0y_2)^2}}{x_0y_0} = \frac{1}{x_0y_0}\begin{vmatrix} x_0 & x_1 & x_2 \\ y_0 & y_1 & y_2 \\ 0 & 1 & i \end{vmatrix}^{\frac{1}{2}} \cdot \begin{vmatrix} x_0 & x_1 & x_2 \\ y_0 & y_1 & y_2 \\ 0 & 1 & -i \end{vmatrix}^{\frac{1}{2}}.$$

73. Generalization by projection. The relation established in § 66 between Euclidean and projective geometry furnishes a source of new theorems in each. A theorem which has been proved for projective geometry can be specialized into a theorem of Euclidean geometry, or a theorem of Euclidean geometry may be generalized so as to furnish a theorem of projective geometry.

The two processes, of generalization and of specialization, may often be combined in a happy way with the principle of duality or with other general methods of projective geometry. Thus a theorem proved for Euclidean geometry can be generalized into a theorem of projective geometry and the dual of the general theorem specialized into a new theorem of Euclidean geometry. As an example, let us take the theorem of Euclid:

A. *The perpendiculars from the vertices of a triangle to the opposite sides meet in a point* (the orthocenter).

The sides of the triangle meet the line at infinity in three points, and the three perpendiculars are lines from the vertices to the conjugates of these three points in the absolute involution. The Euclidean theorem is therefore a special case of the following projective theorem:

B. *The lines joining the vertices of a triangle to the conjugates, with respect to an arbitrary elliptic involution on a line l, of the points in which the opposite sides meet l, are concurrent.*

This is a portion of Theorem 27, Chap. IV, Vol. I, the orthocenter and the three vertices of the triangle being the vertices of a complete quadrangle. But though the Euclidean theorem is a special case, yet the general theorem for elliptic involutions in real geometry may easily be proved by means of it. For, given any elliptic involution whatever and any triangle, the involution can be projected into the absolute involution and the given triangle will go into a triangle of the Euclidean plane. Hence the general theorem, B, that certain three lines meet in a point could fail to be true only if the Euclidean theorem, A, failed.

It is to be noted that this proves the theorem only for a real space and an elliptic involution. In a complex space (§ 5) it might happen that any transformation which carried the involution into the absolute involution would carry the triangle into one whose sides are not all real.

Now consider the plane dual of the projective theorem, B.

B′. *The points of intersection of the sides of a triangle with the conjugates in an arbitrary involution at a point L, of the lines joining the vertices to L, are collinear.*

If the involution at L is taken as the orthogonal involution we have the Euclidean theorem:

A′. *The three sides of a triangle are met in three collinear points by the perpendiculars from a fixed point to the lines joining this point to the opposite vertices.*

The second of the two processes which we are here emphasizing, namely the discovery of Euclidean theorems by specializing projective ones, is brilliantly illustrated in many of the textbooks on projective geometry. We may mention the following:

L. Cremona, Elements of Projective Geometry, Oxford, 1894.
T. Reye, Geometrie der Lage, Leipzig, 1907–1910.
R. Sturm, Die Lehre von den Geometrischen Verwandtschaften, Leipzig, 1909.
R. Böger, Geometrie der Lage, Leipzig, 1900.
H. Grassman, Projective Geometrie der Ebene, Leipzig, 1909.
J. J. Milne, Cross-Ratio Geometry, Cambridge, 1911.
J. L. S. Hatton, Principles of Projective Geometry, Cambridge, 1913.

The reader will find material for the illustration of the second process, namely the discovery of projective theorems by generalizing metric ones, in Euclid's Elements, and even more in such books as the following:

J. Casey, A Sequel to the First Six Books of the Elements of Euclid, Dublin, 1888.
C. Taylor, Ancient and Modern Geometry of Conics, Cambridge, 1881.
J. W. Russell, Elementary Treatise on Pure Geometry, Oxford, 1905.

The class of theorems which are here in question will be dealt with to some extent in the following chapter, and the methods available will be extended in Chap. VI by the study of inversions. But on account of the magnitude of the subject many important theorems will be found relegated to the exercises and many others omitted entirely. In nearly every such case, however, a good treatment can be found in one or another of the books on projective geometry referred to above.

The current textbooks do not often classify theorems on the basis of the geometries to which they belong (§ 34) and the assumptions which are necessary for their proof (§ 17). Some progress has been made on such a classification in the present book (cf. § 83 below), but more remains to be done.

Another criticism on current books is that they employ imaginary points in a rather shy and awkward manner. This is doubtless due to the fact that, previous to a logical treatment of the subject based on definite assumptions, the geometry of reals was regarded as having, somehow, a higher degree of validity than the complex geometry. The reader will often find it easy to abbreviate the proofs of theorems in the literature by a free use of imaginary elements (cf. § 78).

EXERCISES

1. Generalize projectively the following theorems:

(*a*) The medians of a triangle meet in a point.

(*b*) The perpendiculars at the mid-points of the sides of a triangle meet in a point.

(*c*) The diagonals of a parallelogram bisect each other.

2. Let A_1, B_1, C_1 be the points in which the lines joining the vertices A, B, C, respectively, of a triangle to the orthocenter, O, meet the opposite sides. The circle through A_1, B_1 and C_1 contains the mid-points of the pairs AB, BC, CA and of the pairs OA, OB, OC. This circle is called the *nine point* or *Feuerbach circle* of the triangle. Cf. Ex. 7, § 41.

3. A hyperbola whose asymptotes are orthogonal is said to be *equilateral* or *rectangular*. Every hyperbola passing through four points of intersection of two equilateral hyperbolas is an equilateral hyperbola.

4. All equilateral hyperbolas circumscribed to a triangle pass through its orthocenter.

5. The centers of the equilateral hyperbolas circumscribed to a triangle lie on the nine-point circle.

CHAPTER V *

ORDINAL AND METRIC PROPERTIES OF CONICS

74. One-dimensional projectivities. The general discussion of one-dimensional projectivities in Chap. VIII, Vol. I, has a great many points of contact with the ordinal and metric theorems of the last three chapters. For example, a rotation leaving a point O invariant transforms into itself any circle C^2 with O as a center. The transformation effected on the circle by the rotation is a one-dimensional projectivity having the point O as center and the line at infinity as axis. The defining property of the axis of the projectivity in this case is that if a pair of points AB of the circle be rotated into a pair $A'B'$ (i.e. if $\measuredangle AOB$ be congruent to $\measuredangle A'OB'$), then the line AB' is parallel to the line $A'B$, which is a well-known Euclidean theorem.

The proposition that any rotation is a product of two line reflections corresponds to the proposition that any projectivity is a product of two involutions. The point reflection with O as center is commutative with all the other rotations about O and hence effects on C^2 an involution which (§ 79, Vol. I) belongs to all the projectivities effected on C^2 by the rotations of this group. This involution is harmonic (§ 78, Vol. I) to the involution effected on C^2 by any orthogonal line reflection whose axis contains O, and hence all the involutions of the latter sort form a pencil. Thus all the theorems of § 79, Vol. I, can be specialized so as to yield theorems about the group of rotations with O as center.

There are many other applications of the theorems in Chap. VI, Vol. I, to affine and Euclidean geometry (a few of them are indicated in the exercises below), but the main application which we are to consider at present is to the theory of order relations. Let us first recall some of the ordinal theorems which have already been established, and interpret them on the conic sections. Extending the definition of § 4, we shall say:

* In the earlier chapters of this volume we have used only the first seven chapters of Vol. I. The present chapter may advantageously be read in connection with Chaps. VIII–X, Vol. I. Chap. IX is first used in § 77 and Chap. X in § 85.

DEFINITION. A projectivity of a one-dimensional form in any ordered space is *hyperbolic, parabolic,* or *elliptic* according as it has two, one, or no double points.

With regard to involutions, we have already established the following propositions (§ 21): *If an involution preserves sense, each pair separates every other pair. If an involution alters sense, no pair separates any other pair. An involution which does not alter sense is elliptic*; that is to say, *the pairs of a hyperbolic involution do not separate each other. The double points of a hyperbolic involution separate every pair of the involution.*

DEFINITION. If A, B, C, D are four distinct points of a conic, the point O of intersection of the lines AB and CD is called an *interior* point in case the pairs AB and CD separate each other* and an *exterior* point in case these pairs do not separate each other. The set of all interior points is called the *interior* or *inside* of the conic, and the set of all exterior points is called the *exterior* or *outside* of the conic.

The pairs AB and CD are conjugate in the involution with O as center. Hence, if these two pairs separate each other, this involution preserves sense and is such that any two of its pairs separate each other. Hence any two lines through O which meet the conic meet it in pairs of points which separate each other. That is to say, the definition of an interior point is independent of the particular choice of the points A, B, C, D. A like argument applies in case O is exterior. In case the involution with O as center has double points, the lines joining O to these points are tangent to the conic. Hence the next to the last of the propositions about involutions stated above implies that there are no tangents through an *interior* point. These results may be stated as follows:

THEOREM 1. *The points coplanar with a conic fall into three mutually exclusive classes: the conic itself, its interior and its exterior. Each interior point is the center of an involution on the conic which preserves sense, and each exterior point of one which alters sense. All points of a tangent, except the point of contact, are exterior points of the conic.*

* Cf. § 20, particularly the footnote.

Now let O be any interior point. If O' is any point conjugate to O with regard to the conic, there exists (cf. fig. 59) a complete quadrangle $ABCD$ whose vertices are points on the conic such that AB and CD meet in O and AD and CB meet in O'. But by Theorem 7,

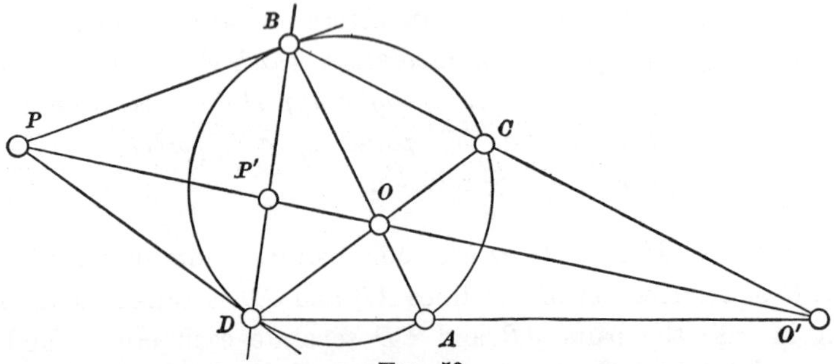

FIG. 59

Chap. II, if AB separates CD, then AD does not separate BC, and hence O' is an exterior point. Hence the polar line of any interior point consists entirely of exterior points. Hence

THEOREM 2. *All points conjugate to an interior point are exterior.*

Suppose, further, that the tangent to the conic at B meets the line OO' in a point P and the line BD meets OO' in a point P' (fig. 59). Then P and P' are conjugate points with regard to the conic. Moreover,

$$ABCD \overline{\wedge} OPO'P'.$$

Since A and C do not separate B and D, it follows that the pair OO' does not separate the pair PP'. That is,

THEOREM 3. *On a line containing an interior point of a conic the pairs of conjugate points with regard to the conic do not separate one another.*

By elementary propositions about poles and polar there follow at once:

COROLLARY 1. *The pole of a line which contains an interior point is an exterior point.*

COROLLARY 2. *The polar of an exterior point contains some interior points.*

In § 78, Vol. I, it was established that any projectivity is a product of two involutions one of which is hyperbolic. Since a hyperbolic involution is opposite, it follows that if the given projectivity is direct, it is a product of two opposite involutions; and if the given projectivity is opposite, it is a product of a direct and an opposite involution. But in the second case the direct involution is, by the argument just made, a product of two opposite involutions. Hence

THEOREM 4. *A direct projectivity is a product of two opposite involutions, and an opposite projectivity is a product of three opposite involutions. An opposite projectivity is also expressible as a product of a direct and an opposite involution.*

In the case of projectivities on a conic, the axis of the product of two involutions is the line joining their centers. Hence we have, as consequences of this theorem,

COROLLARY 1. *Any line in the plane of a conic contains points exterior to the conic.*

COROLLARY 2. *A projectivity whose center is an interior point, and whose axis therefore consists entirely of exterior points, is direct.*

In the fourth exercise, below, we need the following definition:

DEFINITION. The line perpendicular to a tangent to a conic and passing through its point of contact is called the *normal* to the conic at this point.

EXERCISES

1. What transformations of the Euclidean group effect projectivities on l_∞ to which the absolute involution belongs? How are these distinguished from the remaining similarity transformations by their relation to the circular points? What transformations of the Euclidean group are harmonic on l_∞ to the absolute involution?

2. Show that the measure of a line pair as defined in § 72 is the logarithm of the characteristic cross ratio of a certain projectivity on l_∞. Obtain an analogous formula for the measure of an angle in terms of the characteristic cross ratio of a projectivity on a circle.

3. Any noninvolutoric planar collineation which leaves invariant a conic and a line transforms the points of the line by a projectivity to which belongs the involution of conjugate points with regard to the conic.

4. If P is any fixed point of a conic and RQ a variable point pair such that $\measuredangle RPQ$ is a right angle, the lines RQ meet in a fixed point on the normal at P.

5. The lines joining homologous points in a noninvolutoric projectivity on a conic are the tangents of a second conic.

6. If P is any fixed point of a conic and RQ a variable pair of points such that $\measuredangle RPQ$ has constant measure, the lines RQ are the tangents to a second conic.

7. If a projectivity Γ on a line is a product of an involution having double points, A_1 and B_1, followed by another involution, and if $\Gamma^{-1}(A_1) = A_0 \neq A_1$ and $\Gamma(A_1) = A_2$, then A_1 and B_1 are harmonically conjugate with regard to A_0 and A_2 whenever $A_0 \neq A_2$; and $B_1 = A_0$ whenever $A_0 = A_2$.

8. If A_1 and B_1 are a pair of an involution $\mathbf{I}$ which is left invariant by a projectivity Γ, and if $\Gamma^{-1}(A_1) = A_0 \neq A_1$ and $\Gamma(A_1) = A_2 \neq A_0$, then A_0 and A_2 are harmonically conjugate with regard to A_1 and B_1.

9. Let A and A' be any pair of an involution $\mathbf{I}$. If $A \neq A'$, any projectivity Π which transforms $\mathbf{I}$ into itself and leaves A invariant is either the involution, with A and A' as double points, or the identity.

10. Generalize § 80, Vol. I, so as to apply to the group of translations and the equiaffine group, using the fact that the transformations in each of these groups are products of pairs of involutoric projectivities.

75. Interior and exterior of a conic.

THEOREM 5. *Any two points of a conic are the ends of two linear segments one consisting entirely of interior points and the other entirely of exterior points.*

Proof. Let the given points be denoted by A and B, let C and D be any two other points of the conic which separate A and B, and let σ and $\bar{\sigma}$ represent the segments $\overline{ACB}$ and $\overline{ADB}$ on the conic. By the definition of the order relations on the conic, the lines joining C to the points of $\bar{\sigma}$ meet the line AB in the points of a segment $\bar{\sigma}'$ whose ends are A and B, and these points satisfy the definition of interior points. In like manner the lines joining C to points of σ meet the line AB in a segment σ' which is complementary to $\bar{\sigma}'$ and consists entirely of exterior points.

In a real plane the following theorem is a consequence of what we have just proved, but in order to have the result for any ordered plane we give a proof which is entirely general.

THEOREM 6. *Any two interior points of a conic are the ends of a segment consisting entirely of interior points.*

Proof (fig. 60). Let A and C be two interior points. Let A_1 be any point of the conic not on the line AC. The lines A_1C and A_1A are not tangent to the conic, since (Theorem 1) the involutions at A and C are both elliptic. Let A_0 and B_2 respectively be the points, distinct from A_1, in which the lines A_1A and A_1C meet the conic. The two segments of the conic whose ends are A_0 and B_2 are projected by the lines through A_1 into the two segments of the line AC which have A and C as their ends. We shall prove that the segment σ of the line AC which is the projection of the segment complementary to $\overline{A_0A_1B_2}$ consists entirely of interior points.

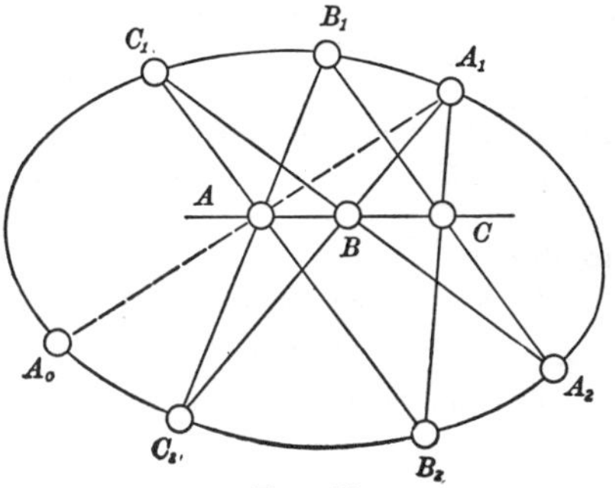

FIG. 60

Let B be any point of σ. The line A_1B then meets the conic in a point C_2 which is separated from A_1 by A_0 and B_2. Let B_2A meet the conic in C_1, let C_1B meet it in A_2, and let A_2C meet it in B_1, so that $A_1B_2C_1A_2B_1C_2$ form a Pascal hexagon whose pairs of opposite sides meet in A, B, C. Since A is an interior point, we have the order $\{C_2A_0B_1A_1\}$. Since B was chosen so that C_2 and A_1 are separated by B_2 and A_0, we have $\{B_2C_2A_0A_1\}$. From these there follows $\{B_2C_2A_0B_1A_1\}$. Transforming this by the involution at A we have $\{C_1B_1A_1C_2A_0\}$. Hence we have $\{B_2C_2A_0C_1B_1A_1\}$. Since the involution with center at C is elliptic, we have $\{B_2B_1A_1A_2\}$. Hence we have $\{B_2C_2A_0C_1B_1A_1A_2\}$. Hence C_2 and A_1 separate A_2 and C_1, and hence B is interior to the conic.

THEOREM 7. *Any two exterior points are ends of a segment consisting entirely of exterior points.*

Proof. Let the two exterior points be E_1 and E_2. If the line E_1E_2 is tangent, all points on it except the points of contact are exterior, since each of these points is the center of a hyperbolic involution on the conic. In this case the theorem is obvious. If the line E_1E_2 meets the conic in two points, the theorem reduces to Theorem 5. If the line E_1E_2 does not meet the conic, and both the segments with E_1 and E_2 as ends should contain interior points, I_1 and I_2 respectively, then neither of the segments whose ends are I_1 and I_2 could consist entirely of interior points, contrary to Theorem 6.

The theorems above are connected with the following algebraic considerations: Any involution can be written in the form

$$(1) \qquad x' = \frac{ax + b}{cx - a}.$$

If we regard a, b, c as a set of homogeneous coördinates in a projective plane, then for every involution (1) there is one and only one point (a, b, c); and inversely for every point (a, b, c) there is a unique involution (1), provided that the point does not satisfy the condition

$$(2) \qquad a^2 + bc = 0.$$

By § 18 the projectivities (1) for which

$$(3) \qquad a^2 + bc > 0$$

are opposite, and those for which

$$(4) \qquad a^2 + bc < 0$$

are direct.

The equation (2) *represents a conic section of which the points satisfying* (3) *are the exterior and those satisfying* (4) *are the interior.* This may be proved as follows:

The conic is given by the parametric representation (§ 82, Vol. I)

$$a : b : c = x : x^2 : -1,$$

and any involution on the conic is given by the transformation (1) of the parameter x. The center of the involution is the point of intersection of the lines containing pairs of the involution. The point $(0, 0, 1)$ of the conic is given by the value 0 of the parameter x and thus is transformed to the point given by the value $x = -b/a$, namely, the point $(-ab, b^2, -a^2)$. The point $(0, 1, 0)$ of the conic is given by $x = \infty$ and thus is transformed to the point given by $x = a/c$, namely, the point $(ac, a^2, -c^2)$. The point of intersection of the lines joining $(0, 0, 1)$ to $(-ab, b^2, -a^2)$ and $(0, 1, 0)$ to $(ac, a^2, -c^2)$ is manifestly $(-a, b, c)$. Hence $(-a, b, c)$ is the center of the involution (1), and therefore is interior to the conic if (4) is satisfied and the involution direct, and exterior to the conic if (3) is satisfied and the involution opposite.

EXERCISES

1. Parabolic projectivities are direct.

2. Two of the three vertices of any self-polar triangle of a conic are exterior points.

3. The center of a hyperbola is an exterior point.

4. The center of a circle is an interior point.

5. In a Euclidean plane all points interior to a circle and all points on it (except the point of contact of the tangent in question) lie entirely on one side of any one of its tangents.

6. If a segment A_1B_1 is contained in a segment A_2B_2, the circle the ends of whose diameter are A_1 and B_1 is composed of points interior to the circle the ends of whose diameter are A_2 and B_2.

7. In a Euclidean plane all points interior to an ellipse lie entirely on one side of any line consisting entirely of exterior points.

8. Any two pairs of conjugate diameters of an ellipse separate each other. Two pairs of conjugate diameters of a hyperbola never separate each other.

9. If O is the center of a conic K^2, the polar reciprocal of a conic C^2 with respect to K^2 will be an ellipse, parabola, or hyperbola according as O is interior to, on, or exterior to C^2.

10. Consider a conic C^2 in a planar net of rationality satisfying Assumption H. The points of the net exterior to the conic fall into two classes $[E]$ and $[F]$ such that two tangents to the conic can be drawn from any point E and no tangent can be drawn to the conic from any point F. On any line in which one E is conjugate to an F with regard to C^2, every E is conjugate to an F. On any line in which one E is conjugate to an E, every E is conjugate to an E and every F to an F. The interior points fall into two classes $[I]$ and $[J]$ such that the pairs of conjugate lines on a point I either both meet C^2 or both do not meet C^2, whereas one member of any pair of conjugate lines on a point J meets C^2 and the other member does not meet C^2.

11. Let the equation of a conic be $f(x_0, x_1, x_2) = 0$ and let the determinant of the coefficients of $f(x_0, x_1, x_2)$ be

$$A = \begin{vmatrix} a_{00} & a_{01} & a_{02} \\ a_{10} & a_{11} & a_{12} \\ a_{20} & a_{21} & a_{22} \end{vmatrix} \neq 0, \qquad a_{ij} = a_{ji}.$$

A point (x_0', x_1', x_2') is interior or exterior according as $A \cdot f(x_0', x_1', x_2')$ is greater or less than zero.

76. Double points of projectivities. The preceding theorems hold for any ordered space. On specializing to a real space we have the additional theorem that a projectivity which alters sense has two double points (§ 4). In the case of involutions this result combined with the theorem that a hyperbolic involution is always opposite gives

THEOREM 8. *The pairs of an elliptic involution always separate one another, and the pairs of a hyperbolic involution never separate one another.*

The last half of this theorem, combined with Theorem 3, gives the condition for the intersection of a line with a conic, a condition which has already been given in a more special form in § 64.

THEOREM 9. *On any line through an interior point of a conic the involution of conjugate points is hyperbolic, and the line meets the conic in the double points of this involution.*

By Cor. 2, Theorem 3, the polar of an exterior point is a line through an interior point. The lines joining the exterior point to the points of intersection of its polar with the conic are tangents. Hence

COROLLARY 1. *Through any exterior point there pass two tangents to a conic.*

COROLLARY 2. *Two involutions, one at least of which is elliptic, have one and only one common pair.*

Proof. The center of an elliptic involution represented on a conic is an interior point. The line joining this point to the center of any other involution meets the conic in two points which are pairs of both involutions. Since any pair of an involution is collinear with the center, the two points so constructed are the only pair common to the two involutions.

A special case of this corollary may be stated in the following form:

COROLLARY 3. *In a given one-dimensional form there is one and only one pair of elements which are conjugate with respect to a given elliptic involution and harmonically separated by a given pair of elements.*

Since a hyperbolic involution is determined by its double points, it is evident that any two hyperbolic involutions are equivalent under the group of all projectivities of a one-dimensional form. The corresponding theorem for elliptic involutions is best seen by representing the involutions on a conic. The two centers I_1, I_2 are interior points, and the line joining them meets the conic in two points C_1, C_2 which do not separate them (Theorem 5). Let O_1 and O_2 be the double points (Theorem 8) of the involution in which I_1I_2 and C_1C_2 are pairs. An involution with either of the points O_1 or O_2 as center will evidently transform the one with I_1 as center into the one with I_2 as center. Hence

COROLLARY 4. *Any two elliptic involutions in the same real one-dimensional form are conjugate under the projective group of that form.*

EXERCISES

1. All involutions which are harmonic to (i.e. commutative with and distinct from) an elliptic involution are hyperbolic.

2. If two points A, B of a line separate each point $P (P \neq A, P \neq B)$ of the line from its conjugate point in a given elliptic involution, A and B are conjugate in this involution.

3. A hyperbolic projectivity is opposite or direct according as a pair of homologous points does or does not separate the double points.

4. Elliptic projectivities are direct.

5. The center of an ellipse is an interior point.

6. The involution determined on the line at infinity of a Euclidean plane by an ellipse is elliptic, by a hyperbola, hyperbolic.

7. Any two ellipses are conjugate under the affine group.*

8. An involution in a flat pencil is either such that every pair of conjugate lines is orthogonal or there is one and only one orthogonal pair of conjugate lines.

9. A conic having two pairs of perpendicular conjugate diameters is a circle.

10. If A_1 and A_2 are the real limiting points of a pencil of circles, each circle of the pencil either contains A_1 and is on the opposite side of the radical axis from A_2, or contains A_2 and is on the opposite side of the radical axis from A_1.

11. Of two circles of a pencil, both containing the same limiting point, one is entirely interior to the other.

12. For any angle, $\measuredangle ABC$, there is one and only one pair l, l' of orthogonal lines through B which separate the lines BA and BC harmonically. One line, l, of the pair contains points P interior to $\measuredangle ABC$, and $\measuredangle ABP$ is congruent to $\measuredangle PBC$. The line l is called the *interior bisector*, and the line l' the *exterior bisector*, of the angle $\measuredangle ABC$.

13. The asymptotes of an equilateral hyperbola bisect any pair of conjugate diameters.

14. The bisectors of the angles of a triangle ABC meet in four points, one in each of the four regions determined by ABC according to § 26. These four points are the centers of four circles inscribed in ABC and are the vertices of a complete quadrilateral of which ABC is the diagonal triangle. The mid-point of the pair BC is the mid-point of the points of contact of either pair of inscribed circles whose centers are collinear with A.

15. Let V and V' be the vanishing points (§ 43) of a projectivity on a line, the notation being so assigned that the point at infinity is transformed to V'. There exist two points A, B which are transformed to two points A', B' such that

$$AV = VB = A'V' = V'B'.$$

* Cf. § 37, Exs. 14 and 15.

77. Ruler-and-compass constructions. The discussion in Chap. IX, Vol. I, reduces any quadratic problem to the problem of finding the points of intersection of an arbitrary line with a fixed conic. According to Theorems 5 and 9 the necessary and sufficient condition that a line coplanar with a conic meet it in two points is that the line pass through an interior point of the conic. Hence this condition will serve to determine the solvability of any problem of the second degree in a real space. Thus the discussion of linear and quadratic constructions, under the projective meaning of these terms, may be regarded as complete.

When we adopt the Euclidean point of view, the fixed conic may be taken as a circle; and therefore every problem of the second degree is reduced to the problem of determining the points of intersection of an arbitrary line with a fixed circle (cf. § 86, Vol. I).

The constructions of elementary Euclidean geometry which are known as ruler-and-compass constructions involve the determination of the points of intersection (whenever existent) of two arbitrary lines, or of an arbitrary line with an arbitrary circle, or of two arbitrary circles. The last of these problems has been shown in § 65 to be reducible to the first and second. Hence any ruler-and-compass construction may be reduced to the problem of finding the intersection of an arbitrary line with a fixed circle.

On account of the special character of the line at infinity, there is not a perfect correspondence between the linear constructions of projective geometry and the Euclidean constructions by means of a ruler. The operations involved in the linear constructions of projective geometry are

(*a*) to join two points by a (projective) line;
(*b*) to take the point of intersection of any two lines.

These are evidently equivalent to the following Euclidean operations:

(1) to join two ordinary points by a line;
(2) to take the point of intersection of two nonparallel lines;
(3′) to draw a line through a given point parallel to a given line.

The first of these operations corresponds to the proposition that two points are on a unique line, the second to the proposition that two nonparallel lines determine a unique point. These operations may be thought of as carried out with a straightedge or ruler whose length is not limited.

The operation (3′) can be effected by means of (1) and (2), together with the following operation:

(3) to find on any ray through a point A, a point C such that the point pair AC is congruent to a preassigned point pair AB.*

For let A be the given point and let BC be the given line. Let O be a point on the line AB in the order $\{ABO\}$ such that BA is congruent to BO. Let $\bar{A}$ be the point of the line OC in the order $OC\bar{A}$ such that CO is congruent to $C\bar{A}$. Then $A\bar{A}$ is evidently parallel to BC.

Thus (1), (2), and (3) serve as a basis for all linear operations in the projective sense. They obviously yield also a certain class of quadratic constructions; but they do not suffice for all quadratic constructions. The latter may be provided for, as explained above, by adjoining the operation of taking the point of intersection with a fixed circle of an arbitrary line through an arbitrary interior point.

For the proof that (3′) is not a consequence of (1) and (2), and that (1), (2), (3) do not provide for all quadratic constructions, the reader is referred to Hilbert, Grundlagen der Geometrie, Chap. VII (4th edition, 1913).

EXERCISES

1. Given three collinear points A, B, C such that AB is congruent to BC, show how to construct a parallel to the line AB through an arbitrary point P by means of the operations (1) and (2) alone.

2. Given two parallel lines, show how to find the mid-point of any pair of points on either of the lines by means of (1) and (2) alone.

3. Given a parallelogram and a point P and a line l in its plane. Through P draw a line parallel to l, making use of the ruler only.

* It is important to notice that the pairs AB and AC have the point A in common. Thus (3) provides merely for drawing a circle through a given point and with a given other point as center. The drawing instrument to which this corresponds is a pair of compasses which snaps together when lifted from the paper, so that it cannot be used to transfer a point pair AB to a point pair $A'B'$ unless $A = A'$. This will be understood by anyone reading the second proposition in Euclid's Elements, which shows how to lay off a point pair congruent to a given point pair on a given ray. The operation (3) may be replaced by the operation of finding on any ray AB a point C such that the point pair AC is congruent to a fixed point pair OP. The instrument for this operation may be thought of as a measuring rod of fixed length (say unit length) without subdivisions. (Cf. the reference to Hilbert, below.)

4. Given a point pair AC and its mid-point B, using the ruler alone, construct the point pair AD such that

$$\frac{AC}{AD} = n.$$

5. Given four collinear points A, A', B, B', construct the fixed point of the parabolic projectivity carrying A to A' and B to B'.

6. Given a projectivity on a line, find a pair of corresponding points A and A' such that a given point M is the mid-point of the segment AA'.

7. Inscribe in a given triangle a rectangle of given area.

8. Given four tangents of a parabola, construct a tangent parallel to a given line.

9. Given three points of a hyperbola and a line parallel to each asymptote, find the point of intersection of the hyperbola with a line parallel to one of the asymptotes.

10. Construct by ruler and compass any number of tangents to a conic given by five of its points; also any number of points of a conic given by five of its tangents.

11. Construct any number of points of a parabola through four given points.

12. Construct any number of points of a parabola touching three given lines and passing through a given point.

13. Through a given point construct an orthogonal pair of lines conjugate with regard to a conic. (If the point is exterior to the conic, these lines are the bisectors of the angles formed by the tangents to the conic from this point.)

78. Conjugate imaginary elements. It has been shown in § 6 that a real projective space S can be regarded as immersed in a complex projective space S′ in such a way that every line of S is a subset of a unique line of S′. Certain additional definitions and conventions have been introduced in § 70. But in both these places little use was made of the properties of imaginary elements beyond their existence and the fact that S′ satisfies Assumptions A, E, P. We shall now prove some of the most elementary theorems about the relation between elements of S and S′.

DEFINITION. Two imaginary points, lines, or planes are said to be *conjugate relative to a real one-dimensional form* of the first or second degree if and only if they are the double elements of an involution in the real form.

As an example consider a real conic C^2 and a line l exterior to it. The conic and the line have in common the double points of an elliptic involution on l. But these points are also the double points of the involution on C^2 whose axis is l. Hence the points common to C^2 and l are conjugate imaginaries both with respect to C^2 and to l. Since any one-dimensional form of the first or second degree whose elements are points is a line or a point conic, and since the double points of any involution on a conic are the intersections of the axis of the involution with the conic, we have

THEOREM 10. *Any two conjugate imaginary points are on a real line.*

By duality we have that any two conjugate imaginary planes are on a real line.

Two conjugate imaginary lines are by definition on a real point, line conic, cone of lines, or regulus. If they are on a real line conic, the plane dual of the argument above shows that they are on a real point. By dualizing in space we obtain the same result for conjugate imaginary lines of a cone of lines. Hence we have

THEOREM 11. *Any two conjugate imaginary coplanar lines are on a real point and any two conjugate imaginary concurrent lines are on a real plane.*

Conjugate imaginary lines on a regulus will be considered in a later chapter.

THEOREM 12. *The lines joining a real point to two conjugate imaginary points not collinear with it are conjugate imaginary lines.*

Proof. The conjugate imaginary points are double points of an elliptic involution on a real line. From any point not on this line this involution is projected into an involution of lines whose double lines are the projections of the given points.

THEOREM 13. *If A_1A_2 and B_1B_2 are two pairs of conjugate imaginary points on different lines, the lines A_1B_1 and A_2B_2 meet in a real point and are conjugate imaginary lines.*

Proof. By hypothesis the lines A_1A_2 and B_1B_2 are real and hence they meet in a real point C. Let B be the conjugate of C in the elliptic involution with A_1 and A_2 as double points. By Corollary 3, Theorem 9, there are two real points P and Q which are paired in this involution and separate B and C harmonically. Let A be the conjugate of C in the elliptic involution with B_1 and B_2 as double points, and let R and S be the two real points which are paired in this involution and separate A and C harmonically. Since any two harmonic sets are projective,

$$CBPQ \underset{\wedge}{=} CARS \quad \text{and} \quad CBPQ \underset{\wedge}{=} CASR.$$

The centers of these two perspectivities are two real points C_1 and C_2, and since each perspectivity transforms two pairs of the elliptic involution on the line A_1A_2 into two pairs of the elliptic involution on the line B_1B_2, it transforms A_1 and A_2 to B_1 and B_2. Hence one of the points C_1 and C_2 is the intersection of the lines A_1B_1 and A_2B_2 and the other that of the lines A_1B_2 and A_2B_1. By Theorem 12 each of these pairs of lines is a pair of conjugate imaginaries.

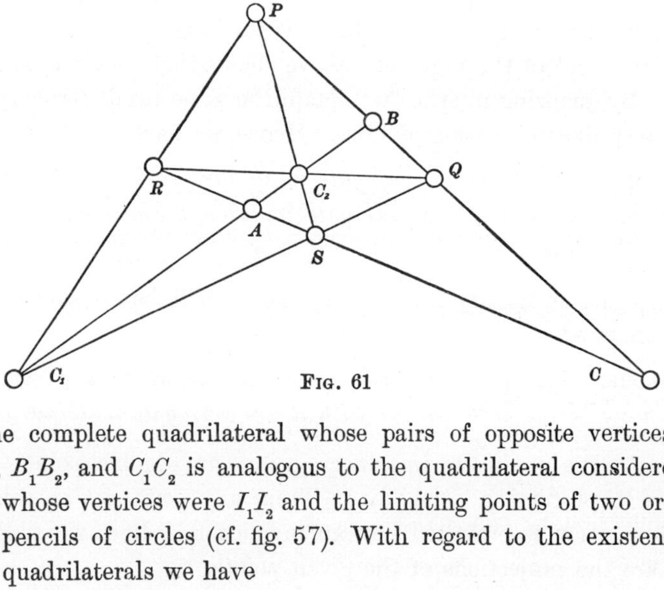

FIG. 61

The complete quadrilateral whose pairs of opposite vertices are A_1A_2, B_1B_2, and C_1C_2 is analogous to the quadrilateral considered in § 71 whose vertices were I_1I_2 and the limiting points of two orthogonal pencils of circles (cf. fig. 57). With regard to the existence of such quadrilaterals we have

THEOREM 14. *Let A_1A_2, B_1B_2, C_1C_2 be the pairs of opposite vertices of a complete quadrilateral. If A_1A_2 and B_1B_2 are pairs of conjugate imaginary points, then C_1 and C_2 are real and the diagonal triangle of the complete quadrilateral is real. If A_1 and A_2 are real and B_1 and B_2 are conjugate imaginaries, then C_1 and C_2 are conjugate imaginaries and the diagonal triangle is real.*

Proof. In the first case C_1 and C_2 are determined as in the proof of the last theorem and hence are real. The diagonal triangle has for its sides the three real lines A_1A_2, B_1B_2, C_1C_2.

In the second case let a be the line through A_2 which is harmonically conjugate to A_2A_1 with respect to the pair of lines A_2B_1 and A_2B_2. Since the latter two lines are conjugate imaginaries and A_2A_1 is real, a is real. The harmonic homology with A_1 as center and a as axis transforms B_1 and B_2 to C_1 and C_2. Hence C_1 and C_2 are conjugate imaginaries and the line C_1C_2 is real.

Relatively to a real frame of reference a real involution is represented by a bilinear equation with real coefficients (§ 58, Vol. I), and its double points appear as the roots of a quadratic equation with real coefficients. Hence the coördinates of a pair of conjugate imaginary points are expressible in the form

$$(x_0 + iy_0,\ x_1 + iy_1,\ x_2 + iy_2,\ x_3 + iy_3)$$

and

$$(x_0 - iy_0,\ x_1 - iy_1,\ x_2 - iy_2,\ x_3 - iy_3),$$

where $x_0, x_1, x_2, x_3, y_0, y_1, y_2, y_3$ are real. Like remarks can be made with regard to the coördinates of a plane or a line, and Theorems 10–14 can easily be proved analytically on this basis. The following theorem appears to be easier to prove analytically than synthetically:

THEOREM 15. *A complex line on a real plane contains at least one real point.*

Proof. Let the equation of the line be

$$u_0x_0 + u_1x_1 + u_2x_2 = 0.$$

This may be expressed in the form

$$(u_0' + iu_0'')\,x_0 + (u_1' + iu_1'')\,x_1 + (u_2' + iu_2'')\,x_2 = 0,$$

where u_0', u_0'', etc. are real. This equation is equivalent, if x_0, x_1, x_2 are required to be real, to

$$u_0'x_0 + u_1'x_1 + u_2'x_2 = 0,$$
$$u_0''x_0 + u_1''x_1 + u_2''x_2 = 0,$$

two equations which are satisfied by at least one real point.

EXERCISES

1. A conic section through three real and two conjugate imaginary points is real.

2. A pair of conjugate imaginary points cannot be harmonically conjugate with regard to another pair of conjugate imaginary points.

3. An imaginary point is on one and only one real line and has one and only one conjugate imaginary point.

79. Projective, affine, and Euclidean classification of conics. Let us regard a real plane π as immersed in a complex plane π', and consider all conics in π' with respect to which the polar of a real point is always a real line.*

Throughout the rest of this chapter the word "conic" shall be used in this sense. The involution of conjugate points with regard to such a conic is one in which real points are paired with real points. Hence, if a conic contains one real point, every real nontangent line through this point contains another point of the conic, and the conic is real. The conics under consideration therefore fall into two classes, the real conics† and those containing no real point.

By § 76, Vol. I, any two real conics are equivalent under the group of projective collineations. The same proposition holds also for any two conics of the other class, as we shall now prove. Let two such conics be denoted by C_1^2 and C_2^2. On an arbitrary real line l they each determine an elliptic involution of conjugate points. By Cor. 4, Theorem 9, there is a projectivity of the line l carrying the involution determined by C_2^2 into that determined by C_1^2. Any projectivity of the real plane which effects this transformation on l will carry C_2^2 into a conic C_3^2 which has the two conjugate imaginary points A_1, A_2 on l in common with C_1^2. A collineation leaving l invariant will now carry the pole of l with regard to C_3^2 to the pole of l with regard to C_1^2; and therefore carries C_3^2 to a conic C_4^2 which has A_1, A_2 and the tangents at these points in common with C_1^2. Let L be the pole of l with regard to C_1^2 and L_1 be any real point of l. By Cor. 3, Theorem 9, there is a pair of points MM_1 which are conjugate with respect to C_1^2 and harmonically separate L and L_1 and also a pair $M'M_1'$ conjugate with respect to C_4^2 and harmonically separating L and L_1. The homology with l as axis, L as center, and carrying M' to M carries C_4^2 to C_1^2. Hence we have

THEOREM 16. *Any two real conics or any two imaginary conics with real polar systems are conjugate under the group of real projective collineations.*

* In § 85 this condition is seen to be equivalent to the condition that the equation of the conic relative to a frame of reference in π shall be expressible with real coefficients. For the present discussion, however, we do not need the general theory of correlation which is used in § 85.

† According to some usage any complex locus which has a real equation is called real. Cf. Pascal's Repertorium der Höheren Mathematik, Vol. II (1910), Chap. XIII (Berzolari). According to this definition both of the above classes of conics would be called real.

If the line l be taken as the line at infinity of a Euclidean plane the argument above shows that any two imaginary conics are also conjugate under the affine group. Since these conics do not meet any real line in real points, they are analogous to ellipses no matter how the line at infinity is chosen. Hence we make the definition:

DEFINITION. An imaginary conic with a real polar system is called an *imaginary ellipse.*

The results just established, together with those stated in Ex. 7, § 76, and Exs. 14 and 15, § 37, may be summarized as follows:

THEOREM 17. *Under the affine group the conics with real polar systems fall into four classes, parabolas, hyperbolas, real ellipses, imaginary ellipses. Any two conics of the same class are equivalent.*

Under the Euclidean group conics must be characterized by their relations to the circular points I_1, I_2. Since a real conic which does not meet l_∞ in real points meets it in conjugate imaginary points, any real conic through I_1 also contains I_2 and is therefore a circle. For the same reason the imaginary conic determined by an elliptic polar system must contain I_2 if it contains I_1.

DEFINITION. An imaginary ellipse with respect to which the pairs of conjugate points on l_∞ are pairs of the absolute involution is called an *imaginary circle.*

THEOREM 18. *Any two real circles or any two imaginary circles are similar.*

Proof. Let the centers, necessarily real, of two circles C^2 and K^2 be O_1 and O_2 respectively. The center O_1 may be transformed to O_2 by a translation T_1. This carries C^2 to a circle C_1^2. Any real line l through O_2 meets C_1^2 in two points C_1 and C_2 and K^2 in two points K_1 and K_2. Since each of these pairs is harmonically conjugate with respect to O_2 and the point at infinity O_∞ of l, the homology T_2 with O_2 as center and l_∞ as axis which carries C_1 to K_1 also carries C_2 to K_2. This homology evidently carries all real points to real points if C_1, C_2, K_1, K_2 are real. If C_1C_2 and K_1K_2 are pairs of conjugate imaginary points, consider (§ 77) the real pair of points PP' harmonically conjugate with regard to C_1C_2 and OO_∞ and the real pair QQ' harmonically conjugate with regard to K_1K_2 and OO_∞. The homology T_2 must carry P and P' to Q and Q' and therefore carries all real points to real points in this case.

Now the conic C_1^2 is fully determined by its points I_1, I_2, C_1, C_2 and its center O_2 and K^2 is fully determined by I_1, I_2, K_1, K_2 and O_2. Hence T_2 carries C_1^2 to K^2. The product T_2T_1 carries C^2 to K^2.

THEOREM 19. *Any two parabolas are similar.*

Proof. Let C^2 and K^2 be two parabolas and let C_∞ and K_∞ be their points of contact with l_∞. Let T_1 be any rotation carrying C_∞ to K_∞ and let $T_1(C^2) = C_1^2$. Let $\overline{K}_\infty$ be the conjugate of K_∞ in the absolute involution and let c be the ordinary line through $\overline{K}_\infty$ tangent to C_1^2 and C its point of contact; also let k be the ordinary line through $\overline{K}_\infty$ tangent to K^2, and K its point of contact. The translation T_2

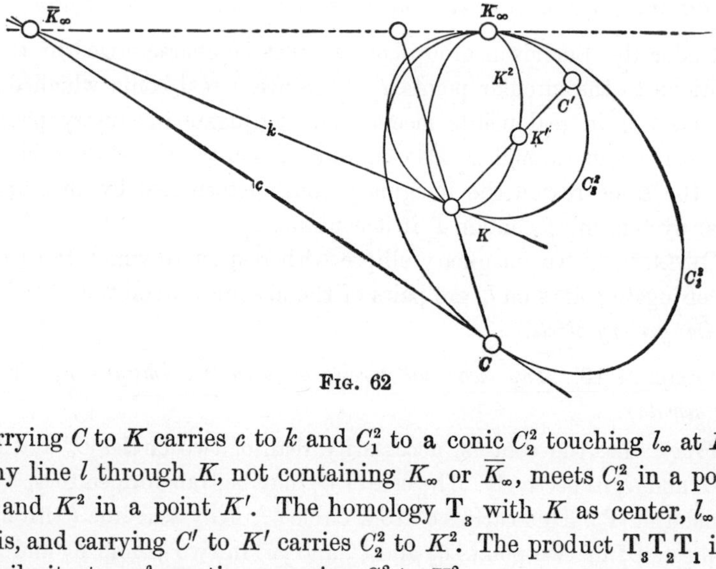

FIG. 62

carrying C to K carries c to k and C_1^2 to a conic C_2^2 touching l_∞ at K_∞. Any line l through K, not containing K_∞ or $\overline{K}_\infty$, meets C_2^2 in a point C' and K^2 in a point K'. The homology T_3 with K as center, l_∞ as axis, and carrying C' to K' carries C_2^2 to K^2. The product $T_3T_2T_1$ is a similarity transformation carrying C^2 to K^2.

No theorem analogous to the last two holds for ellipses and hyperbolas. Suppose an ellipse or a hyperbola C^2 meets l_∞ in C_1 and C_2 and another ellipse or hyperbola K^2 meets it in K_1 and K_2. In case a similarity transformation carries C_1 and C_2 into K_1 and K_2,

$$\text{(5)} \qquad R(I_1I_2, C_1C_2) = R(I_1I_2, K_1K_2).$$

Conversely, if C^2 and K^2 satisfy the condition (5) there evidently exists a rotation carrying C_1 and C_2 to K_1 and K_2. This rotation carries C^2 to a conic C_1^2 which passes through K_1 and K_2. By an argument analogous to the proof of Theorem 18 it can be shown that if C_1^2 and K^2 are both real ellipses, or both imaginary ellipses, or both hyperbolas, there is a similarity transformation carrying C_1^2 to K^2. Hence

THEOREM 20. *Two real ellipses or two imaginary ellipses or two hyperbolas which meet l_∞ in pairs of points C_1C_2 and K_1K_2 are similar if and only if* $R(I_1I_2, C_1C_2) = R(I_1I_2, K_1K_2)$.

EXERCISE

A hyperbola for which $R(I_1I_2, K_1K_2) = -1$ is rectangular (Ex. 3, § 73).

80. Foci of the ellipse and hyperbola. Let C^2 be any hyperbola or real or imaginary ellipse, and let l_1, l_2 be the tangents to C^2 through I_1 and l_3, l_4 the tangents to C^2 through I_2. The circular points I_1, I_2 are one pair of opposite vertices of the complete quadrilateral $l_1l_2l_3l_4$. Let the other two pairs of opposite vertices be F_1F_2 and $F_1'F_2'$ respectively (fig. 63), let a be the line F_1F_2, b the line $F_1'F_2'$, and O the point of intersection of a and b. Also let A_∞ and B_∞ be the points at infinity of the lines a and b respectively. The triangle $OA_\infty B_\infty$ is self-polar with respect to C^2. Hence O is the center of C^2 and is therefore real.

Let X be any real point not on l_1, l_2, l_3, l_4 or C^2. By the dual of the Desargues theorem on conics (§ 46, Vol. I) the tangents to C^2 through X are paired in the same involution with XI_1, XI_2 and XF_1, XF_2 and XF_1', XF_2'. The double lines x_1, x_2 of this involution are harmonically conjugate with regard to XI_1, XI_2 and to the tangents to C^2. Hence they are paired both in the involution of orthogonal lines at X and the involution of lines conjugate with respect to C^2 at X. Hence by Cor. 2, Theorem 9, x_1 and x_2 are real, and are the unique pair of orthogonal lines on X which are conjugate with regard to C^2.

In particular, if $X = O$ it follows that a and b are real and are the only pair of orthogonal and conjugate diameters of C^2. Hence A_∞ and B_∞ are also real. If X is not on a, b, or l_∞, the lines x_1 and x_2 meet a in a pair of real points X_1, X_2 distinct from A_∞ and O. Since F_1 and F_2 are harmonically conjugate with respect to the real pairs X_1X_2 and $A_\infty O$, they are either real or conjugate imaginaries. But since I_1 and I_2 are conjugate imaginaries, by Theorem 14 if one of the pairs F_1F_2 and $F_1'F_2'$ is a pair of real points, the other is a pair of conjugate imaginaries, and conversely. Hence the notation may be so assigned that F_1 and F_2 are real and F_1' and F_2' are conjugate imaginaries.

Let A_1 and A_2 be the points in which a meets C^2 and B_1 and B_2 the points in which b meets C^2. By construction neither of the lines a and b can be tangent to C^2 so that each of the pairs A_1A_2 and B_1B_2 is either real or a pair of conjugate imaginaries.

In case C^2 is an imaginary ellipse, both A_1A_2 and B_1B_2 are necessarily pairs of conjugate imaginaries. In case C^2 is a real ellipse, the line l_∞ does not meet it in any real point, and hence O, the pole of l_∞, is an interior point. Hence both a and b meet C^2 in real points. Hence if C^2 is an ellipse, A_1, A_2, B_1, B_2 are all real. Whether C^2 is an ellipse or a hyperbola, the tangents to C^2 from F_1 are conjugate imaginary lines since they join the real point F_1 to the conjugate

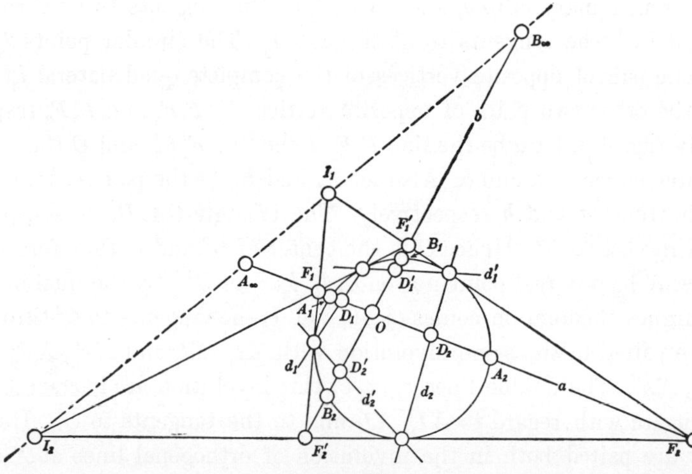

FIG. 63

imaginary points I_1 and I_2. Hence F_1 is interior to C^2, as is also F_2 by a like argument. Hence the line F_1F_2 meets C^2 in real points. Hence if C^2 is a hyperbola, A_1 and A_2 are real. But if C^2 is a hyperbola, O is an exterior point, and hence A_∞, which is harmonically separated from O by A_1 and A_2, must be an interior point. Hence b, the pole of A_∞, does not meet C^2 in real points, and consequently B_1 and B_2 are conjugate imaginaries.

Let the polars of F_1, F_2, F_1', F_2' relative to C^2 be denoted by d_1, d_2, d_1', d_2' respectively. Then d_1 and d_2 being the polars of real points are real; and since their point of intersection is polar to a, it is B_∞, and hence they are parallel to b. In like manner d_1' and d_2' pass through A_∞ and are conjugate imaginaries.

Definition. The lines a and b defined above are called the *axes* of the conic C^2, a being called the *major*, or *principal*, axis and b the *minor*, or *secondary*, axis. Each of the points F_1, F_2, F_1', F_2' is called a *focus*, and each of the points A_1, A_2, B_1, B_2 a *vertex*, of the conic C^2. Each of the lines d_1, d_2, d_1', d_2' is called a *directrix* of C^2.

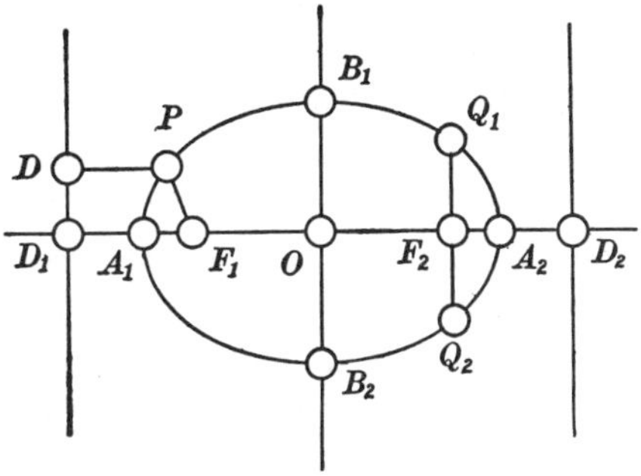

Fig. 64

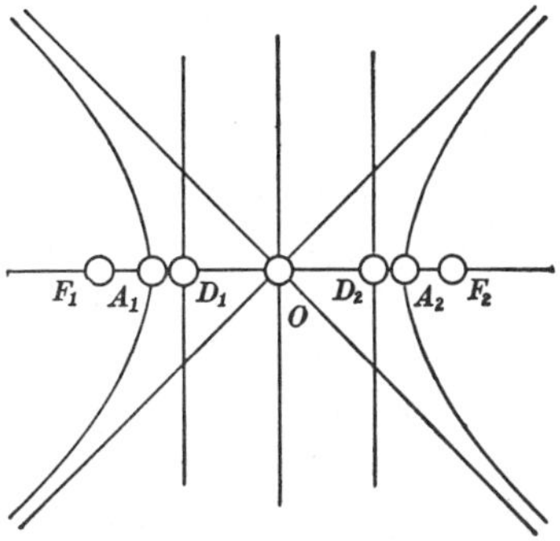

Fig. 65

In the course of the discussion of the complete quadrilateral $l_1l_2l_3l_4$ we have established the following propositions:

Theorem 21. *If C^2 is a hyperbola or a real or imaginary ellipse which is not a circle, its axes are the unique pair of conjugate diameters which are mutually perpendicular. Two of the foci and two of the directrices are real. The real foci lie on the major axis and the real directrices are perpendicular to it. The other two foci are conjugate imaginaries and lie on the minor axis. If C^2 is real, the real foci are interior points and the real directrices are exterior lines. If C^2 is a real ellipse, all four of the vertices are real; if C^2 is a hyperbola, the two vertices on the major axis are real and those on the minor axis are conjugate imaginaries.*

The two tangents to C^2 through F_1 pass also through I_1 and I_2. Pairs of conjugate lines at F_1 are separated harmonically by these two tangents and hence meet l_∞ in pairs of the involution whose double points are I_1 and I_2. If we limit attention to real elements, this may be expressed by saying that the pairs of conjugate lines with respect to C^2 which pass through a focus are orthogonal. Conversely, if the pairs of orthogonal lines at any point P are conjugate with respect to C^2, the double lines of the involution of orthogonal lines at

P would have to coincide with the double lines of the involution of conjugate lines, and hence P would be a focus. Hence

THEOREM 22. *The real foci of a hyperbola or a real or imaginary ellipse are the unique pair of real points at which all pairs of conjugate lines are orthogonal.*

The set of all conics tangent to the four minimal lines l_1, l_2, l_3, l_4 form a range (§ 47, Vol. I). Hence the pairs of tangents to these conics through any point P not on the sides of the diagonal triangle $OA_\infty B_\infty$ form an involution among the pairs of which are the pairs of lines PI_1, PI_2; PF_1, PF_2; and PF_1', PF_2'. Now if P is on C^2, there is only one tangent to C^2 at P, and this tangent is therefore a double line of the involution. This and the other double line have to be harmonically conjugate with respect to PI_1 and PI_2; that is, if C^2 and P are real, the two double lines have to be orthogonal. These double lines must be harmonically conjugate also with respect to PF_1 and PF_2. Thus we have a result which may be expressed as follows (cf. Ex. 12, § 76):

THEOREM 23. *The tangent and the normal to a real ellipse or hyperbola at any real point are the bisectors of the pair of lines joining this point to the real foci.*

In the proof of this proposition we have excepted the vertices of the conic, but the validity of the proposition for these points is self-evident. Another proposition which follows directly from the discussion above is the following, in which we make use of the fact that the pair of real foci determines the pair of imaginary ones, and vice versa.

THEOREM 24. DEFINITION. *The system of all conics having two real or two imaginary foci in common is a range of conics of Type I. The two conics of the set which pass through any real point have orthogonal tangents at this point. Such a range of conics is called a system of* confocal conics *or of* confocals.

The construction for the foci which has been considered in this section, when applied to a circle, reduces to a very simple one. The tangents to the circle at I_1 and I_2 meet in the center of the circle. The center of the circle is therefore sometimes referred to as the *focus* and the line at infinity as the *directrix.*

The term "focus" is derived from the property stated in Theorem 23, in consequence of which, if the conic be regarded as a reflecting surface, all rays of light diverging from one focus will be reflected back to the other focus.

In the rest of the chapter the foci, center, directrices, and axes of an ellipse or a hyperbola will be denoted by the same letters as in this section. The notation has been assigned so that for an ellipse the points are in the order

$$\{D_1A_1F_1OF_2A_2D_2\},$$

and for the hyperbola in the order

$$\{F_1A_1D_1OD_2A_2F_2\},$$

where D_1 and D_2 denote the points of intersection of the principal axis with the directrices d_1 and d_2 respectively.

81. Focus and axis of a parabola. Let C^2 be any parabola. Since it is tangent to l_∞, there are two ordinary tangents to it through I_1 and I_2 respectively; let these be denoted by l_1 and l_2 respectively. Let their point of intersection be denoted by F, their points of contact with C^2 by L_1 and L_2 respectively, and the line L_1L_2 by d. Also let the point of contact of C^2 with l_∞ be denoted by A_∞, the line $A_\infty F$ by a, and the point, other than A_∞, in which a meets C^2, by A.

DEFINITION. The point F is called the *focus*, the line d the *directrix*, the line a the *axis*, the point A the *vertex*, of the parabola C^2.

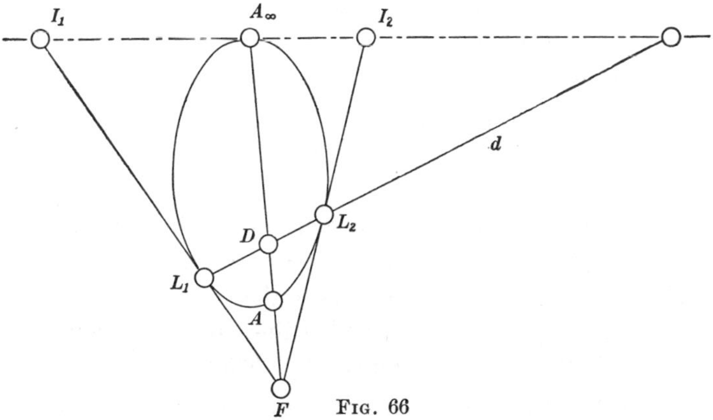

FIG. 66

That the focus, directrix, etc. of a parabola are real may be proved as follows: The transformation from pole to polar with regard to C^2 transforms the absolute involution to an involution of the lines through A_∞ and transforms I_1 and I_2 into $A_\infty L_1$ and $A_\infty L_2$ respectively. The involution in the lines at A_∞ is perspective with an involution among the points of C^2 which has L_1 and L_2 as double points. Hence L_1 and L_2 are conjugate imaginary points. Hence by Theorem 10 the line d is real. Hence its pole, F, is real. Hence the line a joining F to A_∞ is real, and also the point A.

Since the two tangents to C^2 through F pass through I_1 and I_2, any two conjugate lines through F are perpendicular. Conversely, if the pairs of conjugate lines at any point are orthogonal, the tangents through this point must contain I_1 and I_2 respectively. Hence F is the only such point. Since the tangents through F are imaginary, F is interior to C^2, and hence all real points on d are exterior.

The tangent at A is parallel to d, and hence by the construction of d perpendicular to a. Since the tangent at any other ordinary point of C^2 is not parallel to d, it follows that the line a is the only diameter of C^2 which is perpendicular to its conjugate lines. These and other obvious consequences of the definition may be summarized as follows:

THEOREM 25. *The axis of a parabola is real and is the only diameter perpendicular to all its conjugate lines. The focus of a parabola is real and lies on the axis. The focus is the unique point at which all pairs of conjugate lines are orthogonal. It is interior to the parabola. The directrix is real, is the polar of the focus, and is perpendicular to the axis. All real points of the directrix are exterior to the parabola. The vertex is real and is the mid-point of the focus and the point in which the directrix meets the axis.*

The system of all conics tangent to l_1 and l_2 and to l_∞ at A_∞ forms a range of Type II (§ 47, Vol. I) which consists of all parabolas having F as focus and a as axis. The pairs of tangents to these conics through any real point P of the plane are by the dual of Theorem 20, Chap. V, Vol. I, the pairs of an involution in which PI_1 is paired with PI_2 and PF with PA_∞. The tangents to the two conics of the range which pass through P are the double lines of this involution and hence separate PI_1 and PI_2 harmonically. Thus we have

THEOREM 26. *The parabolas with a fixed focus and axis form a range of Type II. The two parabolas of the range which pass through a given point have orthogonal tangents at this point.*

The tangent to either parabola through P is therefore normal to the other. Since these two lines separate PF and PA_∞ harmonically, we have

THEOREM 27. *The tangent and the normal to a parabola at any point are the bisectors of the pair of lines through this point of which one passes through the focus and the other is a diameter.*

EXERCISES

1. If P is any point of an ellipse, the normal at P is the interior bisector of $\angle F_1PF_2$. If P is any point of a hyperbola, the tangent at P is the interior bisector of $\angle F_1PF_2$.

2. At any nonfocal point in the plane of a conic there is a unique pair of orthogonal lines which are conjugate with regard to the conic. In case of an ellipse or a hyperbola these lines harmonically separate the real foci. In case of a parabola they meet the axis in a pair of points of which the focus is the mid-point.

3 For any point P of an axis of a conic there is a unique point P' on the same axis such that any line through P is orthogonal to its conjugate line through P'. The pairs of points P and P' are pairs of an involution (called a *focal involution*) whose double points are the foci of the conic, or, in case of a parabola, the focus and the point at infinity of the axis. If P and P' are on the minor axis, $\angle PF_1P'$ is a right angle. If the conic is a parabola, F is the mid-point of the pair PP'.

4. Of two confocal central conics having a real point in common, one is an ellipse and the other a hyperbola.

5. The tangents at the points in which a conic is met by a line through a focus meet on the corresponding directrix.

6. If two conics have a focus in common, the poles with regard to the two conics of any line through this focus are collinear with the focus.

7. Let P be any point of a conic, and Q the point in which the tangent at P meets a directrix. If F is the corresponding focus, $\angle PFQ$ is a right angle.

8. If a circle passes through the two real foci and a point P of a conic, it will have the two points in which the tangent and normal at P cut the other axis as extremities of a diameter.

9. If a variable tangent meets two fixed tangents in points P and Q respectively, and F is a focus, the measure of $\angle PFQ$ is constant.

10. Let t_1 and t_2 be two tangents of a central conic meeting in a point T; the pair of lines t_1, TF_1 is congruent to the pair TF_2, t_2.

11. The line joining the focus to the point of intersection of two tangents to a parabola makes with either tangent the same angle that the other tangent makes with the axis.

12. Let p be a variable tangent of a parabola, and P a point of p such that the line PF makes a constant angle with p. The locus of P is a tangent to the parabola.

13. The foci of all parabolas inscribed in a triangle lie on a circle.

14. A circle circumscribed to a triangle which is circumscribed to a parabola passes through the focus.

15. The circles circumscribing four triangles whose sides form a complete quadrilateral pass through a point which is the focus of the parabola having the sides of the quadrilateral as tangents.

16. Let P be any point coplanar with, but not on an axis of, a conic C^2. The lines which are at once perpendicular to and conjugate with regard to C^2 to the lines through P are the tangents of a parabola (the *Steiner parabola*). The axes of C^2 are tangents of this parabola.

17. If P and P' are a pair of one focal involution of a central conic, and Q and Q' a pair of the other, P, P', Q, Q' are on an equilateral hyperbola, which may degenerate into a pair of orthogonal lines.

18. Given five points of a conic, construct by ruler and compass the center, the axes, the vertices, the foci, and the directrices. Construct the same elements when five tangents are given.

82. Eccentricity of a conic. Let F be a real focus, and d the corresponding directrix, of a conic C^2 which is not a circle. Let a be the major axis of C^2, and h the line parallel to d such that if a meets d in a point D, and h in a point H, D is the mid-point of the pair FH. Then d is the vanishing line (§ 43) of the harmonic homology Γ with F as center and h as axis.

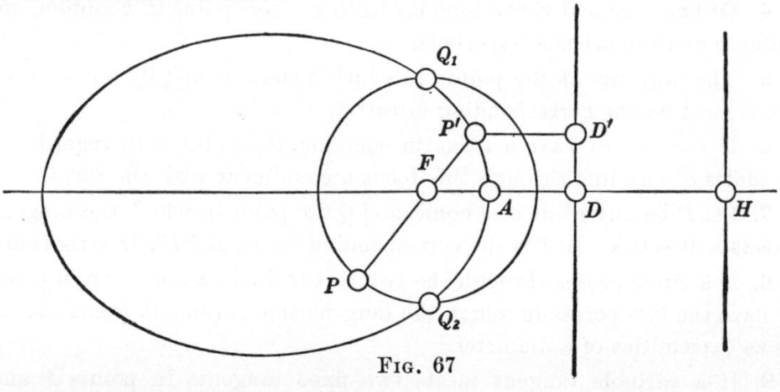

FIG. 67

Since F is a focus, the tangents to C^2 through F pass also through the circular points. Hence the transformation Γ changes C^2 into a circle K^2 with F as center. Now if P is any point of the circle, P' the point of C^2 to which P is transformed by Γ, and D' the point in which the line through P' parallel to FD meets d, it follows by Cor. 2, Theorem 21, Chap. III, that

$$\frac{\text{Dist}\,(P'F)}{\text{Dist}\,(P'D')} = \frac{\text{Dist}\,(PF)}{\text{Dist}\,(FD)}.$$

Since Dist (PF) and Dist (FD) are constants, it follows that

THEOREM 28. DEFINITION. *The ratio of the distances of a point of a conic to a focus and to the corresponding directrix is a constant called the* eccentricity.

The conic C^2 is a parabola if and only if the circle K^2 is tangent to d, the vanishing line of Γ. In this case

$$\text{Dist}\,(FD) = \text{Dist}\,(PF),$$

and hence the eccentricity is unity. The conic C^2 is a hyperbola if and only if K^2 meets d in real points. In this case

$$\text{Dist}\,(FD) < \text{Dist}\,(PF),$$

and hence the eccentricity is greater than one. Applying a like remark to the ellipse we have

THEOREM 29. *A conic section is an ellipse, hyperbola, or parabola according as its eccentricity is less than, greater than, or equal to unity.*

A circle is said to have eccentricity zero, because if P and F be held constant, and D be moved so as to increase FD without limit, the ratio $\text{Dist}\,(PF)/\text{Dist}\,(FD)$ approaches zero.

The eccentricity of a hyperbola or an ellipse is evidently the same relatively to either of its real foci, because the two foci and the corresponding directrices are interchangeable by an orthogonal line reflection whose axis is the minor axis of the conic.

As an immediate corollary of the definition of eccentricity we have

THEOREM 30. *Two real conics are similar if and only if they have the same eccentricity.*

On comparing this theorem with Theorem 20, it is evident that the eccentricity is a function of the cross ratio of the double points of the absolute involution and the points in which the conic meets l_∞. As an example of this relation we have (by comparison with § 72) the theorem that any two hyperbolas whose asymptotes make equal angles have the same eccentricity. The formula connecting the eccentricity of a hyperbola with the angular measure of its asymptotes is given in Ex. 7, below, and the formula for the eccentricity in terms of the cross ratio referred to in Theorem 20 is given in Ex. 9.

Since a real focus of any conic is an interior point, the line through a real focus (e.g. F_2, fig. 64) perpendicular to the principal axis meets the conic in two points, Q_1Q_2. The number $\text{Dist}\,(Q_1Q_2)$ is evidently the same for both foci of an ellipse or hyperbola, and hence is a fixed number for any conic C^2.

DEFINITION. The number $p = \text{Dist}\,(Q_1Q_2)$ is called the *parameter*, or *latus rectum*, of the conic C^2.

In the following exercises e will denote the eccentricity and p the parameter of any conic. For an ellipse or hyperbola a denotes Dist (OA_1) and c denotes Dist (OF_1). For an ellipse b denotes Dist (OB_1). For a hyperbola b denotes $\sqrt{c^2 - a^2}$.

In all cases a radical sign indicates a *positive* square root.

EXERCISES

1. If P is any point of an ellipse, Dist (F_1P) + Dist $(F_2P) = 2\,a$.

2. If P is any point of a hyperbola, Dist (F_1P) − Dist $(F_2P) = \pm\, 2\,a$.

3. In an ellipse Dist $(B_1F_1) = a$ and $a^2 = b^2 + c^2$.

4. Dist $(A_1F_1) \cdot$ Dist $(F_1A_2) = b^2$.

5. In an ellipse or hyperbola $e = \dfrac{c}{a}$ and $p = \dfrac{2\,b^2}{a}$.

6. In a parabola Dist $(AF) = p/4$.

7. The measure θ (§ 67) of the pair of asymptotes of a hyperbola is determined by the equation

$$\cos\theta = 1 - \frac{2}{e^2}.$$

8. For an equilateral hyperbola $e = \sqrt{2}$.

9. The cross ratio $\text{R}\,(C_1C_2,\, I_1I_2) = k^2$ referred to in Theorem 20 is connected with the eccentricity by the relation

$$e^2 = \frac{4\,k}{1 + 2\,k + k^2}$$

in case of an ellipse, and by $$e^2 = \frac{-\,4\,k}{1 - 2\,k + k^2}$$

in case of a hyperbola.

10. Let A^2 and B^2 be the circles with O as center and passing through the vertices A_1 and B_1, respectively, of an ellipse, and let a variable ray making an angle of measure θ with the ray OA meet these circles in X and Y respectively. Then the line through Y parallel to OA_1 meets the line through X parallel to OB_1 in a point P of the conic. If x and y are the coördinates of P relative to the axes of the conic,

$$x = a\cos\theta, \quad y = b\sin\theta.$$

θ is called the *eccentric anomaly* of the point P.

11. Relative to a nonhomogeneous coördinate system in which the principal axis of a conic is the x-axis, and the tangent at a vertex the y-axis, the equation of a parabola, ellipse, and hyperbola, respectively, can be put in the form

$$y^2 = px,$$

$$y^2 = px - \frac{p}{2\,a}x^2,$$

$$y^2 = px + \frac{p}{2\,a}x^2.$$

12. Relative to the asymptotes as axes, the equation of a hyperbola may be written

$$xy = \frac{a^2 + b^2}{4}.$$

13. Relative to any pair of conjugate diameters as axes, an ellipse has the equation

$$\frac{x^2}{a'^2} + \frac{y^2}{b'^2} = 1,$$

and a hyperbola,

$$\frac{x^2}{a'^2} - \frac{y^2}{b'^2} = 1.$$

If A' is a point in which the x-axis meets the conic, Dist $(OA') = a'$. In the case of an ellipse, if B' is one of the points in which the y-axis meets the conic, Dist $(OB') = b'$.

14. The measure of the ordered point triads $OA'B'$ is a constant.

15. The numbers a' and b' satisfy the conditions $a'^2 + b'^2 = a^2 + b^2$ in case of an ellipse and $a'^2 - b'^2 = a^2 - b^2$ in case of a hyperbola.

16. The equation of a system of confocal central conics relative to a system of nonhomogeneous point coördinates in which the axes of the conics are $x = 0$ and $y = 0$ is

$$\frac{x^2}{a^2 - \lambda} + \frac{y^2}{b^2 - \lambda} = 1,$$

where λ is a parameter. In the homogeneous line coördinates such that $u_1x + u_2y + u_0 = 0$ gives the condition that the point (x, y) be on the line $[u_0, u_1, u_2]$, the equation of a system of confocals is $u_0^2 = (a^2 - \lambda)\, u_1^2 + (b^2 - \lambda) u_2^2$.

17. Relative to point coördinates in which the origin is the focus, $y = 0$ the axis of the parabolas, and $x = 0$ perpendicular to the axis, the equation of a system of confocal parabolas is

$$y^2 - 2(p - \lambda)x + \lambda(p - \lambda) = 0.$$

In the corresponding homogeneous line coördinates this is (cf. Ex. 16)

$$pu_2^2 - 2\, u_1u_0 - \lambda(u_1^2 + u_2^2) = 0.$$

83. Synoptic remarks on conic sections. An inspection of the literature will convince one that it would not be practical to include a complete list of the known metric theorems on conic sections in a book like this one. The theorems which we have derived, however, are sufficient to indicate how the rest may be obtained either directly as special cases of projective theorems or as consequences of the focal and affine theorems given in this chapter and Chap. III.

The theorems on conic sections have been classified according to the geometries to which they belong. The most general and elementary which we have considered are those which belong to the proper projective geometry (§ 17), the geometry corresponding to the projective group in any space satisfying Assumptions A, E, P. Theorems of this class are given in Vol. I, particularly in Chaps. V, VIII, X. A second large class contains those theorems which belong to the affine geometry in any proper projective space. These are treated somewhat fully in Chap. III.

The theorems of the class considered in §§ 74, 75 of this chapter belong to the projective geometry of an ordered space. The theorems of § 76 belong to the projective geometry of a real space. Finally, in §§ 80–82 we have been considering theorems of the Euclidean geometry of a real space.

It is quite feasible to make a much finer classification of theorems on conics. This would mean, for example, distinguishing those properties of foci which hold in a parabolic metric geometry in a general space, then those which hold in an ordered space, and then those which are peculiar to the real space.

The theorems which have been under discussion in the remarks above refer in general to figures composed of one conic section and a finite number of points and lines. Theorems regarding more than one conic at a time have not been considered in any considerable number, and the theory of families of conics has not been carried beyond pencils and ranges. For an outline of this subject the reader is referred to the Encyclopädie der Math. Wiss., III C1, §§ 56–90.

EXERCISES

1. The diagonals of the rectangle formed by the tangents at the vertices of an ellipse are conjugate diameters for which $a' = b'$. The angle between this pair of conjugate diameters is less than that between any other pair of conjugate diameters. For this pair of conjugate diameters $a' + b'$ is a maximum. It is a minimum for $a' = a$, $b' = b$.

2. If two orthogonal diameters of a conic meet it in P and Q,

$$\frac{1}{OP^2} + \frac{1}{OQ^2} = \frac{1}{a^2} + \frac{1}{b^2}$$

for an ellipse, and

$$\frac{1}{OP^2} - \frac{1}{OQ^2} = \pm\left(\frac{1}{a^2} - \frac{1}{b^2}\right)$$

for a hyperbola.

3. The locus of a point from which the two tangents to a conic C^2 are orthogonal is a real circle in case C^2 is an ellipse or a hyperbola for which $a > b$; is a pair of conjugate imaginary lines through the center and the circular points in case C^2 is a hyperbola for which $a = b$; is an imaginary circle in case C^2 is a hyperbola for which $a < b$; is the directrix in case C^2 is a parabola. The circle thus defined is called the *director circle* of C^2. Construct it by ruler and compass.

4. A variable tangent to a central conic is met by the lines through a focus which make a fixed angle with it in the points of a circle. In particular, the locus of the foot of a perpendicular from a focus to a tangent is a circle.

5. If t is a variable tangent of a central conic, Dist $(F_1t)\cdot$ Dist $(F_2t)=b^2$. If t' is the other tangent parallel to t, Dist $(F_1t)\cdot$ Dist $(F_1t')=b^2$.

6. If F is a focus of a conic and P_1, P_2 the points of intersection of an arbitrary line through F with the conic,

$$\frac{1}{P_1F}+\frac{1}{FP_2}$$

is a constant.

7. If the tangent to a conic at a variable point P meets the axes in two points T_1 and T_2, and the normal at P meets them in N_1 and N_2, then

$$\begin{aligned}\text{Dist }(PT_1)\cdot\text{Dist }(PT_2)&=\text{Dist }(PN_1)\cdot\text{Dist }(PN_2)\\&=\text{Dist }(PF_1)\cdot\text{Dist }(PF_2).\end{aligned}$$

8. There is a unique circle which osculates* a given conic at a given point P. This is called the *circle of curvature* at P. Its center is called the *center of curvature* for P and lies on the normal at P.

9. Construct by ruler and compass the center of the circle of curvature at an arbitrary point of a given conic.

10. The circle of curvature of a conic C^2 at a point P meets C^2 in one and only one other point, Q. The line PQ is the axis and the point P the center of an elation which transforms K^2 into C^2. The center of curvature is transformed by this elation into the center of the involution on C^2 in which the pairs of orthogonal lines at P meet C^2.

11. The tangent and normal at any point P of a conic C^2 are both tangent to the Steiner parabola (Ex. 16, § 81) determined by this point. The point of contact of the normal with the parabola is the center of the circle of curvature of C^2 at P, and the point of contact of the tangent with the parabola is the pole of the normal with respect to C^2. (For further properties of the circle of curvature, cf. Encyclopädie der Math. Wiss., III C 1, § 36.)

12. The polar reciprocal of a circle with respect to a circle having a point O as center is a conic having O as a focus. (A set of theorems related to this one will be found in Chap. VIII of the book by J. W. Russell referred to in § 73.)

84. Focal properties of collineations. The focal properties of conic sections are closely related to a set of theorems on collineations some of which are given in the exercises below. A good treatment of the subject is to be found in the Collected Papers of H. J. S. Smith, Vol. I, p. 545, and further references in the Encyclopädie der Math. Wiss., III AB 5, § 9.

* Cf. § 47, Vol. I

Let Π be any real projective collineation which does not leave l_∞ invariant, and let p and q be its vanishing lines; so that $\Pi(p) = l_\infty$ and $\Pi(l_\infty) = q$. If I_1 and I_2 are the circular points, let $\Pi^{-1}(I_1) = P_1$, $\Pi^{-1}(I_2) = P_2$, $\Pi(I_1) = Q_1$, $\Pi(I_2) = Q_2$. By the theorems of § 78 the lines P_1I_1 and P_2I_2 meet in a real point A_1, and P_1I_2 and P_2I_1 meet in a real point A_2. If $\Pi(A_1) = B_1$ and $\Pi(A_2) = B_2$, it is clear that the complete quadrilateral whose pairs of opposite vertices are I_1I_2, P_1P_2, A_1A_2 is transformed into one whose pairs of opposite vertices are Q_1Q_2, I_1I_2, B_1B_2. The following propositions are now easily verifiable, and are stated as exercises.

EXERCISES

1. A_1 is such that any ordered pair of lines meeting at A_1 is transformed by Π into a congruent pair of lines. A_2 is such that any two lines meeting in A_2 are transformed by Π into a symmetric pair of lines. No other points have either of these properties.

2. Every conic having a focus at A_1 or A_2 goes to a conic with a focus at B_1 or B_2 respectively.

3. The range of conics having A_1 and A_2 as foci is transformed by Π into the range of conics with B_1 and B_2 as foci; and this is the only system of confocals which goes into a system of confocals.

4. The pencil of circles with A_1, A_2 as limiting points is transformed by Π into that having B_1, B_2 as limiting points; and these are the only two pencils of circles homologous under Π. The radical axes of the two pencils are the two vanishing lines.

5. If P is any point and $\Pi(P) = P'$, then the ordered point triad A_1PA_2 is similar (but not directly similar) to the ordered point triad $B_1P'B_2$.

6. At a point of a Euclidean plane there is in general one and only one pair of perpendicular lines which is transformed into a pair of perpendicular lines by a given affine collineation.

7. In any two projective pencils of lines there is a pair of corresponding orthogonal pairs of lines. The line pairs which are homologous with congruent line pairs form an involution.

8. Any projective collineation which does not leave l_∞ invariant is expressible as a product of a displacement and a homology.

85. Homogeneous quadratic equations in three variables. Reversing the process which is common in analytic geometry, it is possible to derive certain classes of algebraic theorems from the theory of conic sections. We shall illustrate this process in a few important cases and leave the development of further algebraic applications to the reader.

The general homogeneous equation of the second degree can be written in the form

$$\begin{aligned}(6)\qquad & a_{00}x_0^2 + a_{01}x_0x_1 + a_{02}x_0x_2 \\ & + a_{10}x_1x_0 + a_{11}x_1^2 + a_{12}x_1x_2 \\ & + a_{20}x_2x_0 + a_{21}x_2x_1 + a_{22}x_2^2 = 0,\end{aligned}$$

where $a_{ij} = a_{ji}$. Let us first suppose that

$$(7)\qquad A \equiv \begin{vmatrix} a_{00} & a_{01} & a_{02} \\ a_{10} & a_{11} & a_{12} \\ a_{20} & a_{21} & a_{22} \end{vmatrix} \neq 0.$$

In § 98, Vol. I, it has been shown, from the point of view of general projective geometry, that every projective polarity is represented by a bilinear equation of the form

$$\begin{aligned}(8)\qquad & a_{00}x_0x_0' + a_{01}x_0x_1' + a_{02}x_0x_2' \\ & + a_{10}x_1x_0' + a_{11}x_1x_1' + a_{12}x_1x_2' \\ & + a_{20}x_2x_0' + a_{21}x_2x_1' + a_{22}x_2x_2' = 0,\end{aligned}$$

where $a_{ij} = a_{ji}$ and where $A \neq 0$.

It was also shown that every bilinear equation of this form, subject to the condition $A \neq 0$, represents a polarity; that the equation in point coördinates of the fundamental conic of the polarity is (6), which is obtained from (8) by setting $x_i' = x_i$; and that the equation of this conic in line coördinates is

$$(9)\qquad A_{ij}u_iu_j = 0,$$

where A_{ij} is the cofactor of a_{ij} in A.

The coefficients a_{ij} are elements of the geometric number system. Therefore in the case of the real plane they are real numbers, and we have

THEOREM 31. *Every equation of the form* (6) *with real coefficients such that* $a_{ij} = a_{ji}$ *and* $A \neq 0$ *represents a conic whose polar system transforms real points into real lines. Conversely, every conic with regard to which real points have real polars has an equation of the form* (6) *with real coefficients such that* $a_{ij} = a_{ji}$ *and* $A \neq 0$.

In § 79 we have seen that any conic having a real polar system is in one of two classes, and that any two conics of the same class are projectively equivalent. Now it is obvious that

$$x_0^2 + x_1^2 + x_2^2 = 0 \tag{10}$$

is the equation of an imaginary conic, and that

$$x_0^2 + x_1^2 - x_2^2 = 0 \tag{11}$$

is the equation of a real conic. Hence we have

THEOREM 32. *Any quadratic equation in three homogeneous variables whose discriminant A does not vanish is reducible by real linear homogeneous transformation of the variables to the form* (10) *or to the form* (11).

Algebraic criteria to determine whether a given conic C^2 whose equation is in the form (6) belongs to one or the other of these classes may easily be determined by the aid of simple geometric considerations. In case C^2 contains no real points, the line $x_0 = 0$ has no real point in common with it, and the point $u_1 = 0$ (which is on the line $x_0 = 0$) is on no real tangent to it. On the other hand, if the line $x_0 = 0$ contained no real point of C^2, and C^2 were real, this line would consist entirely of exterior points, and hence there would be a tangent to C^2 through the point $u_1 = 0$. Hence a pair of necessary and sufficient conditions that C^2 contain no real points are (1) $x_0 = 0$ is on no point of $C,^2$ and (2) $u_1 = 0$ is on no tangent of C^2.

Substituting $x_0 = 0$ and $x_0' = 0$ in (8), we have the equation of an involution

$$\begin{aligned} &a_{11}x_1x_1' + a_{12}x_1x_2' \\ &+ a_{21}x_2x_1 + a_{22}x_2x_2' = 0, \end{aligned} \tag{12}$$

which, by § 4, is elliptic if and only if $A_{00} > 0$. By a dual argument applied to (9), the necessary and sufficient condition that there be no real tangents to C^2 through the point $u_1 = 0$ is

$$\begin{vmatrix} A_{00} & A_{02} \\ A_{20} & A_{22} \end{vmatrix} > 0. \tag{13}$$

By a well-known theorem on determinants (or a simple computation) this reduces to

$$a_{11} \cdot A > 0.$$

Hence we have

THEOREM 33. *The imaginary conics are those for which*

$$A_{00} > 0 \text{ and } a_{11} \cdot A > 0,$$

and the real ones are those for which not both of these conditions are satisfied and for which $A \neq 0$.

In these conditions it is obvious that A_{00} and a_{11} may be replaced by A_{ii} and a_{jj}, where $i, j = 0, 1, 2$, provided that $i \neq j$.

Let us now investigate the cases where $A = 0$, and first the case in which not all the cofactors A_{00}, A_{11}, A_{22} are zero. To fix the notation, suppose that $A_{00} \neq 0$. Then the bilinear equation (8) is satisfied by $x_0 = A_{00}$, $x_1 = A_{01}$, $x_2 = A_{02}$, no matter what values are taken by x_0', x_1', x_2'. Hence in this case (8) determines a transformation, Γ, of all the points (x_0', x_1', x_2') distinct from (A_{00}, A_{01}, A_{02}) into lines through (A_{00}, A_{01}, A_{02}). A collineation which transforms (A_{00}, A_{01}, A_{02}) to $(1, 0, 0)$ must reduce (8) to

$$(14) \qquad \begin{aligned} &b_{11}x_1x_1' + b_{12}x_1x_2' \\ &+ b_{21}x_2x_1' + b_{22}x_2x_2' = 0 \end{aligned} \qquad b_{12} = b_{21}.$$

It is to be noted that

$$\begin{vmatrix} b_{11} & b_{12} \\ b_{21} & b_{22} \end{vmatrix} \neq 0,$$

because if this determinant vanished, Γ would transform all points (x_0', x_1', x_2') into a single line, and hence A_{00} would vanish. Hence Γ transforms any point (x_0', x_1', x_2') into the line paired in a certain involution with the line joining (x_0', x_1', x_2') to (A_{00}, A_{01}, A_{02}). The double lines of the involution must satisfy the quadratic equation (6).

Comparing with the definitions in § 45, Vol. I, we have that when $A = 0$ and not all the cofactors A_{00}, A_{11}, A_{22} are zero, (6) represents a degenerate conic consisting of two distinct lines and that (8) represents the polar system of the conic. Since the lines represented by (6) are the double lines of a real involution, they are either real or a pair of conjugate imaginaries. In the first case (6) can evidently be transformed by a collineation to

$$(15) \qquad x_1^2 - x_2^2 = 0,$$

and in the second case to

$$(16) \qquad x_1^2 + x_2^2 = 0.$$

The criteria to distinguish the two cases may be found by considering the intersection with (6) of a line $x_i = 0$. This yields imaginary points (just as in the nondegenerate case) if and only if $A_{ii} > 0$, and real points if and only if $A_{ii} \leqq 0$. Hence the case where (6) represents a pair of real lines occurs if and only if $A_{ii} \leqq 0$, for $i = 0, 1, 2$.

Finally, suppose that $A_{00} = A_{11} = A_{22} = A = 0$. In view of the identity,

$$A_{ii}A_{jj} - A_{ij}^2 \equiv a_{kk} \cdot A, \qquad (i \neq j \neq k \neq i) \tag{17}$$

this implies that all the cofactors A_{ij} are zero, and hence that (8) represents the same line, no matter what values are substituted for x_0', x_1', x_2'. Hence (6) represents a single real line (i.e. two coincident real lines), and the polar system (8) transforms all points not on this line into this line. If this line be transformed to $x_1 = 0$, (6) obviously becomes

$$x_1^2 = 0. \tag{18}$$

A degenerate point conic is two distinct or coincident lines. These may always be represented by a quadratic equation which is a product of two linear ones. For such a quadratic $A = 0$, because if $A \neq 0$, the equation has been seen to represent a nondegenerate conic. Hence the theory of degenerate point conics is equivalent to that of homogeneous quadratic equations for which $A = 0$.

The complete projective classification of conics, degenerate or not, may now be stated as an algebraic theorem in the form:

THEOREM 34. *Any homogeneous quadratic equation in three variables may be reduced by a real linear homogeneous transformation,*

$$x_i' = \sum_{j=0}^{2} \alpha_{ij} x_j, \qquad (i = 0, 1, 2), |\alpha_{ij}| \neq 0 \tag{19}$$

to one of the normal forms (10), (11), (16), (15), (18). *The criteria which determine to which one of these forms an equation* (6) *is reducible may be summarized in the following table:*

$A \neq 0$		$A = 0$		
IMAGINARY CONIC	REAL CONIC	IMAGINARY LINE PAIR	REAL LINE PAIR	COINCIDENT REAL LINE PAIR
$a_{11}A > 0$	$a_{11}A \leqq 0$	$A_{00} > 0$	$A_{00} < 0$	$A_{00} = 0$
		or $A_{11} > 0$	or $A_{11} < 0$	$A_{11} = 0$
$A_{00} > 0$	or $A_{00} \leqq 0$	or $A_{22} > 0$	or $A_{22} < 0$	$A_{22} = 0$

Since the algebraic expressions in the above criteria determine conditions on the conic which are independent of the choice of coördinates and thus are invariant under the projective group, it is natural to inquire whether they are algebraic invariants in the sense of § 90, Vol. I. A direct substitution will readily verify that A is a relative invariant of (6).

Suppose we regard the coefficients of (6) as homogeneous coördinates $(a_{00}, a_{11}, a_{22}, a_{01}, a_{10}, a_{12})$ of a point in a five-dimensional space. Then $A = 0$ determines a certain cubic locus in this space the points on which represent degenerate conics. Now if there were any other invariant of (6) under the projective group, say $\phi\,(a_{ij})$, the equation $\phi\,(a_{ij}) = 0$ would represent a locus in this five-dimensional space. But since each nondegenerate conic is projectively equivalent to every other nondegenerate conic, this locus would have to be contained in the locus of $A = 0$. From this it can be proved, by the general theory of loci represented by algebraic equations, that the locus of $\phi\,(a_{ij}) = 0$ coincides with that of $A = 0$, and that hence $\phi\,(a_{ij})$ is rationally expressible in terms of A. Thus A is essentially the only invariant of (6) under the projective group.

The question, however, arises whether there are not other rational functions of the coefficients of (6) which are invariant whenever $A = 0$. If there were such a function, say $\phi\,(a_{ij})$, the conics for which $\phi\,(a_{ij}) = 0$ would be a subclass of the degenerate conics which is transformed into itself by all complex projective collineations. The only class of this sort consists of the coincident line pairs which are given by *two* conditions, $A_{00} = 0$, $A_{11} = 0$. In view of the theorem that a locus represented by two independent algebraic equations cannot be the complete locus of a single algebraic equation, this shows that there is no other invariant of (6) even for the cases in which $A = 0$.

This reasoning could be expressed still more briefly by saying that, while the set of all conics is a five-parameter family, and the set of degenerate conics a four-parameter family given by one condition, the only invariant subset of the degenerate conics is the two-parameter set of coincident line pairs which have to be given by two conditions and so cannot correspond to a single invariant in addition to A.

EXERCISES

1. In case $A = 0$, the lines represented by (6) intersect in the point $(\sqrt{A_{00}}, \sqrt{A_{11}}, \sqrt{A_{22}})$, unless the three cofactors A_{ii} vanish, in which case (6) represents the coincident line pair

$$(\sqrt{a_{00}}x_0 + \sqrt{a_{11}}x_1 + \sqrt{a_{22}}x_2)^2 = 0.$$

2. In case (6) represents a pair of distinct lines, (9) represents their point of intersection counted twice. In case (6) represents a pair of coincident lines, $A_{ij} = 0$ $(i, j = 0, 1, 2)$.

86. Nonhomogeneous quadratic equations in two variables. The affine theory of point conics corresponds to the theory of

$$\begin{aligned} &a_{00} + a_{01}x + a_{02}y \\ &+ a_{10}x + a_{11}x^2 + a_{12}xy \\ &+ a_{20}y + a_{21}yx + a_{22}y^2 = 0, \end{aligned} \tag{20}$$

where the a_{ij}'s satisfy the same conditions as in the last section. The theorem that any nondegenerate conic is an imaginary ellipse, real ellipse, hyperbola, or parabola, and that any two conics of the same class are equivalent under the affine group, translates into the following: Any quadratic equation in two variables, for which $A \neq 0$, is transformable by a transformation of the form

$$\begin{aligned} x' &= a_1x + b_1y + c_1, \\ y' &= a_2x + b_2y + c_2, \end{aligned} \qquad \begin{vmatrix} a_1 & b_1 \\ a_2 & b_2 \end{vmatrix} \neq 0, \tag{21}$$

into one of the following four forms:

$$x^2 + y^2 + 1 = 0, \tag{22}$$

$$x^2 + y^2 - 1 = 0, \tag{23}$$

$$x^2 - y^2 - 1 = 0, \tag{24}$$

$$x^2 + y = 0. \tag{25}$$

To know this it is merely necessary to observe that these equations represent conics of the four types respectively.

The criteria to determine in which class a given conic C^2 belongs may be inferred from the discussion in the last section if we set $x = x_1/x_0$ and $y = x_2/x_0$. It is then evident that $A_{00} > 0$ for an ellipse, $A_{00} = 0$ for a parabola, and $A_{00} < 0$ for a hyperbola. Hence the affine classification of cases where $A \neq 0$ may be summarized in the following table:

$A \neq 0$

IMAGINARY ELLIPSE	REAL ELLIPSE	HYPERBOLA	PARABOLA
$A_{00} > 0$ $a_{11}A > 0$	$A_{00} > 0$ $a_{11}A \leqq 0$	$A_{00} < 0$	$A_{00} = 0$

The cases where $A = 0$ correspond, as in the last section, to degenerate conics. Geometrically the types of figures are obvious, and to obtain the algebraic criteria we need only combine with considerations already adduced, the observation that when $A_{00} = 0$ and either $a_{11} = 0$ or $a_{22} = 0$, then $a_{12} = a_{21} = 0$.

$A = 0$

<table>
<tr><th colspan="2">CONJUGATE IMAGINARY LINES</th><th colspan="3">DISTINCT REAL LINES</th><th colspan="2">COINCIDENT REAL LINES</th></tr>
<tr><th>Concurrent at ordinary point</th><th>Parallel pair</th><th>Concurrent at ordinary point</th><th>Parallel pair</th><th>One at infinity</th><th>Ordinary</th><th>At infinity</th></tr>
<tr><td rowspan="2">$A_{00} > 0$</td><td rowspan="2">$A_{00} = 0$,
$A_{11} > 0$
or
$A_{22} > 0$</td><td rowspan="2">$A_{00} < 0$</td><td colspan="2">$A_{00} = 0$,
$A_{11} < 0$
or
$A_{22} < 0$;</td><td colspan="2">$A_{00} = A_{11} = A_{22} = 0$;</td></tr>
<tr><td>$a_{11} \neq 0$
or
$a_{22} \neq 0$</td><td>$a_{11} = a_{22} = 0$</td><td>$a_{11} \neq 0$
or
$a_{22} \neq 0$</td><td>$a_{11} = a_{22} = 0$</td></tr>
</table>

As normal forms for the first six cases we may take

(26) $$x^2 + y^2 = 0,$$

(27) $$x^2 + 1 = 0,$$

(28) $$x^2 - y^2 = 0,$$

(29) $$x^2 - 1 = 0,$$

(30) $$x = 0,$$

(31) $$x^2 = 0.$$

The case of coincident real lines at infinity does not correspond to any equation in nonhomogeneous coördinates.

Summarizing these results we have the following algebraic theorem:

THEOREM 35. *Any quadratic equation in two variables may be reduced to one and only one of the normal forms* (22)–(31) *by a transformation of the form* (21). *The normal form to which it is reducible is determined by the criteria in the two tables above.*

The question of invariants of (20) under the affine group may be investigated in the manner indicated for the corresponding projective problem in the fine print at the end of the last section. The results of such an investigation are given in the exercises below.

There are no absolute invariants of conics under the projective and affine groups, because two conics would fail to be equivalent under the one group or the other if they determined different values of an absolute invariant, and this would contradict the fact that there are only a finite number of conics distinct under the affine group.

EXERCISES

1. A and A_{00} are invariants of (20) under the affine group.

2. In case $A = A_{00} = 0$, A_{11}/a_{22} and A_{22}/a_{11} are invariants of (20) under the affine group.

3. The homogeneous coördinates of the center of (20) are (A_{00}, A_{01}, A_{02}).

4. If $A_{00} \neq 0$, the translation $\bar{x} = x - \frac{A_{10}}{A_{00}}$, $\bar{y} = y - \frac{A_{20}}{A_{00}}$ transforms (20) into

$$a_{11}\bar{x}^2 + 2\,a_{12}\bar{x}\bar{y} + a_{22}\bar{y}^2 + \frac{A}{A_{00}} = 0.$$

5. If $A \neq 0$ and $A_{00} \neq 0$, the asymptotes of (20) are given by the equation

$$a_{11}\bar{x}^2 + 2\,a_{12}\bar{x}\bar{y} + a_{22}\bar{y}^2 = 0.$$

6. Any diameter of a parabola is parallel to $a_{11}x + a_{12}y = 0$ and to $a_{12}x + a_{22}y = 0$.

87. Euclidean classification of point conics. With respect to a non-homogeneous coördinate system in which the pair of lines $x = 0$ and $y = 0$ is orthogonal and bisected by the lines $x = y$ and $x = -y$, the transformations of the Euclidean group take the form (21) subject to the conditions

$$a_1^2 + a_2^2 = b_1^2 + b_2^2, \qquad a_1b_1 + a_2b_2 = 0, \tag{32}$$

and the displacements are subject to the additional condition

$$\begin{vmatrix} a_1 & b_1 \\ a_2 & b_2 \end{vmatrix} = 1. \tag{33}$$

Since any ellipse or hyperbola is congruent to one whose principal axes are $x = 0$ and $y = 0$, and since any parabola is congruent to a parabola with the origin as vertex and $y = 0$ as its principal axis, it follows that any conic is congruent to a conic having one of the following equations:

$$\frac{x^2}{a^2} + \frac{y^2}{b^2} + 1 = 0, \tag{34}$$

$$\frac{x^2}{a^2} + \frac{y^2}{b^2} - 1 = 0, \tag{35}$$

$$\frac{x^2}{a^2} - \frac{y^2}{b^2} - 1 = 0, \tag{36}$$

$$y^2 - px = 0. \tag{37}$$

The normal forms to which degenerate point conics can be reduced by displacements are evident when one recalls that two pairs of non-parallel lines are congruent when they have the same cross ratio with the circular points and that two pairs of parallel lines are congruent if the lines of each pair are the same distance apart.* By comparison with the second table ($A = 0$) in § 86 we find

$$\frac{x^2}{a^2} + y^2 = 0, \tag{38}$$

$$x^2 + c^2 = 0, \tag{39}$$

$$\frac{x^2}{a^2} - y^2 = 0, \tag{40}$$

$$x^2 - c^2 = 0, \tag{41}$$

$$x = 0, \tag{42}$$

$$x^2 = 0. \tag{43}$$

The group of displacements is extended to the group of similarity transformations by adjoining transformations of the form

$$\begin{aligned} x' &= kx, \\ y' &= ky, \end{aligned} \qquad k \neq 0. \tag{44}$$

Transformations of this sort will reduce the equations (34)–(43) to normal forms in which b, c, and p are all unity.

The criteria for determining to which of these normal forms a conic is reducible under the group of displacements or that of similarity transformations are the same as those already found for the affine group. Two conics whose equations can be reduced to the same normal form are evidently equivalent under the group of displacements if and only if they determine the same values for a and b or c or p, and under the Euclidean group if they determine the same value for a. The numbers a, b, c, p are evidently absolute invariants of the corresponding conics under the group of displacements, and a in (38) and (40) also under the Euclidean group.

The problem of determining a, b, c, p in terms of the coefficients of (20) presents no special difficulty, and will be left to the reader to be considered in connection with the exercises below and those at the end of the next section.

When b, c, p are all unity, a is a function of the eccentricity given by the equations in Exs. 7 and 9, § 82. The same reference gives the connection between the eccentricity and the invariant $\sqrt{-A_{00}}/(a_{11} + a_{22})$.

* The distance apart is the distance of an arbitrary point on one of the parallel lines from the other line. The formula for distance is applied to the case of a pair of conjugate imaginary lines as explained in § 70.

EXERCISES

1. If $A \neq 0$ and $A_{00} \neq 0$, the angular measure of the asymptotes is θ, where

$$\tan\theta = \frac{2\sqrt{-A_{00}}}{a_{11} + a_{22}}.$$

Moreover,
$$\theta = -\frac{i}{2}\log \text{R}(C_1C_2, I_1I_2),$$

where C_1 and C_2 are the points in which the conic meets l_∞, and I_1 and I_2 are the circular points. If $A = 0$ and $A_{00} \neq 0$, these formulas give the angular measure of the lines represented by (20). Derive from this the formula for a in (38) and (40) in terms of the coefficients of (20).

2. A_{00} and $a_{11} + a_{22}$ are absolute invariants of (20) under the group of displacements, and $\sqrt{-A_{00}}/(a_{11} + a_{22})$ under the Euclidean group. If $A \neq 0$ and $a_{11} + a_{22} = 0$, (20) represents an equilateral hyperbola; if $A = 0$ and $a_{11} + a_{22} = 0$, it represents a pair of orthogonal lines or l_∞ and an ordinary line.

3. If $A \neq 0$ and $A_{00} \neq 0$, the axes of (20) are

$$a_{12}(\bar{x}^2 + \bar{y}^2) + (a_{22} - a_{11})\bar{x}\bar{y} = 0,$$

where $\bar{x}$ and $\bar{y}$ are defined as in Ex. 4, § 86.

4. For an ellipse the constants a and b are $\sqrt{\frac{-A}{A_{00}\lambda_1}}$ and $\sqrt{\frac{-A}{A_{00}\lambda_2}}$, where λ_1 and λ_2 are the roots of

$$\lambda^2 - (a_{11} + a_{22})\lambda + A_{00} = 0; \tag{45}$$

and for a hyperbola a and ib are $\sqrt{\frac{-A}{A_{00}\lambda_1}}$ and $\sqrt{\frac{-A}{A_{00}\lambda_2}}$. The discriminant of (45) is $(a_{11} - a_{22})^2 + 4a_{12}^2$.

5. If $A \neq 0$ and $A_{00} = 0$, the parabola (20) touches l_∞ at $(0, a_{12}, -a_{11})$, which is the same as $(0, a_{22}, -a_{12})$. The axis is

$$a_{11}x + a_{12}y + \frac{a_{01}a_{11} + a_{02}a_{12}}{a_{11} + a_{22}} = 0. \tag{46}$$

88. Classification of line conics. The projective classification of line conics is entirely dual to that of point conics and so need not be considered separately. The affine classification, however, corresponds to a new algebraic problem. If the line coördinates are chosen so that

$$u_0x_0 + u_1x_1 + u_2x_2 = 0$$

is the condition that the point (x_0, x_1, x_2) be on the line $[u_0, u_1, u_2]$, the point coördinates being the same as already used, we have the problem of reducing equations of the form (9) to normal forms by means of transformations of the form

$$\begin{aligned} u_0' &= d_0u_0 + d_1u_1 + d_2u_2, \\ u_1' &= \qquad\; + b_2u_1 - a_2u_2, \\ u_2' &= \qquad\; - b_1u_1 + a_1u_2, \end{aligned} \qquad \begin{vmatrix} a_1 & b_1 \\ a_2 & b_2 \end{vmatrix} \neq 0. \tag{47}$$

These are the transformations which leave the line [1, 0, 0] invariant. If

$$d_0 = \begin{vmatrix} a_1 & b_1 \\ a_2 & b_2 \end{vmatrix}, \quad d_1 = \begin{vmatrix} b_1 & c_1 \\ b_2 & c_2 \end{vmatrix}, \quad \text{and} \quad d_2 = \begin{vmatrix} c_1 & a_1 \\ c_2 & a_2 \end{vmatrix},$$

(47) is the same collineation as (21).

The affine classification of nondegenerate line conics is of course the same as that of nondegenerate point conics. To express the criteria in terms of the equation (9) regarded as given primarily,* let us write

(48) $$\alpha \equiv \begin{vmatrix} A_{00} & A_{01} & A_{02} \\ A_{10} & A_{11} & A_{12} \\ A_{20} & A_{21} & A_{22} \end{vmatrix},$$

where the A_{ij}'s are the coefficients of (9), and let α_{ij} denote the cofactor of A_{ij} in α. The point conic associated with (9) must have the equation

(49) $$\sum \alpha_{ij} x_i x_j = 0.$$

By the criteria already worked out, this is an ellipse, hyperbola, or parabola according as the value of

$$\begin{vmatrix} \alpha_{11} & \alpha_{12} \\ \alpha_{21} & \alpha_{22} \end{vmatrix} \equiv A_{00} \cdot \alpha$$

is greater than, less than, or equal to zero; and, in the case of an ellipse, real or imaginary according as $\alpha_{11} > 0$ or $\alpha_{11} \leqq 0$. Thus we have

$$\alpha \neq 0$$

Imaginary Ellipse	Real Ellipse	Hyperbola	Parabola
$\alpha \cdot A_{00} > 0$ $\alpha_{11} > 0$	$\alpha \cdot A_{00} > 0$ $\alpha_{11} \leqq 0$	$\alpha \cdot A_{00} < 0$	$A_{00} = 0$

The normal forms for these four classes are respectively

(50) $$u_0^2 + u_1^2 + u_2^2 = 0,$$

(51) $$u_0^2 - u_1^2 - u_2^2 = 0,$$

(52) $$u_0^2 - u_1^2 + u_2^2 = 0,$$

(53) $$u_1^2 - u_2 = 0.$$

The projective classification of degenerate line conics is dual to that of degenerate point conics, and therefore yields the following three cases: (1) two distinct real points, $\alpha = 0$, $\alpha_{ii} \leqq 0$, one at least

*Instead of in terms of the coefficients of (6).

of α_{00}, α_{11}, α_{22} being different from zero; (2) coincident real points, $\alpha = \alpha_{11} = \alpha_{22} = \alpha_{33} = 0$; (3) conjugate imaginary points, $\alpha = 0$, $\alpha_{ii} > 0$ for at least one value of i.

For the affine classification let us observe that since [1, 0, 0] is the line at infinity, the condition that at least one factor of (9) represent a point at infinity is $A_{00} = 0$. The following criteria are now evident.

$\alpha = 0$

Conjugate Imaginary Points		Distinct Real Points			Coincident Real Points	
Ordinary	At infinity	Both ordinary	One ordinary	Both at infinity	Ordinary	At infinity
$\alpha_{11} > 0$ or $\alpha_{22} > 0$	$\alpha_{00} > 0$, $\alpha_{11} = \alpha_{22} = 0$	$\alpha_{11} < 0$ or $\alpha_{22} < 0$, $A_{00} \neq 0$	$\alpha_{11} < 0$ or $\alpha_{22} < 0$, $A_{00} = 0$	$\alpha_{00} < 0$, $\alpha_{11} = 0$, $\alpha_{22} = 0$	$\alpha_{00} = \alpha_{11} = \alpha_{22} = 0$, $A_{00} \neq 0$	$\alpha_{00} = \alpha_{11} = \alpha_{22} = 0$, $A_{00} = 0$

The normal forms for these cases are respectively

(54) $$u_0^2 + u_1^2 = 0,$$

(55) $$u_1^2 + u_2^2 = 0,$$

(56) $$u_0^2 - u_1^2 = 0,$$

(57) $$u_0 u_1 = 0,$$

(58) $$u_1 u_2 = 0,$$

(59) $$u_0^2 = 0,$$

(60) $$u_1^2 = 0.$$

EXERCISES

1. The two pairs of foci of (9) are the degenerate conics of the range

(61) $$\begin{aligned} &A_{00}u_0^2 + A_{01}u_0u_1 + A_{02}u_0u_2 \\ &+ A_{10}u_1u_0 + (A_{11} - \rho)\, u_1^2 + A_{12}u_1u_2 \\ &+ A_{20}u_2u_0 + A_{21}u_2u_1 + (A_{22} - \rho)\, u_2^2 = 0, \end{aligned}$$

which are given by the values of ρ satisfying

(62) $$A_{00}\rho^2 - (\alpha_{11} + \alpha_{22})\,\rho + \alpha = 0.$$

The discriminant of this quadratic is $(\alpha_{11} - \alpha_{22})^2 + 4\,\alpha_{12}^2$.

2. In case $\alpha = 0$ and $A_{00} \neq 0$, the distance between the points represented by (9) is

$$\frac{2\sqrt{-(a_{11}+a_{22})}}{A_{00}}.$$

3. The normal forms for line conics under the group of displacements are

$$u_0^2 + a^2u_1^2 + b^2u_2^2 = 0, \tag{63}$$

$$u_0^2 - a^2u_1^2 - b^2u_2^2 = 0, \tag{64}$$

$$u_0^2 - a^2u_1^2 + b^2u_2^2 = 0, \tag{65}$$

$$4\,u_0u_1 + pu_2^2 = 0, \tag{66}$$

$$u_0^2 + k^2u_1^2 = 0, \tag{67}$$

$$u_1^2 + c^2u_2^2 = 0, \tag{68}$$

$$u_0^2 - k^2u_1^2 = 0, \tag{69}$$

$$u_0u_1 = 0, \tag{70}$$

$$u_1^2 - c^2u_2^2 = 0, \tag{71}$$

$$u_0^2 = 0, \tag{72}$$

$$u_1^2 = 0. \tag{73}$$

Here a, b, p have the same significance as in (34)–(37); $2\,ki$ is the distance between the two points represented by (67); $2\,k$ is the distance between the two points represented by (69); c is expressible in terms of the cross ratio of the circular points and the two points represented by (68) or (71).

*** 89. Polar systems.** The theorems on the classification of conics (§ 79) may be regarded as completing the discussion of projective polar systems in a real plane. There is, however, a certain amount of interest in making the discussion of polar systems without the intervention of complex elements, and basing it entirely on the most elementary theorems about order relations. This treatment will hold good for a projective space satisfying Assumptions A, E, S, P.

THEOREM 36. *In any projective polar system in an ordered plane the involutions of conjugate points on the sides of a self-polar triangle are all direct, or else one involution is direct and the other two opposite.*

Proof. Let ABC be the self-polar triangle (fig. 68), and let PP' be a pair of points on the side BC and QQ' a pair on the side CA. Let R be the point of intersection of the lines PQ and AB, O that of AP' and BQ', and R' that of CO and AB. Then AP' is the polar of P, BQ' of Q, PQ of O, and CO of R. Hence R and R' are paired in the involution of conjugate points on AB. Let R'' be the point in which $P'Q'$ meets AB: R'' is the harmonic conjugate of R' with respect to A and B.

If the involutions on BC and CA are direct, P and P' separate B and C, and Q and Q' separate C and A. It follows by Theorem 19, Chap. II, that R and R'' do not separate B and A. Hence by Theorems 7 and 8, Chap. II, R' is separated from R by A and B, and hence the involution on the line AB is direct.

On the other hand, if the involutions on BC and CA are not direct, P and P' do not separate B and C, and Q and Q' do not separate C and A. Hence R and R'' do not, and therefore R and R' do, separate A and B. Hence again the third involution is direct.

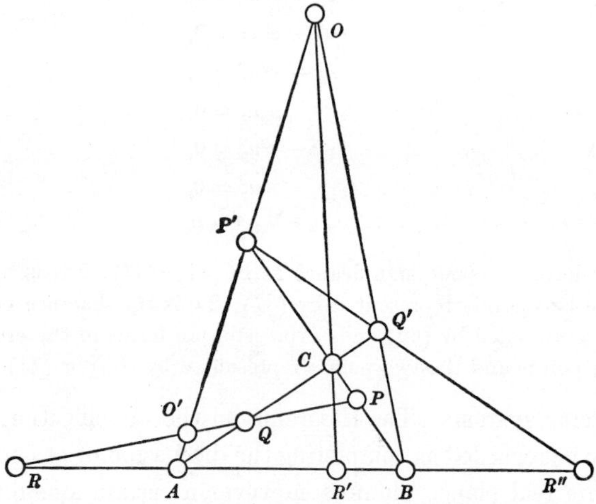

FIG. 68

We have thus shown that at least one of the three involutions is direct; and that if two are direct, so is also the third. From this the statement in the theorem follows.

The reasoning above is valid in any ordered projective space. Specializing to the real space, we have

COROLLARY 1. *The involutions on the sides of a self-polar triangle of a projective polar system in a real plane are all three elliptic, or else two are hyperbolic and the third is elliptic.*

THEOREM 37. *If the involutions of conjugate points on the sides of one self-polar triangle of a projective polar system in an ordered plane are direct, the involution of conjugate points on any line is direct.*

Proof. Let the given self-polar triangle on the sides of which the involutions of conjugate points are direct be ABC. The theorem will follow if we can prove that the involution of conjugate points on any line through a vertex of such a triangle is direct. For any line l meets BC in a point M which has a conjugate point N on BC. By the proposition which we are supposing proved, the involutions on the sides of the self-polar triangle, AMN, are direct; and by a second application of the same proposition, the involution of conjugate points on l is direct. Thus the proof of the theorem reduces to the proof that the involution of conjugate points on any line through A is direct.

Let such a line meet BC in a point P', and let P be the conjugate of P' in the involution on BC. Let Q and Q' be a conjugate pair distinct from A and C on the line AC, and let O, R, R', R'' have the same meaning as in the proof of the last theorem (fig. 68). Also let O' be the conjugate of O on the line AP', i.e. let O' be the intersection of AP' with PQ. Applying Theorem 19, Chap. II, to the triangle ABP' and the lines $O'R$ and OR', it follows that, since C and P do not separate B and P', and R and R' do separate A and B, O and O' are separated by A and P'. Hence the involution of conjugate points on the line AP' is direct.

Corollary 1. *If the involutions on two sides of a self-polar triangle of a polar system in an ordered plane are opposite, then two of the involutions on the sides of any self-polar triangle are opposite and the third is direct.*

Proof. If there were any self-polar triangle not satisfying the conclusion of the theorem, this would, by Theorem 36, be one for which all three involutions were direct. By Theorem 37 it would follow that the involutions on all lines were direct, contrary to hypothesis.

The propositions stated in the last two theorems and in the last corollary may evidently be condensed into the following:

Corollary 2. *Any projective polar system in an ordered plane is either such that the involution of conjugate points on any line is direct, or such that on the sides of any self-polar triangle two of the involutions are opposite and the third direct.*

Applying this result in a real plane, we have that every projective polar system is either such that all involutions of conjugate points are elliptic, or such that on the sides of any self-polar triangle two involutions are hyperbolic and the third elliptic. In the latter case let ABC be a self-polar triangle, AB and AC being the sides upon which the involutions are hyperbolic. Let the double points of the involution on AB be C_1 and C_2, and those of the involution on AC be B_1 and B_2. The polar of C_1 is then the line C_1C. The conic section K^2 through C_1, C_2, B_1, B_2 and tangent to the line C_1C at C_1 has a polar system in which ABC is a self-polar triangle, and in which the given involutions are involutions of conjugate points. By § 93, Vol. I, these conditions are sufficient to determine a polarity. Hence the given polarity is the polar system of K^2. Thus we have

THEOREM 38. DEFINITION. *A projective polar system in a real plane is either the polar system of a real conic, or such that the involution of conjugate points on any line is elliptic. A polar system of the latter type is said to be* elliptic.

The existence of elliptic polar systems is easily seen as follows: Let ABC be any triangle, O any point not on a side of this triangle, P' the point of intersection of OA with BC, Q' the point of intersection of OB with CA, and P and Q any two points separated from P' and Q' by the pairs BC and CA respectively. By the theorems in § 93, Vol. I, there exists a polar system in which the triangle ABC is self-polar and the point O is the pole of the line PQ, and by the theorems in the present section this polar system is elliptic.

CHAPTER VI

INVERSION GEOMETRY AND RELATED TOPICS*

90. Vectors and complex numbers. The properties of the addition of vectors have been derived in § 42 from those of the group of translations. If the operation of multiplication is to satisfy the distributive law,

$$a(b+c) = ab + ac,$$

multiplication by a vector, a, must effect a transformation on the vector field such that $b + c$ is carried into the vector which is the sum of those to which b and c are carried. Since the group of translations is a self-conjugate subgroup of the Euclidean group, any similarity transformation of the vector field satisfies this condition.

Let us then consider the transformations effected on a vector field by the Euclidean group. Any similarity transformation is a product of a translation by a similarity transformation leaving an arbitrary point O invariant. But a translation carries every vector into itself. Hence any similarity transformation has the same effect on the field of vectors as a similarity transformation leaving O invariant. Hence the totality of transformations effected on the vector field by the Euclidean group is identical with the totality of transformations effected on it by the similarity transformations leaving O invariant. Since no such transformation changes every vector into itself, any two of them effect different transformations of the field of vectors. Hence we have

THEOREM 1. *The group of transformations effected by the Euclidean group in a plane upon the field of vectors is isomorphic with the group of similarity transformations leaving an arbitrary point invariant.*

To obtain a definition of multiplication we restrict attention to the group of direct similarity transformations and make use of the fact that if OA and OB are any two nonzero vectors, there is one and but

* The main part of Chap. VII is independent of this chapter. The two chapters may therefore be taken up in reverse order if the reader so desires.

one transformation of this group carrying the points O and A to O and B respectively.

DEFINITION. Relative to an arbitrary vector OA, which is called the *unit vector*, the *product* of two vectors OX (where $X \neq O$) and OY is the vector OZ to which OY is carried by the direct similarity transformation carrying OA to OX, and is denoted by $OX \cdot OY$. In case $X = O$, $OX \cdot OY$ denotes the zero vector.

As obvious corollaries of this definition we have the following two theorems:

THEOREM 2. *The triad of points OAY is directly similar to the triad OXZ if and only if*

$$OZ = OX \cdot OY.$$

THEOREM 3. *The equation*

$$OZ = OX \cdot OY$$

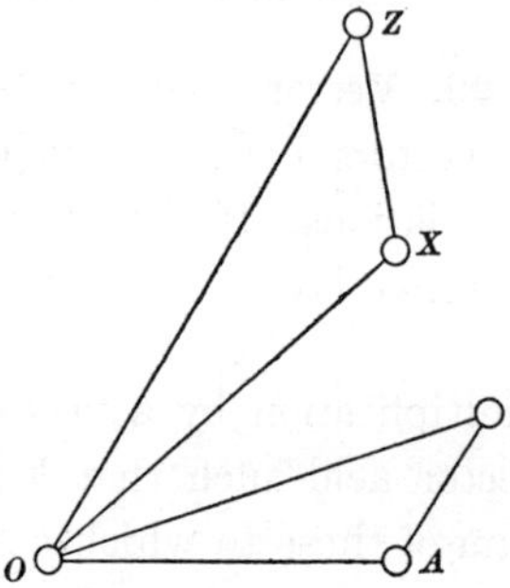

FIG. 69

is satisfied if and only if $\measuredangle AOX + \measuredangle AOY = \measuredangle AOZ$ *and Dist* $(OZ) =$ *Dist* $(OX) \cdot$ *Dist* (OY), *the unit of distance being OA.*

Since the direct similarity transformations leaving a point O invariant form a group, the operation of multiplication must be associative, i.e.

$$OX \cdot (OY \cdot OZ) = (OX \cdot OY) \cdot OZ,$$

and also such that there is a unique inverse for every vector OB for which $O \neq B$, i.e. there must be a vector OY such that

$$OB \cdot OY = OA.$$

The group of direct similarity transformations leaving O invariant is commutative because it consists of the rotations about O (which form a commutative group by § 58) combined with dilations with O as center. Hence the operation of multiplication is commutative, i.e.

$$OX \cdot OY = OY \cdot OX.$$

The fact that the group of translations is self-conjugate under the group of displacements translates into the distributive law,

$$OX \cdot (OY + OZ) = OX \cdot OY + OX \cdot OZ.$$

Recalling the definition of a number system given in Chap. VI, Vol. I, we may summarize these results by saying,

THEOREM 4. *With respect to the operation of addition described in § 42 and of multiplication defined in this section, a planar vector field is a commutative number system.*

In proving this theorem we have made use of no properties of the Euclidean group except such as hold for any parabolic metric geometry for which the absolute involution is elliptic. In case the absolute involution were hyperbolic, exceptions would have to be made corresponding to properties of the minimal lines.

The definition of multiplication of vectors as given here does not conflict with the notion of the ratio of collinear vectors as developed in Chap. III. For the quotient of two collinear vectors is a vector collinear with the unit vector OA, and the system of vectors collinear with OA constitutes a number system isomorphic with the real number system. Thus, if we denote the unit vector by **1**, any vector OX collinear with it may be denoted by

$$x\mathbf{1},$$

where, according to the definition of § 43, x is a real number and where, according to our present definition, x denotes OX itself.

Let us denote a vector OB such that the line OB is perpendicular to the line OA and such that $\text{Dist}(OB) = \text{Dist}(OA)$, by $\boldsymbol{i}$. Then by the definition of multiplication,

$$\boldsymbol{i}^2 = -\mathbf{1}.$$

Any vector collinear with $\boldsymbol{i}$ is expressible in the form $x\boldsymbol{i}$, where x is a vector parallel to **1**, and by Theorem 8, Chap. III, any vector whatever is expressible uniquely in the form

$$a\mathbf{1} + b\boldsymbol{i}.$$

The product of two vectors may be reduced by the associative, distributive, and commutative laws as follows:

$$\begin{aligned}(a\mathbf{1} + b\boldsymbol{i})(c\mathbf{1} + d\boldsymbol{i}) &= (a\mathbf{1} + b\boldsymbol{i})\, c\mathbf{1} + (a\mathbf{1} + b\boldsymbol{i})\, d\boldsymbol{i} \\ &= (ac - bd)\,\mathbf{1} + (bc + ad)\,\boldsymbol{i}.\end{aligned}$$

By comparison with §§ 3 and 14 this shows that

THEOREM 5. *A planar field of vectors is a number system isomorphic with the complex number system, i.e. the geometric number system of a complex line.*

The isomorphism in question is that by which the complex number $a+bi$ corresponds to the vector $a\mathbf{1}+bi$. Supposing that the fundamental points of the scale on the complex line are P_0, P_1, P_∞, this means that there is a correspondence between the complex line and the Euclidean plane in which P_0 corresponds to O, P_1 to A, and every point whose coördinate relative to the scale P_0, P_1, P_∞ is

$$a+bi$$

corresponds to the point Q of the Euclidean plane such that

$$OQ = a\mathbf{1}+bi.$$

One obvious property of this correspondence which we shall have to use later is that the points of the complex line which have real coördinates relative to the scale P_0, P_1, P_∞ correspond to the points of the line OA, or, in other words, that *the points of the chain** $\mathsf{C}(P_0P_1P_\infty)$, *other than* P_∞, *correspond to the points on the real line* OA.

Theorem 5 may be made the basis of a method for the investigation of theorems of Euclidean geometry, particularly those relating to n-lines and circles. The complex numbers may be regarded as the coördinates of the points of the Euclidean plane and many interesting theorems obtained by interpreting simple algebraic equations. Compare the articles by F. Morley, Transactions of the American Mathematical Society, Vol. I, p. 97; Vol. IV, p. 1; Vol. V, p. 467; Vol. VIII, p. 14.

The whole subject is closely related to certain elementary parts of the theory of functions of a complex variable. Cf. an article by F. N. Cole, Annals of Mathematics, 1st Series, Vol. V (1890), p. 121.

91. Correspondence between the complex line and the real Euclidean plane. The operation of addition of vectors has been so defined that

$$OX' = OX + OP,$$

where O and P are fixed and X and X' variable points, may be taken as representing a translation carrying X to X'. The operation of multiplication has been defined so that

$$OX' = OP \cdot OX$$

may be taken to represent a direct similarity transformation carrying O into itself and X to X'. Thus the general direct similarity transformation may be written

$$OX' = OP \cdot OX + OQ.$$

* Cf. § 11. The reader who has omitted the starred sections in Chap. I may take a chain $\mathsf{C}(P_0P_1P_\infty)$ as by definition consisting of those points of a complex line which have real coördinates relative to the scale P_0, P_1, P_∞.

The last theorem may therefore be stated in the following form:

THEOREM 6. *Let Q_0, Q_1, Q_∞ be three arbitrary points of a complex projective line l, and let P_0 and P_1 be two arbitrary points of a Euclidean plane π in whose line at infinity l_∞ an elliptic absolute involution is given. There exists a one-to-one and reciprocal correspondence Γ in which P_0 corresponds to Q_0, P_1 to Q_1, l_∞ to Q_∞, and every ordinary point of π to a point of l distinct from Q_∞. This correspondence is such that to every projective transformation of l leaving Q_∞ invariant, i.e. to every transformation of the form*

(1) $$x' = ax + b, \qquad a \neq 0,$$

there corresponds a direct similarity transformation of π, and conversely.

The question immediately arises, What group of transformations of π corresponds to the general projective group on l, i.e. to the set of transformations

(2) $$x' = \frac{ax+b}{cx+d}, \qquad \begin{vmatrix} a & b \\ c & d \end{vmatrix} \neq 0\,?$$

The transformation of π corresponding to

(3) $$x' = 1/x$$

must change any point P to a point P' such that

$$P_0P' \ \ P_0P = P_0P_1.$$

Hence, by Theorem 3, $\measuredangle PP_0P_1$ is congruent to $\measuredangle P_1P_0P'$. Therefore the orthogonal line reflection with P_0P_1 as axis must carry P to a point P'' of the line P_0P'. If P be regarded as a variable point of a line through P_0, it follows that the correspondence between P' and P'' is projective. In this correspondence P_0 corresponds to the point at infinity of the line P_0P', and each of the points in which this line meets the circle through P_1 with P_0 as center corresponds to itself. Hence the correspondence between P' and P'' on a given line through P_0 is an involution, and P' and P'' are conjugate points with respect to the circle. Hence (§ 71), if P be a variable point of the plane, the correspondence between P' and P'' is an inversion. Hence

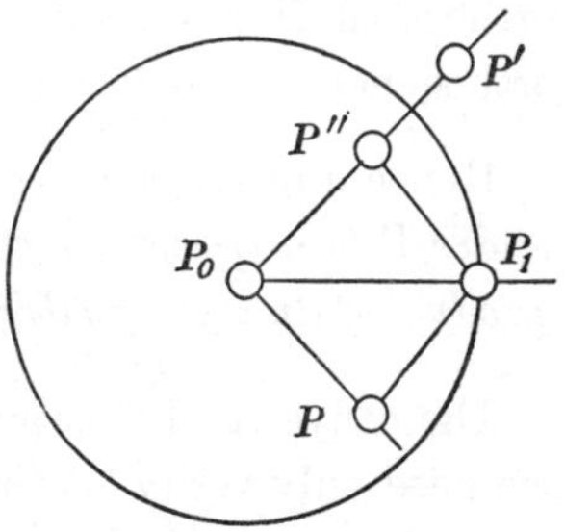

FIG. 70

the transformation of π corresponding to $x' = 1/x$ is the product of the orthogonal line reflection with P_0P_1 as axis and the inversion with respect to the circle through P_1 with P_0 as center.

Now any transformation (2) is evidently (cf. § 54, Vol. I) a product of transformations of the forms (1) and (3). But the transformation (1) has been seen to correspond to a direct similarity transformation, i.e. to a product of a dilation and a displacement. A displacement has been proved in Chap. IV to be a product of two orthogonal line reflections; and a dilation will now be shown to be a product of two or four inversions and orthogonal line reflections.

For consider a dilation Δ with a point O as center and carrying a point A to a point B. If O is not between A and B, there exists (Theorem 8, Chap. V) a pair of points C_1C_2 which separate A and B harmonically and have O as mid-point. Let I_1 be the inversion with respect to the circle with O as center and passing through C_1. The transformation $I_1\Delta$ leaves invariant all points of the circle through A with O as center, and effects a projectivity on each line through O which interchanges O and the point at infinity. The projectivity on each line through O is therefore the involution carrying each point to a conjugate point with regard to the circle through A with O as center. Hence $I_1\Delta$ is an inversion, I_2, with respect to this circle. From $I_1\Delta = I_2$ follows $\Delta = I_1I_2$. If O is between A and B, let Λ be the point reflection with O as center. The product $\Lambda\Delta$ is a dilation such that O is not between A and $\Lambda\Delta(A)$. Hence $\Lambda\Delta$ is a product of two inversions I_1, I_2 and $\Delta = \Lambda I_2 I_1$. Since Λ is a product of two orthogonal line reflections, Δ is a product of four inversions and orthogonal line reflections.

Hence *any projective transformation of a complex line l corresponds under Γ to a transformation of a real Euclidean plane π which is a product of an even number of inversions and orthogonal line reflections.*

The converse of this proposition is also valid. In order to prove it we need only verify (α) that the product of two orthogonal line reflections in π corresponds to a projectivity of l, (β) that the product of an orthogonal line reflection Λ and an inversion P of π corresponds to a projectivity of l, and (γ) that the product of two inversions P_1P_2 of π corresponds to a projectivity of l. The first of these statements is a corollary of Theorem 6.

To prove (β) let us first consider the case where the axis of Λ passes through the center O of P. Let O_1 be one of the points in which the axis of Λ meets the invariant circle of P, X be any point of π, and $X' = \Lambda\text{P}(X)$. The considerations given above in connection with the transformation (3) show that

$$OX' = \frac{OO_1}{OX},$$

and hence that ΛP corresponds to a transformation of l of the same type as (3), i.e. to an involution. Moreover, ΛP is obviously the same as PΛ. In case the axis of Λ does not pass through the center of P, let Λ' be an orthogonal line reflection whose axis passes through the center of P. Then

$$\Lambda\text{P} = \Lambda\Lambda' \cdot \Lambda'\text{P} \quad \text{and} \quad \text{P}\Lambda = \text{P}\Lambda' \cdot \Lambda'\Lambda.$$

The products $\Lambda\Lambda'$ and $\Lambda'\Lambda$ correspond to projectivities by Theorem 6, and $\text{P}\Lambda' = \Lambda'\text{P}$ corresponds to an involution by what has just been proved. Hence ΛP and PΛ correspond to projectivities.

To prove (γ) let Λ be an orthogonal line reflection whose axis contains the centers of P_1 and P_2. Then

$$\text{P}_1\text{P}_2 = \text{P}_1\Lambda \cdot \Lambda\text{P}_2.$$

The products $\text{P}_1\Lambda$ and ΛP_2 correspond to projectivities by (β). Hence P_1P_2 corresponds to a projectivity. Thus we have the important result:

THEOREM 7. *A projective transformation on a complex line corresponds under Γ to a transformation of the real Euclidean plane which is a product of an even number of inversions and orthogonal line reflections, and, conversely, any transformation of the real Euclidean plane of this type corresponds to a projectivity of the complex line.*

92. The inversion group in the real Euclidean plane.

DEFINITION. The transformations of a Euclidean plane and its line at infinity which are products of orthogonal line reflections and inversions are called *circular transformations,* and any circular transformation which is a product of an even number of inversions and orthogonal line reflections is said to be *direct.*

THEOREM 8. DEFINITION. *The set of all circular transformations of a Euclidean plane and its line at infinity in which an absolute involution is given constitute a group which is called* the inversion group. *The set of direct circular transformations form a subgroup of the inversion group, which, if the Euclidean plane is real, is isomorphic with the projective group of a complex line.*

The first part of this theorem is an obvious consequence of the definition, and the second is equivalent to Theorem 7. That not all circular transformations are direct is shown by the special case of an inversion. An inversion is not a direct circular transformation, because it leaves invariant all points of a circle and hence cannot correspond under Γ to a projectivity. Combining Theorems 8 and 6 we have

COROLLARY. *In a real Euclidean plane the group of circular transformations leaving l_∞ invariant is the Euclidean group, and the direct circular transformations leaving l_∞ invariant are the direct similarity transformations.*

The isomorphism between the group of direct circular transformations and the projective group on the line may be used as a source of theorems about the former. Thus the fundamental theorem of projective geometry (Assumption P) translates into the following theorem about the real Euclidean plane:

THEOREM 9. *A direct circular transformation which leaves three ordinary points, or two ordinary points and l_∞, invariant is the identity. There exists a direct circular transformation carrying any three distinct ordinary points A, B, C respectively into three distinct points A', B', C' respectively, or into A', B', and l_∞ respectively.*

Now consider a circular transformation Π which is not direct and which leaves three distinct points A, B, C invariant. By definition

$$\Pi = \Lambda_{2n+1} \cdot \Lambda_{2n} \cdots \Lambda_2 \cdot \Lambda_1,$$

where $\Lambda_i\ (i = 1, 2, \cdots, 2n+1)$ is an inversion or an orthogonal line reflection. Let Λ be an orthogonal line reflection whose axis contains A, B, C, if these points are collinear, or an inversion with respect to the circle containing them in case they are not collinear. Then $\Lambda\Pi$ is a direct circular transformation leaving A, B, C invariant. Hence

$$\Lambda\Pi = 1.$$

Since Λ is of period two, this implies

$$\Pi = \Lambda.$$

The same argument applies in case one of the points A, B, C is replaced by l_∞. Hence we have

THEOREM 10. *A circular transformation which is not direct and leaves invariant three distinct ordinary points A, B, C, or two ordinary points A, B, and l_∞, is an orthogonal line reflection or an inversion according as the invariant points are collinear or not.*

THEOREM 11. *If Π is a circular transformation and Λ an inversion or orthogonal line reflection, $\Pi\Lambda\Pi^{-1}$ is an inversion or orthogonal line reflection.*

Proof. Let A, B, C be three of the invariant points of Λ; then $\Pi\Lambda\Pi^{-1}$ leaves $\Pi(A)$, $\Pi(B)$, $\Pi(C)$ invariant. If

$$\Pi = \Lambda_1\Lambda_2 \cdots \Lambda_n,$$

where $\Lambda_1, \cdots, \Lambda_n$ are orthogonal line reflections or inversions, then

$$\Pi\Lambda\Pi^{-1} = \Lambda_1\Lambda_2 \cdots \Lambda_n\Lambda\Lambda_n \cdots \Lambda_2\Lambda_1,$$

and is thus a product of an odd number of orthogonal line reflections or inversions. Hence by the last theorem it is an orthogonal line reflection or an inversion.

The invariant elements of $\Pi\Lambda\Pi^{-1}$ are those to which the invariant elements of Λ are carried by Π. Since $\Pi\Lambda\Pi^{-1}$ is an inversion or an orthogonal line reflection, we have

COROLLARY 1. *Any circular transformation carries any circle into a circle or into the set of points on an ordinary line and on l_∞. It carries the set of points on l_∞ and an ordinary line into a set of this sort or into a circle.*

COROLLARY 2. *If C^2 and K^2 are any two circles and l any line, there exists a direct circular transformation carrying C^2 to K^2 and one carrying C^2 to the set of all points on l and l_∞.*

Proof. Let A, B, C be any three points of C^2, let A', B', C' be any three points of K^2, and let A', B' be any two points of l. By Theorem 9, there exist direct circular transformations Π and Π' such that

$$\Pi(ABC) = A'B'C' \quad \text{and} \quad \Pi'(ABC) = A'B'l_\infty.$$

Since A', B', C' are not collinear, the set of points into which Π carries C^2 must be a circle; and since there is only one circle containing A', B', C', this circle is K^2. Since there is no circle containing A', B', and l_∞, the set of points into which Π' carries C^2 must be the set of points on l_∞ and an ordinary line. Since the ordinary line contains A' and B', it must be l.

An inversion (§ 71) transforms all lines through its center into themselves and interchanges the center with l_∞. Hence, by the last two corollaries, we have at once

COROLLARY 3. *An inversion carries a circle through its center into the set of points on l_∞ and a line not passing through the center.*

COROLLARY 4. *A pair of circles which touch each other is carried by an inversion into a pair of circles which touch each other, or into a circle and a tangent line together with l_∞, or into two parallel lines and l_∞.*

Proof. Let C^2 and K^2 be two circles which touch each other Since an inversion is a one-to-one reciprocal correspondence except for the origin and l_∞, if neither C^2 nor K^2 passes through the origin, they must be carried into two circles having only one point in common and which therefore touch each other. If C^2 passes through the origin and K^2 does not, C^2 is carried into l_∞ and an ordinary line l, while K^2 is carried into a circle K_1^2 which has one and only one point in common with the line pair $l_\infty l$. Since l_∞ cannot meet K_1^2 in a real point, l meets it in a single point and therefore is tangent. If C^2 and K^2 both pass through the center of inversion, they are transformed into l_∞ and a pair of ordinary lines l, m. Since C^2 and K^2 have only the center of inversion in common and this is transformed into l_∞, the lines l and m can have no ordinary point in common. Hence l and m are parallel.

It was remarked in § 90 (just before the fine print at the end) that the correspondence Γ between the complex line and the real Euclidean plane is such that the points of a certain chain $\mathsf{C}(P_0P_1P_\infty)$, with the exception of P_∞, correspond to the points of a certain Euclidean line l. Since P_∞ corresponds to l_∞, the chain $\mathsf{C}(P_0P_1P_\infty)$ corresponds to the line pair ll_∞. Under the projective group on a line any two chains are equivalent; and under the group of direct circular transformations any circle is equivalent to any circle or any line pair ll_∞ (Cor. 2). Hence we have

THEOREM 12. *The correspondence Γ is such that chains in the complex line correspond to real circles or to line pairs ll_∞, where l is ordinary and l_∞ the line at infinity of the Euclidean plane.*

The theory of chains on a complex line is therefore equivalent to the theory of the real circles and lines of a Euclidean plane. In view of this equivalence we shall freely transform the terminology of the complex line to the Euclidean plane, and vice versa. Thus we shall speak of the cross ratio of four points in the Euclidean plane and of pencils of chains in the complex line. The exercises below contain a number of important theorems some of which can be obtained directly from the definitions in § 71 and some of which can be proved most simply by translating projective theorems on the complex line into the terminology of the Euclidean plane.

DEFINITION. An *imaginary circle* is an imaginary conic through the circular points such that its polar system transforms real points into real lines.

The definition of an inversion given in § 71 applies without change to the case of imaginary circles.

On the geometry of circles in general the reader is referred to the papers by Möbius in Vol. II of his collected works; to those by Steiner in Vol. I (especially pp. 16–83, 461–527) of his collected works; to Vol. II, Chaps. II, III, of the textbook by Doehlemann referred to in Ex. 4; and to the forthcoming book by J. L. Coolidge, A Treatise on the Circle and the Sphere, Oxford, 1916.

EXERCISES

1. An inversion with respect to an imaginary circle is a product of an inversion with respect to a real circle and a point reflection having the same center as the circle.

2. The inverse points on any line through the center O of a circle C^2 are the pairs of an involution having O as center. If A_1 and A_2 are any two inverse points, $OA_1 \cdot OA_2$ is a constant, which in case of a real circle is equal to $(OC)^2$, C being a point of C^2.

3. Two pairs of points AA' and BB' are inverse with respect to a circle with O as center if and only if (1) O is collinear with the pairs AA' and BB', and (2) the ordered triads OAB and $OB'A'$ are similar, but not directly similar.

4. A linkage which consists of a set of six bars OA, OC, AB, BC, CD, DA, jointed movably at the points O, A, B, C, D, and such that Dist $(OA) =$ Dist (OC) and $ABCD$ is a rhombus, is called a "Peaucellier inversor." If O is held fixed and B varies, the locus of D is inverse to that of B with respect to a circle with O as center. If B be constrained, say by an additional link, to move on a circle through O, D describes a line. On the general subject of linkages, cf. K. Doehlemann, Geometrische Transformationen, Vol. II, p. 90, Leipzig, 1908, and A. Emch, Projective Geometry, §§ 62–67, New York, 1905.

5. If A, B, C, D are four points of a Euclidean plane,

$$\text{R}\,(AB, CD) = ke^{i\theta},$$

where $$k = \frac{\text{Dist}\,(AC)}{\text{Dist}\,(AD)} \div \frac{\text{Dist}\,(BC)}{\text{Dist}\,(BD)} \quad \text{and} \quad \theta = \alpha - \beta,$$

where α and β are the measures of $\measuredangle CAD$ and $\measuredangle CBD$ respectively. The number k is invariant under the inversion group, and θ under the group of direct circular transformations. The four points are on a circle or collinear if $\theta = 0$.

6. Construct a point having with three given points a given cross ratio.

7. If Π is any circular transformation, the points $O = \Pi^{-1}(l_\infty)$ and $O' = \Pi(l_\infty)$ are called its vanishing points. The lines through O are transformed by Π into the lines through O'. If X is any point of the plane, and $X' = \Pi\,(X)$, then $\text{Dist}\,(OX) \cdot \text{Dist}\,(O'X')$ is a constant, called the *power* of the transformation (cf. § 43).

8. Let A and B be two points not collinear with O and let $\Pi\,(A) = A'$, $\Pi\,(B) = B'$. The ordered point triads OAB and $O'B'A'$ are directly similar if Π is direct, and similar, but not directly so, if Π is not direct.

9. The equations of an inversion relative to rectangular nonhomogeneous coördinates, having the center of inversion as origin, are

$$x' = \frac{kx}{x^2 + y^2}, \quad y' = \frac{ky}{x^2 + y^2}.$$

The circle of inversion is real or imaginary according as $k > 0$ or $k < 0$.

10. The coördinate system for the real Euclidean plane obtained by means of the isomorphism of the Euclidean group with the projective group leaving a point invariant on a complex line is such that the coördinate z of any point is $x + iy$, where x and y are the coördinates in a system of rectangular nonhomogeneous coördinates and $i^2 = -1$. The points z of a circle satisfy the condition

$$z = \frac{at + b}{ct + d}, \quad \begin{vmatrix} a & b \\ c & d \end{vmatrix} \neq 0,$$

where t is real and variable and a, b, c, d are complex and fixed. If $c = 0$, this circle reduces to a line.

11. The circles orthogonal to $z = \dfrac{at + b}{ct + d}$ are

$$z = \frac{(a + b\beta)\,it + b + a\alpha}{(c + d\beta)\,it + d + c\alpha},$$

where α and β are real.

12. The circles through two points z_1, z_2 are given by

$$z = \frac{atz_1 + z_2}{at + 1}.$$

13. A circle with z_1 as center is given by

$$z - z_1 = ke^{i\theta},$$

where $0 \leqq \theta < 2\pi$ and k is a real constant.

14. The centers of the circles circumscribing the four triangles formed by the sides of a complete quadrilateral are on a circle. This circle is called the *center circle* of the complete quadrilateral. The centers of the center circles of the five complete quadrilaterals formed by the sides of a complete five-line are on a circle called the *center circle* of the five-line. Generalize this result.

93. Generalization by inversion. By the corollary of Theorem 8 the set of direct circular transformations leaving l_∞ invariant is the group of direct similarity transformations, and the set of all circular transformations leaving l_∞ invariant is the Euclidean group. This is the basis of a method of *generalization by inversion* entirely analogous to the *generalization by projection* employed in § 73.

In case a figure F_1 which is under investigation can be transformed by one or more inversions into a known figure F_2, then such of the relations among the elements of F_2 as are invariant under circular transformations must hold good among the corresponding elements of F_1.

In order to apply this method it is necessary to know relations which are left invariant by the circular transformations. The most elementary of these are given in the last section, but perhaps the most important property of an inversion for this purpose is that of *isogonality*, or "preservation of angles."

DEFINITION. If C_1^2 and C_2^2 are two circles having a point Q in common, and m_1 and m_2 are the tangents to C_1^2 and C_2^2 respectively at Q, the measure (according to § 72) of the ordered line pair m_1m_2 is called the *angular measure* of the ordered pair of circles at Q, or simply the *angle* between the two circles at Q. If C_1^2 is any circle, m_2 a line meeting it in a point Q, and m_1 the tangent to C_1^2 at Q, the measure of the ordered line pair m_2m_1 is called the *angle* between m_2 and C_1^2, and the measure of m_1m_2 is called the *angle* between C_1^2 and m_2. The measure of a line pair m_1m_2 is called the *angle** between m_1 and m_2.

THEOREM 13. *An angle a between two circles or a circle and a line or between two lines is changed into $\pi - a$ by an inversion or*

* In accordance with common usage, we are here using the term "angle" to denote a number, in spite of the fact that we use it in § 28 to denote a geometrical figure.

an orthogonal line reflection and is left unaltered by any direct circular transformation.

Proof. The statement with regard to direct circular transformations is an obvious consequence of the one with regard to inversions and orthogonal line reflections. What we have to prove is, therefore, the following:

Let Π be an inversion or an orthogonal line reflection, and let l_1 and l_2 be two lines meeting in a point P such that $\Pi(P) = Q$ is an ordinary point. If l_1 is carried by Π into a line, let this line be denoted by m_1; and if l_1 (together with l_∞) is carried to a circle C_1^2, let m_1 denote the tangent to C_1^2 at Q; likewise, if l_2 is carried by Π into a line, let this line be denoted by m_2; and if l_2 (together with l_∞) is carried to a circle C_2^2, let m_2 denote the tangent to C_2^2 at Q. The two ordered pairs of lines l_1l_2 and m_1m_2 are symmetric.

In case Π is an orthogonal line reflection, $m_1 = \Pi(l_1)$ and $m_2 = \Pi(l_2)$, and the proposition is a direct consequence of the definition of the term "symmetric" (§ 57). Suppose, then, that Π is an inversion having a point O as center.

One of the lines l_1, l_2, say l_1, can be transformed into itself if and only if l_1 is on O. By hypothesis $O \neq P$; hence if $\Pi(l_1) = l_1$, the line l_2 goes into the set of points different from O on a circle C_2^2 through O and Q. Then m_2 is the tangent to C_2^2 at Q. Any line through O which meets l_2 in an ordinary point X meets C_2^2 in the point which corresponds to X under the inversion. Hence the line n_2 through O and tangent to C_2^2 cannot meet l_2 in an ordinary point, and is therefore parallel to l_2. Hence the line pair l_1l_2 is congruent to the pair l_1n_2. The line m_2 is the tangent to C_2^2 at Q. Since l_1n_2 is carried to l_1m_2 by the orthogonal line reflection whose axis is the perpendicular bisector of OQ, the pair l_1n_2 is symmetric with l_1m_2. Hence l_1l_2 is symmetric with l_1m_2.

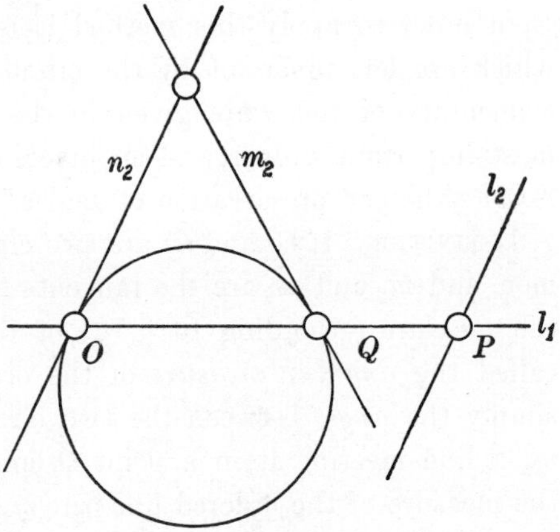

FIG. 71

If neither of the lines l_1, l_2 is transformed into itself, neither passes through O. Let l denote the line OP. Then by the last paragraph ll_1 is symmetric with lm_1, and ll_2 with lm_2. But by Theorem 13, Chap. IV, the symmetry which carries ll_1 to lm_1 must be identical with that which carries ll_2 to lm_2. Hence l_1l_2 is symmetric with m_1m_2.

As an exercise in generalization by inversion let us prove the following:

THEOREM 14. *If three circles C_1^2, C_2^2, C_3^2 meet in a point O in such a way that each pair of them makes an angle $\frac{\pi}{3}$, and also meet by pairs in three other points P, Q, R, the circle (or line) through P, Q and R makes with each of the other circles an angle $\frac{\pi}{3}$.*

Proof. The pair of circles which meet at O obviously make the angle $\frac{\pi}{3}$ at each of the points P, Q, R. An inversion Π with respect to a circle having O as center must therefore change them into the sides of an equilateral triangle. The circle circumscribing this triangle makes the angle $\frac{\pi}{3}$ with each of the sides. But since this circle is the transform of the circle PQR by Π, the conclusion of the theorem follows.

As a second application of the theory of inversion, in combination with projective methods, we may consider the theorem of Feuerbach on the nine point circle (cf. Ex. 2, § 73).

THEOREM 15. *The nine-point circle of a triangle touches the four inscribed circles.*

Proof. Let the given triangle be ABC, and let the mid-points of the pairs BC, CA, AB be A_1, B_1, C_1 respectively. The nine-point circle is the circle containing A_1, B_1, C_1.

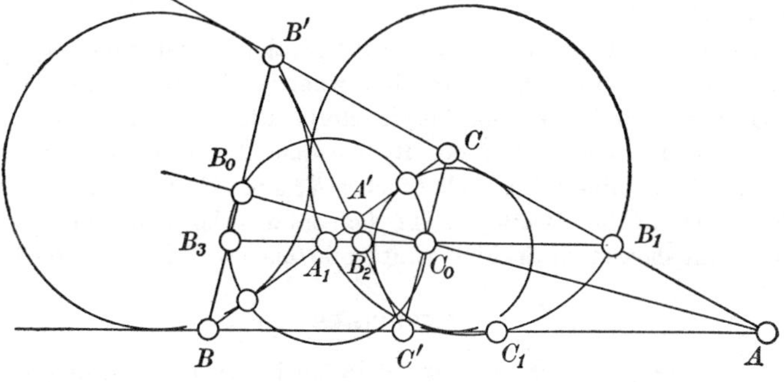

FIG. 72

Let K_1^2 and K_2^2 be the two inscribed circles whose centers are on one of the bisectors of $\measuredangle CAB$. In case K_1^2 and K_2^2 touch the line BC at the same point, this is the mid-point A_1 of the pair BC, the triangle ABC is isosceles, and the nine-point circle obviously touches K_1^2 and K_2^2 at A_1. In every other case there is one line, l, besides AB, BC, CA, which touches both K_1^2 and K_2^2. Let $A'B'C'$ be the points in which l meets the sides BC, CA, AB respectively. Then AA', BB', CC' are the pairs of opposite vertices of a complete quadrilateral circumscribing both K_1^2 and K_2^2, and the diagonal triangle of this quadrilateral is a self-polar triangle both for K_1^2 and K_2^2 (§ 44, Vol. I). Since the side AA' of this triangle is the line of centers of K_1^2 and K_2^2, the other two sides, BB' and CC', are parallel to each other and perpendicular to AA'. Let their points of intersection with AA' be B_0 and C_0 respectively. These two points are conjugate with respect to both circles, and hence must be the limiting points of the pencil of circles containing K_1^2 and K_2^2. The radical axis of the pencil of circles is the perpendicular bisector of the pair B_0C_0, and hence (§ 40) passes through the mid-points of all the pairs BC, $B'C'$, BC', $B'C$, B_0C_0. In particular the radical axis of K_1^2 and K_2^2 passes through A_1, the mid-point of BC. Hence there is a circle G^2 with A_1 as center and passing through B_0 and C_0.

Let Γ be the inversion with respect to G^2. Since this circle passes through B_0 and C_0, it is orthogonal both to K_1^2 and K_2^2 (Theorem 34, § 71), and hence Γ transforms each of these circles into itself. We shall now prove that Γ transforms l into the nine-point circle.

Let B_2 be the point in which A_1B_1 meets l. Since A_1B_1 is parallel to AB, it is not parallel to l, and hence B_2 is an ordinary point. Since A_1B_1 contains the mid-point A_1 of the pair CB and is parallel to BC', it contains the mid-point C_0 of the pair CC'. The involution which Γ effects on the line A_1B_1 must have C_0 as one of its double points and A_1 as its center; hence the other double point must be the point B_3 in which A_1B_1 meets BB', because A_1 is the mid-point of the pair C_0B_3. Thus G^2 passes through B_3 as well as through C_0. But since

$$B_0A'C_0A \overset{B'}{\underset{\wedge}{=}} B_3B_2C_0B_1,$$

B_1 and B_2 are harmonically conjugate with respect to C_0 and B_3. Hence Γ transforms B_2 to B_1.

In like manner it can be shown that if C_2 is the point in which A_1C_1 meets l, Γ transforms C_2 to C_1. Since any line whatever is transformed by Γ to a circle through A_1, it follows that l is transformed to the circle through A_1, B_1, and C_1, i.e. to the nine-point circle. By Theorem 11, Cor. 4, since l is tangent to K_1^2 and K_2^2, the nine-point circle touches K_1^2 and K_2^2. Since it has not been specified which of the bisectors of $\measuredangle CAB$ contains the centers of K_1^2 and K_2^2, this argument shows that the nine-point circle touches all four inscribed circles.

EXERCISES

1. Any three points can be carried by an inversion into three collinear points.

2. Two nonintersecting circles can be carried by an inversion into concentric circles.

3. Any direct circular transformation is a product of an inversion and an orthogonal line reflection.

4. A product of two inversions is an involution if and only if the circles are orthogonal.

5. Of four circles mutually perpendicular by pairs, three can be real.

6. The nine-point circle meets the circle through C_0 having A_1 as center in points of the line $A'B'$.

7. The nine-point circle of a triangle touches the sixteen circles inscribed to the triangle or to any of the triangles formed by pairs of its vertices with the orthocenter.

8. Let three circles C_1^2, C_2^2, C_3^2 meet in a point O, and let P_1, P_2, P_3 be the other points of intersection of the pairs $C_2^2C_3^2$, $C_3^2C_1^2$, $C_1^2C_2^2$ respectively. If Q_1 be any point of C_1^2, Q_2 the point of C_2^2 collinear with and distinct from Q_1 and P_3, and Q_3 the point of C_3^2 collinear with and distinct from Q_2 and P_1, then Q_3, P_2, and Q_1 are collinear.

9. *The problem of Apollonius.* Construct the circles touching three given circles. Cf. Pascal, Repertorium der Höheren Mathematik, II 1, Chap. II, on this and the following exercise.

10. *The problem of Malfatti.* Given a triangle, determine three circles each of which is tangent to the other two and also to two sides of the triangle.

94. Inversions in the complex Euclidean plane. Thus far we have dealt only with a real Euclidean plane. The definition of an inversion given in § 71, however, applies without change in the complex Euclidean plane; i.e. two points A_1, A_2 are inverse with respect to a circle C^2, provided they are conjugate with respect to C^2 and collinear with its center. The transformation thus defined is obviously one to one and reciprocal for all points of the complex projective plane except those on the sides of the triangle OI_1I_2, where O is the center of C^2, and I_1 and I_2 are the circular points at infinity. Any point of l_∞ is carried to O by the inversion, and O is carried to every point of l_∞. The circular point I_1 is transformed to every point of the line OI_1, and every point of the line OI_1 is transformed to I_1. In like manner I_2 is transformed to every point of the line OI_2, and every point of this line is carried to I_2.

DEFINITION. The sides of the triangle OI_1I_2 are called the *singular lines* of the inversion with respect to C^2, and the points on these lines are called its *singular points*.

The principal properties of an inversion may be inferred from the following construction: If A_1 is any point not on a side of the triangle OI_1I_2, let B_1 and B_2 be the points distinct from I_1 and I_2 (fig. 73) in which the lines A_1I_1 and A_1I_2 respectively meet C^2. Let A_2 be the point of intersection of I_1B_2 and I_2B_1. The points A_1 and A_2

are mutually inverse because, by familiar theorems on conics, they are conjugate with regard to C^2 and collinear with O.

From this construction it is evident in the first place that all points, except I_1 of the line A_1I_1, are transformed into points of the line A_2I_2, and vice versa. Hence an inversion transforms the minimal lines through I_1 into the minimal lines through I_2, and vice versa. Moreover, the correspondence between the two pencils of minimal lines is such that if B is a variable point of C^2, the line I_1B always corresponds to I_2B. In other words, the correspondence effected by an inversion between the two pencils of minimal lines is a projectivity generating the invariant circle C^2.

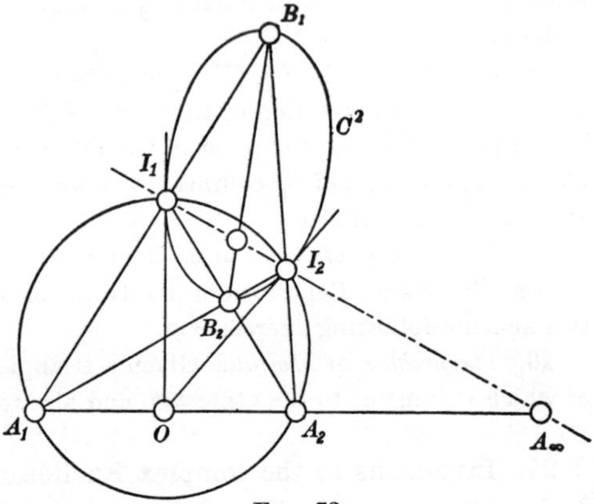

FIG. 73

The definitions of circular and of direct circular transformations, given in § 92, apply without change in the complex Euclidean plane. The result just obtained therefore implies that *any direct circular transformation transforms each pencil of minimal lines projectively into itself, and any nondirect circular transformation transforms each pencil of minimal lines projectively into the other.*

Now suppose that A_1 is a variable point on any line l not containing I_1 or I_2.

(4) $$I_1[A_1] \overset{l}{\underset{\wedge}{=}} I_2[A_1].$$

Since B_1 and B_2 are always on the conic C^2,

(5) $$I_1[A_1] \;\overline{\wedge}\; I_2[B_1],$$

and

(6) $$I_2[A_1] \;\overline{\wedge}\; I_1[B_2].$$

Hence

(7) $$I_2[B_1] \;\overline{\wedge}\; I_1[B_2].$$

But corresponding lines of these two pencils intersect in the variable point A_2, which is therefore always on a conic through I_1 and I_2

or on a line. In the projectivity (5) the line I_2O corresponds to l_∞; in (4) l_∞ corresponds to itself; and in (6) l_∞ corresponds to I_1O. Hence in (7) the line I_2O corresponds to I_1O, and so the circle or line generated by (7) passes through O.

This result may be stated in a form which takes account of the singular elements, as follows: *Any degenerate conic consisting of l_∞ and a nonminimal line is carried by an inversion with respect to C^2 into a conic (degenerate or not) which passes through I_1, I_2, and O.*

Next suppose A_1 to be a variable point on any nondegenerate conic through I_1 and I_2. In this case

$$I_1[A_1] \barwedge I_2[A_1], \tag{8}$$

and hence by the projectivities (5) and (6) we have

$$I_2[A_2] \barwedge I_1[A_2]. \tag{9}$$

Hence A_2 is again on a conic through I_1 and I_2, which can degenerate only if l_∞ corresponds to itself under (9). The latter case implies, by (5) and (6), that I_1O and I_2O correspond under (8) or, in other words, that the locus of A_1 passes through O. Hence *any nondegenerate conic K^2 through I_1 and I_2 corresponds by the inversion with respect to C^2 to a conic through I_1 and I_2, which degenerates into a pair of lines, one of which is l_∞, only in case K^2 passes through O.*

This result, together with the other statement italicized above, amount to an extension of Cors. 1 and 3 of Theorem 11 to the complex Euclidean plane. From our present point of view we can also establish the following theorem, which did not come out of the reasoning in § 92.

THEOREM 16. *The correspondence between two circles which are homologous under an inversion is projective.*

Proof. If A_1 is a variable point of one circle and A_2 of the other, then, in the notation above, $I_2B_1 = I_2A_2$, and hence by (5)

$$I_1[A_1] \barwedge I_2[A_2],$$

which is a necessary and sufficient condition that the correspondence between the two circles be projective (cf. the corollary and definitions following Theorem 10, Chap. VIII, Vol. I).

The same reasoning also applies in case one or both of the conics which are the loci of A_1 and A_2 degenerate. We thus have

COROLLARY. *A projective correspondence is established by an inversion between any two homologous lines or between a line and its homologous set of points on a circle.*

The proof of Theorem 13 on the preservation of angles under a circular transformation applies without change in the complex Euclidean plane. This theorem can also be proved by the use of considerations with regard to the circular points. We shall give the argument for the case of orthogonal circles, leaving it as an exercise for the reader to derive the proof along these lines for the general case.

It has been proved in § 71 that the circles through two points A_1, A_2 are orthogonal to the circles through two points B_1, B_2 if and only if the pairs A_1A_2, B_1B_2, and I_1I_2 are pairs of opposite vertices of a complete quadrilateral (cf. fig. 73). The sides I_1A_1, I_1A_2, I_2A_1, I_2A_2 of such a quadrilateral are transformed by an inversion relative to any circle into four lines through I_1 and I_2. Hence the points A_1, A_2, B_1, B_2 are transformed into four points A_1', A_2', B_1', B_2' such that I_1I_2, $A_1'A_2'$, and $B_1'B_2'$ are pairs of opposite vertices of a complete quadrilateral. Hence the pencils of circles through A_1, A_2 and B_1, B_2 respectively are transformed into two pencils such that the circles of one pencil are orthogonal to those of the other.

With this result it is easy to prove that Theorems 8–11, 13, and their corollaries hold in the complex Euclidean plane, proper exceptions being made so as to exclude minimal lines and pairs of points on minimal lines. This is left as an exercise.

95. Correspondence between the real Euclidean plane and a complex pencil of lines. The correspondence between a complex one-dimensional form and the points of a real Euclidean plane, together with l_∞, can be established in a particularly interesting way if the one-dimensional form be taken as the pencil of lines on one of the circular points of the line at infinity of the Euclidean plane.

Let l_∞ be the line at infinity, and I_1 be one of the circular points. By Theorem 15, Chap. V, each line through I_1 contains at least one real point. No line through I_1, except l_∞, can contain more than one real point; for otherwise it would be a real line, and hence would meet l_∞ in a real point contrary to the fact that I_1 is imaginary. Then each line through I_1, except l_∞, contains one and only one real point of the Euclidean plane. Let us denote by Γ' the correspondence by which l_∞ corresponds to itself and the other lines through I_1 correspond each to the real point which it contains.

By § 94 a direct circular transformation transforms the pencil of lines on I_1 projectively into itself. Hence every direct circular transformation corresponds under Γ' to a projectivity of the lines on I_1.

By Theorem 9 there is one and only one direct circular transformation carrying an ordered triad of distinct points to an ordered triad of distinct points; and by Assumption P there is one and only one projectivity carrying an ordered triad of lines of a pencil to any ordered triad of the pencil. Hence a given projectivity of the pencil of lines on I_1 can correspond under Γ' to only one direct circular transformation. In other words, Γ' sets up a simple isomorphism between the projective group of a complex one-dimensional form and the group of direct circular transformations.

The correspondence between the points of a real line and the lines joining them to I_1 is evidently projective. Since the cross ratio of four points of a real line is real, so is the cross ratio of the lines joining them to I_1. Hence any real line together with l_∞ corresponds under Γ' to a chain. Since any two chains of a one-dimensional form are projectively equivalent, and any circle of the Euclidean plane is equivalent under the inversion group to an ordinary line and l_∞, it follows that under Γ' any chain corresponds to a circle and any circle to a chain.

The correspondence Γ' may be used to transfer the theory of involution from the complex pencil of lines to the Euclidean plane. Let AA', BB', CC' be pairs of opposite vertices of a complete quadrilateral of the Euclidean plane. The pairs of lines joining these point pairs to I_1 are pairs of an involution. Hence

THEOREM 17. *The pairs of opposite vertices of a complete quadrilateral are pairs of an involution, i.e. they are pairs of homologous points in a direct circular transformation of period two.*

In other words, the pairs of opposite vertices of a complete quadrilateral constitute the image under Γ' (and hence under Γ) of a quadrangular set. While the converse of this proposition is not true, the proposition can be generalized by inversion so as to give a construction for the most general quadrangular set in which no four of the six points are on the same circle or line (cf. Ex. 1, below). We shall state the construction in terms of chains.*

THEOREM 18. *Given two pairs of points AA' and BB' and a point C such that no four of the five points are on the same chain. The chains $\mathsf{C}(AB'C)$ and $\mathsf{C}(A'BC)$ either meet in a point D other than C or touch each other at C. In the latter case let D denote C. The chains $\mathsf{C}(DAB)$ and $\mathsf{C}(DA'B')$ meet in a point C' such that AA', BB', CC' are pairs of an involution.*

Proof. Consider the figure in the Euclidean plane (together with l_∞) corresponding under Γ' to the figure described in the theorem. If $\Gamma'(D) \neq l_\infty$, $\Gamma'(D)$ can be transformed to l_∞ by an inversion I. Under $\mathrm{I}\Gamma'$ the four chains $\mathsf{C}(AB'C)$, $\mathsf{C}(A'BC)$, $\mathsf{C}(DAB)$, and $\mathsf{C}(DA'B')$ correspond to Euclidean lines (with l_∞), and hence AA', BB', CC' correspond to the vertices of a complete quadrilateral; so that the theorem reduces to Theorem 17. If $\Gamma'(D) = l_\infty$, the theorem reduces directly to Theorem 17.

COROLLARY. *Three pairs of points on a complex line AA', BB', CC', such that the chains $\mathsf{C}(A'B'C')$, $\mathsf{C}(A'BC)$, $\mathsf{C}(AB'C)$, $\mathsf{C}(ABC')$ are distinct, are pairs of an involution if and only if the four chains have a point in common.*

EXERCISES

1. Three pairs of points of the same chain AA', BB', CC' are in involution if for any point D not in the chain the chains $\mathsf{C}(DAA')$, $\mathsf{C}(DBB')$, $\mathsf{C}(DCC')$ are in the same pencil.

2. Derive Ex. 15, § 81, from the theory of involutions in a plane.

3. If AA', BB', CC' are pairs of opposite vertices of a complete quadrilateral, the three circles having AA', BB', CC' respectively as ends of their diameters belong to the same pencil, and the radical axis of this pencil passes through the center of the circle circumscribing the diagonal triangle of the quadrilateral.

4. Construct the double points of an involution in a Euclidean plane with ruler and compass.

* This puts in evidence the fact that while the geometry of real one-dimensional forms depends essentially on constructions implying the existence of two-dimensional forms, the geometry of the complex projective line could be developed without supposing the existence of points outside the line.

96. The real inversion plane. In a real Euclidean plane an inversion has been seen to be a one-to-one and reciprocal transformation except in that it transforms l_∞ to the center of inversion, and the center to l_∞. An inversion, therefore, is strictly one to one if we regard it as a transformation of the set of objects composed of the points of the real Euclidean plane together with l_∞ regarded as a single object.

DEFINITION. The set of points in a real Euclidean plane, together with the line at infinity regarded as a single object, is called a *real inversion plane*; l_∞ is called the *point at infinity* of the inversion plane. The set of points on a real circle, or on a real line l together with l_∞, is called a *circle* of the inversion plane. An *inversion* is either an inversion in the sense of § 71 with respect to a real or imaginary circle or an orthogonal line reflection. Circular transformations, etc. are defined as in § 92. The set of theorems about the inversion plane, which remain valid when the figures to which they refer are subjected to every transformation of the inversion group, is called the *real inversion geometry.*

Although the point at infinity receives special mention in this definition, from the point of view of the inversion geometry it is not to be distinguished from any other point of the inversion plane. For any point of the inversion plane can be carried to any other point of it by an inversion. In a set of assumptions for the inversion geometry as a separate science, there would be no mention of a point at infinity; just as there is no mention of a line or a plane at infinity in our assumptions for projective geometry.

The inversion geometry has a relation to the Euclidean geometry which is entirely analogous to the relation of the projective geometry to the Euclidean; namely, the set of transformations of the inversion group which leaves one point of the inversion plane invariant is a parabolic metric group in the Euclidean plane obtained by omitting this point from the inversion plane.

A large class of theorems about circles can be stated with the utmost simplicity in terms of the geometry of inversion. For example, the propositions that three noncollinear ordinary points determine a circle and that two ordinary points determine a line combine into the single proposition:

THEOREM 19. *In the inversion plane any three distinct points are on one and but one circle.*

The theorem that there is one and only one circle touching a given circle C^2 at a given point A, and passing through a given point B not on C^2, may be put in the following form, which also includes the proposition that through a given point not on a given line l there is one and but one line parallel to l.

THEOREM 20. *There is one and but one circle through a point A on a circle C^2 and a point B not on C^2, and having no point except A in common with C^2.*

The theory of pencils of circles makes no special mention of the radical axis (§ 71), for the radical axis (with l_∞) is merely one circle of the pencil and is indistinguishable from the other circles. In like manner the center of a circle is not to be distinguished from any other point; for the center is merely the inverse of l_∞, with respect to the circle, and the inversion group does not leave l_∞ invariant.

Thus the theory of pencils of circles in the inversion geometry involves no reference to the radical axis or to the line of centers. A pencil of circles may be defined as follows:

DEFINITION. A *pencil of circles* is either (a) the set of all circles through two distinct points, or (b) the set of all circles orthogonal to the circles of a pencil of Type (a), or (c) the set of all circles through a point of a given circle C^2 and meeting C^2 in no other point. A pencil of circles is said to be *hyperbolic*, *elliptic*, or *parabolic*, according as it is of Types (a), (b), or (c). Any point common to all circles of a pencil is called a *base point* of the pencil.

By comparison with the theorems in the preceding sections it is evident that the pencils of circles of these three types include all the pencils referred to in § 71 and also certain pencils of circles which are regarded as degenerate, from the Euclidean point of view. Thus, consider a pencil of lines through an ordinary point of a Euclidean plane. Each of these lines, with l_∞, constitutes a degenerate circle, and the set of degenerate circles is a pencil according to the definition above. Again, a pencil of parallel lines in the Euclidean plane determines a set of circles $[K^2]$ in the inversion plane which have in common only the one point l_∞. By Theorem 11, Cor. 3, any inversion Γ with a center O transforms $[K^2]$ into a set of circles $[K_1^2]$ through O which have in common no other real points than O.

Since there is one and only one circle of the set $[K_1^2]$ through every point of the Euclidean plane, $[K_1^2]$ must be a pencil of circles of Type (c).

The fundamental theorems about circular transformations may be stated as follows:

THEOREM 21. *A circular transformation is a one-to-one transformation of the inversion plane which carries circles into circles. There is a unique direct circular transformation carrying three distinct points A, B, C to three distinct points A', B', C' respectively. A circular transformation leaving three points invariant is either an inversion relative to the circle through these three points or the identity.*

The theorems on orthogonal circles in § 71, together with the corresponding propositions on circles, lines, and orthogonal line reflections, become:

THEOREM 22. *Two circles are orthogonal if and only if one of them passes through two points which are inverse with respect to the other.*

COROLLARY 1. *Two circles are orthogonal if and only if they belong respectively to two pencils of circles such that the limiting points of one pencil are the common points of the circles of the other pencil.*

COROLLARY 2. *If A_1 and A_2 are inverse with respect to a circle C^2, all circles through A_1 and orthogonal to C^2 pass through A_2.*

The correspondence Γ, which was established in §§ 90, 91, between the Euclidean plane and the complex projective line, is one to one and reciprocal between the inversion plane and the complex line. Since circles and chains correspond under Γ, the inversion geometry is identical with the geometry of chains on a complex line. The direct circular transformations of the inversion plane correspond to the projectivities of the complex line.

It follows from § 90 that the inversion with respect to the chain $\mathsf{C}(Q_0Q_1Q_\infty)$ transforms every point $z = x + iy$ into the conjugate imaginary point $\bar{z} = x - iy$. Hence an inversion with regard to any chain is a transformation projectively equivalent to that by which each point goes to its conjugate imaginary point (cf. § 78). For this reason we make the definition:

DEFINITION. Two points are said to be *conjugate* with respect to a chain if they are inverse with respect to it.

It is easily seen that any nondirect circular transformation is a product of a particular inversion and a direct circular transformation. Hence any nondirect transformation may be written in the form

$$z' = \frac{a\bar{z} + b}{c\bar{z} + d}.$$

We shall return to this subject in § 99.

EXERCISES

1. Construct a set of assumptions for the inversion geometry as a separate science.*

2. Work out the theorems analogous to those of §§ 71, 90–96 for the parabolic metric group in a modular space. Thus obtain a modular inversion geometry. The number of points in a finite inversion plane is $p^2 + 1$ if the number of points on a circle is $p + 1$.

3. The double points of an involution leaving a chain invariant are inverse with respect to the chain.

97. Order relations in the real inversion plane. The more elementary theorems on order relations in the inversion plane follow readily from the corresponding theorems for the Euclidean and projective planes. Suppose we start with a projective plane π'. By leaving out a line l_∞ of π', a Euclidean plane π is determined; and by regarding l_∞ as a point, an inversion plane $\bar{\pi}$ is determined. Any line l of π' which is distinct from l_∞ determines a circle of the inversion plane π; and we now define the order relations on this circle as identical with the projective order relations of l, the point l_∞ taking the place of the point in which l meets l_∞. The order relations on any circle which does not contain l_∞ are determined by § 20.

Since the correspondence effected between any two circles by an inversion is projective (Theorem 16), it follows that the order relations among the points on any circle are unaltered by inversion. Hence order relations on circles are unaltered by circular transformations.

On a complex line the order relations in a chain are identical with the order relations on a real line as developed in §§ 18, 19, 21–24. The correspondence Γ (§§ 90, 91) is such that the order relations of corresponding sets of points on a chain $\mathrm{C}(Q_0 Q_1 Q_\infty)$ and the circle $P_0 P_1 l_\infty$ are identical. Since order relations on circles are unaltered by

* This question has been treated for the three-dimensional case by **M. Pieri,** Giornale di Matematiche, Vol. XLIX (1911), p. 49, and Vol. L, p. 106.

circular transformations, and order relations on chains are unaltered by projectivities, it follows that Γ is such that the order relations of corresponding sets of points on any chain and the corresponding circle are identical. Therefore the theory of order in the inversion plane applies also to the complex line.

Returning to the Euclidean plane π', we know by § 28 that the points not on an ordinary line l fall into two classes such that any two points of the same class are joined by a segment not meeting l, whereas a line joining two points of different classes always meets l. By § 64 any circle containing two points of different classes meets l in two points. We thus have

THEOREM 23. DEFINITION. *The points of an inversion plane not on a circle C^2 fall into two classes, called* the two sides of C^2, *such that two points on the same side of C^2 are joined by a segment of a circle which does not contain any point of C^2, and such that any circle containing two points on different sides of C^2 contains two points of C^2.*

Since order relations on circles are not altered by inversion, there follows:

COROLLARY 1. *If two points are on opposite sides of a circle C^2, the points to which they are transformed by an inversion Π are on opposite sides of $\Pi(C)$.*

On a complex line the points on one side of the chain $\mathsf{C}(Q_0Q_1Q_\infty)$ are evidently those whose coördinates relative to the scale Q_0, Q_1, Q_∞ are $x+iy$, where x is real and y real and positive, and those on the other side are those whose coördinates are $x-iy$. Hence, in general,

COROLLARY 2. *The points D and D' are on opposite sides of a circle through A, B, C if and only if y and y' are of opposite sign in the following two equations:*

$$\mathrm{R}(AB,\ CD) = x + iy, \qquad \mathrm{R}(AB,\ CD') = x' + iy',$$

where x, y, x', y' are all real.

DEFINITION. A throw $\mathsf{T}(AB, CD)$ is said to be *neutral* if $\mathrm{R}(AB, CD)$ is real. Two throws $\mathsf{T}(AB, CD)$ and $\mathsf{T}(A'B', C'D')$ are *similarly* or *oppositely sensed* according as y and y' are of the same or of opposite signs in the equations

$$\mathrm{R}(AB,\ CD) = x + iy \quad \text{and} \quad \mathrm{R}(A'B',\ C'D') = x' + iy',$$

x, y, x', y' being real.

From this definition it is obvious that a direct circular transformation transforms any non-neutral throw into a similarly sensed throw. It is also obvious that an inversion which reduces in the Euclidean plane π to an orthogonal line reflection changes non-neutral throws into oppositely sensed throws. Hence we have

THEOREM 24. *A direct circular transformation carries non-neutral throws into similarly sensed throws, and a nondirect circular transformation carries them into oppositely sensed throws.*

EXERCISES

1. Two circles C^2, K^2 intersecting in two distinct points separate the inversion plane into four classes of points such that two points of the same class are joined by a segment of a circle containing no points of C^2 and K^2, whereas any circle containing points of different classes contains points of C^2 and K^2.

2. Two points which are inverse with respect to a circle are on opposite sides of it.

3. What is the relation between the sense of throws as defined above and the sense of noncollinear point triads in a Euclidean plane as defined in § 30?

4. In a Euclidean plane if a triangle ABC is carried to a triangle $A'B'C'$ by an inversion, the sense $S(ABC)$ is the same as or different from $S(A'B'C')$ according as the center of the inversion is or is not interior to the circle ABC.

5. In the notation of Ex. 7, § 92, if O is interior to a circle C^2, then O' is interior to $\Pi(C^2)$, and every point interior to C^2 is transformed by Π to a point exterior to O'.

98. Types of circular transformations. By § 5 every projectivity on a complex line has one or two double points. On account of the correspondence Γ the same result holds for the direct circular transformations of the real inversion plane.

Let us consider first a transformation Π having but one double point. In the theory of projectivities such a transformation has been called parabolic; and it has been proved that there is one and but one parabolic projectivity leaving a point M invariant and carrying a point A_0 to a point A_1. We have also seen that if A_{-1} is the point which goes to A_0, $\text{R}(MA_0, A_1A_{-1}) = -1$. Hence A_{-1}, A_0, A_1 are on the same chain through M. Since A_{-1}, A_0, M are transformed into A_0, A_1, M respectively, this chain is left invariant by Π.

In like manner any other point B_0 not on the chain $\mathsf{C}(A_0A_1M)$ determines a chain which is left invariant by Π. These two chains cannot have another point than M in common, because this point would have to be left invariant by Π. Thus Π leaves invariant a set of chains through M no two of which have a point in common, and such that there is one and only one chain of the set through any point except M.

If Π be regarded as a transformation of the inversion plane, this means that Π leaves invariant each circle of a pencil of circles of the parabolic type. In the Euclidean plane ϵ, obtained by leaving M out of the inversion plane, this pencil of circles is a system of parallel lines and Π is a direct similarity transformation. Now let us regard ϵ from the projective point of view. The transformation Π leaves all points of the line at infinity of ϵ invariant, because it leaves each of the circular points invariant as well as the point at infinity of the system of parallel lines. Hence Π is a translation in the Euclidean plane ϵ.

This result may be expressed in terms of the inversion plane as follows:

THEOREM 25. *Any direct circular transformation with only one invariant point transforms into itself every pencil of circles of the parabolic type having this point as base point. One and only one of these pencils is such that each circle of the pencil is invariant.*

Returning to the Euclidean plane we have

THEOREM 26. *Any direct similarity transformation which is not a translation or the identity leaves invariant one and only one ordinary point.*

Proof. Regard the Euclidean plane as obtained by omitting one point from an inversion plane. A direct similarity transformation effects a transformation of the direct inversion group and leaves this point invariant. In case it leaves only this point invariant, it has just been seen to be a translation in the Euclidean plane. If not, by the first paragraph of this section it has one and only one other invariant point unless it reduces to the identity.

A similarity transformation leaving an ordinary point O invariant must transform into itself the pencil of lines through this point and the pencil of circles having this point as center.

Two important special cases arise, namely, a rotation about O and a dilation with O as center. Moreover, since there is one and only one direct similarity transformation leaving O invariant and carrying a point P, distinct from O, to a point P', distinct from O, any nonparabolic direct similarity transformation is expressible as a product of a rotation and a dilation.

A rotation which is not a point reflection leaves all circles with O as center invariant, and changes every line through O into another line through O. A dilation which is not a point reflection leaves every line through O invariant, and changes every circle with O as center into another such circle. Hence a product of a dilation and a rotation, neither of which is of period two, leaves invariant no line through O and no circle with O as center. Since either a rotation or a dilation of period two is a point reflection, any direct circular transformation falls under one of the three cases just mentioned or else is a point reflection. Stated in terms of the inversion plane these results become (cf. fig. 56, p. 158):

THEOREM 27. *A direct circular transformation having two fixed points transforms into itself the pencil of circles through the fixed points and also the pencils of circles about these points. The transformation either leaves invariant every circle of one pencil and no circle of the other pencil, or it leaves invariant no circle of either pencil, or it leaves invariant every circle of both pencils and is of period two.*

DEFINITION. A direct circular transformation is said to be *parabolic* if it leaves invariant only one point; to be *hyperbolic* if it leaves invariant two points and all circles through these points; to be *elliptic* if it leaves invariant two points and all circles about these points; to be *loxodromic* if it leaves invariant two points and no circle through the invariant points or about them.

The theorems above are all valid for the complex line if circles be replaced by chains and direct circular transformations by projectivities. The definition is to be understood to apply in the same fashion. Since every nonidentical projectivity on the complex line has one or two double points, the discussion above gives the theorem:

THEOREM 28. *A direct circular transformation (or a projectivity on a complex line) is either parabolic, hyperbolic, elliptic, or loxodromic.*

COROLLARY. *An involution on a complex line is both hyperbolic and elliptic; and any projectivity which is both hyperbolic and elliptic is an involution.*

EXERCISES

1. A projectivity whose double points x_1 and x_2 are distinct from each other and from the point P_∞ of a scale P_0, P_1, P_∞, and whose characteristic cross ratio (§ 73, Vol. I) is k, may be written

$$\frac{x'-x_1}{x'-x_2}=k\frac{x-x_1}{x-x_2}. \tag{10}$$

If one of the double points is P_∞ and the other is x_1, the projectivity may be written

$$x'-x_1=k(x-x_1). \tag{11}$$

The projectivity is hyperbolic if k is real, elliptic if $k=e^{i\theta}$, where θ is real, and loxodromic if neither of these conditions is satisfied.

2. The parabolic projectivities with x_1 as double point may be written in the form

$$\frac{1}{x'-x_1}=\frac{1}{x-x_1}+at, \tag{12}$$

or, in case the double point is P_∞, in the form

$$x'=x+at.$$

In either case a subgroup is obtained by requiring t to be real. The locus of the points to which an arbitrary point is transformed by the transformation of this subgroup is a chain, and the set of such chains constitutes a parabolic pencil of chains.

3. The projectivities (10) and (11) for which

$$k=a^t,$$

where a is constant and t a real variable, form a group (a continuous group of one real parameter, in fact). The locus of the points to which a given point is carried by the transformations of this group or the group considered in Ex. 2 is called a *path curve*. In the nonparabolic cases, if a is real the path curves are chains through the double points. If a is complex and $|a|=1$, they are chains about the double points. If a satisfies neither of these conditions, and the double points are P_0 and P_∞, the path curves are the loci of $x=re^{i\theta}$ satisfying the condition

$$r=\alpha e^{\beta\theta}, \tag{13}$$

where α and β are real constants; if the double points are not specialized, the path curves are projectively equivalent to the system (13). Diagrams illustrating the three types of path curves will be found in Klein and Fricke's Elliptische Modulfunktionen, Vol. I, Abschnitt II.

4. From the Euclidean point of view the r and θ in Ex. 3 are *polar coördinates*, and the loci (13) are *logarithmic spirals* meeting the lines through the origin at the angle $\tan^{-1}(1/\beta)$. (A generalization of the notion of angle analogous to that in § 93 is here taken for granted.) The path curves of a one-parameter group of Euclidean transformations may be a pencil of parallel lines or a pencil of concentric circles or a set of logarithmic spirals congruent to (13).

5. A projectivity having a finite period must be elliptic. A direct similarity transformation having a finite period must be a rotation.

6. A loxodromic projectivity is a product of an elliptic and a hyperbolic projectivity.

7. A projectivity leaving a chain invariant is either hyperbolic or elliptic.

99. Chains and antiprojectivities. The theory of chains on a complex line has been developed in the sections above by combining the general theory of one-dimensional projectivities with the Euclidean theory of circles. It is of course possible, and from some points of view desirable, to develop the theory of chains entirely independently of the Euclidean geometry. The reader is referred for the outlines of such a theory to an article by J. W. Young in the Annals of Mathematics, 2d Series, Vol. XI (1909), p. 33. Many of the properties of chains may be generalized to n dimensions, an *n-dimensional chain* or an *n-chain* being defined as a real n-dimensional space contained in an n-dimensional complex space in such a way that any three points on a line of the real space are on a line of the complex space. (This is the relation between S and S′ in §§ 6 and 70.) A discussion of the theory of these generalized chains will be found in the articles by C. Segre and C. Juel referred to below, and also in those by J. W. Young, Transactions of the American Mathematical Society, Vol. XI (1910), p. 280, and H. H. MacGregor, Annals of Mathematics, 2d Series, Vol. XIV (1912), p. 1.

The transformations,

$$(14)\qquad z' = \frac{a\bar{z}+b}{c\bar{z}+d}, \qquad \begin{vmatrix} a & b \\ c & d \end{vmatrix} = 0,$$

of the complex line which were mentioned at the end of § 96 are analogous to the following class of transformations of the complex projective plane:

$$(15)\qquad \begin{aligned} x_0' &= a_{00}\bar{x}_0 + a_{01}\bar{x}_1 + a_{02}\bar{x}_2, \\ x_1' &= a_{10}\bar{x}_0 + a_{11}\bar{x}_1 + a_{12}\bar{x}_2, \\ x_2' &= a_{20}\bar{x}_0 + a_{21}\bar{x}_1 + a_{22}\bar{x}_2, \end{aligned} \qquad \begin{vmatrix} a_{00} & a_{01} & a_{02} \\ a_{10} & a_{11} & a_{12} \\ a_{20} & a_{21} & a_{22} \end{vmatrix} \neq 0,$$

where $\bar{x}_i$ denotes the complex number conjugate to x_i. These transformations are collineations, because they transform collinear points to collinear points,* but they are not projective collineations. If x_0', x_1', x_2' be replaced by u_0', u_1', u_2', (15) gives the equation of a nonprojective correlation. The analogous formulas in four homogeneous variables will define nonprojective collineations and correlations in space.

DEFINITION. A nonprojective collineation or correlation or a one-dimensional transformation of the type (14) is called an *antiprojectivity.*

The theory of antiprojectivities has been studied by C. Juel, Acta Mathematica, Vol. XIV (1890), p. 1, and more fully by C. Segre, Torino Atti, Vol. XXV (1890), pp. 276, 430 and Vol. XXVI, pp. 35, 592. Their rôle in projective geometry may be regarded as defined by the following theorem due to G. Darboux, Mathematische Annalen, Vol. XVII (1880), p. 55. In this paper Darboux also points out the connection of the geometrical result with the functional equation,

$$f(x+y)=f(x)+f(y).$$

THEOREM 29. *Any one-to-one reciprocal transformation of a real projective line which carries harmonic sets into harmonic sets is projective.*†

Proof. Let Π be any transformation satisfying the hypotheses of the theorem, A, B, C any three points of the line, $\Pi(ABC)=A'B'C'$, and Π' the projectivity such that $\Pi'(A'B'C')=ABC$. Then $\Pi'\Pi(ABC)=ABC$. If we can prove that $\Pi'\Pi$ is the identity, it will follow that $\Pi=\Pi'^{-1}$, and hence that Π is a projectivity.

If $\Pi'\Pi$ were not the identity, it would transform a point P to a point Q distinct from P, while it left invariant all points of the net of rationality $\mathsf{R}(ABC)$. Let L_1, L_2, L_3 be points of this net in the order

$$\{PL_1L_2QL_3\}.$$

By Theorem 8, Chap. V, there would exist two real points S, T which harmonically separate the pairs PL_1 and L_2L_3. The transformation $\Pi'\Pi$ must carry S and T into two points harmonically separating the pairs QL_1 and L_2L_3. But since the latter two pairs separate each

* Cf. § 28, Vol. I.

† Von Staudt, Geometrie der Lage (Nürnberg, 1847), § 9, defined a projectivity of a real line as a transformation having this property. We are using Cremona's definition of a projectivity as a resultant of perspectivities (cf. Vol. I, § 22).

other, by Theorem 8, Chap. V, there is no pair separating them both harmonically. Hence the assumption that $\Pi'\Pi$ is not the identity leads to a contradiction.

COROLLARY 1. *Any collineation or correlation in a real projective space is projective.*

Proof. Since a collineation transforms collinear points into collinear points, it transforms nets of rationality into nets of rationality in such a way that the correspondence between any two homologous nets is projective (cf. §§ 33–35, Vol. I). Hence, according to the theorem above, the correspondence effected by the collineation between any two lines is projective. Hence the collineation is projective.

A like argument proves that a correlation is projective. The reasoning holds without change in a real projective space of n dimensions.

COROLLARY 2. *Any one-to-one reciprocal transformation of the real inversion plane which carries points into points and circles into circles is a transformation of the inversion group.*

Proof. Regard the inversion plane π, minus a point P_∞, as a Euclidean plane π'; let Π be any transformation satisfying the hypotheses of the corollary, let $\Pi(P_\infty) = P'$, and let Π' be an inversion carrying P' to P_∞. Then $\Pi'\Pi$ is a transformation satisfying the hypotheses of the corollary and leaving P_∞ invariant.

Since $\Pi'\Pi$ carries circles through P_∞ into circles, it effects a collineation in π. By the first corollary this collineation is projective. Since it carries circles into circles, it is a similarity transformation. Hence $\Pi'\Pi$ is a transformation, say Π'', of the inversion group in π'. Since $\Pi = \Pi'^{-1}\Pi''$, Π is also in the inversion group.

Translated into the geometry of the complex projective line the last corollary states:

COROLLARY 3. *Any transformation which carries chains into chains is either a projectivity or an antiprojectivity.*

In the light of Corollary 2 it is clear that the whole theory of the inversion group can be developed from the definition of a circular transformation as one which carries points into points and circles into circles. This is the point of view adopted by Möbius in his Theorie der Kreisverwandtschaft, where, however, he used also the unnecessary assumption that the transformation is continuous.

EXERCISES

1. Derive the formulas for antiprojectivities in a modular geometry. Cf. O. Veblen, Transactions of the American Mathematical Society, Vol. VIII (1907), p. 366.

2. Which if any of the following propositions are true? Any one-to-one and reciprocal transformation of a complex projective line which carries harmonic sets of points into harmonic sets of points is either projective or antiprojective. Any one-to-one and reciprocal transformation of a complex projective line which carries quadrangular sets of points into quadrangular sets is either projective or antiprojective. Any collineation or correlation of a complex projective space is either projective or antiprojective.

3. An antiprojectivity carries four collinear points having an imaginary cross ratio into four points whose cross ratio is the conjugate imaginary.

100. Tetracyclic coördinates. The general equation of a circle in a Euclidean plane π with respect to the coördinate system employed in Chap. IV is

$$\alpha_0(x^2+y^2)+2\,\alpha_1 x+2\,\alpha_2 y+\alpha_3=0. \tag{16}$$

Definition. A *degenerate circle* is either a pair of lines joining an ordinary point to the circular points at infinity or a pair of lines ll_∞, where l_∞ is the line at infinity.

Thus (16) represents a nondegenerate circle, provided that the following condition is not satisfied:

$$0=\begin{vmatrix}\alpha_3 & \alpha_1 & \alpha_2\\ \alpha_1 & \alpha_0 & 0\\ \alpha_2 & 0 & \alpha_0\end{vmatrix}\equiv\alpha_0(\alpha_0\alpha_3-\alpha_1^2-\alpha_2^2). \tag{17}$$

The condition $\alpha_0=0$ clearly means that (16) represents a degenerate circle consisting of l_∞ and an ordinary line, unless $\alpha_1=\alpha_2=0$ also, in which case (16) reduces to $\alpha_3=0$. The condition

$$\alpha_0\alpha_3-\alpha_1^2-\alpha_2^2=0 \tag{18}$$

means in case $\alpha_0\neq 0$ that (16) represents a pair of ordinary lines through the circular points. In case $\alpha_0, \alpha_1, \alpha_2, \alpha_3$ are real, these two lines must be conjugate imaginaries. In the rest of this section the α's are supposed real.

Let us now interpret the ordered set of numbers $(\alpha_0, \alpha_1, \alpha_2, \alpha_3)$ as homogeneous coördinates of a point in a projective space of three dimensions, S_3. For every point of S_3, except those satisfying (18), there is a unique circle or line pair ll_∞, where l is ordinary, and vice versa. Hence there is a one-to-one and reciprocal correspondence between the points of S_3 not on the locus (18) and the circles of the inversion plane $\overline{\pi}$ obtained by adjoining l_∞ (regarded as a point) to π.

The points of S_3 which are on the locus (18) and not on $\alpha_0 = 0$ represent pairs of conjugate imaginary lines joining ordinary points of π to I_1 and I_2 respectively. There is one such pair of conjugate imaginary lines of π through each ordinary point of π. The points of S_3 on the locus (18) and not on $\alpha_0 = 0$ may therefore be regarded as corresponding to the points of $\overline{\pi}$, with the exception of l_∞. The only point of S_3 common to $\alpha_0 = 0$ and (18) is (0, 0, 0, 1), and this point may be taken to correspond to l_∞. Thus *the points of* S_3 *not on* (18) *represent circles of the inversion plane* $\overline{\pi}$, *and the points of* S_3 *on* (18) *represent the points of* $\overline{\pi}$.

Stated without the intervention of S_3, this means that the ordered set of numbers $(\alpha_0, \alpha_1, \alpha_2, \alpha_3)$ taken homogeneously and subject to the relation (18) may be regarded as coördinates of the points of $\overline{\pi}$. When not subject to the relation (18) they may be regarded as coördinates of the circles and points in $\overline{\pi}$.

DEFINITION. The ordered sets of four numbers $(\alpha_0, \alpha_1, \alpha_2, \alpha_3)$ subject to (18) are called *tetracyclic coördinates* of the points in $\overline{\pi}$. The same term is applied to any set of coördinates $(\beta_0, \beta_1, \beta_2, \beta_3)$ such that

$$\beta_i = \sum_{j=0}^{3} a_{ij}\alpha_j, \quad |a_{ij}| \neq 0. \qquad (i = 0, 1, 2, 3)$$

The circles (real or imaginary or degenerate) represented by (1, 0, 0, 0), (0, 1, 0, 0), (0, 0, 1, 0), (0, 0, 0, 1) are called the *base* or *fundamental* circles of the coördinate system.

A second particular choice of tetracyclic coördinates is given below.

The points of S_3 on (18) evidently constitute the set of all real points on the lines of intersection of corresponding planes of the two projective pencils

$$(19) \qquad \alpha_0 = \sigma(\alpha_1 + \sqrt{-1}\,\alpha_2) \quad \text{and} \quad \alpha_1 - \sqrt{-1}\,\alpha_2 = \sigma\alpha_3,$$

where the planes determined by the same value of σ are homologous. For (18) is obtained by eliminating σ between these two equations. The lines of intersection of homologous planes are all imaginary, but each contains one real point. This system of lines is, by § 103, Vol. I, a regulus, and the set of points on the lines, by § 104, Vol. I, a quadric surface. The locus (18) is therefore a real quadric surface all of whose rulers are imaginary (cf. also § 105 Vol. I).

The correspondence between the points of S_3 and the circles and points of the inversion plane $\overline{\pi}$ is such that a range of points corresponds to a pencil of circles. For the points of the line joining $(\alpha_0, \alpha_1, \alpha_2, \alpha_3)$ and $(\beta_0, \beta_1, \beta_2, \beta_3)$ correspond to the circles given by the equation

$$(\lambda\alpha_0+\mu\beta_0)(x^2+y^2)+(\lambda\alpha_1+\mu\beta_1)x+(\lambda\alpha_2+\mu\beta_2)y+(\lambda\alpha_3+\mu\beta_3)=0,$$

which represents a pencil of circles, together with its limiting points in case the latter are real.

Any collineation Γ of S_3 which carries the quadric (18) into itself must correspond to a transformation $\overline{\Gamma}$ of $\overline{\pi}$ which carries points into points, circles into circles, and pencils of circles into pencils of circles. $\overline{\Gamma}$ therefore has the property that if a point P of $\overline{\pi}$ is on a circle C^2 of $\overline{\pi}$, then $\overline{\Gamma}(P)$ is on $\overline{\Gamma}(C^2)$. By Theorem 29, Cor. 2, $\overline{\Gamma}$ is a circular transformation. Conversely, any circular transformation of $\overline{\pi}$ carries points to points, circles to circles, and pencils of circles to pencils of circles, and therefore corresponds to a collineation of S_3 which carries the quadric into itself. By Theorem 29, Cor. 1, this collineation is projective. In other words,

THEOREM 30. *The real inversion geometry is equivalent to the projective geometry of the quadric* (18).

COROLLARY. *The projective geometry of the real quadric* (18) *is equivalent to the complex projective geometry of a one-dimensional form.*

A one-to-one correspondence between a complex line and the real quadric (18) may also be set up as follows: Let l be any complex line in the regulus conjugate to that composed of the lines (19). Each of these lines contains one real point, P, of the quadric (18) and one point, Q, of l. The correspondence required is that in which Q corresponds to P.

By properly choosing the constants which enter in the equation of a circle, we may set up the correspondence between the circles of the inversion plane and the points of an S_3 in such a way that the equation of the quadric surface corresponding to the points of the inversion plane has a particularly simple form. The equation of a circle in π may be written

$$(20)\quad \xi_0(x^2+y^2+1)+\xi_1(x^2+y^2-1)+2\,\xi_2 x+2\,\xi_3 y=0.$$

The points $(\xi_0, \xi_1, \xi_2, \xi_3)$ which correspond to points of the inversion plane now satisfy the equation

(21) $$\xi_0^2 = \xi_1^2 + \xi_2^2 + \xi_3^2,$$

and the circles corresponding to the four points (1, 0, 0, 0), (0, 1, 0, 0), (0, 0, 1, 0), and (0, 0, 0, 1) are mutually orthogonal, one of them being imaginary. The coördinates $(\xi_0, \xi_1, \xi_2, \xi_3)$ are connected with $(\alpha_0, \alpha_1, \alpha_2, \alpha_3)$ by the equations

$$\alpha_0 = \xi_0 + \xi_1, \quad \alpha_1 = \xi_2, \quad \alpha_2 = \xi_3, \quad \alpha_3 = \xi_0 - \xi_1,$$

which represent a collineation carrying the quadric (18) into the quadric (21).

If ξ_1/ξ_0, ξ_2/ξ_0, ξ_3/ξ_0 are regarded as nonhomogeneous coördinates with respect to a properly chosen frame of reference in a Euclidean space of three dimensions (cf. Chap. VII), (21) is the equation of a sphere. Hence the real inversion geometry is equivalent to the projective geometry of a sphere.

The latter equivalence may be established very neatly, with the aid of theorems of Euclidean three-dimensional geometry, by the method of stereographic projection. This discussion would naturally come as an exercise in the next chapter. It is to be found in books on function theory. On the whole subject of inversion geometry from this point of view, compare Bôcher, Reihenentwickelungen der Potentialtheorie (Leipzig, 1894), Chap. II.

DEFINITION. A circle C_3^2 is *linearly dependent* on two circles C_1^2 and C_2^2 if and only if it is in the pencil determined by C_1^2 and C_2^2. A circle C^2 is *linearly dependent* on n circles $C_1^2, \cdots, C_n^2$ if and only if it is a member of some finite set of circles $C_{n+1}^2, \cdots, C_{n+k}^2$ such that C_{n+i}^2 is linearly dependent on two of $C_1^2, \cdots, C_{n+i-1}^2 (i = 1, 2, \cdots, k)$. A set of n circles is *linearly independent* if no one of them is linearly dependent on the rest. The set of all circles linearly dependent on three linearly independent circles is called a *bundle.*

EXERCISES

1. The tetracyclic coördinates of a point are proportional to the powers of the point with respect to four fixed circles. If the four circles are mutually orthogonal, the identity which they satisfy reduces to (21).

2. A homogeneous equation of the first degree in tetracyclic coördinates represents a circle.

3. What kind of coördinates are obtained by taking as the base (a) two orthogonal circles and the two points in which they meet? (b) four points?

4. Two points of S_3 correspond to orthogonal circles if and only if they are conjugate with regard to the quadric (21).

5. What set of circles corresponds to the conics in which the quadric (21) is met by the planes of a self-polar tetrahedron?

6. The direct circular transformations of $\overline{\pi}$ correspond to collineations of S_3 which leave each imaginary regulus of (21) invariant, while the others correspond to collineations interchanging the two reguli. The direct circular transformations of $\overline{\pi}$ correspond to direct collineations of S_3 in the sense of § 31, Chap. II.

7. The circles of a bundle correspond to the points of a plane of S_3.

8. The circles common to two bundles constitute a pencil and hence correspond to a line of S_3. Determine the projectively distinct types of pencils of circles on this basis.

9. All circles are linearly dependent on four linearly independent circles.

10. For any bundle of circles there is a point O which has the same power, c^2, with respect to every circle of the bundle. The radical axes of all pairs of circles in the bundle pass through O. In case there is more than one point O, the radical axes of all pairs of circles of the bundle coincide.

11. A bundle of circles may consist of all circles through a point (the set of all lines in a Euclidean plane is a special case of this). In every other case there is a nondegenerate circle orthogonal to all circles of the bundle. This circle has the point O (Ex. 10) as center and consists of the points C such that Dist $(OC) = c$. It is real if and only if c is real. In case c is imaginary let C^2 be the real circle consisting of points C' such that Dist $(OC') = c$; any circle of the bundle meets C^2 in the ends of a diameter.

101. Involutoric collineations. In view of the isomorphism between the real inversion group and the projective group of the real quadric (21), a further consideration of the group of a general quadric will be found apropos. In this connection we need to define certain particular types of involutoric collineations in any projective space. The theorems are all based on Assumptions A, E, P, H_0.

It is proved in § 29, Vol. I, that if ω is any plane and O any point not on ω, there exists a homology carrying any point P to a point P', provided that O, P, P' are distinct and collinear and P and P' are not on ω. It follows by the constructions given in that place that if one point P is transformed into its harmonic conjugate with regard to O and the point in which the line OP meets ω, every point is transformed in this way. It is also obvious that a homology is of period two if and only if it is of this type. Hence we make the following definition:

DEFINITION. A homology of a three-space is said to be *harmonic* if and only if it is of period two. A harmonic homology is also called a *point-plane reflection* and is denoted by $\{O\omega\}$ or $\{\omega O\}$, where O is the center and ω the plane of fixed points.

DEFINITION. If l and l' are two nonintersecting lines of a projective space S_3, the transformation of S_3 leaving each point of l and l' invariant, and carrying any other point P to the point P' such that the line PP' meets l and l' in two points harmonically conjugate with regard to P and P', is called a *skew involution* or a *line reflection in l and l'*. It is denoted by $\{ll'\}$, and l and l' are called its *axes* or *directrices*.

THEOREM 31. *A line reflection $\{ll'\}$ is a product of two point-plane reflections $\{O\omega\} \cdot \{P\pi\}$, where O and P are any two distinct points of l, ω is the plane on P and l', and π is the plane on O and l'.*

Proof. Consider any plane through l, and let L be the point in which it meets l'. In this plane $\{O\omega\}$ and $\{P\pi\}$ effect harmonic homologies whose centers are O and P respectively and whose axes are PL and OL respectively. The product is therefore the harmonic homology whose center is L and axis l. Hence the product $\{O\omega\} \cdot \{P\pi\}$ satisfies the definition of a line reflection whose axes are l and l'.

COROLLARY. *A line reflection is a projective collineation of period two, and any projective collineation of period two leaving invariant the points of two skew lines is a line reflection.*

EXERCISES

1. A projective collineation of period two in a plane is a harmonic homology.

2. A projective collineation of period two in a three-space is a point-plane reflection or a line reflection.

3. Let A, B, C, D be the vertices of a tetrahedron and α, β, γ, δ the respectively opposite faces. The transformations obtainable as products of the three harmonic homologies $\{A\alpha\}$, $\{B\beta\}$, $\{C\gamma\}$ constitute a commutative group of order 8 consisting of four point-plane reflections, three line reflections, and the identity. If the transformations other than the identity be denoted by 0, 1, 2, 3, 4, 5, 6, the multiplication table may be indicated by the modular plane given by the table (1) on p. 3, Vol. I, the rule being that the product of any two transformations corresponding to points i, j of the modular plane is the one which corresponds to the third point on the line joining i and j.

4. Generalize the last exercise to n dimensions. The group of involutoric transformations carrying $n+1$ independent points into themselves is commutative, and such that its multiplication table may be represented by means of a finite projective space of $n-1$ dimensions in which there are three points on each line.

5. A projectivity Γ of a complex line such that for one point P which is not invariant, $\Gamma^n(P) = P$ is such that Γ^n is the identity. If n is the least positive integer for which $\Gamma^n = 1$, Γ is said to be *cyclic of degree n*; the characteristic cross ratio of Γ is an nth root of unity; in case $n = 3$, this cross ratio is said to be *equianharmonic*, and a set of four points having this cross ratio is said to be *equianharmonic*. As a transformation of the inversion group, Γ is equivalent to a rotation of period n.

6. A planar projective collineation of period $n (n > 2)$ is of Type I and the set of transforms of any point is on a conic, or else the collineation is a homology. In the first case, it is projectively equivalent to a rotation; in the second case, to a dilation (in general, imaginary). Consider the analogous problem in three dimensions. (For references on this and the last exercise cf. Encyclopédie des Sc. Math. III 8, § 14. The statements in the Encyclopédie on the planar case are not strictly correct, since they do not sufficiently take the existence of homologies of finite period into account.)

102. The projective group of a quadric. According to the definition in § 104, Vol. I, a quadric may be regarded as the set of points of intersection of the lines of two conjugate reguli. These two reguli may be improper in the sense of Chap. IX, Vol. I, and in the following theorems improper elements are supposed adjoined when needed for the constructions employed.

Definition. If there are proper lines on a quadric, the quadric is said to be *ruled*, otherwise it is said to be *unruled*.

Theorem 32. *A harmonic homology whose center is the pole of its plane of fixed points with regard to a quadric surface Q^2 transforms Q^2 into itself in such a way that the two lines of Q^2 through any fixed point are interchanged.*

Proof. Let O be a point not on Q^2, and ω its polar plane. Any line l of Q^2 meets ω in a unique point K. The plane Ol contains one other line l' of Q^2, and (cf. § 104, Vol. I) l' passes through K. Any line joining O to a point L of l other than K must meet l' in a point L' such that L and L' are harmonically conjugate (§ 104, Vol. I) with regard to O and the point in which OL meets ω. Hence $\{O\omega\}$ interchanges l and l'. From this result the theorem follows at once.

Comparing Theorems 31 and 32, we have

Corollary. *A line reflection $\{ab\}$ such that a and b are polar with respect to a quadric Q^2 transforms Q^2 into itself in such a way that each regulus on Q^2 is transformed into itself.*

Theorem 33. *A projective collineation of a quadric which leaves three points of the quadric invariant, no two of the three points being on the same ruler, is either the identity or a harmonic homology whose center and plane of fixed points are polar with respect to the quadric.*

Proof. Denote the three points by A, B, C, the plane containing them by ω, and the pole of ω by O. Since no two of A, B, C are on a line of Q^2, ω contains no line of Q^2 and hence is not on O. Since three points of the conic in which ω meets the quadric are invariant, all such points are invariant, as is also O. Hence the given collineation is either the identity or a homology. In the latter case it must be a harmonic homology, since any two points of the quadric collinear with O are harmonically conjugate with respect to O and the point in which the line joining them meets ω.

THEOREM 34. *There exists one and only one projective collineation transforming each line of a regulus into itself and effecting a given projectivity on one of these lines. Such a collineation is a product of two line reflections whose axes are lines of the conjugate regulus.*

Proof. Let R_1^2 be a regulus and R_2^2 the conjugate regulus. A projectivity on a line, l, of R_1^2 is by § 78, Vol. I, a product of two involutions, say I and I$'$. Let $\{m_1m_2\}$ be a line reflection such that m_1 and m_2 are lines of R_2^2 through the double points of I, and let $\{m_1'm_2'\}$ be a line reflection such that m_1' and m_2' are lines of R_2^2 through the double points of I$'$. The product of $\{m_1'm_2'\}$ and $\{m_1m_2\}$ effects the given projectivity on l and transforms each line of R_1^2 into itself.

Conversely, any projectivity Γ leaving all lines of R_1^2 invariant effects a projectivity on l which is a product of two involutions I and I$'$. The line reflections $\{m_1m_2\}$ and $\{m_1'm_2'\}$ being defined as before,

$$\{m_1'm_2'\} \cdot \{m_1m_2\} \cdot \Gamma^{-1}$$

leaves all points of l invariant and hence leaves all lines of R_1^2 as well as all lines of R_2^2 invariant. Hence

$$\{m_1'm_2'\} \cdot \{m_1m_2\} \cdot \Gamma^{-1} = 1,$$

and

$$\{m_1'm_2'\} \cdot \{m_1m_2\} = \Gamma.$$

COROLLARY. *The group of permutations of the lines of a regulus effected by the projective collineations transforming the regulus into itself is simply isomorphic with the projective group of a line.*

DEFINITION. A collineation of a quadric which carries each regulus on the quadric into itself is said to be *direct.*

THEOREM 35. *There is one and but one direct collineation of a quadric surface Q^2 carrying an ordered triad of points of Q^2, no two of which are on a line of Q^2, to an ordered triad of points of Q^2 no two of which are on a line of Q^2.*

Proof. Let ABC and PQR be the given ordered triads of points, let a, b, c, p, q, r be the lines of one regulus through the points A, B, C, P, Q, R respectively, and let a', b', c', p', q', r' respectively be the lines of the conjugate regulus through the same points. By the last theorem there is a projective collineation Γ carrying a, b, c to p, q, r respectively while leaving all lines of the conjugate regulus invariant, and also a projective collineation Γ' carrying $a'b'c'$ to $p'q'r'$ respectively while leaving all of the lines a, b, c, p, q, r invariant. The product of Γ and Γ' carries A, B, C to P, Q, R respectively. That there is only one direct collineation having this effect is a corollary of Theorem 33.

Let R_1^2 be the regulus containing the lines a, b, c, and R_2^2 the regulus containing a', b', c'. The two collineations Γ and Γ' which have been used in the proof above are commutative as transformations of R_1^2 because Γ' leaves all lines of R_1^2 invariant, and are commutative as transformations of R_2^2 because Γ leaves all lines of R_2^2 invariant. Hence

$$\Gamma\Gamma' = \Gamma'\Gamma.$$

By Theorem 34, $\quad \Gamma\Gamma' = \{lm\} \cdot \{rs\} \cdot \{l'm'\} \cdot \{r's'\},$

where l, m, r, s are lines of R_1^2, and l', m', r', s' are lines of R_2^2. The collineations $\{rs\}$ and $\{l'm'\}$ are commutative for the same reason that Γ and Γ' are commutative. Hence

$$\Gamma\Gamma' = \{lm\} \cdot \{l'm'\} \cdot \{rs\} \cdot \{r's'\}.$$

The pairs lm and $l'm'$ are two pairs of opposite edges of a tetrahedron the other two edges of which may be denoted by a and b. The product $\{lm\} \cdot \{l'm'\}$ leaves each point of a and b invariant and is involutoric on each of the lines l, l', m, m'. Hence

$$\{lm\} \cdot \{l'm'\} = \{ab\}.$$

The lines a and b are polar with respect to R_1^2 because one of them is the line joining the point ll' to the point mm', and the other the line of intersection of the plane ll' with the plane mm' (cf. § 104, Vol. I).

In like manner $\quad \{pq\} \cdot \{p'q'\} = \{cd\},$

where c and d are polar with respect to R_2^2. Hence we have

THEOREM 36. *Any direct projective collineation* T *of a quadric surface is expressible in the form*

$$\mathrm{T} = \{ab\} \cdot \{cd\},$$

where the line a is polar to the line b, and the line c is polar to the line d.

Since any line reflection whose axes are polar with respect to a quadric is a product of two harmonic homologies whose centers are polar to their planes of fixed points (cf. Theorem 31), the last theorem implies

COROLLARY 1. *Any direct projective collineation of a quadric is a product of four harmonic homologies whose centers are polar to their respective planes of fixed points.*

COROLLARY 2. *Any nondirect projective collineation of a quadric is a product of an odd number of harmonic homologies whose centers are polar to their respective planes of fixed points.*

Proof. If a projective collineation Γ interchanges the two reguli, and Λ is a harmonic homology of the sort described in the statement of the corollary, then $\Gamma\Lambda = \Delta$ is a projective collineation leaving each regulus invariant. By Cor. 1, Δ is a product of an even number of harmonic homologies of the required sort, and hence $\Gamma = \Delta\Lambda$ is a product of an odd number.

103. Real quadrics. The isomorphism between the real inversion group and the projective collineation group of the real quadric (or sphere) (21) may now be studied more in detail. Since a circular transformation leaving three given points of the inversion plane $\overline{\pi}$ invariant is the identity or an inversion (Theorem 21), and since a collineation of S_3 leaving three points of the quadric (21) invariant is the identity or a harmonic homology whose center is polar to its plane of fixed points, it follows that inversions in $\overline{\pi}$ correspond to homologies of S_3. Hence the direct circular transformations of $\overline{\pi}$ correspond to the direct collineations of S_3 transforming (21) into itself.

An involution in $\overline{\pi}$ is a product of two inversions whose invariant circles intersect and are perpendicular. To say that the invariant circles intersect and are perpendicular is to say that they intersect in such a way that one of the circles is transformed into itself by the inversion with respect to the other. Now suppose that $\{O\omega\}$ and $\{P\pi\}$ are the harmonic homologies corresponding to the two inversions. If the points of the quadric on the plane ω are to be transformed among themselves by $\{P\pi\}$, ω must pass through P. In like manner π must pass through O. Hence

$$\{O\omega\} \cdot \{P\pi\} = \{ll'\},$$

where l is the line OP, l' the line $\omega\pi$, and the lines l and l' are polar with respect to the quadric. Hence the involutions in the group of direct circular transformations correspond to the line reflections whose axes are polar with respect to (21).

Thus the theorem that any direct circular transformation of $\overline{\pi}$ is a product of two involutions is equivalent to Theorem 36 applied to the quadric (21). Since an involution in $\overline{\pi}$ always has two double points, we have the additional information, not contained in § 102, that every line reflection transforming the quadric (21) into itself has two and only two fixed points on the quadric. The line joining these two points is obviously one of the axes of the line reflection. Hence the line reflection has two real axes one of which meets the quadric (21) and the other of which does not.

These remarks are enough to show how the real inversion geometry can be made effective in obtaining the theory of the real quadric (21). We shall now show that any real nonruled quadric is projectively equivalent to the quadric (21), from which it follows that the real inversion geometry is equivalent to the projective geometry of any real nonruled quadric.

A nonruled quadric is obviously nondegenerate. In the complex space any two nondegenerate quadrics are projectively equivalent, because any two reguli are projectively equivalent. Since (18) represents a quadric, it therefore follows that every nondegenerate quadric may be represented by an equation of the second degree.

Now let Q^2 be any quadric whose polar system transforms real points into real planes, and let the frame of reference be chosen so that (1, 0, 0, 0), (0, 1, 0, 0), (0, 0, 1, 0), and (0, 0, 0, 1) are vertices of a real self-polar tetrahedron. The plane section by the plane $x_0 = 0$ must be a conic whose equation is of the form

$$a_1x_1^2 + a_2x_2^2 + a_3x_3^2 = 0,$$

and similar remarks can be made about the sections by the planes $x_1 = 0$, $x_2 = 0$, and $x_3 = 0$. From this it follows that Q^2 has the equation

(22) $$a_0x_0^2 + a_1x_1^2 + a_2x_2^2 + a_3x_3^2 = 0,$$

where a_0, a_1, a_2, a_3 are real. The projective collineation

(23) $$x_0' = \sqrt{|a_0|}\,x_0, \quad x_1' = \sqrt{|a_1|}\,x_1, \quad x_2' = \sqrt{|a_2|}\,x_2, \quad x_3 = \sqrt{|a_3|}\,x_3$$

transforms Q^2 into a quadric having one of the following equations

$$x_0'^2 \pm x_1'^2 \pm x_2'^2 \pm x_3'^2 = 0.$$

Any one of the eight quadrics thus represented is obviously equivalent projectively to one of the following three:

(24) $$x_0^2 + x_1^2 + x_2^2 + x_3^2 = 0,$$

(25) $$-x_0^2 + x_1^2 + x_2^2 + x_3^2 = 0,$$

(26) $$-x_0^2 - x_1^2 + x_2^2 + x_3^2 = 0.$$

It is also obvious that (24) is imaginary, that (26) has real rulers, and that (25) is equivalent to (21).

EXERCISES

1. Determine the types of collineations transforming into itself (1) a real unruled quadric, (2) a real ruled quadric, (3) an imaginary quadric having a real polar system.

2. Discuss the projective groups of the three types of quadrics enumerated in the last exercise.

104. The complex inversion plane. A projective plane may be obtained from a Euclidean plane (cf. Introduction, Vol. I) by adjoining ideal points and an ideal line in such a way as to make it possible to regard every collineation as a one-to-one reciprocal transformation of all points in the plane. In like manner the real inversion plane has been obtained from the real Euclidean plane by adjoining a single ideal point which serves as the correspondent of the center of each inversion. Similar considerations will now be adduced showing that an inversion in the complex plane may be rendered one to one and reciprocal by introducing *two intersecting ideal lines.*

In the complex projective plane an inversion has been seen (§ 94) to be a one-to-one reciprocal transformation of all points not on the sides of the singular triangle OI_1I_2, and to effect a projective transformation interchanging the pencil of lines on I_1 with the pencil of lines on I_2. In this projectivity the line I_1I_2 is homologous both with OI_1 and with OI_2.

In the Euclidean plane obtained by omitting the line I_1I_2 from the projective plane, it follows that the inversion is one to one and reciprocal except for points on the two minimal lines, p_0 and m_0, through O. Moreover, it effects a projective correspondence between the set of minimal lines $[p]$ parallel with and distinct from p_0 and the set of minimal lines $[m]$ parallel with and distinct from m_0.

The correspondence between any line p and the homologous line m is incomplete because there is no point on p corresponding to the intersection of m with p_0 and no point on m corresponding to the intersection of p with m_0. This correspondence, however, may be made completely one to one and reciprocal by introducing an ideal point M_∞ on m as the correspondent of the point pm_0 and an ideal point P_∞ on p as the correspondent of the point mp_0. In order to treat all the minimal lines symmetrically, ideal points P'_∞ and M'_∞ must be introduced on p_0 and m_0, respectively, as mutually corresponding points. Also one other ideal point O_∞ is introduced as the correspondent of O.

According to these conventions the line p_0 together with its ideal point P'_∞ is transformed into a set of points consisting of O_∞, M'_∞, and all the points M_∞. This set of points is therefore called an ideal line $\overline{m}_\infty$. In like manner the line m_0 together with its ideal point M_∞ is transformed into a set of points consisting of O_∞, P'_∞, and all the points P_∞; and this set of points is called an ideal line $\overline{p}_\infty$. The Euclidean plane with the lines $\overline{p}_\infty$ and $\overline{m}_\infty$ adjoined is called an inversion plane. Or to state the definition formally and without reference to a particular inversion:

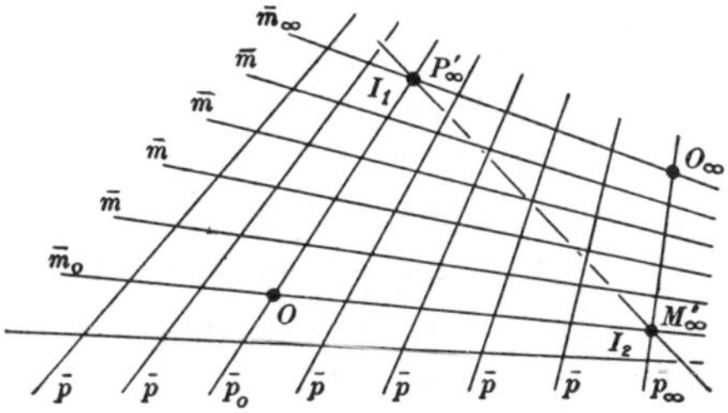

FIG. 74

DEFINITION. Given a complex Euclidean plane π and in it two pencils of minimal lines $[p]$ and $[m]$. By a *complex inversion plane* $\overline{\pi}$ is meant the set of all points of π (referred to as *ordinary points*) together with a set of elements called *ideal points* of which there is one, denoted by P_∞, for each p, and one, denoted by M_∞, for each m, distinct p's and m's determining distinct ideal points, and also one other ideal point which shall be denoted by O_∞. By a *minimal line* of $\overline{\pi}$ is meant (1) the set of points on a p together with the corresponding P_∞, or (2) the set of points on an m together with the corresponding M_∞, or (3) the set of all P_∞'s together with O_∞, or (4) the set of all M_∞'s together with O_∞. The minimal lines of Types (1) and (2) are called *ordinary*, and the lines (3) and (4) are called *ideal.*

A minimal line of Type (1) or (4) will be denoted by $\bar{p}$, of Type (2) or (3) by $\bar{m}$; the minimal lines of Types (3) and (4) are denoted by $\bar{m}_\infty$ and $\bar{p}_\infty$ respectively.

This definition is evidently such that each point of $\bar{\pi}$ is on a unique $\bar{p}$ and on a unique $\bar{m}$.

DEFINITION. By an *inversion* $\bar{\mathrm{I}}$ of $\bar{\pi}$ is meant a transformation defined as follows by an inversion I of π: If p_0 and m_0 are the singular lines of I, $\bar{\mathrm{I}}$ interchanges $\bar{p}_0$ with $\bar{m}_\infty$, $\bar{m}_0$ with $\bar{p}_\infty$, and each $\bar{p}$ containing a p with the $\bar{m}$ containing the m to which p is transformed by I. A point of $\bar{\pi}$ which is the intersection of a $\bar{p}$ and an $\bar{m}$ is transformed to the point which is the intersection of $\bar{\mathrm{I}}\,(\bar{p})$ and $\bar{\mathrm{I}}\,(\bar{m})$. The set of points of $\bar{\pi}$ left invariant by an inversion is called a *nondegenerate circle* of $\bar{\pi}$. A pair of minimal lines, one a $\bar{p}$ and the other an $\bar{m}$, is called a *degenerate circle* of $\bar{\pi}$.

By reference to § 94 it is evident that every circle of π is a subset of the points on a circle of $\bar{\pi}$.

The complex inversion plane is perhaps best understood by setting it in correspondence with a quadric surface, the lines of one regulus on the quadric being homologous with [$\bar{p}$] and those of the other with [$\bar{m}$]. This correspondence may be studied by means of tetracyclic coördinates as in § 100, but it can also be set up by means of a geometric construction as follows:

Regard the complex Euclidean plane π with which we started as immersed in a complex Euclidean space. Let Q^2 be a quadric surface such that OI_1 is a line of one ruling and OI_2 of the other (fig. 74). Through I_1 and I_2 there are two other lines of the two rulings which intersect in a point O_∞. Any point P of the Euclidean plane is joined to O_∞ by a line which meets the quadric Q^2 in a unique point Q other than O_∞ and, conversely, any point of Q^2 which is not on either of the lines $O_\infty I_1$ or $O_\infty I_2$ is joined to O_∞ by a line which meets the Euclidean plane in a point P. Thus there is a correspondence T between the Euclidean plane and the points of Q^2 not on $O_\infty I_1$ or $O_\infty I_2$. This correspondence is such that every minimal line in π of the pencil on I_1 corresponds to a line of the quadric which is in the same ruling with OI_1, and every line of π of the pencil on I_2 corresponds to a line of the quadric which is in the same ruling with OI_2. From this it is evident that if ideal elements are adjoined to π as explained above, the ideal points can be regarded as corresponding to the points of the lines $O_\infty I_1$ and $O_\infty I_2$ so that there is a one-to-one reciprocal correspondence between $\overline{\pi}$ and Q^2.

Now any nondegenerate circle of π is a conic through I_1 and I_2. This is projected from O_∞ by a cone of lines having in common with Q^2 the two lines $O_\infty I_1$ and $O_\infty I_2$. It follows that the cone and Q^2 have also a conic section in common. For let Q_1, Q_2, Q_3 be three of the common points which are not on the lines $O_\infty I_1$ and $O_\infty I_2$; the plane $Q_1Q_2Q_3$ meets the cone in a conic K_1^2 and Q^2 in a conic K_2^2. These two conics have also in common the points in which they meet the lines $O_\infty I_1$ and $O_\infty I_2$ (if these points coincide, K_1^2 and K_2^2 have a common tangent at this point), and hence $K_1^2 = K_2^2$. The conic K_1^2 is nondegenerate, because a nondegenerate cone through O_∞ can have no other line than $O_\infty I_1$ and $O_\infty I_2$ in common with Q^2. Hence every nondegenerate circle of π corresponds under T to a section of Q^2 by a nontangent plane.

Conversely, if K^2 is any nondegenerate conic section which is a plane section of Q^2, it is projected from O_∞ by a cone two of whose lines are $O_\infty I_1$ and $O_\infty I_2$. Hence K^2 corresponds under T to a nondegenerate circle of π.

An inversion in π with respect to a circle C^2 transforms every minimal line of the pencil $[p]$ into that one of $[m]$ which meets it on C^2. Let K^2 be the conic section on Q^2 corresponding under T to C^2. The inversion corresponds under T to a transformation of Q^2 by which every line of one regulus is transformed into the line of the other regulus which meets it in a point of K^2. This is the transformation (Theorem 32) effected by a harmonic homology whose plane of fixed points contains K^2 and whose center is the polar to this plane with respect to Q^2. Hence every inversion in π corresponds under T to a collineation of Q^2 effected by a harmonic homology whose center and plane of fixed points are polar with regard to Q^2. Conversely, every such collineation of Q^2 evidently corresponds under T to an inversion in π. Hence (Theorem 36, Cors. 1 and 2) the inversion group in π is isomorphic under T with the group of projective collineations of Q^2, and the direct circular transformations of π correspond to the projective collineations of Q^2 which carry each regulus into itself.

EXERCISE

Develop the theory of the modular inversion plane, using improper elements in the sense of Chap. IX, Vol. I.

105. Function plane, inversion plane, and projective plane. In the theory of functions of two complex variables

$$F(xy)$$

the two variables x and y are thought of as completely independent of each other. The domain of each is the set of all complex numbers, including ∞. This domain is therefore equivalent to the complex line or to the real inversion plane. Thus the domain of x may be taken to be a real unruled quadric (in particular, a sphere) and the domain of y another real unruled quadric. Or the pair of values (x, y) may be regarded as an *ordered pair of points* on the same real unruled quadric.

Now consider a regulus in the complex projective space and, adopting the notation of the last section (fig. 74), let a scale be established on the lines $\overline{p}_0$ and $\overline{m}_0$ so that O is the zero in each scale. Let x be the coördinate of any point on $\overline{p}_0$ and y of any point on $\overline{m}_0$. Then a pair of values (x, y) determines a unique point on the quadric, i.e. the point of intersection of the line $\overline{m}$ through the point with x as its coördinate, and the line $\overline{p}$ through the point with y as its coördinate. Conversely, the same construction determines a pair of numbers (x, y) for each point of the quadric.

DEFINITION. The set of all ordered pairs (x, y) where x and y are complex numbers, including ∞, is called a *complex function plane*, or the *plane of the theory of functions* of complex variables, or the complex *plane of analysis*. The ordered pairs (x, y) are called *points*. Any point for which $x=\infty$ or $y=\infty$ is said to be *ideal* or *at infinity*, and all other points are called *ordinary*.

The points at infinity of the function plane can be represented conveniently by replacing x by a pair of homogeneous coördinates x_0, x_1 such that $x_1/x_0 = x$, and y by a pair (y_0, y_1) such that $y_1/y_0 = y$. Thus the points of the function plane are represented by

$$(x_0, x_1;\ y_0, y_1),$$

and the ideal points are those satisfying the condition

$$x_0 y_0 = 0.$$

The set of ordinary points of the function plane obviously forms a Euclidean plane in which a line is the locus of an equation of the form

$$ax + by + c = 0.$$

This is equivalent in homogeneous coördinates to

$$(27) \qquad ax_1y_0 + by_1x_0 + cx_0y_0 = 0,$$

an equation which is linear both in the pair of variables x_0, x_1 and in the pair y_0, y_1. The most general equation which is linear in both pairs is

$$(28) \qquad \alpha x_0y_0 + \beta x_0y_1 + \gamma x_1y_0 + \delta x_1y_1 = 0.$$

This reduces to (27) if the condition be imposed that the locus shall contain the point (∞, ∞) which in homogeneous coördinates is $(0, 1;\ 0, 1)$.

DEFINITION. The set of points of the function plane satisfying (28) is called a *circle* (or a *bilinear curve*), and any circle of the form (27) is called a *line*.

The group of transformations which is indicated as most important by problems of elementary function theory has the equations

$$(29) \qquad x' = \frac{p_1x + q_1}{r_1x + s_1}, \qquad \begin{vmatrix} p_1 & q_1 \\ r_1 & s_1 \end{vmatrix} \neq 0,$$

$$y' = \frac{p_2y + q_2}{r_2y + s_2}, \qquad \begin{vmatrix} p_2 & q_2 \\ r_2 & s_2 \end{vmatrix} \neq 0,$$

or, in homogeneous coördinates,

$$(30) \qquad \begin{aligned} x_1' &= p_1x_1 + q_1x_0, & y_1' &= p_2y_1 + q_2y_0, \\ x_0' &= r_1x_1 + s_1x_0, & y_0' &= r_2y_1 + s_2y_0. \end{aligned}$$

This group of transformations clearly transforms circles into circles. The subgroup obtained by imposing the conditions,

$$r_1 = 0, \qquad r_2 = 0,$$

transforms lines into lines because it leaves (∞, ∞) invariant.

Returning to the interpretation of the coördinates x and y on a quadric, it is clear (cf. § 102) that every transformation (29) represents a direct collineation of the quadric, the formula in x determining the transformation of one regulus and the formula in y the transformation of the conjugate regulus. Hence the fundamental group of the function plane is isomorphic with the group of direct projective collineations of a quadric surface.

The parameters x and y which determine the points of a regulus may be connected with the three-dimensional coördinates $(\xi_0, \xi_1, \xi_2, \xi_3)$ by means of the following equations:

$$(31) \qquad \begin{aligned} \xi_0 &= x_1y_1 + x_0y_0, \\ \xi_1 &= x_1y_1 - x_0y_0, \\ \xi_2 &= x_1y_0 + x_0y_1, \\ \xi_3 &= i(x_1y_0 - x_0y_1), \end{aligned}$$

where $i^2 = -1$. For the set of all points $(\xi_0, \xi_1, \xi_2, \xi_3)$ given by these equations are the points on the quadric,

$$(21) \qquad \xi_0^2 = \xi_1^2 + \xi_2^2 + \xi_3^2.$$

Any plane section of this quadric is given by a linear equation in $\xi_0, \xi_1, \xi_2, \xi_3$, which by (31) reduces to a relation of the form (28) among the parameters $x_0, x_1; y_0, y_1$. Hence the circles of the function plane correspond to the plane sections of the quadric (21). In view of the relation already established between the groups it follows that the geometry of a quadric in a complex projective space is identical with that of a complex function plane. In view of § 104 both these geometries are identical with the complex inversion geometry.*

The complex projective plane may be contrasted with the complex inversion plane or function plane in an interesting manner as follows: The homogeneous coördinates $(\alpha_0, \alpha_1, \alpha_2)$ may be regarded as the coefficients of a quadratic equation

$$(32) \qquad \alpha_0 z_0^2 + \alpha_1 z_0 z_1 + \alpha_2 z_1^2 = 0.$$

Every such equation determines two and only two values of z_1/z_0, which may coincide or become infinite (if $\alpha_2 = 0$); and, moreover, two distinct points of the projective plane determine distinct quadratic equations and hence distinct pairs of values of z_1/z_0.

*If one were to confine attention to real values, the definition of the plane of analysis given above would determine a set of elements abstractly equivalent to a real ruled quadric. This is distinct from the real inversion plane, because the latter is equivalent to a real nonruled quadric. For the purposes of the theory of functions of a real variable, however, it is usually desirable to distinguish between $+\infty$ and $-\infty$. If this be done, the function plane is easily seen to be a figure analogous to a rectangle in a Euclidean plane. The group of transformations of such a function plane does not seem to be of great interest from the projective point of view.

The numbers (z_0, z_1) may be taken as homogeneous coördinates on a projective line. Thus there is a one-to-one and reciprocal correspondence between the points of a complex projective plane and the pairs of points on a complex projective line. It is important to notice that the pairs of points on the line *are not ordered pairs,* because a pair of values of z_1/z_0 taken in either order would be the pair of roots of the same quadratic.

Now representing the points of a complex line on a real unruled quadric (e.g. a sphere), we have that the projective plane is in one-to-one reciprocal correspondence with the *unordered* pairs of points of the quadric. On the other hand, we have already seen that the complex projective plane is in one-to-one reciprocal correspondence with the *ordered* pairs of points of the quadric. In either case the points of a pair may coincide.

For further discussion of the subject of this section see "The Infinite Regions of Various Geometries" by M. Bôcher, Bulletin of the American Mathematical Society, Vol. XX (1914), p. 185.

106. Projectivities of one-dimensional forms in general. The theorems of the last four sections have established and made use of the fact that the permutations effected among the lines of a regulus by projective collineations form a group isomorphic with the projective group of a line. Now a regulus is a one-dimensional form of the second degree,* and the notion of one-dimensional projective transformation has been extended to all the other one-dimensional forms (Chap. VIII, Vol. I, particularly § 76). It is therefore to be expected that an analogous extension can be made to the regulus. This we shall now make, but instead of dealing with the regulus in particular, we shall restate the old definition in a form which includes the cases where the regulus is in question.

Definition. A correspondence between any two one-dimensional forms whose elements are of different kinds and not such that all elements of one form are on every element of the other form is said to be *perspective* if it is one-to-one and reciprocal and such that each element of either form is on the corresponding element of the other form.

*The one-dimensional forms of the first and second degrees in three-space are the pencil of points, the flat pencil of lines, the pencil of planes, the point conic, the line conic, the cone of lines, the cone of planes, and the regulus.

This covers the notion of perspectivity as defined in Vol. I between a pencil of points and a pencil of lines or between a pencil of lines and a point conic, etc. It also defines perspectivities between (1) the lines of a regulus and the points on a line of the conjugate regulus, (2) the lines of a regulus and the planes on a line of the conjugate regulus, (3) the lines of a regulus and the points of a conic which is a plane section of the regulus, (4) the lines of a regulus and the planes of a cone tangent to the regulus.

DEFINITION. A correspondence between two one-dimensional forms or among the elements of a single one-dimensional form is *projective* if and only if it is the resultant of a sequence of perspectivities.

This definition comprehends that made in § 22, Vol. I, for forms of the first degree, and extended in § 76, Vol. I, so as to include those of the second degree equivalent under duality to a point conic. In order to justify the new definition, it is necessary to prove that it does not lead to any modification of the relation of perspectivity between one-dimensional forms of the first degree. In other words, we must prove that *any correspondence between two one-dimensional forms of the first degree is projective according to the new definition only if it is projective according to the definition of § 22, Vol. I.*

To prove this theorem it is sufficient to show that a sequence of perspectivities beginning and ending with forms of the first degree and involving forms of the second degree can be replaced by one involving only forms of the first degree. This follows directly from the fact that each one-dimensional form of the second degree is generated by projective one-dimensional forms of the first degree. For example, if a pencil of points $[P]$ is perspective with a regulus $[l]$ and the regulus with a point conic and the point conic with something else, it follows by the theorems of § 103, Vol. I, that $[P]$ is perspective with the pencil of planes $[ml]$, where m is a line of the conjugate regulus and $[ml]$ is perspective with the point conic. Thus the regulus $[l]$ in this sequence of perspectivities is replaced by the pencil of planes $[ml]$. In similar fashion it can be shown by a consideration of the finite number of possible cases that however a form of the second degree may intervene in a sequence of perspectivities, it can be replaced by a form or forms of the first degree. The enumeration of the possible cases is left to the reader, the argument required in each case being obvious.

From this theorem it follows that *the group of projective correspondences of any one-dimensional form with itself is isomorphic with the projective group of a line.* For let Γ be any projectivity of a one-dimensional form F^2 of the second degree (e.g. a regulus), and let Π represent a perspectivity between F^2 and a one-dimensional form F^1 of the first degree (e.g. a line of the conjugate regulus). Then $\Pi\Gamma\Pi^{-1}$ is a projectivity of F^1. In like manner, if Γ' is a projectivity of F^1, $\Pi^{-1}\Gamma'\Pi$ is a projectivity of F^2. Hence Π establishes an isomorphism between the two groups.

***107. Projectivities of a quadric.** An involution on a regulus is the transformation of the lines of the regulus effected by a line reflection whose axes are the double lines of the involution. Since any projectivity of a regulus is a product of two involutions, it may be regarded as effected by a three-dimensional projective collineation which transforms the regulus into itself. Conversely, any direct projective collineation transforming a quadric into itself is a product of two line reflections (Theorem 36) each of which effects an involution on each of the reguli on the quadric.

This relation between the theory of one-dimensional projectivities and the projective group of a quadric may be used to obtain properties of the quadric analogous to the properties of conic sections studied in Chap. VIII, Vol. I. The discussion is based on Assumptions A, E, P, H_0, improper points being adjoined to the space whenever this is required for quadratic constructions.

In Chap. VIII, Vol. I, we have seen that any projectivity on a conic determines a unique point, the center of the projectivity, and that the axes of any two involutions into which the projectivity may be resolved pass through its center. If, now, a projectivity Γ be given on a regulus, any plane π meets the regulus in a conic C^2 on which is determined a projectivity Γ' having a point P as center. This determines a correspondence between the planes π and points P of space which is a null system (§ 108, Vol. I), and hence the axes of the involutions into which the projectivity Γ' can be resolved form a linear complex. The formal proof of this statement follows.

THEOREM 37. *For any nonidentical projectivity of a regulus there exists a linear complex of lines $[l]$ having the property that if l_1 is any line of the complex not tangent to the regulus, there are three lines l_2,*

l_3, l_4 such that l_2 is polar to l_1 and l_3 to l_4 with respect to the regulus, and such that the collineation

$$\{l_1l_2\}\cdot\{l_3l_4\}$$

effects the given projectivity on the regulus. Moreover, every line l_1 having this property belongs to the complex, and so do l_2, l_3, l_4.

Proof. Let R^2 be a regulus and Γ a projectivity of R^2. If l_1l_2 and l_3l_4 are pairs of polar lines such that $\{l_1l_2\}\cdot\{l_3l_4\}$ effects the given projectivity on R^2, let π be any plane containing l_1 and not tangent to R^2. The projectivity Γ on R^2 is perspective with a projectivity Γ' on the conic C^2 in which π meets R^2. Moreover, $\{l_1l_2\}$ and $\{l_3l_4\}$ effect involutions on R^2 which are perspective with involutions I' and I'' on C^2. Thus on C^2

$$\Gamma' = \mathrm{I}'\mathrm{I}''.$$

But (cf. § 77, Vol. I) l_1 is the axis of I' and hence passes through the center of Γ'. A similar argument shows that $l_i\,(i = 2, 3, 4)$ passes through the center of the projectivity perspective with Γ on the conic in which R^2 is met by any plane containing l_i and not tangent to R^2.

Hence all lines l_1, l_2, l_3, l_4 defined as above are contained in the set $[l]$ of all lines l such that if π is any plane on l and not tangent to R^2, l is also on a point P defined as follows: Let C^2 be the conic in which π meets R^2 and Γ' the projectivity on C^2 perspective with the projectivity Γ on R^2; then P is the center of Γ'.

The set $[l]$ obviously contains all lines tangent to R^2 at points of the double lines (if existent) of Γ. If l_1 is any other line of $[l]$ let π be a plane on l_1 and not tangent to R^2, let C^2 be the conic in which π meets R^2, and let Γ' be the projectivity on C^2 perspective with Γ. By § 79, Vol. I, and the definition of $[l]$, Γ' is a product of two involutions having l_1 and another line, l_3, as axes. Let l_2 and l_4 be the polars of l_1 and l_3 respectively. Then $\{l_1l_2\}\cdot\{l_3l_4\}$ effects the perspectivity Γ' on C and hence effects Γ on R^2. By the first paragraph of the proof l_2, l_3, l_4 are all lines of $[l]$. Hence all lines of $[l]$ have the property enunciated in the theorem. It remains to prove that $[l]$ is a linear complex.

By definition, if π is a plane not tangent to R^2 the lines of $[l]$ in π form a flat pencil. If π is tangent to R^2 let p be the line of R^2 on π and q the line of the conjugate regulus on π. In case p is a fixed line of Γ, the lines l on π are the tangents to R^2, i.e. the pencil of lines on π and the point pq. In case p is not a fixed line of Γ, q is a tangent to R^2 which meets a fixed line of Γ and hence is a line of $[l]$. Any other line l_1 of $[l]$ in π must have a polar line l_2 passing through the point pq. Let Γ'' be the projectivity on q perspective with Γ. If Γ is effected by $\{l_1l_2\} \cdot \{l_3l_4\}$, then Γ'' is the product of two involutions, I$'$ and I$''$, which are perspective with the involutions effected on R^2 by $\{l_1l_2\}$ and $\{l_3l_4\}$ respectively. Since l_2 must pass through the point pq, the latter is a double point of I$'$. But when Γ'' is expressed as a product of two involutions, one of these involutions is fully determined by one of its double points in case the latter is not a double point of Γ'' (cf. § 78, Vol. I). Hence the other double point, P, is fixed; and since l_1 must pass through it, it follows that all lines of $[l]$ on π pass through P. Moreover, it is evident that if l_1 is any line (except q) on π and P, l_2 its polar line, and $\{l_3l_4\}$ any line reflection effecting an involution on R^2 which is perspective with I$''$, the projectivity Γ is effected by $\{l_1l_2\} \cdot \{l_3l_4\}$. Hence $[l]$ contains all lines on π and P. Hence $[l]$ is a linear complex by Theorem 24, Chap. XI, Vol. I.

THEOREM 38. *A direct projectivity Γ of a quadric surface Q^2 which does not leave all lines of either regulus invariant determines a linear congruence of lines having the property that if a_1 is any line of the congruence not tangent to Q^2 there exist lines a_2, b_1, b_2 of the congruence such that*

$$\Gamma = \{a_1a_2\} \cdot \{b_1b_2\}. \tag{33}$$

Moreover, each line a_1 having this property belongs to the congruence, and so do a_2, b_1, b_2.

Proof. Γ effects a projectivity on each regulus of Q^2, and each of these reguli by the last theorems determines a linear complex of lines. The two complexes are obviously not identical and hence have a linear congruence in common. Any line a_1 of this congruence is either tangent to Q^2, or such that there exist lines a_2, b_1, b_2 which are in both complexes and such that $\{a_1a_2\} \cdot \{b_1b_2\}$ effects the same projectivity as Γ on both reguli. Hence $\{a_1a_2\} \cdot \{b_1b_2\} = \Gamma$. Moreover, any a_1 for which a_2, b_1, b_2 exist satisfying this condition must, by the last theorem, belong to both complexes and hence belong to this congruence.

COROLLARY 1. *The congruence referred to in the theorem may be degenerate and consist of all lines on a point of Q^2 and on a plane tangent to Q^2 at this point; or it may be parabolic and have a line of the quadric as directrix; or it may be hyperbolic and have a pair* *of polar lines as directrices; or it may be elliptic and have a pair of improper polar lines as directrices.*

Proof. Let C denote the congruence referred to in the theorem and let Π be the polarity by which every point is transformed into its polar plane with respect to Q^2. This polarity transforms any line a_1 of C into its polar line, and the latter, by the theorem, is in C. Hence Π transforms C into itself.

According to § 107, Vol. I, any congruence is either degenerate, parabolic, hyperbolic, or elliptic. If degenerate, it consists of all lines on a point R or a plane ρ, R being on ρ. If Π transforms such a congruence into itself, it must interchange R and ρ, and hence R must be on Q^2 and ρ tangent to Q^2 at R. The congruence C will be of this type if b_1 meets a_1 in a point of Q^2 and does not meet a_2.

If C is parabolic, its one directrix must be transformed into itself by Π, and hence must be a line of Q^2. This case arises if a_1, a_2, b_1, b_2 all meet the same line of Q^2 and do not meet any other line of Q^2.

If C is hyperbolic, Π must either leave the two directrices fixed individually or interchange them. In the first case each directrix must be a line of Q^2, which implies that a_1, a_2, b_1, b_2 all meet two lines of Q^2 and hence that all lines of one regulus are left invariant by Γ, contrary to hypothesis. Hence the second case is the only possible one. It occurs when a_1, a_2, b_1, b_2 do not all meet any line of Q^2, but are met by a pair of real lines.

If C is elliptic, it has two improper directrices* and the reasoning is the same as for the hyperbolic case.

DEFINITION. A line l is said to *meet* or *to be met by* a pair of lines pq if and only if it meets both of them. A pair of lines lm is said to *meet* or *cross* a pair pq if both l and m meet pq.

EXERCISES

1. The lines which cross the distinct pairs of an involution on a regulus together with the lines tangent to the regulus at points of the double lines (if existent) of the involution form a nondegenerate linear complex.

2. If two pairs of polar lines, a_1a_2 and b_1b_2, of a regulus meet each other, the involutions effected by $\{a_1a_2\}$ and $\{b_1b_2\}$ are harmonic (commutative) and their double lines form a harmonic set.

* This may be proved as follows: Let l_1, l_2, l_3, l_4 be lines of C not on the same regulus. Any plane on l_4 meets the regulus R^2 containing l_1, l_2, l_3 in a conic, and l_4 meets this conic in two improper points P_1, P_2. The two lines of the regulus conjugate to R^2 which pass through P_1, P_2 meet l_1, l_2, l_3, l_4 and hence meet all lines of C.

3. Let Γ be a projectivity on a regulus R^2. A variable plane meets R^2 in a conic C^2 on which there is a projectivity Γ' perspective with Γ. The axes of the projectivities Γ' are lines of a linear congruence.

4. Enumerate the types of collineations leaving invariant a quadric (1) in the complex space, (2) in a real space, (3) in various modular spaces.

* 108. Products of pairs of involutoric projectivities.

THEOREM 39. *A direct projective collineation of a quadric surface is a line reflection whose axes are polar, if it interchanges two points of the quadric which are not joined by a line of the quadric.*

Proof. Denote the collineation by Γ, the quadric by Q^2, the two reguli on it by R_1^2 and R_2^2, and the two points which Γ interchanges by A and B. Let a and b be the lines of R_1^2 on A and B respectively, and a' and b' those of R_2^2 on A and B respectively. Since Γ interchanges a and b it effects an involution on R_1^2, and since it interchanges a' and b' it effects an involution on R_2^2. Let l, m be the double lines of the involution on R_1^2, and p, q those of the involution on R_2^2. Γ is evidently the product of $\{lm\}$ by $\{pq\}$ and hence is a line reflection whose axes are the line joining the points lp and mq and the line joining the planes lp and mq. These two lines are polar with regard to Q^2.

THEOREM 40. *Two lines which are not on a quadric Q^2 and do not meet the same line of Q^2 are met by one and but one polar pair of lines.*

Proof. Let one of the given lines meet the quadric in A and A' and the other meet it in B and B'. By Theorem 35 there is a unique direct projective collineation of the quadric which carries A to A', A' to A, and B to B'. By Theorem 39 this is a line reflection $\{lm\}$ and l and m are polar with respect to Q^2. Since $\{lm\}$ transforms A to A', l and m both meet the line AA', and since $\{lm\}$ transforms B to B', l and m both meet the line BB'.

If there were another pair of polar lines l', m' meeting AA' and BB', $\{l'm'\}$ would interchange A and A' and B and B'. By Theorem 35 $\{lm\} = \{l'm'\}$.

COROLLARY. *Two lines which are not on a quadric Q^2 and do not meet the same line of Q^2 are met by two and only two lines which are conjugate to them both with regard to Q^2.*

Proof. This follows directly from the theorem, because two mutually polar lines a, b meeting two lines l and m are both conjugate to

l and m and, moreover, if a line a meets and is conjugate to both l and m its polar line also meets and is conjugate to both l and m.

THEOREM 41. *If a simple hexagon is inscribed in a quadric surface in such a way that no two of its vertices are on a line of the quadric, the three pairs of opposite edges are met each by a polar pair of lines, and these three polar pairs of lines are in the same linear congruence.*

Proof. Let $A_1B_2C_1A_2B_1C_2$ be the simple hexagon. By the last theorem the pair of opposite edges A_1B_2, A_2B_1 is met by a pair of lines c_1, c_2 which are polar with respect to the quadric. In like manner B_2C_1, B_1C_2 are met by a polar pair a_1, a_2, and C_1A_2, C_2A_1 by a polar pair b_1, b_2. Consider the product of line reflections,

$$\Gamma = \{c_1c_2\} \cdot \{b_1b_2\} \cdot \{a_1a_2\}.$$

The line reflection $\{a_1a_2\}$ carries B_1 to C_2, $\{b_1b_2\}$ carries C_2 to A_1, and $\{c_1c_2\}$ carries A_1 to B_2. Likewise $\{a_1a_2\}$ carries B_2 to C_1, $\{b_1b_2\}$ carries C_1 to A_2, and $\{c_1c_2\}$ carries A_2 to B_1. Hence Γ interchanges B_1 and B_2, and by Theorem 39 it is a line reflection. Denoting Γ by $\{d_1d_2\}$ we have

$$\{c_1c_2\} \cdot \{d_1d_2\} = \{b_1b_2\} \cdot \{a_1a_2\}.$$

By Theorem 38 the axes of the four line reflections in this equation are all lines of the same congruence.

In view of the corollaries of Theorems 38 and 40 this theorem may be restated in the following forms:

COROLLARY 1. *If a simple hexagon is inscribed in a quadric in such a way that no two of its vertices are on a line of the quadric, the three polar pairs of lines which meet the pairs of opposite edges are met by a polar pair of lines (which may coincide).*

COROLLARY 2. *If a simple hexagon is inscribed in a quadric surface in such a way that no two of its vertices are on a line of the quadric, each pair of opposite edges is met by a unique pair of lines conjugate to both edges, and the latter three pairs of lines are met by a pair of lines conjugate to each of them. The lines of the last pair may coincide.**

* Bulletin of the American Mathematical Society, Vol. XVI (1909), pp. 55 and 62. A theorem of non-Euclidean geometry from which this may be obtained by generalization has been given by F. Klein, Mathematische Annalen, Vol. XXII (1883), p. 248.

This theorem is closely analogous to Pascal's theorem on conic sections (Chap. V, Vol. I). In the Pascal hexagon the pairs of opposite sides determine three points A, B, C which are collinear. In the hexagon inscribed in a quadric they determine three pairs of lines a_1a_2, b_1b_2, c_1c_2 which are in a linear congruence. In case the vertices of the hexagon are coplanar, the theorem on the quadric reduces directly to Pascal's.

The Pascal theorem may be proved by precisely the method used above. For let $A_1B_2C_1A_2B_1C_2$ be a hexagon inscribed in a conic and let A be the point (B_1C_2, C_1B_2), B be (C_1A_2, A_1C_2), and C be (A_1B_2, B_1A_2). Let $\{Aa\}$, $\{Bb\}$, and $\{Cc\}$ be the harmonic homologies effecting the involutions having A, B, C as centers. By construction the projectivity effected by $\{Cc\} \cdot \{Bb\} \cdot \{Aa\}$ on the conic carries B_1 to B_2, and B_2 to B_1, and hence is an involution. Denoting its center and axis by D and d, we have

$$\{Cc\} \cdot \{Bb\} \cdot \{Aa\} = \{Dd\}.$$

This implies $$\{Bb\} \cdot \{Aa\} = \{Cc\} \cdot \{Dd\}.$$

By the theorems of Chap. VIII, Vol. I, the line AB is the axis of the projectivity effected by $\{Bb\} \cdot \{Aa\}$ and must contain C and D. Hence A, B, C are collinear.

Pascal's theorem is thus based on the proposition that the product of three involutions on a conic is itself an involution if and only if the centers of the three involutions are collinear, i.e. if and only if their axes are concurrent. Let us denote an involution whose double points are L and M by $\{LM\}$, as in Ex. 11, § 52. If the involution is represented on a conic, the double points are joined by the axis of the involution. The proposition above then takes the form: The product $\{L_3M_3\} \cdot \{L_2M_2\} \cdot \{L_1M_1\}$ is an involution if and only if the lines L_1M_1, L_2M_2, L_3M_3 concur. The concurrence of the three lines means either that the three point pairs have a point in common or that they are themselves pairs of an involution. Thus the theorem on involutions may be stated as follows:

THEOREM 42. *In any one-dimensional form a product of three involutions* $\{L_1M_1\}$, $\{L_2M_2\}$, $\{L_3M_3\}$ *is an involution in case the pairs of points* L_1M_1, L_2M_2, L_3M_3 *have a point in common or are pairs of an involution; and the product is not an involution in any other case.*

The double points of the involutions may be either proper or improper (real or imaginary). In order to state the result entirely in terms of proper elements, the involutions may be represented on a conic and the condition stated in terms of the concurrence of their axes, as above; or it may be expressed by saying that they all belong to the same pencil of involutions, or by saying that they are all harmonic to the same projectivity.

This theorem on involutions in a one-dimensional form is fundamental in the theory of those groups of projectivities, in a space of any number of dimensions, which are products of involutoric projectivities. For example, it is essentially the same as Theorem 8, Chap. IV, which was fundamental in the theory of the parabolic metric group in the plane. Corresponding theorems in the Euclidean geometry of three dimensions will be found in §§ 114 and 121, Chap. VII. The same principle appears as Theorem 27, Cor. 1, Chap. III, in connection with the equiaffine group.

These groups are all projective and on that account related to the projective group of a one-dimensional form. But the essential feature which they have in common is that *every transformation of each group is a product of two involutoric transformations of the same group.* On this account, even without their common projective basis, the geometries corresponding to these groups must have many features in common. In particular, whenever there is some class of figures such that if two of the figures are interchanged by a transformation, the transformation is of period two, there must exist a theorem analogous to Pascal's theorem. As examples of this may be cited Theorem 41 above; Ex. 6, § 80, Vol. I; Ex. 1, § 122, below; and in the list of exercises below, Ex. 4, referring to the group of point reflections and translations, Exs. 5, 6 referring to the Euclidean group in a plane, Ex. 7 referring to the equiaffine group. On this subject in particular and also on the general theory of groups generated by transformations of period two, the reader should consult a series of articles by H. Wiener in the Berichte der Gesellschaft der Wissenschaften zu Leipzig, Vol. XLII (1890), pp. 13, 71, 245; Vol. XLIII (1891), pp. 424, 644; and also the article by Wiener referred to in § 45, above. Cf. also § 80, Vol. I.

EXERCISES

1. (Converse of Theorem 41.) If the three pairs of opposite edges of a simple hexagon are met by three pairs of lines a_1a_2, b_1b_2, c_1c_2 in pairs of points which are harmonically conjugate to the pairs of vertices with which they are collinear, and if the lines a_1, a_2, b_1, b_2, c_1, c_2 are in the same linear congruence, then the vertices of the hexagon are on a quadric surface with regard to which a_1a_2, b_1b_2, c_1c_2 are polar pairs of lines.

2. Two pairs of lines which are polar with regard to the same regulus cannot consist of lines of a common regulus.

3. If two lines l and m are met by two pairs of lines which are polar with respect to a quadric, l and m are polar.

4. In a Euclidean plane let A, B, C be the three points of intersection of pairs of opposite sides of a simple hexagon. If A and B are mid-points of the sides containing them, and C is the mid-point of one side containing it, then C is also a mid-point of the other side containing it.

5. Let $A_1B_2C_1A_2B_1C_2$ be a simple hexagon in a Euclidean plane. If the perpendicular bisector of the point pair A_1B_2 coincides with that of A_2B_1, and the perpendicular bisector of B_2C_1 with that of B_1C_2, and the perpendicular bisector of C_2A_1 with that of C_1A_2 then the three perpendicular bisectors meet in a point.

6. Let a, b, c, a', b', c' be six concurrent lines of a Euclidean plane. If there is a pair of lines bisecting each of the pairs ab' and $a'b$, and a pair bisecting bc' and $b'c$, there is a pair bisecting ca' and $c'a$.

7. If the pairs of opposite sides of a simple hexagon are parallel, the lines joining their mid-points are concurrent.

109. Conjugate imaginary lines of the second kind. The theory of antiprojectivities (§ 99) and the extended theory of projectivities of one-dimensional forms (§ 106) will now enable us to complete the theory of conjugate imaginary elements in certain essential details which we were not ready to discuss in § 78. Let S′ be a complex projective space and let S be a three-chain of S′, i.e. a space related to S′ in the manner described in §§ 6 and 70, and let us use the definitions and notations of § 70. The simplest type of antiprojective collineation of S′ is given by the equations

$$(34) \qquad x_0' = \bar{x}_0, \quad x_1' = \bar{x}_1, \quad x_2' = \bar{x}_2, \quad x_3' = \bar{x}_3.$$

The frame of reference is such that the points of S have real coördinates. The transformation changes each point

$$(\alpha_0 + i\beta_0, \ \alpha_1 + i\beta_1, \ \alpha_2 + i\beta_2, \ \alpha_3 + i\beta_3),$$

where the α's and β's are real, into the point

$$(\alpha_0 - i\beta_0, \ \alpha_1 - i\beta_1, \ \alpha_2 - i\beta_2, \ \alpha_3 - i\beta_3).$$

These two points if distinct are joined by the real line

$$(\alpha_0 + \lambda\beta_0, \ \alpha_1 + \lambda\beta_1, \ \alpha_2 + \lambda\beta_2, \ \alpha_3 + \lambda\beta_3)$$

and are the double points of the involution determined by the transformation of the parameter λ,

$$\lambda' = -\frac{1}{\lambda}.$$

Comparing with the definition of conjugate imaginary points in § 78, it is clear that (34) is the transformation by which every point of S′ goes to its conjugate imaginary point, the points of S being regarded as real.

From the fact that the transformation (34) leaves no imaginary point invariant, it follows that it cannot leave any imaginary line or plane invariant. For the real line through an imaginary point P of the given line or plane is left invariant by (34), and hence P would be left invariant by (34). On the other hand, (34) leaves every real element invariant and hence leaves every elliptic involution in a real one-dimensional form invariant. Since (34) cannot leave the double elements of such an involution invariant, it must interchange them. Hence (34) interchanges any element of S′ with the element which is its conjugate imaginary according to the definition of § 78.

The definition of § 78 defines the notion of conjugate imaginary elements for all one-dimensional forms of the first or second degrees, and the theorems of that section cover all cases except that of a pair of conjugate imaginary lines which are the double lines of an elliptic involution in the lines of a regulus.

DEFINITION. An imaginary line which is a double line of an elliptic involution in a flat pencil is said to be of *the first kind,* and one which is a double line of an elliptic involution in a regulus is said to be of *the second kind.*

THEOREM 43. *Any imaginary line is either of the first or of the second kind.*

Proof. Let l be an imaginary line. It cannot contain two real points, else it would be a real line (§ 70). Hence it contains one or no real point. In the first case let O be the real point on l, P one of the imaginary points on l, and $\bar{P}$ the imaginary point conjugate to P. The line $P\bar{P}$ is real, and hence the plane $OP\bar{P}$ is real. Hence by § 78 the lines OP and $O\bar{P}$ are the double lines of an elliptic involution in the pencil of real lines on the point O and the plane $OP\bar{P}$.

In the second case let P, Q and R be three points of l and let $\bar{P}$, $\bar{Q}$ and $\bar{R}$ be their respective conjugate imaginary points. The lines $P\bar{P}$, $Q\bar{Q}$, $R\bar{R}$ are real and no two of them can intersect, for if they did l would be on a real plane, and we should have the case considered in the last paragraph. Hence these lines determine a regulus R_1^2 in S. On the real line $P\bar{P}$ there is by § 78 an elliptic involution having P and $\bar{P}$ as its imaginary double points. Hence there is an elliptic involution in the regulus R_2^2, conjugate to R_1^2, having l as one double line and a line $\bar{l}$ through $\bar{P}$ as the other. The lines l and $\bar{l}$ are conjugate imaginary lines by definition, and satisfy the definition of imaginary lines of the second kind. Since (34) transforms each element into its conjugate element, it is clear that $\bar{l}$ contains $\bar{Q}$ and $\bar{R}$ as well as $\bar{P}$.

The system of real lines obtained by joining each point of l to its conjugate imaginary point on $\bar{l}$ is, by the reasoning above, a set of lines of the real space S, no two of which intersect. Any four of them determine a linear congruence (§ 107, Vol. I) C in S and also a linear congruence $\bar{C}$ of S′. The congruence C has the property that each of its lines is contained in a line of $\bar{C}$, and $\bar{C}$ evidently is the set of all lines joining points of l to points of $\bar{l}$. Hence C is an elliptic congruence according to the definition of § 107, Vol. I, and consists of all real lines meeting l and $\bar{l}$. Hence the system of real lines joining points of l to their conjugate imaginary points is an elliptic congruence in S, or in other words:

THEOREM 44. *An imaginary line of the second kind is a directrix of an elliptic congruence.*

The observation, made in the argument above, that there is one line of a certain elliptic congruence through each point of an imaginary line of the second kind, shows that an elliptic congruence may be taken as a real image of a complex one-dimensional form. This of course implies that the whole of the real inversion geometry can be carried over into the theory of the elliptic congruence and *vice versa.* Cf. the exercises below.

The relations between the imaginary lines of the second kind and the regulus and elliptic congruence are fundamental in the von Staudt theory of imaginaries which has been referred to in § 6. In addition to the references given in that place, the reader may consult the Encyclopédie des Sciences Mathématiques, III 8, § 19, and III 3, §§ 14, 15.

EXERCISES

1. An elliptic congruence in a real space has a pair of conjugate imaginary lines of the second kind as directrices.

2. The correspondence by which each point of an imaginary line l corresponds to its conjugate imaginary point is an antiprojectivity between l and its conjugate imaginary line.

3. Under the projective group of a real space any imaginary point is transformable into any other imaginary point, any imaginary line of the first kind into any imaginary line of the first kind, and any imaginary line of the second kind into any imaginary line of the second kind; an imaginary line of the first kind is not transformable into one of the second kind.

4. There is a one-to-one reciprocal correspondence between the points of a complex line and the lines of an elliptic congruence in a real space in which the points of a chain correspond to the lines of a regulus. By means of this correspondence, make a study of the elliptic congruence and its group.

5. Let S_3' be a three-dimensional complex space. Any five noncoplanar points of S_3' determine a unique three-chain, which is a real S_3. This S_3 is related to S_3' in the manner described in §§ 6 and 70. Through any point P of S_3' not on S_3, there is (§ 78) a unique line which contains a line of S_3 (i.e. a chain C_1) as a subset. On this chain C_1 there is a unique elliptic involution having P as a double point. Let $\overline{P}$ be the other double point of this involution. P and $\overline{P}$ are the conjugate imaginary points with regard to the real space S_3, and the transformation of S_3' by which each point P not on S_3 goes to $\overline{P}$, and each point on S_3 is left invariant, may be called a *reflection in the three-chain* S_3. Any transformation which is a product of an odd number of reflections in three-chains is an antiprojective collineation, and any transformation which is a product of an even number of reflections in three-chains is a projective collineation. Every collineation is expressible in this form.

110. The principle of transference. We have seen how the geometry of the inversion group in the plane, arising initially as an extension of the Euclidean group, is equivalent to the projective geometry of the complex line and also to that of a real quadric which may be specialized as a sphere. We have also seen the equivalence of the projective groups of all one-dimensional forms in any properly projective space. Since the regulus is a one-dimensional form, this gave a hold on the group of the general quadric. The latter group in a complex space has been seen to be isomorphic with the complex inversion group and also with the fundamental group of the function plane.

At each step we have helped ourselves forward by transferring the results of one geometry to another, combining these with easily obtained theorems of the second geometry, and thus extending our knowledge of both. This is one of the characteristic methods of modern geometry. It was perhaps first used with clear understanding by O. Hesse,* and was formulated as a definite geometrical principle (Uebertragungsprinzip) by F. Klein in the article referred to in § 34.

This principle of transference or of carrying over the results of one geometry to another may be stated as follows: *Given a set of elements* [*e*] *and a group G of permutations of these elements, and a set of theorems* [*T*] *which state relations left invariant by G. Let* [*e'*] *be another set of elements, and G' a group of permutations of* [*e'*]. *If there is a one-to-one reciprocal correspondence between* [*e*] *and* [*e'*]

* Gesammelte Werke, p. 531.

in which G is simply isomorphic with G′, the set of theorems [T] determines by a mere change of terminology a set of theorems [T′] which state relations among elements e′ which are left invariant by G′.

This principle becomes effective when the method by which [e] and G are defined is such as to make it easy to derive theorems which are not so easily seen for [e′] and G′. This has been abundantly illustrated in the present chapter, but the series of geometries equivalent to the projective geometry on a line could be much extended. Some of the possible extensions are mentioned in the exercises below.

From the example of the conic and the quadric surface (§ 107) it is clear that in order to carry results over from the theory of a set [e] and a group G to a set [e′] and a group G′ it is not necessary that the correspondence be one-to-one. The transference of theorems is, however, no longer a mere translation from one language, as it were, to another, but involves a study of the nature of the correspondence.

DEFINITION. Given a set of elements [e] and a group G of permutations of [e], the set of theorems [T] which state relations among the elements of [e] which are left invariant by G and are not left invariant by any group of permutations containing G is called a *generalized geometry* or *a branch of mathematics*.*

This is, of course, a generalization of the definition of a geometry employed in §§ 34 and 39. At the time when the rôle of groups in geometry was outlined by Klein, the only sets [e] under consideration were continuous manifolds, i.e. complex spaces of n dimensions or loci defined by one or more analytic relations among the coördinates of points in such spaces. The older writers restrict the term "geometry" by means of this restriction on the set [e]. But in view of the existence of modular spaces and other sets of elements determining sets of theorems more nearly identical with ordinary geometry than some of those admitted by Klein's original definition, it seems desirable to state the definition in the form adopted above.

In case the set of theorems [T] is arranged deductively, as explained in the introduction to Vol. I, it becomes a mathematical science. The problem of the foundation of such a science is that of determining, if possible, a finite set of assumptions from which [T] may be deduced.

* The generalized conception of a geometry is discussed very clearly in the article by G. Fano in the Encyclopädie der Math. Wiss. III AB 4b. A number of special cases are outlined in the latter half of the article.

EXERCISES

1. If a projective collineation interchanges the two reguli on a quadric, homologous lines of the two reguli meet in points of a plane.

* **2.** Let R^2 be a regulus, ω a plane not tangent to R^2, and O the pole of ω (ω may conveniently be regarded as the plane at infinity of a Euclidean space). A projectivity Γ of R^2 may be effected by a collineation Γ' leaving all lines of the conjugate regulus invariant. This collineation multiplied by the harmonic homology $\{O\omega\}$ gives a collineation Γ'' interchanging the two reguli. By Ex. 1, Γ'' determines a unique plane. Let P be the point polar to Γ'' with regard to R^2. The correspondence thus determined between the projectivities Γ of R^2 and the points of space not on R^2 is one to one and reciprocal. It is such that projectivities which are harmonic (§ 80, Vol. I) correspond to conjugate points with respect to R^2, and all the involutions correspond to points of ω.

* **3.** The construction of Ex. 2 sets up a correspondence between the projectivities of a one-dimensional form and the points of a three-dimensional space which are not on a certain quadric. The same correspondence may be obtained by letting a projectivity

$$x' = \frac{a_0 x + a_1}{a_2 x + a_3}$$

correspond to the point (a_0, a_1, a_2, a_3). The relations between the one-dimensional and three-dimensional projective geometries thus obtained have been studied by C. Stéphanos, Mathematische Annalen, Vol. XXII (1883), p. 299.

* **4.** Develop the theory of the twisted cubic curve in space along the following lines: (1) Define it algebraically. (2) Give a geometric definition. (3) Prove that Definitions (1) and (2) are equivalent. (4) Derive the further theorems on the cubic as far as possible from the geometric definition. It will be found that the properties of this cubic can be obtained largely from those of conic sections and one-dimensional projectivities in view of an isomorphism of the groups in question. The theorems should be classified according to the principle laid down in § 83.

* **5.** A *rational curve* in a space of k dimensions is a locus given parametrically as follows:

$$x_0 = R_0(t), \quad x_1 = R_1(t), \cdots, \quad x_n = R_n(t),$$

where $R_0(t), \cdots, R_n(t)$ are rational functions of t. In case $k = n$ and the locus is not contained in any space of less than n dimensions, the curve is a *normal curve.* Develop the theories of various rational curves along the lines outlined in Ex. 4. For reference cf. § 28 of the encyclopedia article by Fano referred to above and articles by several authors in recent volumes of the American Journal of Mathematics.

* **6.** The linear dependence of conic sections may be defined by substituting "point conic" or "line conic," as the case may be, for "circle" in the definition given at the end of § 100. Develop the theory of linear families of conics of one, two, three, and four dimensions, using the principle of correspondence whenever possible and classifying theorems according to the principle laid down in § 83. Cf. Encyclopédie des Sc. Math. III 18.

CHAPTER VII

AFFINE AND EUCLIDEAN GEOMETRY OF THREE DIMENSIONS

111. Affine geometry. DEFINITION. Let π_∞ be an arbitrary but fixed plane of a projective space S. The set of points of S not on π_∞ is called a *Euclidean space* and π_∞ is called the *plane at infinity* of this space. The plane π_∞ and the points and lines on π_∞ are said to be *ideal* or *at infinity*; all other points, lines, and planes of S are said to be *ordinary*. When no other indication is given, a point, line, or plane is understood to be ordinary. Any projective collineation transforming a Euclidean space into itself is said to be *affine*; the group of all such collineations is called the *affine group of three dimensions*, and the corresponding geometry the *affine geometry of three dimensions*.

DEFINITION. Two ordinary lines which have an ideal point in common are said to be *parallel* to each other. Two ordinary planes which have an ideal line in common, or an ordinary line and an ordinary plane which have an ideal point in common, are said to be *parallel* to each other.

In particular, a line or plane is said to be parallel to itself or to any plane or line which it is on. For ordinary points, lines, and planes we have as an obvious consequence of the assumptions and definitions of Chap. I, Vol. I, the following theorem:

THEOREM 1. *Through a given point there is one and only one line parallel to a given line. Through a given point there is one and only one plane parallel to a given plane. If two lines, l and l', are not in the same plane there is one and only one plane through a given point parallel to l and l'. If l and l' are parallel, any plane through l is parallel to l'.*

Another obvious though important theorem is the following:

THEOREM 2. *The transformations effected in an ordinary plane π by the affine group in space constitute the affine group of the Euclidean plane consisting of the ordinary points of π.*

In consequence of this theorem we have the whole affine plane geometry as a part of the affine geometry of three dimensions, and we shall take all the definitions and theorems of Chap. III for granted without further comment.

This discussion is valid for any space satisfying Assumptions A, E. The affine geometry of an ordered space (A, E, S) has already been considered in § 31, and certain additional theorems are given in Exs. 5–7 below.

EXERCISES

1. The lines joining the mid-points of the pairs of vertices of a tetrahedron meet in a point.

2. Classify the quadric surfaces from the point of view of real affine geometry. Develop the theory of diametral lines and planes. The real projective classification of the nondegenerate quadrics has been given in § 103. The affine classification is given in the Encyclopédie des Sc. Math. III 22, § 19.

***3.** Classify the linear congruences from the point of view of the real affine geometry. Cf. § 107, Vol. I.

***4.** Classify the linear complexes from the point of view of real affine geometry. Cf. § 108, Vol. I.

5. With respect to the coördinate system used in § 31 the points of the line joining $A=(a_1, a_2, a_3)$ and $B=(b_1, b_2, b_3)$ are

$$\left(\frac{a_1+\lambda b_1}{1+\lambda},\ \frac{a_2+\lambda b_2}{1+\lambda},\ \frac{a_3+\lambda b_3}{1+\lambda}\right),$$

B corresponding to $\lambda=\infty$ and the point at infinity to $\lambda=-1$. The segment AB consists of the points for which $\lambda>0$ and its two prolongations of those for which $\lambda<-1$ and $-1<\lambda<0$ respectively.

6. Two points D and D' are on the same side of the plane ABC if and only if

$$S(ABCD)=S(ABCD').$$

7. Using the notation of § 101 and dealing with an ordered Euclidean space, $\{O\omega\}$ is an affine collineation which alters sense if O or ω is at infinity and $\{ll'\}$ is an affine collineation which does not alter sense if l or l' is at infinity. In an ordered projective space $\{ll'\}$ is, and $\{O\omega\}$ is not, a direct collineation.

112. Vectors, equivalence of point triads, etc. DEFINITION. An elation having π_∞ as its plane of fixed points is called a *translation.* If l is an ordinary line on the center of the translation, the translation is said to be *parallel* to l.

The properties of the group of translations follow in large part ·om the following evident theorem.

THEOREM 3. *The transformations effected in an ordinary plane* π *by the translations leaving* π *invariant constitute the group of translations of the Euclidean plane composed of the ordinary points of* π.

As corollaries of this we have statements about translations in space which are verbally identical with Theorems 3–7, Chap. III. Theorem 8, Chap. III, generalizes as follows:

COROLLARY. *If OX, OY, and OZ are three noncoplanar lines and* T *any translation, there exists a unique triad of translations* T_x, T_y, T_z *parallel to OX, OY, OZ respectively and such that*

$$T = T_x T_y T_z.$$

The theory of congruence under translations generalizes to space without change, and the contents of §§ 39 and 40 may be taken as applying to the affine geometry in three-space. In like manner the definition of a field of vectors and of addition of vectors is carried over to space if the words "Euclidean plane" be replaced by "Euclidean space." The theorems of § 42 then apply without change.

We arrive at this point on the basis of Assumptions A, E, H_0. Adding Assumption P we take over the theory of the ratio of collinear vectors from §§ 43, 44. Some of the theorems to which it may be applied without essential modifications of the methods used in the planar case are given in the exercises below.

The definition of equivalence of ordered point triads in § 48 is such that if a plane π be carried by an affine collineation to a plane π', any two equivalent point triads of π are carried to two equivalent point triads of π'. Moreover, the definition of measure of ordered point triads in § 49 is such that if two coplanar ordered point triads ABC, DEF are carried by an affine collineation to $A'B'C'$, $D'E'F'$ respectively,

$$(1) \qquad \frac{m\,(ABC)}{m\,(DEF)} = \frac{m\,(A'B'C')}{m\,(D'E'F')}.$$

This result in view of Theorem 39, Chap. III, depends on the corresponding theorem about the ratios of collinear vectors. In (1) the unit of measure in any plane is regarded as entirely independent of the unit of measure in every other plane, but nevertheless the ratio of the measures is an invariant of the affine group. Certain ratios of ratios of measures are invariants of the projective group (cf. Ex. 17 below).

The notion of equivalence of ordered point triads may be extended as follows:

DEFINITION. Two ordered point triads ABC and $A'B'C'$ are *equivalent* if and only if ABC may be carried by a translation to an ordered triad $A''B''C''$ which is equivalent in the sense of § 48, Chap. III, to $A'B'C'$.

The fundamental propositions with regard to equivalence, as developed in § 48, remain valid under the extended definition. Thus if $ABC \backsimeq A_1B_1C_1$ and $A_1B_1C_1 \backsimeq A_2B_2C_2$, $ABC \backsimeq A_2B_2C_2$; if $ABC \backsimeq A_1B_1C_1$, $A_1B_1C_1 \backsimeq ABC$, etc.

This extension of the notion of equivalence carries with it a corresponding restriction of the idea of measure, i.e. measure is now defined as in § 49, with the added proviso that the unit triad in any plane shall be equivalent to the unit triad in any parallel plane.

The method by which the theory of equivalence of ordered point triads was developed in Chap. III does not generalize directly to the case of ordered tetrads in three-dimensional space.* We shall therefore give an algebraic definition of the measures of an ordered set of four points, leaving it to the reader to develop the corresponding synthetic theory (cf. Ex. 13 below).

DEFINITION. By the *measure* of an ordered tetrad of points A_1, A_2, A_3, A_4 *relative to an ordered tetrad OPQR as unit* is meant the number

$$(2)\qquad \begin{vmatrix} 1 & a_{11} & a_{12} & a_{13} \\ 1 & a_{21} & a_{22} & a_{23} \\ 1 & a_{31} & a_{32} & a_{33} \\ 1 & a_{41} & a_{42} & a_{43} \end{vmatrix} = m\,(A_1A_2A_3A_4),$$

where (a_{i1}, a_{i2}, a_{i3}) are nonhomogeneous coördinates of A_i $(i = 1, 2, 3, 4)$ in a coördinate system in which O, P, Q, R are $(0, 0, 0)$, $(1, 0, 0)$, $(0, 1, 0)$, $(0, 0, 1)$ respectively. Two ordered tetrads are said to be *equivalent* if and only if they have the same measure. In real affine geometry the number $\frac{1}{6}|m\,(A_1A_2A_3A_4)|$ is called the *volume* of the tetrahedron $A_1A_2A_3A_4$ relative to the unit tetrahedron $OPQR$ and is denoted by $v\,(A_1A_2A_3A_4)$.

The theory of the equivalence of point pairs, triads, tetrads, etc. is the most elementary part of vector analysis and the Grassmann *Ausdehnungslehre*. This subject in particular, and the affine geometry

* Cf. M. Dehn, Mathematische Annalen, Vol. LV (1902), p. 465.

of three dimensions in general, is worthy of a much more extensive treatment than it is receiving here. We have referred only to that part of the subject which is essential to the study of the Euclidean geometry of three dimensions.

In the following exercises the coördinate system is understood to be that which is described in the definition of measure of ordered tetrads above. The vectors OP, OQ, OR are taken as units of measure for the respectively parallel systems of vectors. The ordered point triads OPQ, OQR, ORP are taken as units of measure for the respectively parallel systems of ordered point triads.

Definition. By the *projection* of a set of points $[X]$ on the x-axis is meant the set of points in which this axis is met by the planes through the points X and parallel to the plane $x=0$; and the projection on the y- and z-axes have analogous meanings.

By the *projection* of a set of points $[X]$ on the plane $x=0$ is meant the set of points in which this plane is met by the lines on points X and parallel to the x-axis; and the projections on the planes $y=0$ and $z=0$ have analogous meanings.

EXERCISES

1. The measures of ordered tetrads of points are unaltered by transformations

$$x' = b_{11}x + b_{12}y + b_{13}z + b_{10},$$
$$y' = b_{21}x + b_{22}y + b_{23}z + b_{20}, \qquad (3)$$
$$z' = b_{31}x + b_{32}y + b_{33}z + b_{30},$$

subject to the condition $\Delta = 1$, where

$$\Delta = \begin{vmatrix} b_{11} & b_{12} & b_{13} \\ b_{21} & b_{22} & b_{23} \\ b_{31} & b_{32} & b_{33} \end{vmatrix}. \qquad (4)$$

This group is called the *equiaffine* group and also the *special linear* group. The group for which $\Delta^2 = 1$ leaves volumes invariant.

2. Ratios of measures of ordered tetrads of points are left invariant by the affine group.

3. In an ordered space two ordered sets of points $ABCD$ and $A'B'C'D'$ are in the same sense or not according as $m(ABCD)$ and $m(A'B'C'D')$ have the same sign or not.

4. The product of two line reflections $\{ll'\}$ and $\{mm'\}$ (cf. § 101) is a translation if l' and m' are at infinity and l and m are parallel.

5. Determine the subgroups of the group of translations in space.

6. The projections of a point pair P_1P_2 on the x-, y-, and z-axes respectively have the measures

$$\alpha = x_2 - x_1, \quad \beta = y_2 - y_1, \quad \gamma = z_2 - z_1,$$

and those of the ordered point triad OP_1P_2 on the planes $x = 0$, $y = 0$, $z = 0$ respectively have the measures

$$\lambda = \begin{vmatrix} y_1 & z_1 \\ y_2 & z_2 \end{vmatrix}, \quad \mu = \begin{vmatrix} z_1 & x_1 \\ z_2 & x_2 \end{vmatrix}, \quad \nu = \begin{vmatrix} x_1 & y_1 \\ x_2 & y_2 \end{vmatrix}.$$

These numbers satisfy the relation

$$\alpha\lambda + \beta\mu + \gamma\nu = 0.$$

Any two points $P_1'P_2'$ of the line P_1P_2 such that Vect P_1P_2 = Vect $P_1'P_2'$ determine the same six numbers $\alpha, \beta, \gamma, \lambda, \mu, \nu$. These numbers are proportional to the Plücker coördinates (cf. § 109, Vol. I) of the line P_1P_2.

7. Using the notations of Ex. 6, $\lambda = m(OPP_1P_2)$, $\mu = m(OQP_1P_2)$, $\nu = m(ORP_1P_2)$. If $\alpha', \beta', \gamma', \lambda', \mu', \nu'$ are the numbers analogous to $\alpha, \beta, \gamma, \lambda, \mu, \nu$ determined by an ordered pair P_3P_4,

$$m(P_1P_2P_3P_4) = \alpha\lambda' + \beta\mu' + \gamma\nu' + \lambda\alpha' + \mu\beta' + \nu\gamma'.$$

8. The measures of the projections of an ordered point triad $P_1P_2P_3$ on the planes $x = 0$, $y = 0$, $z = 0$ respectively are

$$u_1 = \begin{vmatrix} y_1 & z_1 & 1 \\ y_2 & z_2 & 1 \\ y_3 & z_3 & 1 \end{vmatrix} \quad u_2 = -\begin{vmatrix} x_1 & z_1 & 1 \\ x_2 & z_2 & 1 \\ x_3 & z_3 & 1 \end{vmatrix} \quad u_3 = \begin{vmatrix} x_1 & y_1 & 1 \\ x_2 & y_2 & 1 \\ x_3 & y_3 & 1 \end{vmatrix}.$$

The homogeneous coördinates of the plane $P_1P_2P_3$ are (u_0, u_1, u_2, u_3), where

$$u_0 = \begin{vmatrix} x_1 & y_1 & z_1 \\ x_2 & y_2 & z_2 \\ x_3 & y_3 & z_3 \end{vmatrix} = m(OP_1P_2P_3).$$

9. If P_1, P_2, P_3, P_4 are four noncoplanar points and P_3', P_4' are two points collinear with P_3 and P_4, then Vect $(P_3'P_4')$ = Vect (P_3P_4) if and only if $m(P_1P_2P_3P_4) = m(P_1P_2P_3'P_4')$.

10. If P_1, P_2, P_3, P_4 are four noncoplanar points and the lines P_1P_2, $P_1'P_2'$, $P_1''P_2''$ have a point in common and

$$\text{Vect}(P_1P_2) = \text{Vect}(P_1'P_2') + \text{Vect}(P_1''P_2''),$$

then
$$m(P_1P_2P_3P_4) = m(P_1'P_2'P_3P_4) + m(P_1''P_2''P_3P_4).$$

***11.** Study barycentric coördinates and the barycentric calculus for three-dimensional space. Cf. § 51, § 27, and references to Möbius in § 49.

***12.** Study the measure of n-points in space, generalizing the exercises in § 49.

***13.** Define two ordered tetrads $ABCD$ and $A'B'C'D'$ as equivalent provided that (1) $A = A'$, $B = B'$, $C = C'$, and the line DD' is parallel to the plane ABC, or (2) if there are a finite number of ordered tetrads $t_1, \cdots, t_n$ such that $ABCD$ is in relation (1) to t_1, t_1 in a like relation to t_2, t_3 to $t_4, \cdots$.

and t_n to $A'B'C'D'$. Develop a theory of equivalence as nearly as possible analogous to that of § 48. Show that two tetrads are equivalent in this sense if and only if they are equivalent according to the definition in the text.

***14.** An elation whose center is at infinity and whose plane of fixed points is ordinary is called a *simple shear*. The set of all products of simple shears is the equiaffine group. Develop the theory of the equiaffine group on this basis. Is it possible to generalize § 52 to space?

15. If a plane meets the sides $A_0A_1, A_1A_2, \cdots, A_nA_0$ of a simple polygon $A_0A_1A_2 \cdots A_n$ in points $B_0, B_1, \cdots, B_n$, respectively,

$$\frac{A_0B_0}{A_1B_0} \cdot \frac{A_1B_1}{A_2B_1} \cdots \frac{A_nB_n}{A_0B_n} = 1.$$

16. If a quadric surface (§ 104, Vol. I) meets the lines $A_0A_1, A_1A_2, \cdots, A_nA_0$ respectively in the pairs of points $B_0C_0, B_1C_1, \cdots, B_nC_n$, respectively,

$$\frac{A_0B_0}{A_1B_0} \cdot \frac{A_0C_0}{A_1C_1} \cdot \frac{A_1B_1}{A_2B_1} \cdot \frac{A_1C_1}{A_2C_1} \cdots \frac{A_nB_n}{A_0B_n} \cdot \frac{A_nC_n}{A_0C_n} = 1.$$

***17.** Six points of a plane no three of which are collinear satisfy the following identity:

$$m(123)\,m(456) - m(124)\,m(563) + m(125)\,m(634) - m(126)\,m(345) \equiv 0.$$

The ratio of any two terms in this sum is a projective invariant. These propositions are given by W. K. Clifford in the Proceedings of the London Mathematical Society, Vol. II (1866), p. 3, as the foundation of the theory of two-dimensional projectivities. Develop the details of the theory outlined by Clifford. Cf. also Möbius, Der barycentrische Calcul, § 221.

113. The parabolic metric group. Orthogonal lines and planes. DEFINITION. Let Σ_∞ be an arbitrary but fixed polar system in the plane at infinity π_∞. This polar system shall be called the *absolute* or *orthogonal polar system*. The conic whose points lie on their polar lines with respect to Σ_∞ is, if existent, called the *circle at infinity*. The group of all collineations leaving Σ_∞ invariant is called the *parabolic metric group* and its transformations are called *similarity transformations*. Two figures conjugate under this group are said to be *similar*.

DEFINITION. Two ordinary planes or two ordinary lines are *orthogonal* or *perpendicular* if and only if they meet π_∞ in conjugate lines or points of the absolute polar system Σ_∞. An ordinary line and plane are *orthogonal* or *perpendicular* if and only if they meet π_∞ in a point and line which are polar with regard to Σ_∞. A line perpendicular to itself, i.e. a line through a point of the circle at infinity, is called a *minimal* or *isotropic line.* A plane perpendicular to itself, i.e. a plane meeting π_∞ in a tangent to the circle at infinity, is called a *minimal* or *isotropic plane.*

As the analogue of Theorems 2 and 3 we have

THEOREM 4. *The similarity transformations which leave an ordinary nonminimal plane* π *invariant, effect in* π *the transformations of a parabolic metric group in the Euclidean plane consisting of the ordinary points of* π.

Generalizing Theorem 1, Chap. IV, we have

THEOREM 5. *At every point O of a Euclidean space the correspondence between the lines and their perpendicular planes is a polar system, the projection of* Σ_∞. *All the lines through O perpendicular to a given line are on the plane perpendicular to the given line at O; and all the planes through O perpendicular to a given plane are on the line through O perpendicular to this plane. If existent, the isotropic lines through a point O constitute a cone of lines, and the isotropic planes through O the cone of planes tangent to this cone of lines.*

COROLLARY 1. *Two perpendicular nonminimal planes meet in a nonminimal line, and two perpendicular nonminimal lines are parallel to a nonminimal plane.*

COROLLARY 2. *If a plane 1 is perpendicular to a plane 2, and 2 is parallel to a plane 3, then 1 is perpendicular to 3. If a plane 1 is perpendicular to a line 2, and 2 is parallel to a line or plane 3, then 1 is perpendicular to 3. If a line 1 is perpendicular to a plane 2, and 2 is parallel to a line or plane 3, then 1 is perpendicular to 3. If a line 1 is perpendicular to a line 2, and 2 is parallel to a line 3, then 1 is perpendicular to 3.*

THEOREM 6. *Two nonparallel lines not both parallel to the same minimal plane are met by one and only one line perpendicular to them both; this line is not minimal.*

Proof. Let A_∞ and B_∞ be the points in which the given lines meet π_∞. By hypothesis $A_\infty \neq B_\infty$, and the line $A_\infty B_\infty$ is not tangent to the circle at infinity. Let C_∞ be the pole of the line $A_\infty B_\infty$ with respect to Σ_∞. The required common intersecting perpendicular is the line through C_∞ meeting the two given lines; this line is obviously unique and not minimal.

EXERCISE

The planes perpendicular to the edges of a tetrahedron at the mid-points of the pairs of vertices meet in a point O. The line perpendicular to any face of the tetrahedron at the center of the circle through the three vertices in this face passes through O.

114. Orthogonal plane reflections. DEFINITION. A homology of period two whose center, P, is a point at infinity polar in the absolute polar system to the line at infinity of its plane of fixed points, π, is called an *orthogonal reflection in a plane* or an *orthogonal plane reflection* or a *symmetry with respect to a plane*, and may be denoted by $\{\pi P\}$.* The plane of fixed points is called the *plane of symmetry* of any two figures which correspond in the homology.

Since the center and the line at infinity of the plane of fixed points of an orthogonal reflection in a plane are pole and polar with respect to Σ_∞, we have

THEOREM 7. *An orthogonal reflection in a plane is a transformation of the parabolic metric group.*

By a direct generalization of Theorems 3 and 4, Chap. IV, we obtain the following:

THEOREM 8. (1) *If π and ρ are two parallel nonminimal planes, the product $\{\rho R\} \cdot \{\pi P\}$ is a translation parallel to any line perpendicular to π and ρ.* (2) *If T is a translation parallel to a nonminimal line l, π any plane perpendicular to l, and ρ the plane perpendicular to l passing through the mid-point of the point pair in which π and $\mathrm{T}(\pi)$ meet l, then*

$$\mathrm{T} = \{\rho R\} \cdot \{\pi P\};$$

and if σ is the plane perpendicular to l passing through the mid-point of the pair in which π and $\mathrm{T}^{-1}(\pi)$ meet l,

$$\mathrm{T} = \{\pi P\} \cdot \{\sigma S\}.$$

(3) *A translation parallel to a minimal line l is a product of four orthogonal plane reflections.*

THEOREM 9. *A product $\Lambda_n \Lambda_{n-1} \cdots \Lambda_1$ of orthogonal plane reflections is expressible in the form $\Lambda'_n \Lambda'_{n-1} \cdots \Lambda'_1 \mathrm{T}$ or $\mathrm{T}' \Lambda'_n \Lambda'_{n-1} \cdots \Lambda'_1$, where $\Lambda'_1, \Lambda'_2, \cdots, \Lambda'_n$ are orthogonal plane reflections whose planes of*

* In the rest of this chapter this notation will be used in the sense here defined and not in the more general sense of § 101.

fixed points all contain an arbitrary point O, and T *and* T′ *are translations. In case O is left invariant by* $\Lambda_n\Lambda_{n-1}\cdots\Lambda_1$, T *and* T′ *reduce to the identity.*

Proof. Let Λ_i' $(i=1, 2, \dots n)$ denote the orthogonal plane reflection whose plane of fixed points is the plane through O parallel to the plane of fixed points of Λ_i. Then by Theorem 8, $\Lambda_i\Lambda_i'=T_i$, T_i being a translation. Hence $\Lambda_i=T_i\Lambda_i'$ and

$$(5)\qquad \Lambda_n\Lambda_{n-1}\cdots\Lambda_1=T_n\Lambda_n'T_{n-1}\Lambda_n'\cdots T_1\Lambda_1'.$$

By the generalization to space of Theorem 11, Cor. 2, Chap. III, if Σ is any affine collineation and T a translation, $T\Sigma=\Sigma T'$, where T′ is a translation. By repeated application of this proposition, (5) reduces to

$$\Lambda_n\Lambda_{n-1}\cdots\Lambda_1=\Lambda_n'\Lambda_{n-1}'\cdots\Lambda_1'T=T'\Lambda_n'\Lambda_{n-1}'\cdots\Lambda_1',$$

where T and T′ are translations.

In case O is a fixed point for the product $\Lambda_n\Lambda_{n-1}\cdots\Lambda_1$, since it is also left invariant by each of the reflections Λ_i', it is left invariant by T and T′. Hence in this case T and T′ reduce to the identity.

THEOREM 10. *If* Λ_1, Λ_2, Λ_3 *are three orthogonal plane reflections whose planes of fixed points meet in a line l, ordinary or ideal, the product* $\Lambda_3\Lambda_2\Lambda_1$ *is an orthogonal plane reflection whose plane of fixed points contains l.*

Proof. One of the chief results obtained in Chap. VIII, Vol. I, can be put in the following form:* If T_1, T_2, T_3 are harmonic homologies leaving a conic invariant and such that their centers are collinear, $T_3T_2T_1$ is a harmonic homology leaving the conic invariant. For by Theorem 19 of that chapter, and its corollary, the product T_2T_1 is expressible in the form T_3T, where T is a harmonic homology whose center and axis are polar with respect to the conic, the axis being concurrent with those of T_1, T_2, and T_3; and from $T_2T_1=T_3T$ follows $T_3T_2T_1=T_3T_3T=T$.

Now if Λ_1, Λ_2, Λ_3 are orthogonal plane reflections whose planes of fixed points meet in an ordinary line l their centers are collinear. Hence they effect in π_∞ three harmonic homologies whose centers are the poles of their axes with respect to the absolute polar system and whose centers are collinear. Hence $\Lambda_3\Lambda_2\Lambda_1$ effects a harmonic homology in the plane at infinity and its axis, m_∞, passes

* Cf. the fine print in § 108.

through the point at infinity of l. Since l and m_∞ are both lines of fixed points of $\Lambda_3\Lambda_2\Lambda_1$, all points of the plane π containing l and m_∞ are invariant. Hence $\Lambda_3\Lambda_2\Lambda_1$ effects a homology having the pole of m_∞ with respect to Σ_∞ as center. Since this homology is of period two in π_∞ it must be an orthogonal plane reflection.

In case the planes of fixed points of Λ_1, Λ_2, Λ_3 are parallel we have by Theorem 8 (1) that $\Lambda_2\Lambda_1$ is a translation parallel to a line perpendicular to these planes, i.e. parallel to a nonminimal line. Hence by Theorem 8 (2) there exists an orthogonal plane reflection, Λ_4, such that

$$\Lambda_2\Lambda_1 = \Lambda_3\Lambda_4$$

or

$$\Lambda_3\Lambda_2\Lambda_1 = \Lambda_4.$$

COROLLARY. *If* $\{\lambda_1 L_1\}$ *and* $\{\lambda_2 L_2\}$ *are two orthogonal plane reflections, and* λ_1' *is any ordinary nonminimal plane in the same pencil with* λ_1 *and* λ_2, *there exists a plane* λ_2' *and points* L_1' *and* L_2' *such that*

$$\{\lambda_2 L_2\} \cdot \{\lambda_1 L_1\} = \{\lambda_2' L_2\} \cdot \{\lambda_1' L_1'\}.$$

Proof. By the theorem, if L_1' is the point at infinity of a line perpendicular to λ_1', there exists an orthogonal plane reflection $\{\lambda_2' L_2'\}$ such that

$$\{\lambda_2 L_2\} \cdot \{\lambda_1 L_1\} \cdot \{\lambda_1' L_1'\} = \{\lambda_2' L_2'\},$$

and hence

$$\{\lambda_2 L_2\} \cdot \{\lambda_1 L_1\} = \{\lambda_2' L_2'\} \cdot \{\lambda_1' L_1'\}.$$

115. Displacements and symmetries. Congruence. We may now generalize directly from § 57, Chap. IV:

DEFINITION. A product of an even number of orthogonal plane reflections is called a *displacement* or *rigid motion.* A product of an odd number of orthogonal plane reflections is called a *symmetry.*

THEOREM 11. *The set of all displacements and symmetries is a self-conjugate subgroup of the parabolic metric group and contains the set of all displacements as a self-conjugate subgroup.*

DEFINITION. Two figures such that one can be transformed into the other by a displacement are said to be *congruent.* Two figures such that one can be transformed into the other by a symmetry are said to be *symmetric.*

THEOREM 12. *If a figure* F_1 *is congruent to a figure* F_2, *and* F_2 *to a figure* F_3, *then* F_1 *is congruent to* F_3. *If* F_1 *is symmetric with* F_2, *and* F_2 *with* F_3, *then* F_1 *is congruent to* F_3. *If* F_1 *is congruent to* F_2, *and* F_2 *symmetric with* F_3, *then* F_1 *is symmetric with* F_3.

THEOREM 13. *Any displacement leaving an ordinary point O invariant is a product of two orthogonal plane reflections whose planes of fixed points contain O.*

Proof. Consider a product of four orthogonal plane reflections, whose planes of fixed points pass through O.

$$\Gamma = \{\lambda_4 L_4\} \cdot \{\lambda_3 L_3\} \cdot \{\lambda_2 L_2\} \cdot \{\lambda_1 L_1\}.$$

Let l be the line of intersection of λ_1 and λ_2, m that of λ_3 and λ_4, and let λ be a plane containing l and m, where in case $l = m$, λ is chosen so as not to be minimal. If λ is nonminimal, by the corollary of Theorem 10 there exist orthogonal plane reflections $\{\mu M\}$, $\{\nu N\}$ such that

$$\{\lambda_2 L_2\} \cdot \{\lambda_1 L_1\} = \{\lambda L\} \cdot \{\mu M\},$$

and

$$\{\lambda_4 L_4\} \cdot \{\lambda_3 L_3\} = \{\nu N\} \cdot \{\lambda L\}.$$

Hence

$$\Gamma = \{\nu N\} \cdot \{\lambda L\} \cdot \{\lambda L\} \cdot \{\mu M\} = \{\nu N\} \cdot \{\mu M\}.$$

In case λ is minimal* $\{\lambda_1 L_1\}$ transforms λ to the other minimal plane through l (i.e. the other plane containing l and a tangent to the circle at infinity), and $\{\lambda_2 L_2\}$ transforms this plane back to λ. In like manner the product $\{\lambda_4 L_4\} \cdot \{\lambda_3 L_3\}$ leaves λ invariant. Hence λ is left invariant by Γ. On the other hand the line l is obviously not left invariant by Γ, and therefore Γ does not leave all points at infinity invariant. Hence Γ leaves at most two tangents to the circle at infinity invariant, and thus leaves at most two minimal planes through O invariant. Let λ_2' be any plane of the bundle containing λ_2 and λ_3 which does not meet λ_1 in a line of an invariant minimal plane of Γ. By the corollary of Theorem 10 there exists a plane λ_3' and points L_2' and L_3' such that

$$\{\lambda_3 L_3\} \cdot \{\lambda_2 L_2\} = \{\lambda_3' L_3'\} \cdot \{\lambda_2' L_2'\},$$

and hence such that

$$\Gamma = \{\lambda_4 L_4\} \cdot \{\lambda_3' L_3'\} \cdot \{\lambda_2' L_2'\} \cdot \{\lambda_1 L_1\}.$$

Now let l be the line of intersection of λ_1 and λ_2', m that of λ_3' and λ_4, and λ' the plane containing l and m. If λ' were minimal it would, as argued above for λ, be invariant under Γ, whereas λ_2' was so chosen that l cannot be in such a plane. Hence the argument in the previous paragraph can be applied to the last expression obtained for Γ.

* This case obviously does not arise in the real Euclidean geometry (§ 116), so that this paragraph may be omitted if one is interested only in that case. It is needed, however, in complex geometry.

Thus, in any case, a product of four orthogonal plane reflections whose planes of fixed points pass through O reduces to a product of two such reflections. By Theorem 9 any displacement leaving O invariant is a product of an even number, say $2n$, of orthogonal reflections in planes through O. This may be reduced to a product of two orthogonal reflections in planes through O by $n-1$ applications of the result proved above.

COROLLARY. *An orthogonal plane reflection is not a displacement.*

Proof. Let O be a point of the plane of fixed points of an orthogonal plane reflection Λ. If Λ were a displacement it would, by the theorem, be a product of two orthogonal plane reflections containing O and hence could only have a single line of fixed points.

DEFINITION. A displacement which is a product of two orthogonal plane reflections whose planes of fixed points have an ordinary line l in common is called a *rotation about* l, and l is called the *axis* of the rotation. If the axis is a minimal line the rotation is said to be *isotropic* or *minimal.*

THEOREM 14. *The product of two orthogonal reflections in perpendicular planes is a rotation of period two. It transforms every point P not on its axis to a point P' such that the axis is perpendicular to the line PP' at the mid-point of the pair PP'. It leaves invariant the points of its axis and the points in which any plane perpendicular to its axis meets the plane at infinity. Its axis cannot be a minimal line.*

Proof. Consider any plane π perpendicular to the planes of fixed points of the two orthogonal plane reflections Λ_1 and Λ_2. By the first corollary of Theorem 5 the axis of $\Lambda_2\Lambda_1$ is nonminimal and hence π is nonminimal. In π the transformations effected by Λ_1 and Λ_2 are orthogonal line reflections in the sense of Chap. IV, and their product is a point reflection (Theorem 5, Chap. IV) in the plane. From this the theorem follows in an obvious way.

DEFINITION. The product of two orthogonal reflections in perpendicular planes is called an *involutoric rotation* or an *orthogonal line reflection* or a *half turn.* If l is its axis and l' the polar with respect to Σ_∞ of the point at infinity of l, it may be denoted by $\{ll'\}$.*

* In the rest of this chapter this notation will be used in the sense here defined and not in the more general sense of § 101.

THEOREM 15. DEFINITION. *The product of the orthogonal plane reflections in three perpendicular planes is a transformation carrying each point P to a point P' such that the point O of intersection of the three planes is the mid-point of the pair PP'. A transformation of this sort is called a* point reflection *or* symmetry *with respect to the point O as center. It is not a displacement. The points P and P' are said to be* symmetric *with respect to O.*

Proof. In the plane at infinity the three orthogonal plane reflections effect the three harmonic homologies whose centers and axes are the vertices and respectively opposite sides of a triangle. The product therefore leaves all points at infinity invariant. It also leaves O invariant and is evidently of period two on the line of intersection of any two of the planes of fixed points of the orthogonal plane reflections. Hence it is a homology of period two with O as center and π_∞ as plane of fixed points. It is not a displacement, since by Theorem 13 a displacement leaving O invariant would have a line of fixed points passing through O.

THEOREM 16. *The transformations effected in a nonminimal plane π by the displacements leaving π invariant constitute the group of displacements and symmetries of the parabolic metric group whose absolute involution is that determined by Σ_∞ on the line at infinity of π.*

Proof. Let Γ be any displacement leaving π invariant, O an arbitrary point of π, and T the translation carrying O to $\Gamma(O)$. Then $T^{-1}\Gamma(O) = O$, and hence, by Theorem 13, $T^{-1}\Gamma$ is a rotation. Moreover, $T^{-1}\Gamma$ leaves π invariant.

It is obvious from the definition of a rotation that it can leave π invariant only in case its axis is perpendicular to π or in case it is of period two and its axis is a line of π. If $T^{-1}\Gamma$ falls under the first of these cases, it effects a rotation in π according to the definition of rotation in Chap. IV, and thus Γ effects a displacement in π. If $T^{-1}\Gamma$ falls under the second of these cases it effects, and therefore Γ also effects, a symmetry in π according to the definition in Chap. IV.

COROLLARY 1. *The transformations effected in a nonminimal plane π by the displacements and symmetries leaving π invariant constitute the group of displacements and symmetries of the parabolic metric group whose absolute involution is that determined by Σ_∞ on the line at infinity of π.*

Corollary 2. *If O is an arbitrary point, any displacement Γ is expressible in the forms*

$$\Gamma = \mathrm{TP} \quad \text{and} \quad \Gamma = \mathrm{P'T'},$$

where T, T′ *are translations and* P, P′ *rotations leaving O invariant.*

Proof. As in the proof of the theorem above, let T be the translation carrying O to $\Gamma(O)$. Then $\mathrm{T}^{-1}\Gamma(O) = O$ and hence, by Theorem 13, $\mathrm{T}^{-1}\Gamma$ is a rotation, P. Hence $\Gamma = \mathrm{TP}$. If T′ is the translation carrying O to $\Gamma^{-1}(O)$, it follows in like manner that $\Gamma\mathrm{T}'(O)$ is a rotation P′ and hence that $\Gamma = \mathrm{P'T'^{-1}}$.

Corollary 3. *The transformations effected on a nonminimal line p by the displacements leaving p invariant constitute the group composed of all parabolic transformations and involutions leaving the point at infinity of p invariant.*

EXERCISES

1. Two point pairs are congruent if they are symmetric.

2. The set of all point reflections and translations forms a group which, unlike the analogous group in the plane (§ 45), is not a subgroup of the group of displacements. The product of two point reflections is a translation, and any translation is expressible as a product of two point reflections, one of which is arbitrary.

3. Study the theory of congruence in a minimal plane.

4. A rotation leaves no point invariant which is not on its axis. It leaves invariant all planes perpendicular to its axis and no others unless it is of period two, when it is an orthogonal line reflection.

116. Euclidean geometry of three dimensions. The last theorem may be regarded as the fundamental theorem of the parabolic metric geometry in space, for by means of it all the results of the two-dimensional parabolic metric geometry become immediately applicable.

Suppose now that we consider a three-space satisfying Assumptions A, E, H, C, R (or A, E, K), i.e. a real projective space. Suppose also that Σ_∞ be taken to be an elliptic polar system,* i.e. the polar system of an imaginary ellipse (§ 79). Then in any plane the parabolic metric geometry reduces to the Euclidean geometry and the displacements which leave this plane invariant are Euclidean displacements.

* The existence and properties of an elliptic polar system may be determined without recourse to imaginaries (in fact, on the basis A, E, P, S), as in § 89.

A set of assumptions for the Euclidean geometry of three dimensions is composed of I–XVI, given in §§ 29 and 66. We have seen in § 29 that I–IX are satisfied by a Euclidean space of three dimensions. Assumption XI is a consequence of Theorem 12, and Assumptions X, XII–XVI of Theorems 11 and 16. Hence *in a real three-space, if* Σ_∞ *is an elliptic polar system the parabolic metric geometry is the Euclidean geometry.*

The general remarks in § 66 are applicable to the three-dimensional case as well as to the two-dimensional one.

It was stated in § 66 that the congruence assumptions are no longer strictly independent when a full continuity assumption is added, because by introducing ideal elements and an arbitrary Σ_∞ (as in the present chapter) a relation of congruence may be defined for which the statements in X–XVI are theorems which can easily be proved. This view is not accepted by certain well-known mathematicians, who hold that the arbitrariness in the definition of the absolute involution somehow conceals a new assumption.* It may, therefore, be well to restate the matter here.†

Assumptions I–IX, XVII are categorical for the Euclidean space; i.e. if two sets of objects [P] and [Q] satisfy the conditions laid down for points in the assumptions, there is a one-to-one reciprocal correspondence between [P] and [Q] such that the subsets called lines of [P] correspond to the subsets called lines of [Q]. Thus the internal structure of a Euclidean space is fully determined by Assumptions I–IX, XVII. The group leaving invariant the relations described in these assumptions is the affine group, and all the theorems of the affine geometry are consequences of these assumptions. The latter may therefore be characterized as the assumptions of affine geometry.

Among the theorems of the affine geometry is one which states that there is an infinity of subgroups, each one conjugate to all the rest and such that the set of theorems belonging to it constitutes the Euclidean geometry. Each of these groups is capable of being called the Euclidean group, and there is no theorem about one of them which is not true about all of them. The set of theorems stating relations invariant under any one of these groups is the Euclidean geometry. This set of theorems is the same whichever Euclidean group be selected, i.e. *the Euclidean geometry is a unique body of theorems.*

Each Euclidean group has a self-conjugate subgroup of displacements which defines a relation called congruence having the properties stated in

* Cf. the remarks on a paper by the writer in the article by Enriques, Encyclopédie des Sc. Math. III 1, § 12.

† This discussion should be read in connection with the remarks on foundations of geometry in the introduction to Vol. I and in § 13 of this volume; also in connection with the remarks on the geometry corresponding to a group, §§ 34, 39, 110.

Assumptions X–XVI. Moreover, any relation which satisfies these assumptions is associated with a group of displacements which is self-conjugate under a Euclidean group.

Thus Assumptions X–XVI characterize the relation of congruence as completely as possible, i.e. any relation satisfying these assumptions must be that determined by one of the infinitely many groups of displacements. The set of theorems about congruence is unique and is the Euclidean geometry.

The relation between the affine geometry and the Euclidean geometry is analogous to that between the Euclidean geometry and the geometry belonging to any non-self-conjugate subgroup of a Euclidean group. Consider, for example, the subgroup obtained by leaving a particular point O invariant. A relation which is left invariant by this group may be defined as follows:

DEFINITION. A point P is *nearer* than a point Q if and only if Dist (OP) $<$ Dist (OQ). P and Q are *equally near* if Dist $(OP) =$ Dist (OQ).

There is an element of arbitrary choice in this definition, just as there is in the choice of an absolute involution to define the notion of congruence. Moreover, the geometry of *nearness* is just as truly a geometry as is the Euclidean geometry.* It would be easy to put down a set of assumptions (XVIII–N) in terms of *near* regarded as an undefined relation, which would state the abstract properties of this relation, just as X–XVI state the abstract properties of congruence.

Another non-self-conjugate subgroup of the Euclidean group which gives rise to an interesting geometry is the group leaving invariant a line and a plane on this line. In terms of this group the notions of *forward* and *backward* and *up* and *down* can be defined, and the geometry corresponding to this group is a set of propositions embodying the abstract theory of this set of relations.

It is a theorem of Euclidean geometry that the Euclidean group has subgroups with the properties involved in these geometries, just as it is a theorem of affine geometry that the affine group has Euclidean subgroups and a theorem of projective geometry that the projective group has affine subgroups.

Assumptions I–IX, XVII have a different rôle from X–XVI or XVIII–N, in that they determine the set of objects (points and lines, etc.) which are presupposed by all the other assumptions. The choice of these assumptions is logically arbitrary. The choice of such sets of "assumptions" as X–XVI is not arbitrary; it must correspond to a properly chosen group of permutations of the objects determined by I–IX, XVII. When independence proofs are given for Assumptions X–XVI, it is done by giving new interpretations to the term "congruence," not to "point" or "line."

* It is even possible to give a psychological significance to this geometry. The normal individual has a certain place, say home, in terms of nearness to which other places are thought of; here O is the central point of home. In astronomy stars are regarded as near or the contrary, according to their distance from the sun; here O is the center of the sun.

The point of view of the writer is that if X–XVI or XVIII–N are to be regarded as independent assumptions, their independence is of a lower grade than that of I–IX, XVII. They constitute a definition by postulates of a relation (congruence or nearness) among objects (points, lines, etc.) already fully determined. Their significance is that they characterize that subset of the theorems deducible from I–IX, XVII which corresponds to any Euclidean group and which therefore is the Euclidean geometry.

EXERCISES

*** 1.** Develop the geometry corresponding to some non-self-conjugate subgroup of the Euclidean group. Determine a set of mutually independent assumptions characterizing this geometry.

2. The identity is the only transformation of the Euclidean group which leaves fixed two points A and B and two rays (cf. definition in § 16) AC and AD orthogonal to each other and to the line AB.

3. If a and b are any two rays having a common origin, O, and on different lines, there is a unique orthogonal line reflection and a unique orthogonal plane reflection transforming a into b.

4. If A, B, C, D are any four points no three of which are collinear, there exists a unique rotation leaving the line AB invariant and transforming C into a point of the plane ABD on the same side of AB with D.

5. Any transformation of the Euclidean group which leaves a line pointwise invariant and preserves sense is a rotation.

6. Any transformation of the Euclidean group which leaves a line pointwise invariant and alters sense is an orthogonal reflection in a plane containing this line.

7. There is one and only one displacement which transforms three mutually orthogonal rays OA, OB, OC into three mutually orthogonal rays $O'A'$, $O'B'$, $O'C'$, provided that $S(OABC) = S(O'A'B'C')$.

***117. Generalization to *n* dimensions.** The discussion of the Euclidean and affine geometries in §§ 111–116 is so arranged that it will generalize at once to any number of dimensions. It is recommended to the reader to carry out this generalization in detail, at least in the four-dimensional case.

The elementary theorems of alignment for four dimensions are given in § 12, Vol. I. The definition of a Euclidean four-space is given in § 28, Vol. II. The generalization of § 111 is obvious on comparing these two sections. A four-dimensional translation may be defined as a projective collineation leaving invariant all points of the three-space at infinity and also all lines through one of these points. The generalization of § 112 then follows at once.

A three-dimensional polar system may be defined as the polar system of a proper or improper regulus (Chap. XI, Vol. I; cf. also §§ 100–108, Vol. II), or it may be studied *ab initio* by generalizing Chap. X, Vol. I. The notion of perpendicular lines, planes, and three-spaces then follows at once and also the theorems generalizing those of § 113. An orthogonal reflection in an S_3 is next defined as a projective collineation of period two, leaving invariant a point P at infinity and each point of a three-space whose plane at infinity is polar to P in the absolute polar system. All the theorems of §§ 114, 115 up to Theorem 13 then generalize at once. Theorems 13–15 must be modified, in view of the fact that there are more than one type of four-dimensional displacements leaving a point invariant. Theorem 16 holds unchanged.

Finally, it can be proved as in § 116 that in case of a real space and an elliptic polar system the parabolic metric geometry satisfies a set of axioms for Euclidean geometry of four dimensions. This set differs from the one used above, in that VIII is replaced by

VIII′. *If A, B, C, D are four noncoplanar points, there exists a point E not in the same S_3 with A, B, C, D, and such that every point is in the same S_4 with A, B, C, D, E.*

The introduction of nonhomogeneous coördinates in a space of n dimensions may be made by direct generalizations of § 69, Vol. I. The formulas for the affine group, the group of translations, the Euclidean group, and the group of displacements are then easily seen to be identical with those given in the sections below, except that the summations from 0 or 1 to 3 must in each case be replaced by summations from 0 or 1 to n.

118. Equations of the affine and Euclidean groups. With respect to a nonhomogeneous coördinate system in which π_∞ is the singular plane, the affine group is evidently the set of all projectivities of the form

$$(6)\qquad \begin{aligned} x' &= a_{11}x + a_{12}y + a_{13}z + a_{10}, \\ y' &= a_{21}x + a_{22}y + a_{23}z + a_{20}, \\ z' &= a_{31}x + a_{32}y + a_{33}z + a_{30}, \end{aligned}$$

where
$$\Delta \equiv \begin{vmatrix} a_{11} & a_{12} & a_{13} \\ a_{21} & a_{22} & a_{23} \\ a_{31} & a_{32} & a_{33} \end{vmatrix} \neq 0,$$

and the variables and coefficients are elements of the geometric number system.

In the system of homogeneous plane coördinates in which the plane at infinity is represented by [1, 0, 0, 0], this group takes the form

$$
\begin{aligned}
u_0' &= b_{00}u_0 + b_{01}u_1 + b_{02}u_2 + b_{03}u_3, \\
u_1' &= \qquad\quad\; b_{11}u_1 + b_{12}u_2 + b_{13}u_3, \\
u_2' &= \qquad\quad\; b_{21}u_1 + b_{22}u_2 + b_{23}u_3, \\
u_3' &= \qquad\quad\; b_{31}u_1 + b_{32}u_2 + b_{33}u_3.
\end{aligned} \tag{7}
$$

In an ordered space the affine group has a subgroup consisting of all transformations for which Δ is positive. This group has been considered in § 31. It also has obvious subgroups consisting of all transformations for which $\Delta^2 = 1$ and for which $\Delta = 1$.

The equations of a translation parallel to the x-axis are evidently $x' = x + a$, $y' = y$, $z' = z$, and similar expressions represent a translation parallel to any other axis. Hence by the corollary of Theorem 3 the equations of the group of translations are

$$
\begin{aligned}
x' &= x + a, \\
y' &= y + b, \\
z' &= z + c.
\end{aligned} \tag{8}
$$

If the coördinates are so chosen that the planes $\bar{x} = 0$, $\bar{y} = 0$, $\bar{z} = 0$ are mutually orthogonal, the equations of the circle at infinity in terms of the corresponding homogeneous coördinates are

$$a\bar{x}_1^2 + b\bar{x}_2^2 + c\bar{x}_3^2 = 0, \qquad \bar{x}_0 = 0.$$

These are reducible by the transformation

$$x_0 = \bar{x}_0, \quad x_1 = \sqrt{a}\bar{x}_1, \quad x_2 = \sqrt{b}\bar{x}_2, \quad x_3 = \sqrt{c}\bar{x}_3 \tag{9}$$

to

$$x_1^2 + x_2^2 + x_3^2 = 0, \qquad x_0 = 0. \tag{10}$$

In the real geometry a, b, c are positive if the polar system is elliptic (§ 85), and the transformation (9) carries real points to real points. The formulas (9) are the only ones in the present section in which irrational expressions appear. Hence the rest of the discussion holds for any space satisfying Assumptions A, E, P, H_0. In any such space it is easily seen that (10) represents a conic whose polar system may be taken as Σ_∞, but it does not follow, as in the real case, that any improper conic can be reduced to this form. The situation here is entirely analogous to that obtaining in § 62.

In the three-dimensional homogeneous plane coördinates, π_∞ and the planes tangent to the circle at infinity (10) satisfy the equation

$$(11) \qquad u_1^2 + u_2^2 + u_3^2 = 0.$$

Any plane

$$(12) \qquad u_0 + u_1 x' + u_2 y' + u_3 z' = 0$$

is the transform under a collineation of the form (6) of the plane

$$(13) \qquad (u_0 + a_{10}u_1 + a_{20}u_2 + a_{30}u_3) + (a_{11}u_1 + a_{21}u_2 + a_{31}u_3)\, x + (a_{12}u_1 + a_{22}u_2 + a_{32}u_3)\, y + (a_{13}u_1 + a_{23}u_2 + a_{33}u_3)\, z = 0.$$

Hence (11) is the transform of

$$(14) \qquad (a_{11}^2 + a_{12}^2 + a_{13}^2)\, u_1^2 + (a_{21}^2 + a_{22}^2 + a_{23}^2)\, u_2^2 + (a_{31}^2 + a_{32}^2 + a_{33}^2)\, u_3^2 + 2\,(a_{11}a_{21} + a_{12}a_{22} + a_{13}a_{23})\, u_1u_2 + 2\,(a_{11}a_{31} + a_{12}a_{32} + a_{13}a_{33})\, u_1u_3 + 2\,(a_{21}a_{31} + a_{22}a_{32} + a_{23}a_{33})\, u_2u_3 = 0.$$

In order that (11) and (14) shall represent the same locus, we must have

$$(15) \qquad a_{11}^2 + a_{12}^2 + a_{13}^2 = a_{21}^2 + a_{22}^2 + a_{23}^2 = a_{31}^2 + a_{32}^2 + a_{33}^2,$$
$$a_{11}a_{21} + a_{12}a_{22} + a_{13}a_{23} = a_{11}a_{31} + a_{12}a_{32} + a_{13}a_{33} = a_{21}a_{31} + a_{22}a_{32} + a_{23}a_{33} = 0.$$

These conditions are equivalent to the equation (cf. § 95, Chap. X, Vol. I)

$$(16) \qquad \begin{pmatrix} a_{11} & a_{12} & a_{13} \\ a_{21} & a_{22} & a_{23} \\ a_{31} & a_{32} & a_{33} \end{pmatrix} \cdot \begin{pmatrix} a_{11} & a_{21} & a_{31} \\ a_{12} & a_{22} & a_{32} \\ a_{13} & a_{23} & a_{33} \end{pmatrix} = \begin{pmatrix} \rho & 0 & 0 \\ 0 & \rho & 0 \\ 0 & 0 & \rho \end{pmatrix},$$

where $\rho = a_{11}^2 + a_{12}^2 + a_{13}^2$.

If the matrix $(a_{11}a_{22}a_{33}) = A$ be interpreted as the matrix of a planar collineation, as in § 95, Vol. I, this states that the product of the collineation by the collineation represented by the transposed matrix is the identity. Hence the product of the two matrices in the reverse order is a matrix representing the identity. This means that

$$a_{11}^2 + a_{21}^2 + a_{31}^2 = a_{12}^2 + a_{22}^2 + a_{32}^2 = a_{13}^2 + a_{23}^2 + a_{33}^2,$$

and

$$a_{11}a_{12} + a_{21}a_{22} + a_{31}a_{32} = a_{11}a_{13} + a_{21}a_{23} + a_{31}a_{33} = a_{12}a_{13} + a_{22}a_{23} + a_{32}a_{33} = 0.$$

Since the determinants of a matrix and of its transposed matrix are equal, we have

$$\Delta^2 = \rho^3 = (a_{11}^2 + a_{12}^2 + a_{13}^2)^3 = (a_{11}^2 + a_{21}^2 + a_{31}^2)^3.$$

DEFINITION. A matrix such that its product by a given matrix A is the identical matrix (§ 95, Vol. I) is called the *inverse* of A and is denoted by A^{-1}. A square matrix whose transposed matrix is equal to its inverse is called *orthogonal.* A linear transformation,

$$(17)\qquad \begin{aligned} x' &= a_{11}x + a_{12}y + a_{13}z, \\ y' &= a_{21}x + a_{22}y + a_{23}z, \\ z' &= a_{31}x + a_{32}y + a_{33}z, \end{aligned}$$

whose matrix $(a_{11}a_{22}a_{33})$ is orthogonal, is said to be *orthogonal.*

The results at which we have arrived may now be expressed in part as follows:

THEOREM 17. *The transformations of the parabolic metric group can be written in the form*

$$(18)\qquad \begin{aligned} x' &= \rho\,(a_{11}x + a_{12}y + a_{13}z + k_1), \\ y' &= \rho\,(a_{21}x + a_{22}y + a_{23}z + k_2), \\ z' &= \rho\,(a_{31}x + a_{32}y + a_{33}z + k_3), \end{aligned}$$

where the matrix $(a_{11}a_{22}a_{33})$ *is orthogonal.*

From the form of these equations we obtain the following corollaries:

COROLLARY 1. *Any transformation* (18) *of the Euclidean group is the product of an orthogonal transformation, a translation, and a homology of the form*

$$(19)\qquad \begin{aligned} x' &= \rho x, \\ y' &= \rho y, \\ z' &= \rho z. \end{aligned}$$

COROLLARY 2. *A homology* (19) *is commutative with any collineation leaving the origin invariant.*

Since an orthogonal matrix is any matrix satisfying (16) with $\rho = 1$, we have

COROLLARY 3. *The product of two orthogonal transformations is orthogonal. The determinant of an orthogonal transformation is* $+1$ *or* -1.

In view of the formula for the inverse of a matrix (§ 95, Vol. I), we have

COROLLARY 4. *A matrix* $(a_{11}a_{22}a_{33})$ *is orthogonal if and only if*

$$A_{ij} = \Delta a_{ji}, \qquad (i = 1, 2, 3;\ j = 1, 2, 3) \tag{20}$$

where Δ *is the determinant of the matrix and* A_{ij} *the cofactor of* a_{ij}.

The matrix of an orthogonal transformation of period two is its own inverse and hence its own transposed. Hence

COROLLARY 5. *An orthogonal transformation is of period two if and only if* $a_{ij} = a_{ji}$.

The double points of any orthogonal transformation (17) must satisfy the equations

$$\begin{aligned} (a_{11} - 1)x + a_{12}y + a_{13}z &= 0, \\ a_{21}x + (a_{22} - 1)y + a_{23}z &= 0, \\ a_{31}x + a_{32}y + (a_{33} - 1)z &= 0. \end{aligned} \tag{21}$$

The determinant of the coefficients of these equations is

$$D_1 = \Delta - (A_{11} + A_{22} + A_{33}) + (a_{11} + a_{22} + a_{33}) - 1.$$

But since the transformation is orthogonal, $A_{ii} = \Delta a_{ii}$. Hence the determinant of (21) reduces to

$$D_1 = (1 - \Delta)(a_{11} + a_{22} + a_{33} - 1).$$

Another determinant which is of importance in the theory of orthogonal transformations is that of the equations

$$\begin{aligned} (a_{11} + 1)x + a_{12}y + a_{13}z &= 0, \\ a_{21}x + (a_{22} + 1)y + a_{23}z &= 0, \\ a_{31}x + a_{32}y + (a_{33} + 1)z &= 0. \end{aligned} \tag{22}$$

Any point satisfying these equations is transformed into its symmetric point with respect to the origin. The orthogonal transformation therefore transforms the line joining these points into itself and effects an involution with the origin as center on this line. The determinant of the equations (22) is

$$D_2 = \Delta + (A_{11} + A_{22} + A_{33}) + (a_{11} + a_{22} + a_{33}) + 1,$$

which reduces to

$$D_2 = (1 + \Delta)(a_{11} + a_{22} + a_{33} + 1).$$

Let us now consider an orthogonal transformation (17) which we shall denote by Σ. If $\Delta = -1$ for Σ, $D_2 = 0$, and hence there is at least one point which is carried by Σ into its symmetric point with respect to the origin. The plane through the origin perpendicular to the line joining these points is left invariant by Σ. On the other hand, $D_1 \neq 0$ unless

$$a_{11} + a_{22} + a_{33} = 1, \tag{23}$$

and hence Σ leaves no other point than the origin invariant unless (23) is satisfied. Suppose now that (23) is satisfied. A cofactor of an element a_{ii} of the main diagonal of D_1 is

$$A_{ii} - (a_{jj} + a_{kk}) + 1,$$

where $i \neq j \neq k \neq i$. By (20) this reduces to

$$-(a_{11} + a_{22} + a_{33}) + 1,$$

which vanishes. The cofactor of an element $a_{ij} (i \neq j)$ of D_1 is

$$A_{ij} + a_{ji},$$

and by (20) this vanishes when $\Delta = -1$. Thus we have that if $\Delta = -1$ and (23) is satisfied, Σ has a plane of fixed points. Since it transforms one point into its symmetric point with respect to the origin, it must be an orthogonal plane reflection. Thus we have proved

THEOREM 18. *An orthogonal transformation for which* $\Delta = -1$ *always has an invariant plane. It either leaves no point except the origin invariant or it is an orthogonal plane reflection. The latter case occurs if and only if* $a_{11} + a_{22} + a_{33} = 1$.

By comparison with Corollary 5 above we have

COROLLARY. *An orthogonal transformation for which* $\Delta = -1$ *is an orthogonal plane reflection if and only if* $a_{12} = a_{21}$, $a_{23} = a_{32}$, *and* $a_{13} = a_{31}$.

Let us now consider an orthogonal transformation Σ for which $\Delta = 1$. In this case $D_1 = 0$, and hence there is always a line of fixed points passing through the origin. Let Λ_1 be an orthogonal plane reflection containing a line of fixed points of Σ. Then $\Sigma\Lambda_1$ is an orthogonal transformation for which $\Delta = -1$ and for which there are other fixed points than the origin. By the last theorem, therefore, it is an orthogonal plane reflection Λ_2. From $\Sigma\Lambda_1 = \Lambda_2$ follows $\Sigma = \Lambda_2\Lambda_1$. We therefore have

THEOREM 19. *An orthogonal transformation for which* $\Delta = 1$ *is a rotation.*

COROLLARY 1. *An orthogonal transformation for which* $\Delta = -1$ *is a symmetry.*

Any transformation (18) for which $\rho = 1$ is a product of an orthogonal transformation and a translation. It is therefore either a displacement or a symmetry. By Theorem 16, Cor. 1, a homology (19) for which $\rho^2 \neq 1$ is not a displacement or a symmetry. Hence we have

COROLLARY 2. *The subgroup of* (18) *for which* $\rho = 1$ *and* $\Delta = 1$ *is the group of displacements.*

COROLLARY 3. *The subgroup* of (18) *for which* $\rho = 1$ *and* $\Delta^2 = 1$ *is the group of displacements and symmetries.*

The coördinate system which has been employed above is such that the planes $x = 0, y = 0, z = 0$ are mutually orthogonal. Moreover, the displacement

$$x' = y, \quad y' = z, \quad z' = x,$$

leaves (0, 0, 0) invariant and transforms (1, 0, 0) to (0, 1, 0) and (0, 1, 0) to (0, 0, 1). Hence the pairs (0, 0, 0) (1, 0, 0), (0, 0, 0) (0, 1, 0), and (0, 0, 0) (0, 0, 1) are congruent. Coördinates satisfying these conditions are said to be *rectangular.*

EXERCISES

1. The group of displacements and symmetries leaves the quadratic form

$$u_1^2 + u_2^2 + u_3^2$$

absolutely invariant.

2. Two point pairs $(a, b, c)(a', b', c')$ and $(x, y, z)(x', y', z')$ are congruent if and only if $(a - a')^2 + (b - b')^2 + (c - c')^2 = (x - x')^2 + (y - y')^2 + (z - z')^2$.

3. Two planes

$$u_1x + u_2y + u_3z + u_0 = 0,$$
$$v_1x + v_2y + v_3z + v_0 = 0$$

are orthogonal if and only if $u_1v_1 + u_2v_2 + u_3v_3 = 0.$

4. Three planes

$$u_{i1}x + u_{i2}y + u_{i3}z + u_{i0} = 0, \qquad (i = 1, 2, 3)$$

the coefficients being such that

$$u_{i1}^2 + u_{i2}^2 + u_{i3}^2 = 1, \qquad (i = 1, 2, 3)$$

are mutually perpendicular if and only if the matrix $(u_{11}u_{22}u_{33})$ is orthogonal.

5. The three ordered triads of numbers (a_{i1}, a_{i2}, a_{i3}), $i = 1, 2, 3$, are direction cosines of mutually perpendicular vectors if and only if the matrix $(a_{11}a_{22}a_{33})$ is orthogonal.

119. Distance, area, volume, angular measure. The definition (§ 67) of distance between two points extends without modification to the three-dimensional case. The distance between a point O and a plane π is the distance between O and the point P in which

π is met by the line through O perpendicular to π. The distance between two lines $l_1 l_2$ is Dist $(P_1 P_2)$, where P_1 and P_2 are the points in which the common intersecting perpendicular line meets l_1 and l_2 respectively.

If the notion of equivalence of ordered point triads (§ 112) be extended by regarding two ordered triads as equivalent whenever they are congruent, it is obvious that any triad is equivalent to triads in any plane whatever and not merely, as in § 112, to triads in a system of parallel planes. Moreover, if ABC are noncollinear points such that AB is congruent to AC, the ordered triad ABC is congruent and therefore equivalent to the ordered triad ACB. Hence

$$ABC \backsimeq BCA \backsimeq CAB \backsimeq ACB \backsimeq CBA \backsimeq BAC,$$

i.e. according to the extended definition, any ordered triad is equivalent to any permutation of itself.

Since $m(ABC) = -m(ACB)$, the definition of measure (§ 49) cannot be extended to correspond to the new conception of equivalence. On the other hand, the notion of area (§ 68) of a triangle is directly applicable. The situation here is entirely analogous to that described in § 67 with regard to the measure of a vector and the distance between two points. The formal definition may be made as follows:

DEFINITION. Let OPQ be a triangle (called the *unit triangle*) which is such that the lines OP and OQ are orthogonal and the point pairs OP and OQ are congruent to the unit of distance. Then if $A'B'C'$ is a triangle coplanar with OPQ and congruent to ABC, the positive number

$$\tfrac{1}{2}\,|\,m(A'B'C')| = a(ABC),$$

where $m(A'B'C')$ is the measure (§ 49) of the ordered triad $A'B'C'$ relative to the ordered triad OPQ, is called the *area of the triangle ABC.*

The definition of the measure of an ordered tetrad and of the volume of a tetrahedron may be taken from § 112, with the proviso that the unit tetrad $OPQR$ is such that the lines OP, OQ, OR are mutually orthogonal and the point pairs OP, OQ, OR congruent to the unit of distance.

The definition of the measure of angle may be taken over literally from § 69. Since, however, any symmetry in a plane can be effected by a three-dimensional displacement, the indetermination in the measure of an angle is such that any angle whose measure is β also has the measure $k\pi + \beta$, where k is a positive or negative integer. The measure of an angle may therefore be subjected to the condition $0 \leq \beta < \pi$ or $-\pi/2 < \beta \leqq \pi/2$.

DEFINITION. The *angular measure* of a pair of intersecting lines ab is the smallest value between 0 and 2π, inclusive, of the measures of the four angles $\measuredangle a_1 b_1$ formed by a ray a_1 of a and a ray b_1 of b. It is denoted by $m(ab)$. If a and b do not intersect, $m(ab)$ denotes $m(a'b)$, where a' is a line having a point in common with b and parallel to a. The *angular measure* of two planes π, π' is the angular measure of two lines l, l' perpendicular to π and π' respectively.

The following statements are easily proved and will be left to the reader as exercises (cf. § 72): In the case where a and b do not intersect, the value of $m(ab)$ is independent of the choice of a'. Although in Euclidean plane geometry $0 \leqq m(ab) < \pi$, in the three-dimensional case

$$0 \leqq m(ab) < \frac{\pi}{2}.$$

If l_1 and l_2 are any two lines parallel to a and b respectively, and i_1 and i_2 are the minimal lines through the intersection of l_1 and l_2, $m(ab)$ is the smaller of the two numbers

$$\theta_1 = -\frac{i}{2}\log \mathrm{R}_x(l_1 l_2, i_1 i_2) \quad \text{and} \quad \theta_2 = -\frac{i}{2}\log \mathrm{R}_x(l_1 l_2, i_2 i_1),$$

that determination of the logarithm in each case being chosen for which $0 \leqq \theta_1 < \pi$ and $0 \leqq \theta_2 < \pi$.

The numbers which we have been defining in this section are some of the simplest absolute invariants of the group of displacements. The algebraic formulas for these invariants and some others are stated in the exercises below. In every case the radical sign indicates a *positive* root. By the angle between two vectors OA and OB is meant the measure of $\measuredangle AOB$.

The *orthogonal projection* of a set of points $[P]$ on a plane π is the set of points in which the lines perpendicular to π through the points P meet π. The *orthogonal projection* of a set of points $[P]$ on a line l is the set of points in which the planes perpendicular to l through the points P meet l.

The exercises refer to four distinct noncoplanar points $P_1 = (x_1, y_1, z_1)$, $P_2 = (x_2, y_2, z_2)$, $P_3 = (x_3, y_3, z_3)$, $P_4 = (x_4, y_4, z_4)$, no two of which are collinear with the origin. The coördinate system is rectangular, and O, P, Q, R denote the points (0, 0, 0), (1, 0, 0), (0, 1, 0), (0, 0, 1) respectively, as in § 112.

EXERCISES

1. Dist $(P_1P_2) = \sqrt{(x_1 - x_2)^2 + (y_1 - y_2)^2 + (z_1 - z_2)^2}$.

2. The cosines of the angles between a vector OP_1 and the x-, y-, and z-axes respectively are

$$\frac{x_1}{\sqrt{x_1^2 + y_1^2 + z_1^2}}, \quad \frac{y_1}{\sqrt{x_1^2 + y_1^2 + z_1^2}}, \quad \frac{z_1}{\sqrt{x_1^2 + y_1^2 + z_1^2}}.$$

These are referred to as the *direction cosines* of the vector OP_1. If $r =$ Dist (P_1P_2), the direction cosines of the vector P_1P_2 are

$$\frac{x_2 - x_1}{r}, \quad \frac{y_2 - y_1}{r}, \quad \frac{z_2 - z_1}{r}.$$

3. The equation of a plane perpendicular to the line OP_1 is

$$x_1x + y_1y + z_1z = k.$$

4. The distance from the point P_1 to the plane $\alpha x + \beta y + \gamma z = \delta$ is

$$\left|\frac{\alpha x_1 + \beta y_1 + \gamma z_1 - \delta}{\sqrt{\alpha^2 + \beta^2 + \gamma^2}}\right|.$$

5. If Q_1 is the orthogonal projection of P_2 on the line OP_1, then

$$\frac{x_1x_2 + y_1y_2 + z_1z_2}{\sqrt{x_1^2 + y_1^2 + z_1^2}}$$

is Dist(OQ_1) in case Q_1 and P_1 are on the same side of O, and $-$ Dist(OQ_1) in case Q_1 and P_1 are not on the same side of

$$x_1x_2 + y_1y_2 + z_1z_2 = \text{Dist } OP_1 \cdot \text{Dist } OP_2 \cdot \cos \measuredangle P_1OP_2.$$

6. $m(P_1P_2P_3P_4) =$ Dist$(P_1P_2) \cdot$ Dist$(P_3P_4) \cdot r \cdot \sin\theta$, where r is the distance between the lines P_1P_2 and P_3P_4, and θ the angle between the vectors P_1P_2 and P_3P_4.

7. If θ denotes the measure of $\measuredangle P_1OP_2$, and l, m, n the direction cosines of a vector OK perpendicular to the plane OP_1P_2 and such that $S(OP_1P_2K) = S(OPQR)$,

$$\begin{vmatrix} y_1 & z_1 \\ y_2 & z_2 \end{vmatrix} = \text{Dist}(OP_1) \cdot \text{Dist}(OP_2) \cdot \sin\theta \cdot l,$$

$$\begin{vmatrix} z_1 & x_1 \\ z_2 & x_2 \end{vmatrix} = \text{Dist}(OP_1) \cdot \text{Dist}(OP_2) \cdot \sin\theta \cdot m,$$

$$\begin{vmatrix} x_1 & y_1 \\ x_2 & y_2 \end{vmatrix} = \text{Dist}(OP_1) \cdot \text{Dist}(OP_2) \cdot \sin\theta \cdot n.^*$$

8. With respect to the coördinate system employed in § 118, the angle between two lines which meet π_∞ in $(0, \alpha_1, \alpha_2, \alpha_3)$ and $(0, \beta_1, \beta_2, \beta_3)$ is

$$\theta = -\frac{i}{2}\log\frac{\alpha_1\beta_1 + \alpha_2\beta_2 + \alpha_3\beta_3 + \sqrt{(\alpha_1\beta_1 + \alpha_2\beta_2 + \alpha_3\beta_3)^2 - (\alpha_1^2 + \alpha_2^2 + \alpha_3^2)(\beta_1^2 + \beta_2^2 + \beta_3^2)}}{\alpha_1\beta_1 + \alpha_2\beta_2 + \alpha_3\beta_3 - \sqrt{(\alpha_1\beta_1 + \alpha_2\beta_2 + \alpha_3\beta_3)^2 - (\alpha_1^2 + \alpha_2^2 + \alpha_3^2)(\beta_1^2 + \beta_2^2 + \beta_3^2)}}$$

9. If four planes $\alpha, \beta, \gamma, \delta$ meet on a line,

$$R(\alpha\beta, \gamma\delta) = \frac{\sin(\alpha\gamma)}{\sin(\alpha\delta)} \div \frac{\sin(\beta\gamma)}{\sin(\beta\delta)},$$

where $(\alpha\gamma)$ denotes the angular measure of the ordered pair of planes $\alpha\gamma$.

* Cf. Ex. 6, § 112.

120. The sphere and other quadrics. DEFINITION. A *sphere* is the set of all points $[P]$ such that the point pairs OP, where O is a fixed point, are all congruent to a fixed point pair OP_0. In case the line OP_0 is minimal, the sphere is said to be *degenerate*; otherwise it is *nondegenerate.* The point O is called the *center* of the sphere.

By comparison with the definition in § 60 it is clear that any section of a nondegenerate sphere by a nonminimal plane is a circle. In case the circle at infinity exists, two perpendicular sections C_1^2 and C_2^2 of a sphere S by nonminimal planes constitute with the circle at infinity three conic sections intersecting one another in pairs of distinct points. By § 105, Vol. I, there is one and but one quadric surface containing them. A nonminimal plane π through the center of the sphere meets this quadric in a conic section which contains at least two points of the circles C_1^2 and C_2^2 and two points of the circle at infinity. This conic is therefore a circle containing the points of the sphere S which are in π. Hence the sphere S is identical with the set of all ordinary points of the quadric surface containing C_1^2, C_2^2, and the circle at infinity. Since O is the center of each circle in which S is met by a nonminimal plane through O, O is the pole of the plane at infinity with regard to the quadric. Since a circle in a nonminimal plane contains the ordinary points of a nondegenerate conic, it follows that the quadric surface is nondegenerate, i.e. is a quadric which contains two proper or improper reguli.

In case the circle at infinity does not exist, improper elements may be adjoined as explained in § 85, Vol. I, so that the circle at infinity exists in the resulting improper space. The argument in the paragraph above thus applies to any space whatever which satisfies Assumptions A, E, P, H_0. Thus we have

THEOREM 20. *A nondegenerate sphere consists of the ordinary points of a nondegenerate quadric surface S^2 such that all pairs of points in the plane at infinity conjugate with regard to S^2 are conjugate with regard to the absolute polar system. The center of the sphere is the pole of the plane at infinity relative to this quadric.*

Comparing the definition above with Theorem 7, Chap. IV, we have

COROLLARY. *A degenerate sphere with a point O as center consists of all ordinary points on the cone of minimal lines through O, except O itself.*

Had a degenerate circle in the plane been defined in the same way that a degenerate sphere is defined above, it would have been found to consist of points on only one minimal line through O, since in the plane the group of displacements leaves each minimal line invariant.

The Euclidean classification of quadric surfaces may now be made in a manner entirely analogous to the Euclidean classification of conic sections in Chap. V. After completing the projective classification (§ 103) and the affine classification (§ 111, Ex. 2) and obtaining the properties of diameters and diametral planes, the principal remaining problem is that of determining the *axes*, an axis being defined as a line through the center of the quadric perpendicular to its conjugate planes.

A line l and a plane π meet the plane at infinity in a point L_∞ and a line p_∞ respectively. If l and π are perpendicular, L_∞ and p_∞ are polar with respect to Σ_∞. If l and π are conjugate with regard to a quadric Q^2, L_∞ and p_∞ are polar with respect to the conic (real, imaginary, or degenerate) in which Q^2 meets π_∞. Hence the problem of finding the axes is reduced to that of finding the points which have the same polar lines with respect to two conics. This problem has been treated in § 101, Vol. I, for the case where both conics are nondegenerate. In general the two conics have one and but one common self-polar triangle. Hence, in general, a quadric surface has three axes which are mutually orthogonal. The determination of the other cases which may arise is a problem (Ex. 5, below) requiring a comparatively simple application of methods and theorems which we have already explained.

The classification of point quadrics includes that of cones and conic sections, the properties of cones and conics in three-dimensional Euclidean geometry being by no means dual to each other. In connection with this it is of interest to prove the following theorem, which embodies perhaps the oldest definition of a conic.

THEOREM 21. *Any nondegenerate real conic is perspective with a circle.*

Proof. Let C^2 be a given conic and K^2 a circle in a different plane having a common tangent and point of contact with C^2. By Theorem 11, Chap. VIII, Vol. I, C^2 and K^2 are sections of the same cone.

COROLLARY. *Any cone of lines is a projection of a circle from a point.*

EXERCISES

1. The equation of a sphere of center (a, b, c) in rectangular coördinates is

$$(x-a)^2+(y-b)^2+(z-c)^2=k.$$

2. The set of points on the lines of intersection of homologous planes in the corresponding pencils,

$$x_2+\sqrt{-1}\,x_3=\lambda(x_0+x_1),$$
$$x_0-x_1=\lambda(x_2-\sqrt{-1}\,x_3),$$

is a sphere.

3. A *right circular cone* is a projection of a circle from a point from which the extremities of any diameter are projected by a pair of perpendicular lines. Any conic may be regarded as the plane section of a right circular cone.

***4.** Develop the theory of stereographic projection of a sphere on a plane (cf. § 100).

***5.** Classify the quadric surfaces from the point of view of Euclidean geometry. Having made the classification geometrically, find normal forms for the equations of the quadrics of the different classes and the criteria to determine to which class a given quadric belongs. This is analogous to the work in Chap. V.

***6.** Classify the linear complexes from the point of view of Euclidean geometry.

***7.** Starting with a definition of an inversion with respect to a sphere analogous to that of an inversion with respect to a circle (§ 71), develop the theory of the inversion group of three-dimensions. This should be done both in the real and complex cases and the real and complex inversion spaces studied.

121. Resolution of a displacement into orthogonal line reflections. The properties of the group of displacements are closely bound up with the theorem that any displacement is a product of two orthogonal line reflections. In proving this theorem we shall place no restriction on the absolute polar system Σ_∞, except that it be nondegenerate, and shall base our reasoning on Assumptions A, E, H_0 only. We are therefore obliged to consider transformations which do not exist in the Euclidean geometry, namely those with minimal lines as axes.

DEFINITION. The line at infinity polar in Σ_∞ to the center of a translation is called the *axis* of the translation. If the axis is tangent to the circle at infinity, the translation is said to be *isotropic* or *minimal.*

THEOREM 22. *A product of two orthogonal line reflections whose axes l and m are parallel is a translation whose axis is the line at infinity of any plane perpendicular to the plane of l and m and parallel to l. Conversely, let* T *be any translation and l any nonminimal line meeting its axis; then if m is the line containing the mid-points* *of every pair of points, L and $\mathrm{T}(L)$, for which L is on l, and if l' is the pole in Σ_∞ of the point at infinity of l,*

$$\mathrm{T} = \{ml'\} \cdot \{ll'\}.$$

Proof. If the axes l and m of two orthogonal line reflections $\{ll'\}$ and $\{mm'\}$ are parallel, they meet π_∞ in a point P_∞. Each of the orthogonal line reflections effects in π_∞ a harmonic homology whose axis l is the polar of P_∞ in Σ_∞. Hence the product leaves all points at infinity invariant. In the plane of l and m the product $\{ml'\} \cdot \{ll'\}$ effects a planar translation parallel to any line perpendicular to l. Therefore the product $\{ml'\} \cdot \{ll'\}$ is a translation in space parallel to this line. Its axis, therefore, is the line at infinity of any plane perpendicular to the plane of l and m and parallel to l.

The converse follows directly in the same manner as the analogous statement in Theorem 4, Chap. IV.

THEOREM 23. *Any displacement is a product of two orthogonal line reflections.*

Proof. In case the displacement, which we shall denote by Δ, is a translation the theorem reduces to Theorem 22. In any other case Δ is a product of a rotation and a translation (Theorem 16, Cor. 2), i.e.

$$\Delta = \{R_\infty \rho\} \cdot \{P_\infty \pi\} \cdot \mathrm{T},$$

where T is a translation which may be the identity. Thus Δ effects in the plane at infinity a product of two harmonic homologies whose centers and axes are P_∞, p_∞ and R_∞, r_∞ respectively, where p_∞ is the line at infinity of π and r_∞ that of ρ.

Let Q be an arbitrary ordinary point and $Q' = \Delta(Q)$. Let l be the line of intersection of the planes joining Q to p_∞ and Q' to r_∞. These planes cannot be parallel, because p_∞ and r_∞ do not coincide; and l cannot contain P_∞ or R_∞, because P_∞ is not on p_∞ and R_∞ is not on r_∞.

Let O be an ordinary point of l such that neither of the lines OQ and OQ' contains P_∞ or R_∞. (If the lines OQ and OQ' coincide, they coincide with l.) Let P be the mid-point of OQ, R the mid-point of OQ', and let p and r be the lines PP_∞ and RR_∞ respectively. Then p and r are such that there exist orthogonal line reflections $\{pp_\infty\}$ and $\{rr_\infty\}$ such that

$$\{rr_\infty\}(Q') = O,$$

$$\{pp_\infty\}(O) = Q.$$

Hence

$$\{pp_\infty\} \cdot \{rr_\infty\} \cdot (Q') = Q.$$

Moreover, $\{pp_\infty\}\cdot\{rr_\infty\}$ effects the inverse of the transformation effected in the plane at infinity by Δ. Hence $\{pp_\infty\}\cdot\{rr_\infty\}\cdot\Delta$ leaves invariant all points at infinity as well as Q, and hence

$$\{pp_\infty\}\cdot\{rr_\infty\}\cdot\Delta=\mathbf{1},$$

or

$$\Delta=\{rr_\infty\}\cdot\{pp_\infty\}.$$

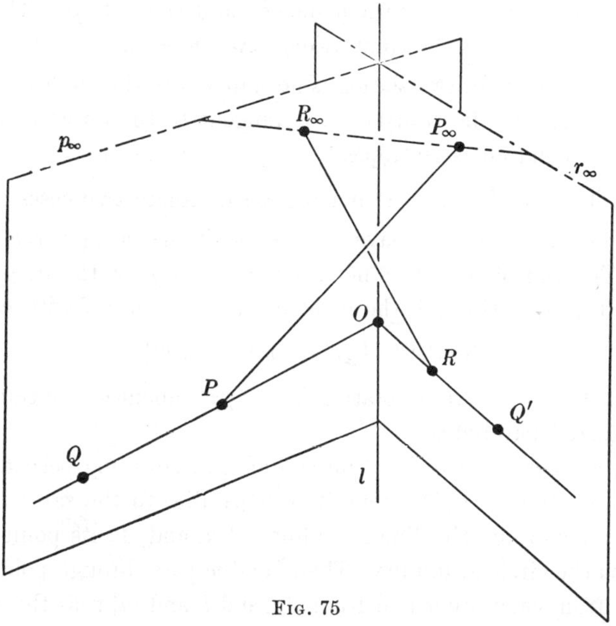

Fig. 75

It is now very easy to enumerate the possible types of displacements. A displacement Δ being expressed in the form $\{ll'\}\cdot\{mm'\}$, the following cases can arise:*

I. The lines l and m intersect in an ordinary point O. Δ is a rotation which is the product of the orthogonal reflections in the planes perpendicular to l and m respectively at O. Two subcases must be distinguished:

(*a*) The plane containing l and m is not minimal. Δ is a rotation about the common intersecting perpendicular of l and m.

(*b*) The plane containing l and m is minimal. Δ is an isotropic rotation about the line joining O to the point in which the plane of

* It is to be remembered that neither l nor m can be minimal.

l and m touches the circle at infinity. It evidently effects a parabolic transformation in the pencil of planes meeting its axis and also effects an elation in the fixed plane on the axis.

II. The lines l and m are parallel. If we denote their common point at infinity by P_∞, and its polar line with respect to Σ_∞ by p_∞, Theorem 22 states that Δ is a translation whose axis is the line polar in Σ_∞ to the point in which the plane of l and m meets p_∞. The latter point is the center of the translation. Two cases arise:

(*a*) The axis of the translation is not tangent to the circle at infinity.

(*b*) The axis of the translation is tangent to the circle at infinity, and the translation is isotropic.

III. The lines l and m do not intersect. Again two cases arise:

(*a*) The lines l and m have a common intersecting perpendicular line a (Theorem 6) which is not minimal. Let p be the line parallel to m and passing through the point of intersection of l with a. Then

$$\Delta = \{ll'\} \cdot \{pp'\} \cdot \{pp'\} \cdot \{mm'\}.$$

Thus Δ is the product of a rotation $\{ll'\} \cdot \{pp'\}$ about a by a translation $\{pp'\} \cdot \{mm'\}$ parallel to a.

(*b*) The lines l and m have no common intersecting perpendicular. In this case they are (Theorem 6) both parallel to the same minimal plane α. Let a_∞ be the line at infinity of α, and A_∞ its point of contact with the circle at infinity. Then l and m pass through points of a_∞ distinct from each other and from A_∞, and l' and m' pass through A_∞. Therefore Δ effects a transformation of Type III (§ 40, Vol. I) in the plane at infinity, with A_∞ as its fixed point and a_∞ as its fixed line. It also effects a parabolic transformation in the pencil of planes with a_∞ as axis. Thus its only fixed point is A_∞, its only fixed line a_∞, and its only fixed plane π_∞.

DEFINITION. A displacement of Type IIIa, i.e. a product of a non-isotropic rotation by a translation parallel to its axis, is called a *twist* or *screw motion*. The axis of the rotation is called the *axis* of the twist.

THEOREM 24. *A displacement which interchanges two distinct ordinary points is an orthogonal line reflection.*

Proof. Denote the given points by A and B. The given displacement Δ cannot be a translation, because a translation carrying a point A to a point B would carry B to a point C such that B is the mid-point of the pair AC. Nor can Δ be a twist or a transformation of Type IIIb, because either of these types effects the same transformation as a translation on a certain system of parallel planes, and hence no point can be transformed involutorically. And Δ cannot be an isotropic rotation, because in this case it would effect a parabolic transformation in the planes on its axis and an elation in the one fixed plane on the axis. Hence Δ is a nonisotropic rotation. By reference to § 115 it follows that Δ must be an orthogonal line reflection.

THEOREM 25. *If* Λ_1, Λ_2, Λ_3 *are three orthogonal line reflections whose axes are parallel or have a common intersecting perpendicular* l, *the product* $\Lambda_3\Lambda_2\Lambda_1$ *is an orthogonal line reflection whose axis is parallel to the other three axes in the first case and is an intersecting perpendicular of* l *in the second case.*

Proof. In case the three axes are parallel, by Theorem 22, $\Lambda_2\Lambda_1$ is a translation which is also expressible as the product of Λ_3 by another orthogonal line reflection Λ_4, so that

$$\Lambda_2\Lambda_1 = \Lambda_3\Lambda_4,$$

and hence

$$\Lambda_3\Lambda_2\Lambda_1 = \Lambda_4.$$

In case the three axes have a common intersecting perpendicular l, the orthogonal line reflections effect involutions on l having the point at infinity of l as a common double point. Hence (§ 108, Theorem 42) the product $\Lambda_3\Lambda_2\Lambda_1$ effects an involution on l whose double points are the point at infinity and an ordinary point P. Hence, by Theorem 24, $\Lambda_3\Lambda_2\Lambda_1$ is an orthogonal line reflection Λ_4. Since P is left invariant by Λ_4, it is on the axis of Λ_4; and this axis is perpendicular to l because Λ_4 leaves l invariant.

EXERCISE

The product of an isotropic rotation by a translation parallel to its axis is an isotropic rotation about an axis in the same minimal plane.

122. Rotation, translation, twist. Let us now require the absolute polar system to be elliptic, as in the real Euclidean geometry. In this case there are no minimal lines, and hence the possible types of displacement are reduced to Ia, IIa, IIIa. Thus we have

THEOREM 26. *In case the absolute polar system is elliptic any displacement is a rotation or a translation or a twist.*

With this assumption about the absolute polar system we have a particularly simple method for the combination of displacements which depends on Theorem 25. Suppose that we wish to combine two displacements $\{l_2l_2'\}\cdot\{l_1l_1'\}$ and $\{l_4l_4'\}\cdot\{l_3l_3'\}$. Let a be a common intersecting perpendicular of l_1 and l_2, and b of l_3 and l_4, and let m be a common intersecting perpendicular of a and b. Then the product Δ of the two displacements satisfies the following conditions:

$$\begin{aligned}\Delta &= \{l_4l_4'\}\cdot\{l_3l_3'\}\cdot\{l_2l_2'\}\cdot\{l_1l_1'\}\\ &= \{l_4l_4'\}\cdot\{l_3l_3'\}\cdot\{mm'\}\cdot\{mm'\}\cdot\{l_2l_2'\}\cdot\{l_1l_1'\}.\end{aligned}$$

By the theorem just proved there exist two orthogonal line reflections $\{pp'\}$, $\{qq'\}$ such that

(24) $$\{l_4l_4'\}\cdot\{l_3l_3'\}\cdot\{mm'\}=\{qq'\}$$

and

(25) $$\{mm'\}\cdot\{l_2l_2'\}\cdot\{l_1l_1'\}=\{pp'\}.$$

Hence $$\Delta=\{qq'\}\cdot\{pp'\}.$$

Another way of phrasing this argument is as follows:

By (24), $$\{l_4l_4'\}\cdot\{l_3l_3'\}=\{qq'\}\cdot\{mm'\},$$

and, by (25), $$\{l_2l_2'\}\cdot\{l_1l_1'\}=\{mm'\}\cdot\{pp'\}.$$

Hence $$\Delta=\{qq'\}\cdot\{mm'\}\cdot\{mm'\}\cdot\{pp'\}=\{qq'\}\cdot\{pp'\}.$$

The analogy of this process with that of the composition of vectors is very striking. A vector is denoted by two points. A displacement is denoted by $\Lambda_2\cdot\Lambda_1$ where Λ_2 and Λ_1 are the orthogonal line reflections of which it is the product. In order to add two vectors AB and CD we choose an arbitrary point O and determine points P and Q such that

$$AB=PO \text{ and } CD=OQ.$$

Then we have $$AB+CD=PO+OQ=PQ.$$

In the case of two displacements $\Lambda_2\Lambda_1$ and $\Lambda_4\Lambda_3$ we find an orthogonal line reflection Λ (which is not arbitrary but is determined according to Theorem 25), for which there are two others, Λ_5 and Λ_6, such that

$$\Lambda_2\Lambda_1=\Lambda\Lambda_5 \text{ and } \Lambda_4\Lambda_3=\Lambda_6\Lambda.$$

Hence $$\Lambda_4\Lambda_3\Lambda_2\Lambda_1=\Lambda_6\Lambda\Lambda\Lambda_5=\Lambda_6\Lambda_5.$$

Similar remarks can be made with regard to any group of transformations which are products of pairs of involutoric transformations. See § 108 and, particularly, the series of articles by H. Wiener which are there referred to.

The resolution of a general displacement into a product of two rotations of period two is a special solution of the problem to express a given displacement Δ as a product $\mathrm{P}\Lambda$ where P and Λ are rotations, Λ being of period two. The general solution of this problem may be found very simply in terms of the special one as follows:

Let P be any point of space, and let a be any line through P such that

$$\Delta = \{bb'\} \cdot \{aa'\}.$$

Let p be the line through P perpendicular to a and intersecting b, and let π be the plane through P perpendicular to p. Then any line l on P and π may be taken as the axis of Λ. This is obvious if $l = a$. If $l \neq a$, the product $\{aa'\} \cdot \{ll'\}$ is a rotation about p, because l and a are perpendicular to p at P. Hence

$$\Delta \cdot \{ll'\} = \{bb'\} \cdot \{aa'\} \cdot \{ll'\} = \mathrm{P}$$

is a rotation about an axis through the point of intersection of b and p. Hence

$$\Delta = \mathrm{P}\Lambda \tag{26}$$

where

$$\Lambda = \{ll'\}.$$

Moreover, if l be any line through P and not in π, $\{aa'\} \cdot \{ll'\}$ is a rotation about a line q perpendicular to a and l and hence distinct from p. Since q is perpendicular to a and not identical with p, it does not meet b. Hence the displacement

$$\Delta \cdot \{ll'\} = \{bb'\} \cdot \{aa'\} \cdot \{ll'\}$$

is not a rotation. Hence the pencil of lines on P and π is the set of all lines on P which are axes of the rotations Λ of period two such that $\Delta = \mathrm{P}\Lambda$ where P is a rotation.

This argument applies to any ordinary point P. There is no difficulty in seeing that any point at infinity is also the center of a flat pencil of lines any one of which may be chosen as the axis of Λ in (26). From this it follows by Theorem 24, Chap. XI, Vol. I, that the set of all lines which are axes of Λ's satisfying (26) form a linear complex. The argument for the case when P is at infinity is left as an exercise for the reader (Ex. 7). By another application of Theorem 24, Chap. XI, Vol. I, it is easy to prove that the axes of the rotations P which satisfy (26) are the lines of another linear complex. This is also left as an exercise (Ex. 8). Other instances of the resolution of a general displacement into displacements of special types are given in Exs. 9–11. These exercises all connect closely with those given in the next section

DEFINITION. A twist Γ such that Γ^2 is a translation is called a *half twist.*

An orthogonal line reflection is a special case of a half twist, and any half twist is a product of two orthogonal line reflections whose axes are perpendicular.

EXERCISES

1. If the three common intersecting perpendiculars of the pairs of opposite edges of a simple hexagon are also the lines joining the mid-points of the pairs of vertices on opposite edges, they have a common intersecting perpendicular.

2. If the product of three orthogonal line reflections is another line reflection, the three axes are parallel or are all met by a common perpendicular.

3. For any three congruent figures F_1, F_2, F_3 there exists a figure F and three lines l_1, l_2, l_3 such that

$$F_1 = \{l_1 l_1'\} F, \quad F_2 = \{l_2 l_2'\} F, \quad F_3 = \{l_3 l_3'\} F.$$

(See the note by G. Darboux on p. 351 of Leçons de Cinématique, Paris, 1897, by G. Koenigs, where the theorem is credited in part to Stéphanos.)

4. The axes of two harmonic orthogonal line reflections meet and are perpendicular.

5. For any pair of orthogonal line reflections there is a third which is harmonic to both.

6. Under what conditions are two displacements commutative?

7. For any displacement Δ there exists a linear complex C of lines such that every ordinary line of C is an axis of a rotation Λ of period two such that

$$\Delta = \mathrm{P}\Lambda$$

where P is a rotation. No line not in C is an axis of such a Λ.

8. If Δ is a displacement which is not of period two, the axes of the rotations P determined in Ex. 7 form a linear complex C_1 which has in common with C all the lines perpendicular to the axis of Δ.

9. Any displacement Δ can be put in the form

$$\Delta = \Lambda \mathrm{P}$$

where Λ and P are rotations and Λ is of period two. The axes of the Λ's satisfying this condition constitute the ordinary lines of the complex C (Ex. 7) and those of the P's the ordinary lines of C_1 (Ex. 8).

10. Any displacement Δ can be put in the form

$$\Delta = \mathrm{P}_2 \cdot \mathrm{P}_1 \tag{27}$$

where P_1 and P_2 are rotations or translations. If Δ is not a rotation or translation, the axis of P_1 or of P_2 can be chosen arbitrarily. The axes of the P_1's which satisfy (27) are carried into the axes of the corresponding P_2's by a correlation Γ.

11. Any displacement Δ can be put in the form

$$\Delta = \mathrm{PH} \tag{28}$$

where P is a rotation or translation and H a half twist. The axis either of P or of H can be chosen arbitrarily. For any P and H satisfying (28) there exists a rotation or translation P′ and a half twist H′ such that

$$\Delta = \mathrm{HP'} \text{ and } \Delta = \mathrm{H'P}.$$

12. Every symmetry is expressible as a product in either order of an orthogonal reflection in a plane π and a rotation about a line l perpendicular to π.

13. The mid-points of pairs of points which correspond under a symmetry are the points of the plane π (Ex. 12) or else coincide with the point $l\pi$. The planes perpendicular to the lines joining these pairs at their mid-points pass through the point $l\pi$.

14. Every symmetry transformation is expressible as a product in either order of an orthogonal plane reflection and an orthogonal line reflection.

15. Determine the types of symmetry transformations which are distinct under the Euclidean group.

123. Properties of displacements. The main properties of displacements which we have found may be stated as follows for the real Euclidean geometry:

Any displacement Δ has a unique axis a which is a line at infinity only in case Δ is a translation. The displacement is a product of two orthogonal line reflections, i.e.

$$\Delta = \{l_2 l_2'\} \cdot \{l_1 l_1'\}.$$

The lines l_1 and l_2 meet a in two points A_1 and A_2 and are perpendicular to it. Let the measure of the angle between l_1 and l_2 be θ and the distance between A_1 and A_2 be d. Then Δ is the resultant of a translation T parallel to a which carries every point X to a point X' such that

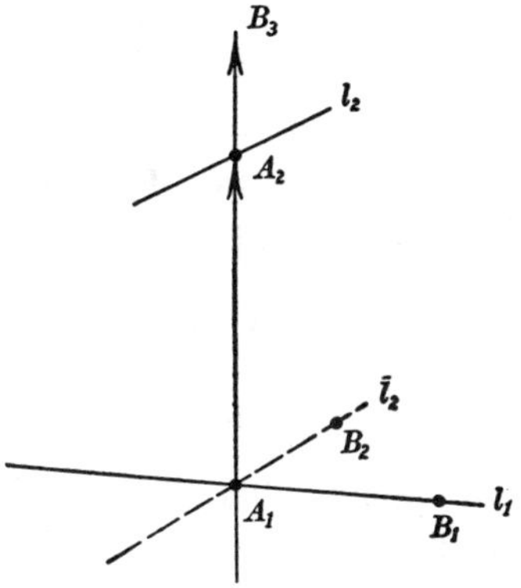

Fig. 76

$$\mathrm{Dist}(XX') = 2\,d,$$

and a rotation P with a as axis which carries each plane π on d to a plane π' such that the angular measure of π and π' is $2\,\theta$.

Definition. The numbers $2\,\theta$ and $2\,d$ respectively are called the *angle of rotation* and *distance of translation* respectively of Δ.

The rotation P such that $\Delta = \mathrm{TP} = \mathrm{PT}$ is

$$\mathrm{P} = \{\bar{l}_2\bar{l}'_2\} \cdot \{l_1 l'_1\},$$

where $\bar{l}_2$ is the line through A_1 parallel to l_2. Let B_1 and B_2 be two points of l_1 and $\bar{l}_2$ respectively, so chosen that the measure of $\measuredangle B_1A_1B_2$ is θ (and not $\pi - \theta$).* Let one of the two sense-classes (§ 31) in the Euclidean space be designated as positive.

If $0 \neq \theta \neq \frac{\pi}{2}$, there are two points B_3, B'_3 on a such that

$$\mathrm{Dist}\,(A_1B_3) = \mathrm{Dist}\,(A_1B'_3) = \tan\theta.$$

These points are on opposite sides of the plane $A_1B_1B_2$ and hence $S(A_1B_1B_2B_3) \neq S(A_1B_1B_2B'_3)$. Let B_3 be that one of these points for which $S(A_1B_1B_2B_3)$ is positive. If $\theta = 0$, let $B_3 = A_1$. It is easily seen that this determination of B_3 is the same for any choice of B_1 and B_2 subject to the conditions imposed above. Hence *any displacement* Δ *for which* $\theta \neq \frac{\pi}{2}$ *determines uniquely a line a and two vectors* A_1A_2 *and* A_1B_3, *which are parallel to a if a is ordinary.* If a is ideal, Δ is a translation and A_1B_3 zero.

Conversely, an ordinary line a and two vectors parallel to a determine a unique displacement Δ. For let A_1 be any point of a, and l_1 any line through A_1 and perpendicular to a. Then the first vector determines a unique point A_2 and the second a unique point B_3. There are two lines $\bar{l}_2$, $\bar{\bar{l}}_2$ through A_1 perpendicular to a and such that $m(l_1\bar{l}_2) = m(l_1\bar{\bar{l}}_2) = \theta$ where $\tan\theta = \mathrm{Dist}\,B_1B_3$. Let B_1 be an arbitrary point of l_1, and $\bar{B}_2$, $\bar{\bar{B}}_2$ points of $\bar{l}_2$, $\bar{\bar{l}}_2$ respectively, such that θ is the measure of $\measuredangle B_1A_1\bar{B}_2$ and $\measuredangle B_1A_1\bar{\bar{B}}_2$. Then let B_2 be that one of $\bar{B}_2$ and $\bar{\bar{B}}_2$ such that $S(A_1B_1B_2B_3)$ is positive, and let l_2 be the line through A_2 parallel to A_1B_2. The displacement determined is

$$\Delta = \{l_2l'_2\} \cdot \{l_1l'_1\}.$$

Hence *any displacement* Δ *which is not a half twist determines and is determined by a line a and two vectors* A_1A_2 *and* A_1B_3. From this it is plain that if it be desired to specify a displacement by means of parameters or coördinates, it is necessary to give a set of numbers which will determine the line a (e.g. the Plücker coördinates of

* The measure of any pair of lines in three-dimensional Euclidean geometry satisfies the condition $0 \leqq \theta \leqq \frac{\pi}{2}$. Cf. § 119.

the line) and two additional numbers which will specify the vectors A_1A_2 and A_1B_3. This question is considered from various points of view in the following sections.

For a treatment of the general problem of parameter representations of displacements and, indeed, of the whole theory of displacements, see the articles by E. Study, Mathematische Annalen, Vol. XXXIX (1891), p. 441, and Sitzungsberichte der Berliner Mathematischen Gesellschaft, Vol. XII (1913), p. 36. The exercises in this section and the last one are largely drawn from the first of these articles and from the articles by Wiener, referred to above.

EXERCISES

1. Let l be the axis of a twist, a any ray perpendicular to and intersecting l, and b the ray into which a is displaced. Let c be the ray with origin at the mid-point of the segment joining the origin of a and b and bisecting the angle between the rays through this point parallel to a and b respectively. (Two rays are parallel if they are on parallel lines and on the same side of the line joining their origins.) The given twist is the product of the line reflection whose axis contains a by the line reflection whose axis contains c.

2. The product of three rotations whose axes have a point in common and whose angles of rotation are respectively double the angles between the ordered pairs of planes determined by the pairs of axes in a definite order, is the identity.

3. The rotations P and P′ described in Ex. 11, § 122, have the same *angle of rotation*, and the half twists H and H′ described in the same exercise have the same *distance of translation*.

4. There exists an orthogonal line reflection interchanging two congruent ordered pairs of points A_1B_1 and A_2B_2 if and only if A_1B_2 is congruent to A_2B_1.

5. There is a unique orthogonal line reflection carrying a given sense-class on a line l to a given sense-class on a line l'. The axes of the two orthogonal line reflections carrying a line l to a line l' are perpendicular to each other and to the common intersecting perpendicular of l and l' at the mid-point of the pair of points in which the latter meets l and l'.

6. If an ordered triad of noncollinear points $A_1B_1C_1$ is congruent to an ordered triad $A_2B_2C_2$, the axis of the displacement carrying A_1, B_1, C_1 to A_2, B_2, C_2 respectively meets orthogonally the axis of the orthogonal line reflection which carries A_1 and B_1 to two points A_1' and B_1' of the line A_2B_2 such that $S(A_1'B_1') \neq S(A_2B_2)$.

7. If three noncollinear points A_1, A_2, A_3 are displaced into A_2, A_3, A_4 respectively, the axis of the displacement is the common intersecting perpendicular of the line joining A_2 to the mid-point of A_1A_3 and the line joining A_3 to the mid-point of A_2A_4.

8. Show how to construct the axis of the displacement carrying an ordered point triad $A_1B_1C_1$ to a congruent ordered triad $A_2B_2C_2$.

9. If a line l be displaced to a line l', the mid-points of pairs of congruent points are the points of a line $\bar{l}$ or are identical; the planes perpendicular to the lines joining the pairs of congruent points at their mid-points meet on a line $\bar{\bar{l}}$ or are parallel or coincide. Under what circumstances do the different cases arise?

10. If a plane α be displaced to a plane α', the mid-points of the pairs of congruent points are the points of a plane $\bar{\alpha}$ or the points of a line or coincide; the planes perpendicular to the lines joining the pairs of congruent points at their mid-points pass through a point $\bar{\bar{A}}$ or all meet on a line or coincide. Under what circumstances do the different cases arise?

11. Let Δ be a displacement, P a variable point of space, $P' = \Delta(P)$, $\bar{P}$ the mid-point of the pair PP', and π the plane through $\bar{P}$ perpendicular to the line PP' if $P \neq P'$. Then if Δ is not a half twist, the transformations T_1 such that $\mathrm{T}_1(P) = \bar{P}$ and T_2 such that $\mathrm{T}_2(\bar{P}) = P'$ are affine collineations and

$$\mathrm{T}_2\mathrm{T}_1 = \Delta = \mathrm{T}_1\mathrm{T}_2.$$

If Δ is not a rotation, the transformation Γ such that $\Gamma(P) = \pi$ is a projective correlation such that $\Gamma(\pi) = P'$; i.e. such that

$$\Gamma^2 = \Delta.$$

If Δ is not a rotation or a half twist, the transformation N such that $\mathrm{N}(\bar{P}) = \pi$ is a projective correlation, and in fact is the null-system of the complex C referred to in Ex. 7, § 122. These transformations also satisfy the equations

$$\mathrm{T}_1 = \mathrm{N}\Gamma, \quad \mathrm{T}_2 = \Gamma\mathrm{N}, \quad \mathrm{N}\Delta = \Delta\mathrm{N}.$$

12. Using the notations of Ex. 11, if α is any plane, $\Delta(\alpha) = \alpha'$, and $\mathrm{T}_2(\alpha) = \bar{\alpha}$, then $\bar{\alpha}$ bisects the pair of planes α and α', and $\mathrm{T}_1(\bar{\alpha}) = \alpha'$.

13. In the correlation N the lines $\bar{l}$ and $\bar{\bar{l}}$ defined by Ex. 9 correspond. The plane $\bar{\alpha}$ and the point $\bar{\bar{A}}$ defined in Ex. 10 also correspond in N.

14. The linear complex C (Ex. 7, § 122) contains every line $\bar{l}$ which coincides with the line $\bar{\bar{l}}$ determined by the same line l (Ex. 9). Hence it is the set of those lines $\bar{l}$ which are perpendicular to the lines joining corresponding points of l and l', and it is also the set of lines $\bar{\bar{l}}$ which intersect the lines joining corresponding points of l and l'.

15. The affine collineation T_1 (Ex. 11) carries the axis of P (Ex. 11, § 122) to that of H′.

16. The correlation Γ (Ex. 11) carries the axis of P_1 (Ex. 10, § 122) to that of P_2.

17. The transformations T^{-1}, T_2, Γ, Γ^{-1} all carry C (Ex. 7, § 122) into C_1 (Ex. 8, § 122).

124. Correspondence between the rotations and the points of space. If we confine attention to the rotations leaving a point O invariant,*

* By the reasoning in § 90 it is clear that this amounts to considering the effect of all displacements on the field of vectors.

the considerations of the last section simplify considerably. The points A_1 and A_2 may be taken as coincident with O, and the point B_3 shall be denoted by R. Then every noninvolutoric rotation P corresponds to a definite point R on its axis. An involutoric rotation (orthogonal line reflection) may be taken to correspond to the point at infinity of its axis. Hence the rotations leaving O invariant correspond in a one-to-one and reciprocal way to the points of the real projective space consisting of the given Euclidean space and its points at infinity.

Let OX, OY, OZ be axes of a rectangular coördinate system with O as center such that $S(OXYZ)$ is the positive sense-class. Whenever R is distinct from the origin, denote the measures of $\measuredangle ROX$, $\measuredangle ROY$, $\measuredangle ROZ$ by α, β, γ respectively. Then the coördinates of R are

$$x = \tan\theta \cos\alpha,$$
$$y = \tan\theta \cos\beta,$$
$$z = \tan\theta \cos\gamma.$$

Let $(\alpha_0, \alpha_1, \alpha_2, \alpha_3)$ be the homogeneous coördinates of R, so chosen that if R is ordinary,

$$X = \frac{\alpha_1}{\alpha_0}, \qquad Y = \frac{\alpha_2}{\alpha_0}, \qquad Z = \frac{\alpha_3}{\alpha_0};$$

and if R is at infinity, $\alpha_0 = 0$. In either case we may take

$$\alpha_0 = \cos\theta, \quad \alpha_1 = \sin\theta\cos\alpha, \quad \alpha_2 = \sin\theta\cos\beta, \quad \alpha_3 = \sin\theta\cos\gamma.$$

According to Theorem 23 any rotation $(\alpha_0, \alpha_1, \alpha_2, \alpha_3)$ is expressible as a product of two involutoric rotations $(0, \lambda_1, \lambda_2, \lambda_3)$ and $(0, \mu_1, \mu_2, \mu_3)$. According to the convention just introduced, the λ's and μ's may be regarded as direction cosines. Hence, by Exs. 5 and 7, § 119,

$$(29) \quad \alpha_0 = \lambda_1\mu_1 + \lambda_2\mu_2 + \lambda_3\mu_3, \quad \alpha_1 = \begin{vmatrix} \lambda_2 & \lambda_3 \\ \mu_2 & \mu_3 \end{vmatrix}, \quad \alpha_2 = \begin{vmatrix} \lambda_3 & \lambda_1 \\ \mu_3 & \mu_1 \end{vmatrix}, \quad \alpha_3 = \begin{vmatrix} \lambda_1 & \lambda_2 \\ \mu_1 & \mu_2 \end{vmatrix}.$$

Two fundamental problems now arise: (1) to express the coördinates of the point representing the resultant of two rotations in terms of the coördinates of the points representing the rotations, and (2) to write the equations of a rotation in terms of the parameters $(\alpha_0, \alpha_1, \alpha_2, \alpha_3)$.

The formulas (29) are a special case of the formulas which furnish the solution of the first of these problems. The formulas for the general case may be found by an application of the method for compounding rotations described in § 122. Let the two rotations correspond to $A=(\alpha_0, \alpha_1, \alpha_2, \alpha_3)$ and $B=(\beta_0, \beta_1, \beta_2, \beta_3)$ respectively. Let μ_1, μ_2, μ_3 be direction cosines of a line perpendicular to OA and OB. Then the rotation $(\alpha_0, \alpha_1, \alpha_2, \alpha_3)$ is expressible by means of the formulas (29) and $(\beta_0, \beta_1, \beta_2, \beta_3)$ by the following:

$$(30)\quad \beta_0=\mu_1\nu_1+\mu_2\nu_2+\mu_3\nu_3,\ \beta_1=\begin{vmatrix}\mu_2 & \mu_3\\ \nu_2 & \nu_3\end{vmatrix},\ \beta_2=\begin{vmatrix}\mu_3 & \mu_1\\ \nu_3 & \nu_1\end{vmatrix},\ \beta_3=\begin{vmatrix}\mu_1 & \mu_2\\ \nu_1 & \nu_2\end{vmatrix}.$$

According to the principle explained in § 122, the point $(\gamma_0, \gamma_1, \gamma_2, \gamma_3)$ which represents the product of $(\alpha_0, \alpha_1, \alpha_2, \alpha_3)$ followed by $(\beta_0, \beta_1, \beta_2, \beta_3)$ is

$$(31)\quad \gamma_0=\lambda_1\nu_1+\lambda_2\nu_2+\lambda_3\nu_3,\ \gamma_1=\begin{vmatrix}\lambda_2 & \lambda_3\\ \nu_2 & \nu_3\end{vmatrix},\ \gamma_2=\begin{vmatrix}\lambda_3 & \lambda_1\\ \nu_3 & \nu_1\end{vmatrix},\ \gamma_3=\begin{vmatrix}\lambda_1 & \lambda_2\\ \nu_1 & \nu_2\end{vmatrix}.$$

The result of eliminating the λ's, μ's, and ν's from these equations is

$$(32)\quad \begin{aligned}\gamma_0&=\alpha_0\beta_0-\alpha_1\beta_1-\alpha_2\beta_2-\alpha_3\beta_3,\\ \gamma_1&=\alpha_1\beta_0+\alpha_0\beta_1+\alpha_3\beta_2-\alpha_2\beta_3,\\ \gamma_2&=\alpha_2\beta_0-\alpha_3\beta_1+\alpha_0\beta_2+\alpha_1\beta_3,\\ \gamma_3&=\alpha_3\beta_0+\alpha_2\beta_1-\alpha_1\beta_2+\alpha_0\beta_3.\end{aligned}$$

This is most easily verified by substituting (29), (30), and (31) in (32). The rotation $(\gamma_0, \gamma_1, \gamma_2, \gamma_3)$ which is the product of $(\alpha_0, \alpha_1, \alpha_2, \alpha_3)$ and $(\beta_0, \beta_1, \beta_2, \beta_3)$ must be that given by (32); for if not, there would be some case in which (32) would not be satisfied by the values of $\alpha_0, \beta_0, \gamma_0$, etc. given by (29), (30), and (31).

The formulas (32), which are due to O. Rodrigues, Journal de Mathématiques, Vol. V (1840), p. 380, are the same as those for the multiplication of quaternions. Cf. § 127.

The problem (2) of expressing the coefficients of the equations (17) of a rotation in terms of the coördinates of the corresponding point $(\alpha_0, \alpha_1, \alpha_2, \alpha_3)$ may be solved very easily by the formulas and theorems of § 118, in the case of rotations of period two. The involutoric rotation corresponding to $(0, \lambda_1, \lambda_2, \lambda_3)$ is, in fact,

$$(33)\quad \begin{aligned}x'&=(2\lambda_1^2-1)x+2\lambda_1\lambda_2 y+2\lambda_1\lambda_3 z,\\ y'&=2\lambda_1\lambda_2 x+(2\lambda_2^2-1)y+2\lambda_2\lambda_3 z,\\ z'&=2\lambda_1\lambda_3 x+2\lambda_2\lambda_3 y+(2\lambda_3^2-1)z.\end{aligned}$$

This is easily verified, because (1) the matrix is orthogonal and its determinant is +1, (2) the transformation leaves the point $(\lambda_1, \lambda_2, \lambda_3)$

invariant, (3) the matrix is symmetric and hence corresponds to a transformation of period two.

To obtain the equations of the transformation corresponding to $(\alpha_0, \alpha_1, \alpha_2, \alpha_3)$ it would be sufficient to take the product of (33) and the corresponding transformation in terms of μ_1, μ_2, μ_3 and compare with equations (29). The algebraic computations involved would, however, be more complicated than in the following method, which is based on a simple observation with regard to collineations whose equations are of the form

$$
\begin{aligned}
\alpha_0 x &= \alpha_0 \bar{x} + \alpha_3 \bar{y} - \alpha_2 \bar{z}, \\
\alpha_0 y &= -\alpha_3 \bar{x} + \alpha_0 \bar{y} + \alpha_1 \bar{z}, \\
\alpha_0 z &= \alpha_2 \bar{x} - \alpha_1 \bar{y} + \alpha_0 z.
\end{aligned} \tag{34}
$$

If $\bar{P} = (\bar{x}, \bar{y}, \bar{z})$ and $P = (x, y, z)$, then the vector $O\bar{P}$ is perpendicular to the vector $\bar{P}P$, because

$$\bar{x}(x - \bar{x}) + \bar{y}(y - \bar{y}) + \bar{z}(z - \bar{z}) = 0. \tag{35}$$

The transformation (34) also has the obvious property of leaving invariant all points on the line joining the origin to $(\alpha_1, \alpha_2, \alpha_3)$.

Conversely, if a collineation

$$
\begin{aligned}
\rho x &= a_{11} \bar{x} + a_{12} \bar{y} + a_{13} \bar{z}, \\
\rho y &= a_{21} \bar{x} + a_{22} \bar{y} + a_{23} \bar{z}, \\
\rho z &= a_{31} \bar{y} + a_{32} \bar{y} + a_{33} \bar{z},
\end{aligned} \tag{36}
$$

has the property that whenever $\bar{P} = (\bar{x}, \bar{y}, \bar{z})$ is distinct from $P = (x, y, z)$, OP is perpendicular to $P\bar{P}$, the relation (35) requires that $a_{ij} = -a_{ji}$ whenever $i \neq j$ and that $\rho = a_{11} = a_{22} = a_{33}$. If, moreover, (36) leaves all points of the line joining the origin to $(\alpha_1, \alpha_2, \alpha_3)$ invariant, it must be either of the form (34) or of the form

$$
\begin{aligned}
\alpha_0 x &= \alpha_0 \bar{x} - \alpha_3 \bar{y} + \alpha_2 \bar{z}, \\
\alpha_0 y &= \alpha_3 \bar{x} + \alpha_0 \bar{y} - \alpha_1 \bar{z}, \\
\alpha_0 z &= -\alpha_2 \bar{x} + \alpha_1 \bar{y} + \alpha_0 \bar{z}.
\end{aligned} \tag{34'}
$$

It is also to be observed that the determinant of Transformations (34) and (34′) is $\alpha_0 A$, where

$$A = \alpha_0^2 + \alpha_1^2 + \alpha_2^2 + \alpha_3^2. \tag{37}$$

This determinant can vanish for real α's only if $\alpha_0 = 0$.

Now consider an orthogonal transformation (17) representing a rotation P which is not of period two. Let P be an arbitrary point, $P' = \mathrm{P}(P)$, and $\bar{P}$ the mid-point of P and P'. The relation between P and $\bar{P}$ is given by the equations*

$$
(38)\qquad
\begin{aligned}
2\bar{x} &= (a_{11}+1)x + a_{12}y + a_{13}z,\\
2\bar{y} &= a_{21}x + (a_{22}+1)y + a_{23}z,\\
2\bar{z} &= a_{31}x + a_{32}y + (a_{33}+1)z.
\end{aligned}
$$

The line $\bar{P}P$ is perpendicular to $O\bar{P}$ and (38) must have the same invariant points as P. Hence if P is the rotation corresponding to $(\alpha_0, \alpha_1, \alpha_2, \alpha_3)$, the equations of the transformation from $\bar{P}$ to P must be of the form (34) or (34′).

Forming the determinants analogous to (19) in § 31, we see that $S(OP\bar{P}R)$, where $R = (\alpha_0, \alpha_1, \alpha_2, \alpha_3)$, is positive if $\bar{P}$ is given by (34) and negative if $\bar{P}$ is given by (34′). Hence (38) must be the inverse of (34). Solving the equations (34) we have

$$
(39)\qquad
\begin{aligned}
\bar{x} &= \frac{\alpha_0^2+\alpha_1^2}{A}x + \frac{\alpha_1\alpha_2-\alpha_0\alpha_3}{A}y + \frac{\alpha_1\alpha_3+\alpha_0\alpha_2}{A}z,\\
\bar{y} &= \frac{\alpha_1\alpha_2+\alpha_0\alpha_3}{A}x + \frac{\alpha_0^2+\alpha_2^2}{A}y + \frac{\alpha_2\alpha_3-\alpha_0\alpha_1}{A}z,\\
\bar{z} &= \frac{\alpha_1\alpha_3-\alpha_0\alpha_2}{A}x + \frac{\alpha_2\alpha_3+\alpha_0\alpha_1}{A}y + \frac{\alpha_0^3+\alpha_3^2}{A}z.
\end{aligned}
$$

Since (38) and (39) must be the same transformation, we have

$$
(40)\qquad
\begin{aligned}
a_{11} &= 2\frac{\alpha_0^2+\alpha_1^2}{A}-1, & a_{12} &= 2\frac{\alpha_1\alpha_2-\alpha_0\alpha_3}{A}, & a_{13} &= 2\frac{\alpha_1\alpha_3+\alpha_0\alpha_2}{A},\\
a_{21} &= 2\frac{\alpha_1\alpha_2+\alpha_0\alpha_3}{A}, & a_{22} &= 2\frac{\alpha_0^2+\alpha_2^2}{A}-1, & a_{23} &= 2\frac{\alpha_2\alpha_3-\alpha_0\alpha_1}{A},\\
a_{31} &= 2\frac{\alpha_1\alpha_3-\alpha_0\alpha_2}{A}, & a_{32} &= 2\frac{\alpha_2\alpha_3+\alpha_0\alpha_1}{A}, & a_{33} &= 2\frac{\alpha_0^2+\alpha_3^2}{A}-1.
\end{aligned}
$$

These are the formulas, due to Euler, for expressing the coefficients of an orthogonal transformation in terms of the homogeneous parameters $\alpha_0, \alpha_1, \alpha_2, \alpha_3$.

* The transformation from P to $\bar{P}$ is that denoted by $\mathbf{T}_1$ in Ex. 11, § 123.

The formulas for the α's in terms of the a_{ij}'s may be obtained by taking linear combinations of Equations (40):

$$1+a_{11}+a_{22}+a_{33}=\frac{4\,\alpha_0^2}{A},\quad a_{21}-a_{12}=4\frac{\alpha_0\alpha_3}{A},\quad a_{13}-a_{31}=\frac{4\,\alpha_0\alpha_2}{A},$$

$$a_{32}-a_{23}=\frac{4\,\alpha_0\alpha_1}{A}.$$

From this it follows that

(41) $\alpha_0:\alpha_1:\alpha_2:\alpha_3=1+a_{11}+a_{22}+a_{33}:a_{32}-a_{23}:a_{13}-a_{31}:a_{21}-a_{12}.$

125. Algebra of matrices. The algebra of the last section may be put in a most compact form by means of matrix notation. This requires one or two new definitions. The *sum* of two matrices is defined by means of the following equation:

$$(42)\quad \begin{pmatrix} a_{11} & a_{12} & a_{13}\\ a_{21} & a_{22} & a_{23}\\ a_{31} & a_{32} & a_{33}\end{pmatrix}+\begin{pmatrix} b_{11} & b_{12} & b_{13}\\ b_{21} & b_{22} & b_{23}\\ b_{31} & b_{32} & b_{33}\end{pmatrix}=\begin{pmatrix} a_{11}+b_{11} & a_{12}+b_{12} & a_{13}+b_{13}\\ a_{21}+b_{21} & a_{22}+b_{22} & a_{23}+b_{23}\\ a_{31}+b_{31} & a_{32}+b_{32} & a_{33}+b_{33}\end{pmatrix}.$$

This operation obviously satisfies the associative and commutative laws, namely

$$A+(B+C)=(A+B)+C,$$

$$A+B=B+A,$$

where A, B, C stand for matrices.

Multiplication of matrices has been defined in § 95, Vol. I, i.e.

$$(43)\qquad (a_{ij})\cdot(b_{ij})=(c_{ij}),$$

where $c_{ij}=\sum_{k=1}^{3}a_{ik}b_{kj}$. Under this definition it is clear that

$$A(B+C)=AB+AC$$

and

$$(B+C)A=BA+CA.$$

Also it has already been proved that

$$(AB)C=A(BC).$$

It is now easy to see that, under these definitions, matrices have most of the properties of a noncommutative number system in the sense of Chap. VI, Vol. I, the matrices

$$\begin{pmatrix}0&0&0\\0&0&0\\0&0&0\end{pmatrix}\quad\text{and}\quad\begin{pmatrix}1&0&0\\0&1&0\\0&0&1\end{pmatrix}$$

taking the rôles of 0 and 1 respectively. The matrices of the form

$$\begin{pmatrix}x&0&0\\0&x&0\\0&0&x\end{pmatrix}$$

form by themselves a number system which is isomorphic with the number system of the geometry. Such a matrix may be called a *scalar* and be denoted by x.

Now let us denote the orthogonal matrix of the equations of a rotation (17) by R, and let the skew symmetric matrix

$$\begin{pmatrix} 0 & \frac{\alpha_3}{\alpha_0} & \frac{-\alpha_2}{\alpha_0} \\ \frac{-\alpha_3}{\alpha_0} & 0 & \frac{\alpha_1}{\alpha_0} \\ \frac{\alpha_2}{\alpha_0} & \frac{-\alpha_1}{\alpha_0} & 0 \end{pmatrix}$$

be denoted by S. Then the matrix of the transformation (34) is $1+S$ and the matrix of the transformation (38) is $\frac{1}{2}(1+R)$. The comparing of coefficients of (38) and of (39) amounts to writing

$$1+R=2(1+S)^{-1}.$$

This equation may be transformed as follows:

$$R=2(1+S)^{-1}-1,$$
$$R=2(1+S)^{-1}-(1+S)(1+S)^{-1},$$
$$R=(1-S)(1+S)^{-1}.$$

The last equation, however, states a relation which is obvious from the point of view of matrices. For if S be any skew symmetric matrix, the transposed of S is $-S$. Since the product of the transposed matrices of the two given matrices is the transposed of the product, the transposed of

$$(1-S)(1+S)^{-1}$$

is

$$(1+S)(1-S)^{-1},$$

which is also its inverse. Hence, whenever

$$R=(1-S)(1+S)^{-1},$$

R is orthogonal.

This equation may be solved as follows:

$$\begin{aligned} 1+R &= (1+S)(1+S)^{-1}+(1-S)(1+S)^{-1} \\ &= 2(1+S)^{-1}, \end{aligned}$$
$$(1+R)^{-1}=\tfrac{1}{2}(1+S),$$
$$2(1+R)^{-1}-1=S,$$
$$2(1+R)^{-1}-(1+R)(1+R)^{-1}=S,$$
$$(1-R)(1+R)^{-1}=S,$$

which gives the formula for a skew symmetric matrix in terms of an orthogonal matrix.

The operation of taking the inverse of a matrix is defined (cf. § 95, Vol. I) in case the determinant of the matrix is distinct from zero. In the operations above, this is a restriction on the matrix $1+R$ and, by comparison with Equations (22), is seen to mean that no point must be transformed by the rotation corresponding to R into its symmetric point with respect to the origin.

The generalization from three-rowed to n-rowed matrices is obvious, and we thus have the skew symmetric and orthogonal matrices of n rows connected by the relations

$$R=(1-S)(1+S)^{-1}, \tag{44}$$

$$S=(1-R)(1+R)^{-1}. \tag{45}$$

The equations between the corresponding elements in the matrices which enter in the first of these two matrix equations are the formulas given by Cayley (Collected Works, Cambridge, 1889, Vol. I, p. 332), expressing the n^2 coefficients of an orthogonal transformation as rational functions of $\frac{n(n-1)}{2}$ parameters.

126. Rotations of an imaginary sphere. The group of rotations leaving a point invariant may be regarded as a subgroup of the collineations of a sphere having this point as center. Let us consider the imaginary sphere

$$x_0^2+x_1^2+x_2^2+x_3^2=0 \tag{46}$$

and apply some of the results obtained in § 102. If a collineation

$$\begin{aligned} x_0' &= c_{00}x_0+c_{01}x_1+c_{02}x_2+c_{03}x_3,\\ x_1' &= c_{10}x_0+c_{11}x_1+c_{12}x_2+c_{13}x_3,\\ x_2' &= c_{20}x_0+c_{21}x_1+c_{22}x_2+c_{23}x_3,\\ x_3' &= c_{30}x_0+c_{31}x_1+c_{32}x_2+c_{33}x_3, \end{aligned} \tag{47}$$

carries each line of one regulus on the sphere into itself, any point (x_0, x_1, x_2, x_3) satisfying the condition (46) must be carried into a point (x_0', x_1', x_2', x_3') satisfying the condition

$$x_0'^2+x_1'^2+x_2'^2+x_3'^2=0, \tag{48}$$

which states that it is on the sphere, and the condition

$$x_0x_0'+x_1x_1'+x_2x_2'+x_3x_3'=0, \tag{49}$$

which states that it is on the plane tangent at (x_0, x_1, x_2, x_3). Substituting (47) in (48) we have, as in § 118,

$$\sum_{i=0}^{3} c_{i0}^2 = \sum_{i=0}^{3} c_{i1}^2 = \sum_{i=0}^{3} c_{i2}^2 = \sum_{i=0}^{3} c_{i3}^2,$$

$$c_{0i}c_{0j} + c_{1i}c_{1j} + c_{2i}c_{2j} + c_{3i}c_{3j} = 0 \quad \text{if} \quad i \neq j.$$

Substituting (47) in (49) we have

$$c_{ij} = -c_{ji} \quad \text{if} \quad i \neq j,$$

$$c_{00} = c_{11} = c_{22} = c_{33}.$$

The matrix of the equations (47) must therefore be of the form

$$(50) \qquad \begin{pmatrix} \alpha_0 & \alpha_1 & \alpha_2 & \alpha_3 \\ -\alpha_1 & \alpha_0 & -\alpha_3 & \alpha_2 \\ -\alpha_2 & \alpha_3 & \alpha_0 & -\alpha_1 \\ -\alpha_3 & -\alpha_2 & \alpha_1 & \alpha_0 \end{pmatrix}$$

or

$$(51) \qquad \begin{pmatrix} \beta_0 & \beta_1 & \beta_2 & \beta_3 \\ -\beta_1 & \beta_0 & \beta_3 & -\beta_2 \\ -\beta_2 & -\beta_3 & \beta_0 & \beta_1 \\ -\beta_3 & \beta_2 & -\beta_1 & \beta_0 \end{pmatrix}.$$

On multiplying together two matrices of one of these forms, the product is seen to be of the same form; whereas if two matrices of different forms are multiplied together, the product does not satisfy the condition $c_{ij} = -c_{ji}$, $i \neq j$. Hence the matrices of the form (50) must represent the projective collineations leaving all lines of one regulus on (46) invariant, and those of the form (51) must represent the projective collineations leaving all lines of the other regulus invariant. Hence, by § 102, any direct projective collineation leaving the sphere invariant is represented by a product of a matrix of type (50) by one of type (51).

A rotation is a direct collineation leaving invariant both the sphere and the plane at infinity $x_0 = 0$. A collineation (47) leaves $x_0 = 0$ invariant if and only if $c_{01} = c_{02} = c_{03} = 0$. But on multiplying (50) and (51) it is clear that this can happen only if $\alpha_0 = \rho\beta_0$, $\alpha_1 = -\rho\beta_1$, $\alpha_2 = -\rho\beta_2$, $\alpha_3 = -\rho\beta_3$, ρ being any number except zero. Hence the matrix representing a rotation is $A\bar{A}$, where

$$A = \begin{pmatrix} \alpha_0 & \alpha_1 & \alpha_2 & \alpha_3 \\ -\alpha_1 & \alpha_0 & -\alpha_3 & \alpha_2 \\ -\alpha_2 & \alpha_3 & \alpha_0 & -\alpha_1 \\ -\alpha_3 & -\alpha_2 & \alpha_1 & \alpha_0 \end{pmatrix} \quad \text{and} \quad \bar{A} = \begin{pmatrix} \alpha_0 & -\alpha_1 & -\alpha_2 & -\alpha_3 \\ \alpha_1 & \alpha_0 & -\alpha_3 & \alpha_2 \\ \alpha_2 & \alpha_3 & \alpha_0 & -\alpha_1 \\ \alpha_3 & -\alpha_2 & \alpha_1 & \alpha_0 \end{pmatrix}.$$

The matrix of the product $A\bar{A}$ is

$$\begin{pmatrix} \alpha_0^2+\alpha_1^2+\alpha_2^2+\alpha_3^2 & 0 & 0 & 0 \\ 0 & \alpha_0^2+\alpha_1^2-\alpha_2^2-\alpha_3^2 & 2(\alpha_1\alpha_2-\alpha_0\alpha_3) & 2(\alpha_1\alpha_3+\alpha_0\alpha_2) \\ 0 & 2(\alpha_1\alpha_2+\alpha_0\alpha_3) & \alpha_0^2+\alpha_2^2-\alpha_1^2-\alpha_3^2 & 2(\alpha_2\alpha_3-\alpha_0\alpha_1) \\ 0 & 2(\alpha_1\alpha_3-\alpha_0\alpha_2) & 2(\alpha_2\alpha_3+\alpha_0\alpha_1) & \alpha_0^2+\alpha_3^2-\alpha_1^2-\alpha_2^2 \end{pmatrix},$$

which agrees with (40) of § 124.

Hence the *parameters* $(\alpha_0, \alpha_1, \alpha_2, \alpha_3)$ *in the Euler formulas may be regarded as the elements of a matrix of the form* (50) *which represents the projectivity effected on one of the reguli of* (46) *by the rotation.*

If two rotations effect projectivities A and B respectively on a regulus, the product of the rotations effects the projectivity BA on the regulus (§ 102). Hence the product of two rotations whose parameters are $(\alpha_0, \alpha_1, \alpha_2, \alpha_3)$ and $(\beta_0, \beta_1, \beta_2, \beta_3)$ respectively has the parameters $(\gamma_0, \gamma_1, \gamma_2, \gamma_3)$, where

$$\begin{pmatrix} \gamma_0 & \gamma_1 & \gamma_2 & \gamma_3 \\ -\gamma_1 & \gamma_0 & \gamma_3 & -\gamma_2 \\ -\gamma_2 & -\gamma_3 & \gamma_0 & \gamma_1 \\ -\gamma_3 & \gamma_2 & -\gamma_1 & \gamma_0 \end{pmatrix} = \begin{pmatrix} \beta_0 & \beta_1 & \beta_2 & \beta_3 \\ -\beta_1 & \beta_0 & -\beta_3 & \beta_2 \\ -\beta_2 & \beta_3 & \beta_0 & -\beta_1 \\ -\beta_3 & -\beta_2 & \beta_1 & \beta_0 \end{pmatrix} \cdot \begin{pmatrix} \alpha_0 & \alpha_1 & \alpha_2 & \alpha_3 \\ -\alpha_1 & \alpha_0 & -\alpha_3 & \alpha_2 \\ -\alpha_2 & \alpha_3 & \alpha_0 & -\alpha_1 \\ -\alpha_3 & -\alpha_2 & \alpha_1 & \alpha_0 \end{pmatrix}.$$

This yields the same formulas as (32) in § 124.

EXERCISE

A parameter representation for the sphere (46) is

$$x_0 = i(\lambda_1\mu_1 + \lambda_0\mu_0),$$
$$x_1 = \lambda_1\mu_1 - \lambda_0\mu_0,$$
$$x_2 = \lambda_1\mu_0 + \lambda_0\mu_1,$$
$$x_3 = i(\lambda_1\mu_0 - \lambda_0\mu_1),$$

where $i^2 = -1$. The two reguli on the sphere are the sets of lines for which λ_1/λ_0 and μ_1/μ_0 respectively are constant. The transformation whose matrix is (50) is given by the projectivity

$$\lambda_0' = (\alpha_0 + i\alpha_1)\lambda_0 + (\alpha_3 - i\alpha_2)\lambda_1,$$
$$\lambda_1' = -(\alpha_3 + i\alpha_2)\lambda_0 + (\alpha_0 - i\alpha_1)\lambda_1.$$

127. Quaternions. The definitions of sum and product of matrices in § 125 for three-rowed matrices clearly apply to matrices of any number of rows. With this understanding the sum of two matrices of the form (50) is obviously a matrix of the same form. The same has been seen in the last section to be true of the products of two such matrices. Hence the set of all such matrices is carried into itself by the operations of addition and multiplication of matrices defined in § 125.

Let us introduce the notation

$$1=\begin{pmatrix}1&0&0&0\\0&1&0&0\\0&0&1&0\\0&0&0&1\end{pmatrix},\qquad i=\begin{pmatrix}0&1&0&0\\-1&0&0&0\\0&0&0&-1\\0&0&1&0\end{pmatrix},$$

$$j=\begin{pmatrix}0&0&1&0\\0&0&0&1\\-1&0&0&0\\0&-1&0&0\end{pmatrix},\quad k=\begin{pmatrix}0&0&0&1\\0&0&-1&0\\0&1&0&0\\-1&0&0&0\end{pmatrix}.$$

Then any matrix of the sort we are considering is expressible in the form

$$\alpha_0 1+\alpha_1 i+\alpha_2 j+\alpha_3 k.$$

The matrices i, j, k satisfy the following multiplication table:

(52)

	i	j	k
i	-1	k	$-j$
j	$-k$	-1	i
k	j	$-i$	-1

It has been seen in § 125 that matrices satisfy the associative and commutative laws of addition, the associative laws of multiplication, and the distributive laws. They obviously do not, in the present case, satisfy the commutative law of multiplication. Addition is performed by the rule

$$(53)\qquad \begin{aligned}&(\alpha_0 1+\alpha_1 i+\alpha_2 j+\alpha_3 k)+(\beta_0 1+\beta_1 i+\beta_2 j+\beta_3 k)\\&\qquad=(\alpha_0+\beta_0)\,1+(\alpha_1+\beta_1)\,i+(\alpha_2+\beta_2)\,j+(\alpha_3+\beta_3)\,k,\end{aligned}$$

and multiplication by the rule

$$(54)\qquad \begin{aligned}&(\alpha_0 1+\alpha_1 i+\alpha_2 j+\alpha_3 k)\cdot(\beta_0 1+\beta_1 i+\beta_2 j+\beta_3 k)\\&\qquad=\gamma_0 1+\gamma_1 i+\gamma_2 j+\gamma_3 k,\end{aligned}$$

where

$$(55)\qquad \begin{aligned}\gamma_0&=\alpha_0\beta_0-\alpha_1\beta_1-\alpha_2\beta_2-\alpha_3\beta_3,\\ \gamma_1&=\alpha_0\beta_1+\alpha_1\beta_0+\alpha_2\beta_3-\alpha_3\beta_2,\\ \gamma_2&=\alpha_0\beta_2-\alpha_1\beta_3+\alpha_2\beta_0+\alpha_3\beta_1,\\ \gamma_3&=\alpha_0\beta_3+\alpha_1\beta_2-\alpha_2\beta_1+\alpha_3\beta_0.\end{aligned}$$

From (53) it is clear that the operation of subtraction can be performed on any two matrices of this form. From (55) it is clear that $(\beta_0 1 + \beta_1 i + \beta_2 j + \beta_3 k)^{-1}$ exists whenever the determinant

$$\begin{vmatrix} \beta_0 & -\beta_1 & -\beta_2 & -\beta_3 \\ \beta_1 & \beta_0 & \beta_3 & -\beta_2 \\ \beta_2 & -\beta_3 & \beta_0 & \beta_1 \\ \beta_3 & \beta_2 & -\beta_1 & \beta_0 \end{vmatrix} \equiv (\beta_0^2 + \beta_1^2 + \beta_2^2 + \beta_3^2)^2$$

is different from zero. This condition is satisfied whenever β_0, β_1, β_2, β_3 are real.

Hence when α_0, α_1, α_2, α_3 are real, the matrices of the form (50) constitute a noncommutative number system in the sense of Chap. VI, Vol. I. This number system is, in fact, the Hamiltonian system of quaternions. Compare the references at the end of the next section, particularly p. 178 of the article in the Encyclopädie and the article by Dickson in the Bulletin of the American Mathematical Society.

EXERCISE

A system of quaternions may be defined as a set of objects $[q]$ such that (1) for every ordered pair of vectors a, b there is a q, which we shall denote by $\binom{a}{b}$; (2) for every q there is at least one pair of vectors; (3) two pairs of vectors OA, OB and OA', OB' correspond to the same q if and only if the ordered triads OAB and $OA'B'$ are coplanar and directly similar in their common plane; (4) the q's are subject to operations of addition and multiplication defined by the equations

$$\binom{a}{b} + \binom{c}{b} = \binom{a+c}{b}, \qquad (b \neq 0)$$

$$\binom{a}{b} \times \binom{b}{c} = \binom{a}{c}. \qquad (b \neq 0 \neq c)$$

Prove that a system of q's satisfies the fundamental theorems of a number system with the exception of the commutative law of multiplication. See G. Koenigs, Leçons de Cinématique (Paris, 1897), p. 464.

128. Quaternions and the one-dimensional projective group. On comparing (32) and (55) it is clear that there is a correspondence between quaternions, taken homogeneously, and the rotations leaving a point invariant in which if two quaternions q_1, q_2 correspond to the rotations P_1, P_2 respectively, the product $q_2 q_1$ corresponds to $\mathrm{P}_2\mathrm{P}_1$. The group of rotations is isomorphic with the group of projective transformations of the circle at infinity and hence with the projective group of any complex one-dimensional form. There must, therefore, be a relation between quaternions and the one-dimensional projectivities,

$$x' = \frac{\alpha x + \beta}{\gamma x + \delta}.$$

The simplest way to obtain a number system corresponding to these transformations is to apply the operations of addition and multiplication as defined above to two-rowed matrices, i.e.

$$\begin{pmatrix} \alpha_1 & \beta_1 \\ \gamma_1 & \delta_1 \end{pmatrix} + \begin{pmatrix} \alpha_2 & \beta_2 \\ \gamma_2 & \delta_2 \end{pmatrix} = \begin{pmatrix} \alpha_1 + \alpha_2 & \beta_1 + \beta_2 \\ \gamma_1 + \gamma_2 & \delta_1 + \delta_2 \end{pmatrix},$$

$$\begin{pmatrix} \alpha_1 & \beta_1 \\ \gamma_1 & \delta_1 \end{pmatrix} \cdot \begin{pmatrix} \alpha_2 & \beta_2 \\ \gamma_2 & \delta_2 \end{pmatrix} = \begin{pmatrix} \alpha_1\alpha_2 + \beta_1\gamma_2 & \alpha_1\beta_2 + \beta_1\delta_2 \\ \gamma_1\alpha_2 + \delta_1\gamma_2 & \gamma_1\beta_2 + \delta_1\delta_2 \end{pmatrix}.$$

If we write

$$e_1 = \begin{pmatrix} 1 & 0 \\ 0 & 0 \end{pmatrix}, \quad e_2 = \begin{pmatrix} 0 & 1 \\ 0 & 0 \end{pmatrix}, \quad e_3 = \begin{pmatrix} 0 & 0 \\ 1 & 0 \end{pmatrix}, \quad e_4 = \begin{pmatrix} 0 & 0 \\ 0 & 1 \end{pmatrix},$$

we have

$$\begin{pmatrix} \alpha & \beta \\ \gamma & \delta \end{pmatrix} = \alpha e_1 + \beta e_2 + \gamma e_3 + \delta e_4.$$

The units e_1, e_2, e_3, e_4 satisfy the multiplication table

	e_1	e_2	e_3	e_4
e_1	e_1	e_2	0	0
e_2	0	0	e_1	e_2
e_3	e_3	e_4	0	0
e_4	0	0	e_3	e_4

Although these matrices satisfy the associative and distributive laws of addition and multiplication and the commutative law of addition, it is clear that they do not constitute a number system, because it is possible to have $ab = 0$ when $a \neq 0$ and $b \neq 0$. Nevertheless, if we write

$$1 = e_1 + e_4, \quad i = \sqrt{-1}\,(e_1 - e_4), \quad j = e_2 - e_3, \quad k = \sqrt{-1}\,(e_2 + e_3),$$

any matrix $\begin{pmatrix} \alpha & \beta \\ \gamma & \delta \end{pmatrix}$ is expressible linearly in $1, i, j, k$; and

$$i^2 = j^2 = k^2 = -1, \quad ij = -ji = k, \quad jk = -kj = i, \quad ki = -ik = j.$$

Hence the system of two-rowed matrices

$$\begin{pmatrix} \alpha & \beta \\ \gamma & \delta \end{pmatrix},$$

where $\alpha, \beta, \gamma, \delta$ are complex numbers, is equivalent to the set of elements

(56) $$a1 + bi + cj + dk,$$

where 1, i, j, k satisfy the multiplication table (52) of quaternions. The elements (56) are quaternions, properly so called, only when a, b, c, d are real. When a, b, c, d are ordinary complex numbers, the elements (56) do not form a number system in the sense of Chap. VI, Vol. I, because there can be elements x, y both different from 0 such that $xy = 0$.

It is interesting to note that 1, i, j, k are the matrices

$$\begin{pmatrix}1 & 0\\ 0 & 1\end{pmatrix},\quad \begin{pmatrix}\sqrt{-1} & 0\\ 0 & -\sqrt{-1}\end{pmatrix},\quad \begin{pmatrix}0 & 1\\ -1 & 0\end{pmatrix},\quad \begin{pmatrix}0 & \sqrt{-1}\\ \sqrt{-1} & 0\end{pmatrix},$$

which represent the identity, and three mutually harmonic involutions

$$x' = -x,\quad x' = -\frac{1}{x},\quad x' = \frac{1}{x}.$$

If the projectivities are represented on a conic, these three involutions have the vertices of a self-polar triangle as centers.

The matrix represented by

$$\alpha_0 1 + \alpha_1 i + \alpha_2 j + \alpha_3 k$$

is

$$\begin{pmatrix}\alpha_0 + \sqrt{-1}\,\alpha_1 & \alpha_2 + \sqrt{-1}\,\alpha_3\\ -\alpha_2 + \sqrt{-1}\,\alpha_3 & \alpha_0 - \sqrt{-1}\,\alpha_1\end{pmatrix},$$

and its determinant is

$$\alpha_0^2 + \alpha_1^2 + \alpha_2^2 + \alpha_3^2.$$

The geometric significance of this remark is obvious on comparison with the exercise in § 126.

The relation between quaternions and the one-dimensional projective group was discovered by B. Peirce (cf. Chap. VI by A. Cayley in Tait's Quaternions, 3d edition, Cambridge, 1890). It is an instance of a general relation, noted by H. Poincaré, between any linear associative algebra and a corresponding linear group. On this subject see E. Study, Mathematical Papers from the Chicago Congress (New York, 1896), p. 376, and Encyclopädie der Math. Wiss., I A 4, § 12; Lie-Sheffers, Kontinuierliche Gruppen (Leipzig, 1893), Chap. XXI; and L. E. Dickson, Bulletin of the American Mathematical Society, Vol. XXII (1915), p. 53. On the general subject of linear associative algebra see L. E. Dickson, Linear Algebras, Cambridge Tracts in Mathematics, No. 16, 1914; and the article by E. Study and E. Cartan in the Encyclopédie des Sciences Mathématiques, I 5.

***129. Representation of rotations and one-dimensional projectivities by points.** The parameter representation of the rotations about a point which we based in § 124 on a Euclidean construction has now been seen to be connected in the closest way with the theory of the one-dimensional projective group. It is therefore of interest to set up the correspondence between the points of space and the rotations about a point in a form which puts in evidence also the correspondence between the points of space and the one-dimensional projectivities. This has been studied in detail in the memoir by Stéphanos referred to in Ex. 3, § 110. It will be merely outlined here, because the proofs are all simple applications of theorems which should by this time be familiar to the reader. The construction given below has the advantage over the one given in § 123 of being valid in a general projective space.

Let S^2 be an arbitrary sphere. (In order to connect with our previous work S^2 may be taken as the imaginary sphere $x^2+y^2+z^2+1=0$). Let R_1^2 and R_2^2 be the two reguli on S^2, O the center of S^2, and C_∞^2 the circle at infinity.

An arbitrary rotation P leaving O invariant determines and is fully determined by a projectivity Γ of C_∞^2, and hence is fully determined by its effect on three points P_1, P_2, P_3 of C_∞^2. If l_1, l_2, l_3 are the lines of R_1^2 on P_1, P_2, P_3 respectively, and m_1, m_2, m_3 the lines of R_2^2 on the points P(P_1), P(P_2), P(P_3) respectively, the planes l_1m_1, l_2m_2, l_3m_3 meet in a point R. *Let R correspond to* P *and to* Γ (cf. Ex. 2, § 110).

The following propositions are now easily established by reference to theorems on one-dimensional forms:

The point R is on the axis of P and is independent of the choice of P_1, P_2, P_3.

If the line OR meets S^2 in two points Q_1Q_2, R (Q_1Q_2, OR) is the cross ratio of Γ.

The involutions correspond to points of the plane at infinity.

Pairs of inverse projectivities correspond to pairs of points having O as mid-point.

Harmonic projectivities (§ 80, Vol. I) of C_∞^2 correspond to points which are conjugate with respect to S^2.

The projectivities of C_∞^2 harmonic to a given projectivity correspond to the points of a plane. Such a set of projectivities may be called a *bundle of projectivities.*

The projectivities common to two bundles correspond to the points of a line and may be called a *pencil* of projectivities.

A pencil of involutions according to this definition is the same as a pencil of involutions according to the definition in § 78, Vol. I.

The product of the projectivities corresponding to points R_1 and R_2, not collinear with O, corresponds to a point R_3 obtained by the following construction: Let l', l'' be the lines of R_1^2 through the points in which OR_1 meets S^2, and let m', m'' be the lines of R_2^2 through the points in which OR_2 meets S^2. The line through R_1 meeting m' and m'' intersects the line through R_2 meeting l' and l'' in the point R_3. If l' and l'' coincide, the line meeting them is understood to be tangent to S^2, and a similar convention is adopted in case m' and m'' coincide.

If R_1 be regarded as fixed and R_2 as variable, R_3 is connected with R_2 by the relation

$$R_3 = \Lambda(R_2),$$

where Λ is a projective collineation leaving the lines l', l'' pointwise invariant. In case $l' = l''$, Λ is a collineation of the type in which all points and planes on l' are invariant and each plane on l' is transformed by an elation whose center is the point of contact of this plane with S^2.

If R_3 be regarded as fixed and R_1 as variable, the transformation defined by the relation

$$R_2 = \Delta(R_1)$$

is a collineation interchanging the reguli R_1^2 and R_2^2, and carrying each line l of R_1^2 into the line m of R_2^2 in the plane $R_3 l$, and each line m of R_2^2 into the line l of R_1^2 in the plane Om.

The propositions above are derivable from Assumptions A, E, P. In a real space we have

The rotations represented by points of a line all carry a certain ray with O as origin to a certain other ray with O as origin. Conversely, all rotations carrying a given ray with O as origin to a second ray with O as origin are represented by points of a line.

The necessary and sufficient condition that two rotations P_1, P_2 be harmonic is that there exists a ray r such that $\mathrm{P}_1(r)$ is opposite to $\mathrm{P}_2(r)$.

The representation of rotations by points given in § 124 is identical with the one given in this section, in case S^2 is imaginary. In case S^2 is real, the real points of space represent imaginary rotations.

If S^2 is a ruled quadric and C_∞^2 a real conic, the construction above gives a representation of the real projectivities of a one-dimensional form by the points of space not on S^2. The sets of points $[D]$ and $[O]$ representing the direct and opposite projectivities respectively are such that any two points of the same set can be joined by a segment consisting of points of this set, whereas any segment joining a D to an O contains a point of S^2. The sets $[D]$ and $[O]$ are called the two *sides* of S^2.

EXERCISES

1. Study the configuration formed by the points representing the rotations which carry into itself (*a*) a regular tetrahedron; (*b*) a cube; (*c*) a regular icosahedron. (Cf. Stéphanos, loc. cit., p. 348.)

2. A real quadric (ruled or not) determines two sets of points, its *sides*, such that two points of the same side can be joined by a segment consisting entirely of points of this side and such that any segment joining two points of different sides contains one point of the quadric. If the quadric is not ruled, one and only one of its sides contains all points of a plane. This side is called the *outside* or *exterior*, and the other the *inside* or *interior*.

130. Parameter representation of displacements. Simple algebraic considerations will enable us to extend the parameter representation of rotations considered in the sections above so as to cover the case of displacements in general. We will suppose the general displacement given in the form

$$
\begin{aligned}
x_0' &= a_{00}x_0,\\
x_1' &= a_{10}x_0 + a_{11}x_1 + a_{12}x_2 + a_{13}x_3,\\
x_2' &= a_{20}x_0 + a_{21}x_1 + a_{22}x_2 + a_{23}x_3,\\
x_3' &= a_{30}x_0 + a_{31}x_1 + a_{32}x_2 + a_{33}x_3,
\end{aligned} \tag{57}
$$

where the matrix $(a_{11}a_{22}a_{33})$ is orthogonal. According to § 126, if $a_{10} = a_{20} = a_{30} = 0$, the matrix of (57) is expressible in the form $A\bar{A}$, A and $\bar{A}$ being defined at the bottom of page 336.

Now observe that if

$$
B = \begin{pmatrix} 2\beta_0 & 0 & 0 & 0\\ 2\beta_1 & 0 & 0 & 0\\ 2\beta_2 & 0 & 0 & 0\\ 2\beta_3 & 0 & 0 & 0 \end{pmatrix}, \tag{58}
$$

and C is any four-rowed matrix, $C \cdot B$ is a matrix in which all elements except those of the first column are zero. From this it follows that $A(\bar{A}-B)$ will be of the form (57). In fact, if we require also that

$$\alpha_0\beta_0+\alpha_1\beta_1+\alpha_2\beta_2+\alpha_3\beta_3=0, \tag{59}$$

we have

$$\begin{pmatrix} \alpha_0 & \alpha_1 & \alpha_2 & \alpha_3 \\ -\alpha_1 & \alpha_0 & -\alpha_3 & \alpha_2 \\ -\alpha_2 & \alpha_3 & \alpha_0 & -\alpha_1 \\ -\alpha_3 & -\alpha_2 & \alpha_1 & \alpha_0 \end{pmatrix} \cdot \begin{pmatrix} \alpha_0-2\beta_0 & -\alpha_1 & -\alpha_2 & -\alpha_3 \\ \alpha_1-2\beta_1 & \alpha_0 & -\alpha_3 & \alpha_2 \\ \alpha_2-2\beta_2 & \alpha_3 & \alpha_0 & -\alpha_1 \\ \alpha_3-2\beta_3 & -\alpha_2 & \alpha_1 & \alpha_0 \end{pmatrix}$$

$$=\begin{pmatrix} \alpha_2^0+\alpha_1^2+\alpha_2^2+\alpha_3^2 & 0 & 0 & 0 \\ 2(\alpha_1\beta_0-\alpha_0\beta_1+\alpha_3\beta_2-\alpha_2\beta_3) & \alpha_0^2+\alpha_1^2-\alpha_2^2-\alpha_3^2 & 2(\alpha_1\alpha_2-\alpha_0\alpha_3) & 2(\alpha_1\alpha_3+\alpha_0\alpha_2) \\ 2(\alpha_2\beta_0-\alpha_3\beta_1-\alpha_0\beta_2+\alpha_1\beta_3) & 2(\alpha_1\alpha_2+\alpha_0\alpha_3) & \alpha_0^2+\alpha_2^2-\alpha_1^2-\alpha_3^2 & 2(\alpha_2\alpha_3-\alpha_0\alpha_1) \\ 2(\alpha_3\beta_0+\alpha_2\beta_1-\alpha_1\beta_2-\alpha_0\beta_3) & 2(\alpha_1\alpha_3-\alpha_0\alpha_2) & 2(\alpha_2\alpha_3+\alpha_0\alpha_1) & \alpha_0^2+\alpha_3^2-\alpha_1^2-\alpha_2^2 \end{pmatrix}.$$

Hence the coefficients of (57) are given in terms of two sets of homogeneous parameters $\alpha_0, \alpha_1, \alpha_2, \alpha_3$; $\beta_0, \beta_1, \beta_2, \beta_3$ by the equations (40), together with $a_{00}=1$ and

$$\begin{aligned} a_{10}&=2(\alpha_1\beta_0-\alpha_0\beta_1+\alpha_3\beta_2-\alpha_2\beta_3)A, \\ a_{20}&=2(\alpha_2\beta_0-\alpha_3\beta_1-\alpha_0\beta_2+\alpha_1\beta_3)A, \\ a_{30}&=2(\alpha_3\beta_0+\alpha_2\beta_1-\alpha_1\beta_2-\alpha_0\beta_3)A, \end{aligned} \tag{60}$$

provided that the α's and β's are connected by the relation (59). Conversely, the α's and β's are determined by the coefficients of (57) according to the equations (41) and the following:

$$\begin{aligned} \beta_0:\beta_1:\beta_2:\beta_3 &= a_{10}(a_{32}-a_{23})+a_{20}(a_{13}-a_{31})+a_{30}(a_{21}-a_{12}): \\ &-a_{10}(1+a_{11}+a_{22}+a_{33})-a_{20}(a_{21}-a_{12})+a_{30}(a_{13}-a_{31}): \\ &a_{10}(a_{21}-a_{12})-a_{20}(1+a_{11}+a_{22}+a_{33})-a_{30}(a_{32}-a_{23}): \\ &-a_{10}(a_{13}-a_{31})+a_{20}(a_{32}-a_{23})-a_{30}(1+a_{11}+a_{22}+a_{33}). \end{aligned} \tag{61}$$

The last equations are obtained by solving (59) and (60) simultaneously for the β's and substituting the values of the a's given by (41).

It remains to find the formulas for the parameters ($\alpha_0'', \alpha_1'', \alpha_2'', \alpha_3''$; $\beta_0'', \beta_1'', \beta_2'', \beta_3''$) of a displacement Δ'' which is such that $\Delta''=\Delta'\cdot\Delta$, where Δ has the parameters ($\alpha_0, \alpha_1, \alpha_2, \alpha_3$; $\beta_0, \beta_1, \beta_2, \beta_3$) and Δ' the parameters ($\alpha_0', \alpha_1', \alpha_2', \alpha_3'$; $\beta_0', \beta_1', \beta_2', \beta_3'$).

We have seen that the matrix of Δ is of the form $A(\bar{A}-B)$, where A and $\bar{A}$ are of the form given at the bottom of page 336 and B is given by (58). In like manner Δ' can be expressed in the analogous form $A'(\bar{A}'-B')$ and Δ'' in the form $A''(\bar{A}''-B'')$. Since the β's do not enter into any coefficients of (57) except a_{10}, a_{20}, a_{30}, it is clear that α_0'', α_1'', α_2'', α_3'' are given by the formulas (32), or, in other words, that $A''=A'A$. By definition,

$$\begin{aligned} A''(\bar{A}''-B'') &= A'(\bar{A}'-B')A(\bar{A}-B) \\ &= A'\bar{A}'A\bar{A}-A'\bar{A}'AB-A'B'A\bar{A}+A'B'AB. \end{aligned}$$

In view of (59), the elements of the first row of AB are all zero. Hence all the elements of $B'AB$ are zeros. Hence

$$A'B'AB=0.$$

Since A and $\bar{A}'$ are the matrices of transformations of two conjugate reguli, each transformation leaving all the lines of the other regulus invariant, they are commutative. Hence

$$A''(\bar{A}''-B'')=A'A\bar{A}'\bar{A}-A'A\bar{A}'B-A'AA^{-1}B'A\bar{A}.$$

But
$$A^{-1}=A^{*}\cdot\frac{1}{\alpha_0^2+\alpha_1^2+\alpha_2^2+\alpha_3^2},$$

where
$$A^{*}=\begin{pmatrix} \alpha_0 & -\alpha_1 & -\alpha_2 & -\alpha_3 \\ \alpha_1 & \alpha_0 & \alpha_3 & -\alpha_2 \\ \alpha_2 & -\alpha_3 & \alpha_0 & \alpha_1 \\ \alpha_3 & \alpha_2 & -\alpha_1 & \alpha_0 \end{pmatrix},$$

and
$$B'A\bar{A}=B'\cdot(\alpha_0^2+\alpha_1^2+\alpha_2^2+\alpha_3^2).$$

Hence

$$A''(\bar{A}''+B'')=A'A(\bar{A}'\bar{A}-\bar{A}'B-A^{*}B'). \tag{62}$$

Since $A''=A'A$ and $\bar{A}''=\bar{A}'\bar{A}$, it follows that

$$B''=\bar{A}'B+A^{*}B'. \tag{63}$$

Hence

$$\begin{aligned} \beta_0'' &= \alpha_0'\beta_0-\alpha_1'\beta_1-\alpha_2'\beta_2-\alpha_3'\beta_3+\alpha_0\beta_0'-\alpha_1\beta_1'-\alpha_2\beta_2'-\alpha_3\beta_3', \\ \beta_1'' &= \alpha_1'\beta_0+\alpha_0'\beta_1-\alpha_3'\beta_2+\alpha_2'\beta_3+\alpha_1\beta_0'+\alpha_0\beta_1'+\alpha_3\beta_2'-\alpha_2\beta_3', \\ \beta_2'' &= \alpha_2'\beta_0+\alpha_3'\beta_1+\alpha_0'\beta_2-\alpha_1'\beta_3+\alpha_2\beta_0'-\alpha_3\beta_1'+\alpha_0\beta_2'+\alpha_1\beta_3', \\ \beta_3'' &= \alpha_3'\beta_0-\alpha_2'\beta_1+\alpha_1\beta_2+\alpha_0\beta_3+\alpha_3\beta_0'+\alpha_2\beta_1'-\alpha_1\beta_2'+\alpha_0\beta_3'. \end{aligned} \tag{64}$$

Rewriting (32) in our present notation, we also have

$$(65)\quad \begin{aligned} \alpha_0'' &= \alpha_0'\alpha_0 - \alpha_1'\alpha_1 - \alpha_2'\alpha_2 - \alpha_3'\alpha_3, \\ \alpha_1'' &= \alpha_0'\alpha_1 + \alpha_1'\alpha_0 + \alpha_2'\alpha_3 - \alpha_3'\alpha_2, \\ \alpha_2' &= \alpha_0'\alpha_2 - \alpha_1'\alpha_3 + \alpha_2'\alpha_0 + \alpha_3'\alpha_1, \\ \alpha_3' &= \alpha_0'\alpha_3 + \alpha_1'\alpha_2 - \alpha_2'\alpha_1 + \alpha_3'\alpha_0. \end{aligned}$$

The formulas (64) and (65) can be put into a very convenient form by means of the notation of biquaternions.* Let us define a biquaternion as any element of a number system whose elements are expressions of the form

$$(66)\quad s = (\alpha_0 + \alpha_1 i + \alpha_2 j + \alpha_3 k) + \epsilon(\beta_0 + \beta_1 i + \beta_2 j + \beta_3 k),$$

where the α's and β's are numbers of the geometric number system, i, j, k are subject to the multiplication table (52), and ϵ is subject to the rules

$$\epsilon^2 = 0, \qquad \epsilon x = x\epsilon,$$

where x is any other element, and where the elements (66) are added and multiplied according to the usual rules for addition and multiplication of polynomials.

If the product of s and s', where

$$s' = (\alpha_0' + \alpha_1' i + \alpha_2' j + \alpha_3' k) + \epsilon(\beta_0' + \beta_1' i + \beta_2' j + \beta_3' k),$$

be denoted by

$$s'' = s' \cdot s = (\alpha_0'' + \alpha_1'' i + \alpha_2'' j + \alpha_3'' k) + \epsilon(\beta_0'' + \beta_1'' i + \beta_2'' j + \beta_3'' k),$$

the $\alpha_0'', \cdots, \beta_3''$ are given by the formulas (64) and (65).

For a more complete study of the parameter representation of displacements, see E. Study, Geometrie der Dynamen (particularly II, § 21), Leipzig, 1903.

EXERCISES

1. The parameters of a twist may be taken so that α_1, α_2, α_3 are the direction cosines of the axis of the twist; $\alpha_0 = \cot\theta$, where 2θ is the angle of rotation; and $\beta_0 = d$, where $2d$ is the distance of translation.

2. Find the equations of T_1, T_2, Γ, N, etc. as defined in the exercises of § 123.

***3.** Find a parameter representation for the displacements in a plane which is analogous to the one studied above (cf. Study, Leipziger Berichte, Vol. XLI (1889), p. 222).

* W. K. Clifford, Preliminary Sketch of Biquaternions, Mathematical Papers (London, 1882), p. 181. The system of biquaternions here used is one of the three systems of hypercomplex numbers known by this name. See § 146, below.

GENERAL EXERCISES

Classify each theorem in this list of exercises according to the type of projective space in which it may be valid and according to the geometry to which it belongs.

1. A homology whose plane of fixed points is ideal is called a *dilation* or *expansion*. Any transformation of the Euclidean group is either a displacement or a dilation or the product of a rotation by a dilation.

2. Any transformation of the Euclidean group leaves at least one line invariant.

3. Any transformation of the Euclidean group is either a displacement or a dilation or the product of a displacement by a dilation whose center is on a fixed line of the displacement.

4. Let l be a line which is invariant under a transformation Γ of the Euclidean group, and let k be the characteristic cross ratio (§ 73, Vol. I) of the projectivity effected by Γ on l. Γ is a displacement or symmetry if and only if $k = \pm 1$.

5. Any transformation of the Euclidean group which alters sense can be expressed as a product $\Delta P \Lambda$, where Δ is a dilation or the identity, P an orthogonal plane reflection, Λ an orthogonal line reflection or the identity.

6. If two triangles in different planes are perspective, and the plane of one be rotated about the axis of perspectivity, the center of perspectivity will describe a circle in a plane perpendicular to the axis of perspectivity (Cremona, Projective Geometry, Chap. XI).

7. The planes tangent to the circle at infinity constitute a degenerate plane quadric. With any real nondegenerate quadric this determines a range of quadrics, i.e. a family of quadrics of the form

$$f(u_1, u_2, u_3) + \lambda(u_1^2 + u_2^2 + u_3^2) = 0,$$

where $f(u_1, u_2, u_3)$ is the equation in plane coördinates of the given quadric. This is called a *confocal system of quadrics*. Besides the circle at infinity this range contains three other degenerate quadrics, an imaginary ellipse, a real ellipse, and a hyperbola. There is one quadric of the range tangent to any plane of space. There are three quadrics of the range through any point of space, and their tangent planes at this point are mutually orthogonal.

8. Let $[l]$ and $[m]$ be two bundles of lines related by a projective transformation Γ. There is one and, in general, only one set of three mutually perpendicular lines l_1, l_2, l_3 transformed by Γ to three mutually perpendicular lines m_1, m_2, m_3. There are two real pencils of lines in $[l]$ which are transformed by Γ into congruent pencils of $[m]$. What special cases arise? Cf. Encyclopédie des Sc. Math., III, 8, § 9.

9. Let Γ be a collineation of space. The planes $\Gamma(\pi_\infty)$ and $\Gamma^{-1}(\pi_\infty)$ are called the *vanishing planes* of Γ. Through each point of space there is a pair of lines each of which is transformed by Γ into a congruent line (i.e. pairs of points go into congruent pairs). These lines are all parallel to $\Gamma^{-1}(\pi_\infty)$.

10. A collineation Γ which does not leave the plane at infinity invariant determines two systems of confocal quadrics such that the one system is carried by Γ into the other. Cf. § 84 and the references given there.

11. Let T be a direct-similarity transformation of a plane, A_1 a variable point of this plane, $A_2 = \mathrm{T}(A_1)$, and A_3 a point such that the variable triangle $A_1A_2A_3$ is directly similar to a fixed triangle $B_1B_2B_3$. Then the transformations from A_1 to A_3 and from A_2 to A_3 are direct-similarity transformations. Both of these transformations have the same finite fixed elements as T.*

12. Let T be an affine transformation, A_1 a variable point, $A_2 = \mathrm{T}(A_1)$, and A_0 a point such that the ratio A_0A_1/A_0A_2 is constant. The transformation P from A_1 to A_0 is directly similar and has the same fixed elements as T. If T is a similarity transformation, so is P.

13. If T_1 and T_2 are affine transformations, A_0 a variable point, $A_1 = \mathrm{T}_1(A_0)$, $A_2 = \mathrm{T}_2(A_0)$, and A_3 a point such that $A_1A_0A_2A_3$ is a parallelogram, the transformation from A_0 to A_3 is affine.

* On this and the following exercises cf. Encyclopädie der Math. Wiss. III AB 9, pp. 914–915.

CHAPTER VIII

NON-EUCLIDEAN GEOMETRIES

131. Hyperbolic metric geometry in the plane. According to the point of view explained in § 34 there must be a geometry corresponding to the projective group of a conic section. The case of a real conic in a real plane is one of extreme interest because of its close analogy with the Euclidean geometry, as will be seen at once.

DEFINITION. An arbitrary but fixed conic of a plane π is called *the absolute conic* or *the absolute.* The interior of this conic is called the *hyperbolic plane.* Points interior to the conic are called *ordinary points* or *hyperbolic points,* and those on the conic or exterior to it are called *ideal points.* A line consisting entirely of ideal points is called an *ideal line,* and the set of ordinary points on any other line is called an *ordinary line* or a *hyperbolic line.* The group of all projective collineations leaving the absolute conic invariant is called the *hyperbolic (metric) group of the plane,* and the corresponding geometry is called the *hyperbolic plane geometry.*

Let us at first assume only that the plane π is ordered (A, E, S, P). On this basis we have as a consequence the theorems in §§ 74, 75 on the interior of a conic, that the points of an ordinary line satisfy the definition in § 23 of a linear convex region. This determines the meaning of the terms "segment," "ray," "between," "precede," etc. as applied to collinear ordinary points and sets of points in the hyperbolic plane. The ordinal properties of the hyperbolic plane may be summarized as follows:

THEOREM 1. *The hyperbolic plane satisfies Assumptions I–VI given for the Euclidean plane in § 29.*

Proof. Assumptions I, II, III, V are direct consequences of the proposition that the points of an ordinary line constitute a linear convex region. Assumption VI, that the interior of a conic contains at least three noncollinear points, is an obvious consequence of §§ 74, 75.

The hypothesis of Assumption IV is that three points A, B, C are noncollinear and that two other points D and E satisfy the order relations $\{BCD\}$ and $\{CEA\}$. The conclusion is that there exists a point F on the line DE and between A and B. To prove this it is necessary to show (1) that the point of intersection F of the projective lines DE and AB is interior to the absolute conic and (2) that F is between A and B. Let l be a line exterior to the conic, and let its points of intersection with the lines AB, BC, CA respectively be F_∞, D_∞, E_∞. By hypothesis and § 75, the pair DD_∞ is not separated by BC and the pair EE_∞ is separated by AC. Hence, by § 26, the pair FF_∞ is separated by AB. Since F_∞ is exterior to the conic, F is interior (§ 75) and between A and B.

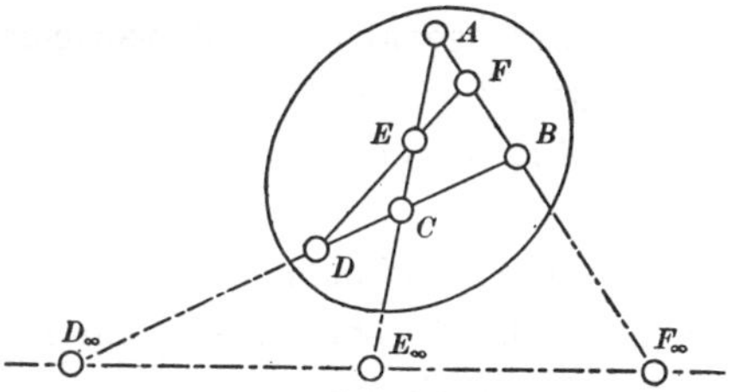

FIG. 77

THEOREM 2. *The hyperbolic plane does not satisfy Assumption IX, § 29. On the contrary, if a is any line and A any point not on a there are infinitely many lines on A and coplanar with a which do not meet a.*

Proof. By § 75 the projective line containing a also contains an infinity of points exterior to the absolute. Any line of the hyperbolic plane contained in the projective line joining A to one of these points fails to meet a.

DEFINITION. If a projective line containing a line a of a hyperbolic plane meets the absolute conic in two points B_∞, C_∞, and A is any ordinary point not on a, the ordinary lines contained in the projective lines AB_∞ and AC_∞ are said to be *parallel* to a. The segments AB_∞ and AC_∞, consisting entirely of points interior to the absolute, constitute, together with A, two rays which are also said to be *parallel* to a.

If the projective plane π be supposed real, the points B_∞ and C_∞ exist for every line a, and hence we have

THEOREM 3. *In the real hyperbolic plane there are two and only two lines which pass through any point A and which are parallel to a line a not on A. There are two and only two rays with A as end parallel to a.*

This theorem of course does not require full use of continuity assumptions. It would also be valid if we assumed merely that any line through an interior point of a conic meets the conic (cf. § 76).

DEFINITION. The points on the absolute are sometimes called *points at infinity* or *infinite points*; and the points exterior to the absolute, *ultra-infinite points.*

132. Orthogonal lines, displacements, and congruence.

DEFINITION. Two lines (or two points) are said to be *orthogonal* or *perpendicular* to each other if they are conjugate with respect to the absolute.

Of two perpendicular points one is, of course, always ultra-infinite, but no analogous statement holds for perpendicular lines. From the corresponding theorems on conics we deduce at once

THEOREM 4. *The pairs of perpendicular lines on an ordinary point are pairs of a direct involution. Through an ordinary point there is one and but one line perpendicular to a given ordinary line.*

DEFINITION. A transformation of π which effects an involution on the absolute conic whose axis contains ordinary points is called an *orthogonal line reflection.* A transformation of π which effects an involution on the absolute conic whose center is an ordinary point is called a *point reflection.* A product of two orthogonal line reflections is called a *displacement.* A product of an odd number of orthogonal line reflections is called a *symmetry.* Two figures such that one can be carried to the other by a displacement are said to be *congruent,* and two figures such that one can be carried to the other by a symmetry are said to be *symmetric.*

An orthogonal line reflection is a harmonic homology whose center and axis are pole and polar with respect to the absolute conic. Since the axis contains an interior point, the center is exterior and the involution effected on the absolute alters sense (§ 74). Conversely, it follows from § 74 that an involution on the absolute conic which alters sense is effected by a harmonic homology whose center is exterior to the absolute conic, — i.e. by an orthogonal line reflection.

Since any direct projectivity is a product of two opposite involutions (§ 74), the displacements as defined above are identical with the projective collineations which transform the absolute conic into itself with preservation of sense. In particular, a point reflection is a displacement. On the other hand, the symmetries are the projective collineations which carry the absolute into itself and interchange the two sense-classes on the absolute.

From these remarks it is evident that the theory of displacements can be obtained from the theorems on projectivities of a conic in Chap. VIII, Vol. I, and in Chap. V, Vol. II. Some of the theorems may also be obtained very easily as projective generalizations of simple Euclidean theorems.

In proving these theorems we shall suppose that we are dealing with the real projective plane and not merely with an ordered plane as in Theorem I. It would be sufficient, however, to assume merely that every opposite involution is hyperbolic (i.e. that every line through an interior point of a conic meets it), for this proposition is the only consequence of the continuity of the real plane which we use in our arguments.

Let us first prove that Assumption X (§ 66) of the Euclidean geometry holds for the hyperbolic geometry. It is to be shown that if A, B are two distinct points, then on any ray c with an end C there is a unique point D such that AB is congruent to CD. The points A and C are the centers of elliptic involutions on the absolute. It is shown in § 76 that one such involution can be transformed into any other by either a direct or an opposite involution. Hence there is a displacement Δ carrying A to C.

The absolute conic may be regarded as a circle C^2 in a Euclidean plane whose line at infinity is the pole of C with regard to the absolute. In this case C is the center of the Euclidean circle, and the hyperbolic displacements are the Euclidean rotations leaving C invariant. The required theorem now follows from the Euclidean proposition that there is one and only one rotation carrying B to a point D of a ray having C as end. The point D is interior to C^2 because B is.

Assumption XI, § 66, holds good in the hyperbolic geometry because the displacements form a group. Assumption XII may be proved for the hyperbolic geometry by the argument used in § 66 for the Euclidean case. The same is true of Assumption XIII if we understand by the mid-point of a pair AB the ordinary point which is harmonically separated by the pair AB from a point conjugate to it with respect to the absolute.

DEFINITION. A *circle* is the set $[P]$ of all points such that the point pairs OP where O is a fixed point are all congruent to a fixed point pair OP_0.

If the absolute be identified, as in the proof of Assumption X above, with a Euclidean circle C^2, and O with its center, it is obvious that the circles of the hyperbolic plane having O as center are identical with the Euclidean circles interior to and concentric with C^2. Hence we obtain from the properties of a pencil of concentric Euclidean circles (§ 71)

THEOREM 5. DEFINITION. *A circle in the hyperbolic plane is a conic entirely interior to the absolute. It touches the absolute in two conjugate imaginary points A, B, and the tangents at these points pass through the center of the circle. The polar of the center passes through A and B and is called the* axis *of the circle. All its real points are exterior to the absolute conic.*

It will be proved in § 134 (Theorem 7, Cor. 1) that two circles can have at most two real points in common. Once this is established, the proof of Assumption XIV in § 66 applies without change to the hyperbolic geometry.

Assumption XV is proved in § 134 as Cor. 2 of Theorem 7.

Assumption XVI may be proved as follows: Let A, B, C be three points in the order $\{ABC\}$, and let P_∞ and Q_∞ be the points in which the line AB meets the absolute conic, the notation being assigned so that we have $\{P_\infty ABCQ_\infty\}$. Let B_1, B_2, B_3, $\cdots$ be points in the order $\{P_\infty ABB_1B_2B_3\cdots\}$ such that AB is congruent to each of the pairs BB_1, B_1B_2, etc. Choose a scale (Chap. VI, Vol. I) in which $P_\infty AQ_\infty$ correspond to 0, 1, ∞ respectively, and let b be the coördinate of B. By the hypothesis about the order relations, $b > 1$. The displacement carrying AB to BB_1 is a projectivity of the line AB which leaves P_∞ and Q_∞ respectively invariant and transforms A to B. Hence it has the equation

$$x' = bx$$

with respect to the scale P_∞, A, Q_∞. The coördinates of B_1, B_2, B_3, $\cdots$ are therefore b^2, b^3, b^4, $\cdots$ respectively. The coördinate of C is, by the hypothesis that $\{ABC\}$, some positive number c greater than b. There are at most a finite number of values of

$b^n (n = 1, 2, \cdots)$ between b and c. Hence there are at most a finite number of the points $B_1, B_2, \cdots$ between B and C. This is what is stated in Assumption XVI.

We have now seen, taking for granted two results which will be proved in § 134, that all the assumptions (cf. §§ 29 and 66) of Euclidean plane geometry except the assumption about parallel lines are satisfied in the real hyperbolic plane, and that the parallel-line assumption is not satisfied.

EXERCISES

1. If corresponding angles of two triangles are congruent, the corresponding sides are congruent.

2. The absence of a theory of similar triangles in hyperbolic geometry is due to what fact about the group of the geometry?

3. The perpendiculars at the mid-points of the sides of a triangle meet in a point (which may be ideal).

***4.** Classify the conic sections from the point of view of hyperbolic geometry.

133. Types of hyperbolic displacements. According to § 77, Vol. I, any displacement has a center and an axis which it leaves invariant. If the center is interior, the axis meets the absolute in two conjugate imaginary points, and the displacement effects an elliptic transformation on the absolute. If the center is exterior, the axis meets the absolute in two real points, and the displacement effects a hyperbolic transformation on the absolute. If the center is on the absolute, the axis is tangent, and the displacement effects a parabolic transformation on the absolute.

In the first case, the points into which a displacement and its powers carry a point distinct from its center are, by definition, on a circle which is transformed into itself by the given rotation.

In the second case, since the displacement is a product of two orthogonal line reflections whose axes pass through the center, it is obvious that the displacement leaves invariant any conic C^2 which touches the absolute in the two points in which it is met by the axis of the displacement. Such a conic is obtained from the absolute by a homology whose center and axis are the center and axis of the displacement in question. From this it follows in an obvious way that C^2 is entirely interior or entirely exterior to the absolute. We are interested in the case in which C^2 is interior.

Let the points of contact of C^2 with the absolute K^2 be P and Q respectively. Since the center of the displacement O and the line PQ are polar with respect to C^2, P and Q are the ends of two segments σ, τ of points of C^2 which are (in the hyperbolic plane) on opposite sides of the line PQ. Any line through O and a point of the hyperbolic plane is perpendicular to PQ and meets σ, PQ, and τ in three points S, M, T respectively. If S', M', T' are the points analogously determined by another line through O, let $\overline{M}$ be the mid-point of the pair MM'. Then the displacement which is the product of the orthogonal line reflection with $O\overline{M}$ as axis by that with OM' as axis carries S, M, T to S', M', T' respectively.

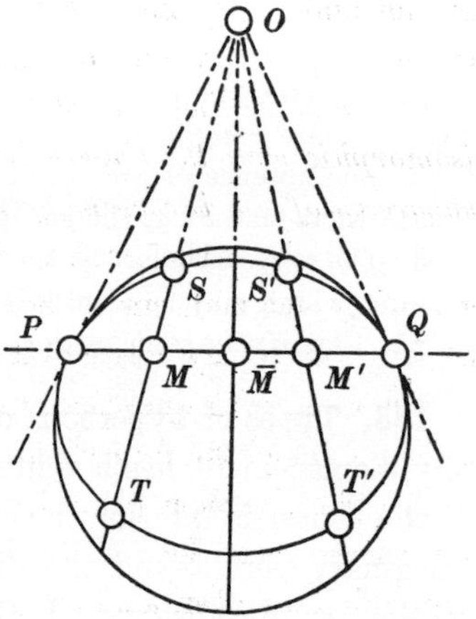

FIG. 78

This result may be expressed by saying that σ is the locus of a point S', on a given side of PQ, such that if M' is the foot of the perpendicular from S' to PQ, $S'M'$ is congruent to SM. For this reason σ and τ are called *equidistantial curves* of PQ.

A point A can be carried into a point B by a displacement leaving a given line l, not on A, invariant, if and only if the two points are on the same equidistantial curve of l. The equidistantial curves have some of the properties of parallel lines in the Euclidean geometry.

A displacement which effects a parabolic transformation on the absolute is a product of two orthogonal line reflections whose axes intersect in the center O of the displacement. Hence the displacement leaves invariant any conic which has contact of the third order (see § 47, Vol. I) with the absolute at O. And by the same reasoning as employed in the second case, a point P can be transformed into a point P' by a displacement which is parabolic on the absolute with a fixed point at O if and only if P and P' are on a conic having contact of the third order with the absolute at O.

DEFINITION. A conic interior to the absolute and having contact of the third order with it is called a *horocycle*.

The circles, equidistantial curves, and horocycles are all *path curves* of one-parameter groups of rotations.

134. Interpretation of hyperbolic geometry in the inversion plane. Although the theory of conics touching a fixed conic in pairs of points has not been taken up explicitly in this book, we have in the inversion geometry a body of theorems from which the part of it needed for our present purpose can be obtained by the principle of transference.

It has been seen in § 94, Theorem 16, that any transformation of the inversion group which carries a circle K^2 into itself effects a projective transformation of this circle into itself. Moreover, there is one and only one direct circular transformation which effects a given projectivity on K^2. Hence *the group of direct circular transformations leaving a circle of the inversion plane invariant is simply isomorphic with the hyperbolic metric group, and the geometry of this subgroup of the inversion group is the hyperbolic geometry.*

The circles orthogonal to K^2 have the property that there is one and only one such circle through each pair of distinct points interior to K^2. Since they also are transformed into themselves by the group which is here in question, it is to be expected that they correspond to the lines of the hyperbolic plane. This may be proved as follows:

Let the inversion plane be represented by a sphere S^2 in a Euclidean three-space. Let K^2 be the circle in which S^2 is met by a plane π through its center, and let us regard the points of π interior to K^2 as a hyperbolic plane. The circles of S^2 orthogonal to K^2 are those in which S^2 is met by planes perpendicular to π. Hence if we let each point P of S^2 on one side of K^2 correspond to the point P' of π such that the line PP' is perpendicular to π, a correspondence Γ is established between the hyperbolic plane and the points on one side of a circle K^2 in the inversion plane in such a way that the lines of the hyperbolic plane correspond to the circles orthogonal to K^2. Moreover, since the direct circular transformations of the inversion plane are effected by three-dimensional collineations leaving S^2 invariant, the direct circular transformations leaving K^2 invariant correspond under Γ to displacements and symmetries of the hyperbolic plane. Thus we have

THEOREM 6. *There is a one-to-one reciprocal correspondence Γ between the points of a hyperbolic plane as defined in § 131 and the points on one side of a circle K^2 in an inversion plane (or inside a circle of the Euclidean plane) in which sets of collinear points of the* *hyperbolic plane correspond to sets of points on circles orthogonal to K^2, and in which displacements and symmetries of the hyperbolic plane correspond to direct circular transformations leaving K^2 invariant.*

THEOREM 7. *In the correspondence Γ the circles of the hyperbolic plane correspond to circles of the inversion plane which are entirely on one side of K^2.*

Proof. Let C^2 be any circle entirely on one side of K^2, and let O and O' be the two points which are inverse with respect to both K^2 and C^2, i.e. the limiting points of the pencil of circles containing C^2 and K^2 (§§ 71, 96). In the Euclidean plane obtained by omitting O' from the inversion plane, O is the center of both K^2 and C^2, and hence the direct circular transformations leaving K^2 and C^2 invariant are the rotations about O and the orthogonal line reflections whose axes are on O. These correspond under Γ to the displacements and symmetries of the hyperbolic plane which leave O invariant. Hence the points of C^2 correspond to a circle of the hyperbolic plane.

Since any circle of the hyperbolic plane may be displaced into one whose center corresponds under Γ to O, the argument just made shows that every circle of the hyperbolic plane may be obtained as the correspondent under Γ of a circle of the inversion plane which is interior to K^2.

This theorem enables us to carry over a large body of theorems on circles from the Euclidean geometry to the hyperbolic. For example, we have at once the following corollaries:

COROLLARY 1. *Two circles in the hyperbolic plane can have at most two real points in common.*

COROLLARY 2. *If the line joining the centers of two circles in the hyperbolic plane meets them in pairs of points which separate each other, the circles meet in two points, one on each side of the line.*

The first of these corollaries, on comparison with Theorem 5, yields the following projective theorem: *Two conics interior to a real conic and touching it in pairs of conjugate imaginary points can have at most two real points in common, and always have two conjugate imaginary points in common.*

THEOREM 8. *In the correspondence Γ equidistantial curves of the hyperbolic plane correspond to those portions of circles intersecting K^2, not orthogonally, which are on one side of K^2. Two equidistantial* *curves which are parts of one conic in the hyperbolic plane are parts of circles inverse to each other with respect to* K^2.

Proof. A circle K_1^2 of S^2 which intersects K^2 in two points P, Q without being perpendicular to it is a section of S^2 by a plane not perpendicular to π. The correspondence Γ transforms this circle into a conic section C^2 in π which is the projection of K_1^2 from the point at infinity of a line perpendicular to π. The tangents to K_1^2 at P and Q are transformed into tangents to K^2. Hence C^2 touches K^2 at P and Q.

The portions of K_1^2 on the two sides of K^2 on S^2 correspond to the two segments of C^2 having P and Q as ends; but only one of these portions of K_1^2 is on the side of K^2 which is in correspondence with the hyperbolic plane by means of Γ. The segment of C^2 which is not in correspondence with this portion of K_1^2 is evidently in correspondence with a portion of the circle into which K_1^2 is transformed by the three-dimensional orthogonal reflection with π as plane of fixed points.

This proves that the part of any circle K_1^2 of the inversion plane which is on one side of K^2 corresponds under Γ to an equidistantial curve E_1, and that that part of the circle inverse to K_1^2 with respect to K^2 which is on the same side of K^2 corresponds to the equidistantial curve E_2 which is part of the same conic with E_1. That any equidistantial curve is in correspondence with a portion of some circle of the inversion plane is easily proved by an argument like that used in the last theorem.

Corollary 1. *In the correspondence* Γ *a circle touching* K^2 *corresponds to a horocycle of the hyperbolic plane.*

Since each equidistantial curve corresponds to a portion of a circle of the inversion plane, it follows that two equidistantial curves can have at most two real points in common. It must be noted that two conics containing each an equidistantial curve can have four real points in common, since each conic accounts for two equidistantial curves.

In like manner two horocycles can have at most two real points in common, and, still more generally,

Corollary 2. *Two loci each of which is a circle, horocycle, or equidistantial curve can have at most two points in common.*

EXERCISES

1. Show that Γ may be extended so that the ultra-infinite lines of the hyperbolic plane correspond to imaginary circles of the inversion plane which are orthogonal to K^2.

2. Study the theory of pencils of circles, equidistantial curves, and horocycles in the hyperbolic plane by means of the correspondence Γ. (A list of the theorems will be found in an article by E. Ricordi, Giornale di Matematiche, Vol. XVIII (1880), p. 255, and in Chap. XI of Non-Euclidean Geometry by J. L. Coolidge, Oxford, 1909.)

3. Develop the theory of conics touching a fixed conic in pairs of points.

135. Significance and history of non-Euclidean geometry. In proving the two corollaries of Theorem 7 we have completed the proof (§ 132) that the congruence assumptions of § 66 are satisfied in the hyperbolic plane. Combining this result with Theorems 1 and 2, we have

THEOREM 9. *In the real hyperbolic plane geometry, Assumptions I–VI, $\overline{VII}$, X–XVI of the assumptions for Euclidean plane geometry in §§ 29 and 66 are true, and Assumption IX is false.*

COROLLARY. *Assumption XVII of § 29 is true in the hyperbolic plane geometry.*

The existence of the hyperbolic geometry therefore furnishes a proof of the independence* of Assumption IX as an assumption of Euclidean geometry. This assumption is equivalent to, though not identical in form with, Euclid's parallel postulate.† And it is the interest in the parallel postulate which has been the chief historical reason for the development of the hyperbolic geometry.

The question whether the postulate of Euclid was independent or not was raised very early. In fact, the arrangement of propositions in Euclid's Elements shows that he had worked on the question himself. The effort to prove the postulate as a theorem continued for centuries, and in the course of time a considerable number of theorems were shown to be independent of this assumption. Eventually the question arose, what sort of theorems could be proved by taking the contrary of Euclid's assumption as a new assumption.

*Cf. § 2, Vol. I, and § 13, Vol. II.

†Cf. Vol. I, p. 202, of Heath, The Thirteen Books of Euclid's Elements, Cambridge, 1908.

This question seems to have been taken up systematically for the first time by G. Saccheri,* who obtained a large body of theorems on this basis, but seems to have been restrained from drawing, or at least publishing, more radical conclusions by the weight of religious disapproval. The credit for having propounded the body of theorems based on a contradiction of the parallel postulate as a self-consistent mathematical science, i.e. as a non-Euclidean geometry, belongs to J. Bolyai † (1832) and N. I. Lobachevski ‡ (1829), although many of the ideas involved seem to have been already in the possession of C. F. Gauss.§ It was not, however, until it had been shown by Beltrami ‖ that the hyperbolic plane geometry could be regarded as the geometry of a pseudospherical surface in Euclidean space, that an independence proof (cf. Introduction, Vol. I) for the parallel assumption could be said to have been given. The work of Beltrami depends on the investigation by Riemann ¶ of the differential geometry ideas at the basis of geometry (1854). Riemann seems to deserve the credit for the discovery of the elliptic geometry (§§ 141–143 below), though it is not clear that he distinguished between the two types of elliptic geometry.**

The proof of the existence of a non-Euclidean geometry was made capable of a simpler form by the discovery of A. Cayley †† (1859) that a metric geometry can be built up, using a conic as absolute. The relation of Cayley's work to other branches of geometry and the previous studies of non-Euclidean geometry was made plain by F. Klein ‡‡ in connection with his elucidation of the rôle of groups in geometry. The representation of the hyperbolic plane by means of the interior

* Euclides ab omni naevo vindicatus, Milan, 1733. German translation in "Die Theorie der Parallellinien von Euklid bis auf Gauss," by F. Engel and P. Staeckel, Leipzig, 1896.

† English translation by G. B. Halsted, under the title "The Science Absolute of Space," 4th ed., Austin, Texas, 1896.

‡ German translation by Engel, under the title "Zwei geometrische Abhandlungen," Leipzig, 1898. Cf. also a translation by Halsted of another work entitled "The Theory of Parallels," Austin, Texas, 1892.

§ Werke, Vol. VIII, pp. 157–268.

‖ Saggio di interpretazione della geometria non-euclidea, Giornale di Matematiche, Vol. VI (1868), p. 284.

¶ English translation by W. K. Clifford, in Nature, Vol. VIII (1873), and in Clifford's "Mathematical Papers" (London, 1882), p. 55.

** Cf. F. Klein, Autographierte Vorlesungen über nicht-euklidische Geometrie, Vol. I (Göttingen, 1892), p. 287.

†† Collected Works, Vol. II (Cambridge, 1889), p. 583.

‡‡ Mathematische Annalen, Vol. IV (1871), p. 573.

of a circle (§ 134), and the representation of the elliptic plane given in Ex. 12, § 141, are due to R. De Paolis* and H. Poincaré.†

For the history of non-Euclidean geometry and an exposition of parts of it, the reader is referred to R. Bonola, Non-Euclidean Geometry, English translation by H. S. Carslaw, Chicago, 1912. Other texts in English are J. L. Coolidge, Non-Euclidean Geometry, Oxford, 1909; Manning, Non-Euclidean Geometry, Boston, 1901; D. M. Y. Sommerville, The Elements of Non-Euclidean Geometry, London, 1914; H. S. Carslaw, The Elements of Non-Euclidean Plane Geometry and Trigonometry, London, 1916. Besides these we may mention D. M. Y. Sommerville's Bibliography of Non-Euclidean Geometry, London, 1911.

There are numerous other geometries closely related to the non-Euclidean geometries touched on in this chapter. Of particular interest are the geometries associated with Hermitian forms investigated by G. Fubini (Atti del Reale Istituto Veneto, Vol. LXIII (1904), p. 501) and E. Study,‡ and the geometry of the Physical Theory of Relativity.§

136. Angular measure. The measure of angles may be defined precisely as in the Euclidean geometry, and we carry over the definitions and theorems of § 69 without modification. If we represent the absolute and an arbitrary point O by a Euclidean circle C^2 and its center, the Euclidean rotations about O are identical with the hyperbolic rotations about O, and hence the two angular measures as determined by the method of § 69 are identical. By § 72, if a and b are two lines intersecting in O, and θ is the measure of the smallest angle $\measuredangle AOB$ for which A is a point of a and B a point of b,

$$\theta = -\frac{i}{2}\log \text{R}(ab,\, i_1 i_2), \tag{1}$$

where i_1 and i_2 are the minimal lines through O. Since i_1 and i_2 are the tangents to C^2 through O, it follows that (1) may be taken as the formula for the measure of any ordered pair of lines a, b in the

* Atti della R. Accademia dei Lincei, Ser. 3, Vol. II (1877–1878), p. 31.

† Acta Mathematica, Vol. I (1882), p. 8, and Bulletin de la Société mathématique de France, Vol. XV (1887), p. 203.

‡ Mathematische Annalen, Vol. LX (1905), p. 321.

§ Cf. F. Klein, Jahresbericht der Deutschen Mathematiker-Vereinigung, Vol. XIX (1910), p. 281, and the article by Wilson and Lewis referred to in § 48 above.

hyperbolic plane if i_1 and i_2 are understood to be the tangents to the absolute through the point of intersection of a and b.

If the hyperbolic plane is represented as in § 134 by the interior of a circle C^2, the angular measure of any two hyperbolic lines is identical with the Euclidean measure of the angle (§ 93) between the two circles orthogonal to C^2 which represent them. This has just been seen for the case where the two circles are lines through the center of C^2. In the general case a point A of intersection of the two circles orthogonal to C^2 may be transformed to the center of C^2 by a direct circular transformation Λ. The transformation Λ as a direct circular transformation leaves Euclidean angular measure invariant (§ 93), and as a displacement of the hyperbolic plane leaves hyperbolic angular measure invariant. Since the two measures are identical at the center of C^2, they must also be identical at A.

As an application of this result we may prove the following remarkable theorem:

THEOREM 10. *The sum of the angles of a triangle is less than π.*

Proof. Let the triangle be ABC, and let the absolute and the point A be represented by a Euclidean circle C^2 and its center. Then the hyperbolic lines AB and AC are represented by Euclidean lines through the center of C^2, and the hyperbolic line BC is represented by a circle K^2 through B and C orthogonal to C^2 (fig. 79).

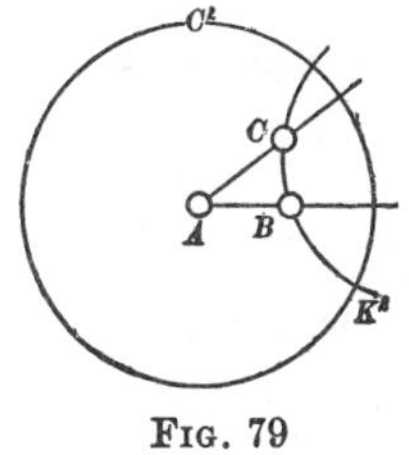

FIG. 79

The hyperbolic measures of the angles at A, B, and C respectively are equal to the Euclidean measures of $\measuredangle BAC$ and two angles formed by AB and AC with the tangents to K^2 at B and C respectively. The sum of these three angles is easily seen to be less than that of the angles of the Euclidean (rectilineal) triangle ABC. Hence it is less than π.

The theorem that the sum of the angles of a triangle is π may be substituted for Assumption IX as an assumption of Euclidean geometry;* the proposition just proved can be taken as the corresponding assumption of hyperbolic geometry; and the proposition that the sum of the angles of a triangle is greater than π can be taken as an assumption for elliptic geometry.

* On the history of this theorem cf. Bonola, loc. cit., Chap. II. This reference will also be found useful in connection with the exercises.

EXERCISES

*__1.__ Prove from Assumptions I–VI, X–XVI that if the sum of the angles of one triangle is greater than, equal to, or less than π, the corresponding statement also holds for all other triangles.

*__2.__ Prove from Assumptions I–VI, X–XVI that the sum of the angles of a triangle is less than or equal to π.

137. Distance. Since the conic section is a self-dual figure, it is to be expected that the formula for the measure of point-pairs is analogous to (1). As a matter of fact, we shall only modify the factor $-i/2$. If A and B are two ordinary points, let A_∞, B_∞ be the points in which the line AB meets the absolute, the notation being assigned so that the points are in the order $\{A_\infty ABB_\infty\}$. Then $R(AB, A_\infty B_\infty)$ is positive (§ 24), and hence $\log R(AB, A_\infty B_\infty)$ has a real value. We define the distance between A and B by means of the equation

$$\text{Dist}(AB) = \gamma \log R(AB, A_\infty B_\infty), \tag{2}$$

where γ is an arbitrary constant and the real determination of the logarithm is taken.

It is seen at once that

$$\text{Dist}(AB) = \text{Dist}(BA),$$

because

$$R(AB, A_\infty B_\infty) = R(BA, B_\infty A_\infty),$$

and that if A, B, C are collinear points in the order $\{ABC\}$,

$$\text{Dist}(AB) + \text{Dist}(BC) = \text{Dist}(AC),$$

because

$$R(AB, A_\infty B_\infty) \cdot R(BC, A_\infty B_\infty) = R(AC, A_\infty B_\infty).$$

Moreover, it is evident from the properties of the collineations transforming a conic into itself that a necessary and sufficient condition for the congruence of two point-pairs AB, CD is

$$R(AB, A_\infty B_\infty) = R(CD, C_\infty D_\infty),$$

where A_∞, B_∞ are chosen as above and C_∞, D_∞ are chosen analogously. Hence a necessary and sufficient condition for the congruence of AB and CD is

$$\text{Dist}(AB) = \text{Dist}(CD).$$

Hence the distance function defined above is fully analogous to that used in Euclidean geometry (§ 67). The constant γ may be determined by choosing a fixed point-pair OP as the unit of distance. We then have

$$\frac{1}{\gamma} = \log R(OP, O_\infty P_\infty). \tag{3}$$

138. Algebraic formulas for distance and angle. Let us consider the symmetric bilinear form

$$\begin{aligned} f(X, X') = {} & a_{00}x_0x_0' + a_{01}x_0x_1' + a_{02}x_0x_2' \\ & + a_{01}x_1x_0' + a_{11}x_1x_1' + a_{12}x_1x_2' \\ & + a_{02}x_2x_0' + a_{12}x_2x_1' + a_{22}x_2x_2' \end{aligned}$$

and the covariant form

$$\begin{aligned} F(u, u') = {} & A_{00}u_0u_0' + A_{01}u_0u_1' + A_{02}u_0u_2' \\ & + A_{01}u_1u_0' + A_{11}u_1u_1' + A_{12}u_1u_2' \\ & + A_{02}u_2u_0' + A_{12}u_2u_1' + A_{33}u_2u_2', \end{aligned}$$

where the A_{ij}'s are defined as in § 85. With respect to homogeneous coördinates, $f(X, X) = 0$ is the equation of a point conic, and $F(u, u) = 0$ of the line conic composed of the tangents to $f(X, X) = 0$. Let us take this conic as the absolute and derive the formulas for the measure of distance and of angle.

Let $Y = (y_0, y_1, y_2)$ and $Z = (z_0, z_1, z_2)$ be two distinct points. The points of the line joining them are

$$\lambda Y + \mu Z = (\lambda y_0 + \mu z_0, \quad \lambda y_1 + \mu z_1, \quad \lambda y_2 + \mu z_2),$$

and the points in which this line meets $f(X, X) = 0$ are determined by the values of λ/μ satisfying the equation

$$0 = f(\lambda Y + \mu Z, \lambda Y + \mu Z) = \lambda^2 f(Y, Y) + 2\lambda\mu f(Y, Z) + \mu^2 f(Z, Z).$$

These values are

$$\frac{\lambda_1}{\mu_1} = \frac{-f(Y, Z) + \sqrt{f^2(Y, Z) - f(Y, Y)f(Z, Z)}}{f(Y, Y)},$$

$$\frac{\lambda_2}{\mu_2} = \frac{-f(Y, Z) - \sqrt{f^2(Y, Z) - f(Y, Y)f(Z, Z)}}{f(Y, Y)}.$$

Let us denote the two points of the absolute corresponding to (λ_1, μ_1) and (λ_2, μ_2) by I_1 and I_2 respectively. Then

$$\text{Dist}(YZ) = \gamma \log R(YZ, I_1I_2).$$

Since (λ, μ) is $(1, 0)$ for Y and $(0, 1)$ for Z, we have (§ 65, Vol. I)

$$R(YZ, I_1I_2) = \frac{\mu_1\lambda_2}{\lambda_1\mu_2}.$$

Hence

$$(4) \qquad \begin{aligned} \text{Dist}(YZ) &= \gamma \log \frac{f(Y, Z) + \sqrt{f^2(Y, Z) - f(Y, Y)f(Z, Z)}}{f(Y, Z) - \sqrt{f^2(Y, Z) - f(Y, Y)f(Z, Z)}} \\ &= \gamma \log \frac{\left(f(Y, Z) + \sqrt{f^2(Y, Z) - f(Y, Y)f(Z, Z)}\right)^2}{f(Y, Y)f(Z, Z)}. \end{aligned}$$

By precisely the same reasoning applied to the dual case we have for the measure of a pair of lines $u=(u_0, u_1, u_2)$, $v=(v_0, v_1, v_2)$.

$$(5)\qquad m(u, v) = -\frac{i}{2}\log\frac{F(u, v)+\sqrt{F^2(u, v)-F(u, u)F(v, v)}}{F(u, v)-\sqrt{F^2(u, v)-F(u, u)F(v, v)}}$$
$$= -\frac{i}{2}\log\frac{\left(F(u, v)+\sqrt{F^2(u, v)-F(u, u)F(v, v)}\right)^2}{F(u, u)F(v, v)}.$$

Denoting Dist(Y, Z) by d, we obtain

$$(6)\qquad e^{\frac{d}{2\gamma}} = \frac{f(Y, Z)+\sqrt{f^2(Y, Z)-f(Y, Y)f(Z, Z)}}{\sqrt{f(Y, Y)f(Z, Z)}},$$

and hence

$$(7)\qquad \cosh\frac{d}{2\gamma} = \frac{e^{\frac{d}{2\gamma}}+e^{-\frac{d}{2\gamma}}}{2} = \sqrt{\frac{f^2(Y, Z)}{f(Y, Y)f(Z, Z)}},$$

and

$$(8)\qquad \sinh\frac{d}{2\gamma} = \frac{e^{\frac{d}{2\gamma}}-e^{-\frac{d}{2\gamma}}}{2} = \sqrt{\frac{f^2(Y, Z)-f(Y, Y)f(Z, Z)}{f(Y, Y)f(Z, Z)}}.$$

In like manner, if $\theta = m(uv)$,

$$(9)\qquad e^{i\theta} = \frac{F(u, v)+\sqrt{F^2(u, v)-F(u, u)F(v, v)}}{\sqrt{F(u, u)F(v, v)}}.$$

$$(10)\qquad \cos\theta = \sqrt{\frac{F^2(u, v)}{F(u, u)F(v, v)}}.$$

$$(11)\qquad \sin\theta = i\sqrt{\frac{F^2(u, v)-F(u, u)F(v, v)}{F(u, u)F(v, v)}}$$
$$= \sqrt{\frac{F(u, u)F(v, v)-F^2(u, v)}{F(u, u)F(v, v)}}.$$

For a further discussion of these formulas see Clebsch-Lindemann, Vorlesungen über Geometrie, Vol. II, Part III, Leipzig, 1891.

***139. Differential of arc.** The homogeneous coördinates of all points not on the absolute,

$$(12)\qquad f(X, X) = 0,$$

may be subjected to the relation

$$(13)\qquad f(X, X) = C,$$

where C is a constant. Since $f(X, X)$ is quadratic, this determines two sets of coördinates (x_0, x_1, x_2) for each point of the hyperbolic plane instead of an infinity of sets as in unrestricted homogeneous coördinates.*

Some definite determination of the values of each of the homogeneous coördinates is manifestly necessary in order to apply the processes of differential calculus to formulas in homogeneous coördinates. The particular relation $f(X, X) = C$ has the advantage, among others, of not being singular for any point not on the absolute.

Suppose now that (x_0, x_1, x_2) describes a locus determined by the condition that x_0, x_1, x_2 are functions of a parameter t. Then, in the familiar notation,†

$$\begin{aligned}\frac{ds}{dt} &= \underset{\Delta t=0}{L} \frac{\text{Dist}\,(X, X+\Delta X)}{\Delta t} \\ &= \underset{\Delta t=0}{L} \frac{2\gamma \sinh \frac{1}{2\gamma} \text{Dist}\,(X, X+\Delta X)}{\Delta t} \\ &= \underset{\Delta t=0}{L} \frac{2\gamma}{\Delta t}\sqrt{\frac{f^2(X, X+\Delta X) - f(X, X)f(X+\Delta X, X+\Delta X)}{f(X, X)f(X+\Delta X, X+\Delta X)}},\end{aligned}$$

by (8). Since $f(Y+Y', Z) = f(Y, Z) + f(Y', Z)$, this reduces to

$$\begin{aligned}\left(\frac{ds}{dt}\right)^2 &= \underset{\Delta t=0}{L} \frac{4\gamma^2}{(\Delta t)^2} \\ &\quad \frac{(f(X,X)+f(X,\Delta X))^2 - f(X,X)(f(X,X)+2f(X,\Delta X)+f(\Delta X,\Delta X))}{f(X,X)\,(f(X,X)+2f(X,\Delta X)+f(\Delta X,\Delta X))} \\ &= \underset{\Delta t=0}{L}\, 4\gamma^2 \frac{f^2\left(X, \frac{\Delta X}{\Delta t}\right) - f(X, X)f\left(\frac{\Delta X}{\Delta t}, \frac{\Delta X}{\Delta t}\right)}{f(X,X)\,(f(X,X)+2f(X,\Delta X)+f(\Delta X,\Delta X))} \\ &= 4\gamma^2 \frac{f^2\left(X, \frac{dX}{dt}\right) - f(X, X)f\left(\frac{dX}{dt}, \frac{dX}{dt}\right)}{f^2(X, X)},\end{aligned}$$

* If (x_0, x_1, x_2) are interpreted as rectangular coördinates in a Euclidean space of three dimensions, $f(X, X) = C$ is the equation of a quadric surface, and we have a correspondence in which each point of the hyperbolic plane corresponds to a pair of points of the quadric surface. By properly choosing $f(X, X)$, this correspondence can be reduced to that given in § 134 between the hyperbolic plane and the surface of a sphere.

† We are applying theorems of calculus here on the same basis that we have employed algebraic theorems in other parts of the work.

in which $\frac{dX}{dt}$ represents $\left(\frac{dx_0}{dt}, \frac{dx_1}{dt}, \frac{dx_2}{dt}\right)$. In differential notation this formula is

$$(14) \qquad ds^2 = 4\,\gamma^2 \frac{f^2(X, dX) - f(X, X)f(dX, dX)}{f^2(X, X)}.$$

By duality we have a corresponding formula for the differential of angle,

$$(15) \qquad d\theta^2 = \frac{F^2(u, du) - F(u, u)\,F(du, du)}{F^2(u, u)}.$$

These formulas are independent of the particular determination of our coördinates by means of the relation (13). If we differentiate (13) we obtain

$$f(X, dX) = 0,$$

so that for this particular determination of coördinates

$$(16) \qquad ds^2 = -4\,\gamma^2 \frac{f(dX, dX)}{f(X, X)} = -4\,\gamma^2 \frac{f(dX, dX)}{C}.$$

Let us now choose the homogeneous cöordinate system so that

$$f(X, X) = x_1^2 + x_2^2 - 4\,\gamma^2 x_0^2,$$

and choose $C = -4\,\gamma^2$ so that, for points not on the absolute,

$$(17) \qquad x_1^2 + x_2^2 - 4\,\gamma^2 x_0^2 = -4\,\gamma^2.$$

If γ is real and not zero, we are dealing with hyperbolic geometry, and

$$(18) \qquad \begin{aligned} ds^2 &= f(dX, dX) \\ &= dx_1^2 + dx_2^2 - 4\,\gamma^2 dx_0^2. \end{aligned}$$

If we substitute $\qquad u = \frac{2\,x_1}{1 + x_0}, \qquad v = \frac{2\,x_2}{1 + x_0}$

in the value for ds^2 given in (18), we obtain

$$(19) \qquad ds^2 = \frac{du^2 + dv^2}{\left[1 - \frac{u^2 + v^2}{16\,\gamma^2}\right]^2}.$$

Regarding u and v as parameters of a surface in a Euclidean space, (19) gives the linear element of the surface (cf. Eisenhart, Differential Geometry, § 30). This is a surface for which, in the usual notation of differential geometry, $E = G$ and $F = 0$. The curvature of this surface is constant and equal to $-1/4\,\gamma^2$ (cf. Clebsch-Lindemann, loc. cit., Vol. II, p. 525). From this it follows that the hyperbolic plane geometry in the neighborhood of any point is equivalent to the geometry on a portion of a surface of constant negative curvature.

If we substitute $u = x_1/x_0$ and $v = x_2/x_0$ in (18), we obtain

$$ds^2 = 4\gamma^2 \frac{(4\gamma^2 - v^2)du^2 + 2\,uv\,du\,dv + (4\gamma^2 - u^2)dv^2}{(4\gamma^2 - u^2 - v^2)^2}.$$

This is the form of linear element used by Beltrami in the paper cited above. This form is such that geodesics are given by linear equations in u and v. Hence geodesics of the surface correspond to lines of the hyperbolic plane.

It is to be noted that the curvature of a surface, while often defined in terms of a Euclidean space in which the surface is supposed to be situated, is a function of E, F, and G and therefore an internal property of the surface, i.e. a property stated in terms of curves ($u = c$ and $v = c$) in the surface and entirely independent of its being situated in a space.

Another remark which may save misunderstanding by a beginner is that the geometries corresponding to real values of γ are identical. The choice of γ amounts to a determination of the unit of length, as was shown in § 137.

EXERCISES

1. Express the differential of angle in terms of (x_0, x_1, x_2) and their derivatives (cf. Clebsch-Lindemann, loc. cit., Vol. II, p. 477).

***2.** Develop the theory of areas in the hyperbolic plane. For a treatment by differential geometry cf. Clebsch-Lindemann, loc. cit., p. 489. For a development by elementary geometry of a theory of areas of polygons which is equally available in hyperbolic, parabolic, and elliptic geometry, see A. Finzel, Mathematische Annalen, Vol. LXXII (1912), p. 262.

140. Hyperbolic geometry of three dimensions. A *hyperbolic space* of three dimensions is the interior (cf. Ex. 2, § 129) of a nonruled quadric surface, called the *absolute quadric*, and the hyperbolic geometry of three dimensions is the set of theorems stating properties of this space which are not disturbed by the projective collineations leaving the quadric invariant. The definitions of the terms "displacement," "congruent," "perpendicular," etc. are obtained by direct generalization of the definition in § 132 and the corresponding definitions in the chapters on Euclidean geometry. They will be taken for granted in what follows, without being formally written down.

The fundamental theorems on congruence may be obtained from the observations (1) that any displacement of space leaving a plane invariant effects in this plane a displacement or a symmetry in the sense of § 132, and (2) that no two displacements of space leaving a plane invariant effect the same displacement or symmetry in this plane. From this we infer, by reference to § 135,

THEOREM 11. *In the real three-dimensional hyperbolic geometry Assumptions I–XVI of §§ 29 and 66 are all true except Assumption IX, which is false.*

By § 100 there is a simple isomorphism between the displacements of a hyperbolic space and the direct circular transformations of the inversion plane. Hence the theorems of inversion geometry or of the theory of projectivities of complex one-dimensional forms can all be translated into theorems of hyperbolic geometry. The reader who carries this out in detail will find that many of the theorems of Chap. VI assume very interesting forms when carried over into the hyperbolic geometry.

In particular, if an *orthogonal line reflection*, or *half turn*, is defined as a line reflection (§ 101) whose directrices are polar with respect to the absolute, it follows at once that every displacement is a product of two orthogonal line reflections. With this basis the theory of displacements is very similar to the corresponding theory in Euclidean geometry, but many of the proofs are simpler.

The formulas for distance and angle are identical with those of § 138, and the differential formulas with those of § 139 if $f(X, X')$ be understood to be a bilinear form in (x_0, x_1, x_2, x_3) and (x'_0, x'_1, x'_2, x'_3).

EXERCISES

1. The product of three half turns is a half turn if and only if their three ordinary directrices have a common intersecting perpendicular line.

2. If a simple hexagon be inscribed in the absolute, the common intersecting perpendicular lines of pairs of opposite edges are met by a common intersecting perpendicular line (cf. § 108).

3. Determine the projectively distinct types of displacements.

***4.** Defining a *horosphere* as a real quadric interior to the absolute and transformable into the absolute by means of an elation whose center is on the absolute and whose plane of fixed points is tangent to the absolute, prove that the hyperbolic geometry of a horosphere is equivalent to the Euclidean plane geometry.

***5.** Classify the quadric surfaces from the point of view of hyperbolic geometry.

***6.** Given the existence of a hyperbolic space, define a set of ideal points such that the extended space is projective. Cf. R. Bonola, Giornale di Matematiche, Vol. XXXVIII (1900), p. 105, and F. W. Owens, Transactions of the American Mathematical Society, Vol. XI (1910), p. 140.

***7.** Obtain theorems analogous to those in the exercises of §§ 122, 123 with regard to the hyperbolic displacements.

***8.** Study the theory of volumes in hyperbolic geometry by methods of differential geometry.

141. Elliptic plane geometry. Definition. The geometry corresponding to the group of projective collineations in a real* projective plane π which leave an imaginary ellipse E^2 invariant is called the *two-dimensional elliptic geometry* or *elliptic plane geometry.* The imaginary conic E^2 is called the *absolute conic* or the *absolute.* The projective plane π is sometimes referred to as the *elliptic plane.*

The order relations in this geometry are of course identical with those of the projective plane (Chap. II). The congruence relations are defined as in § 132, with suitable modifications corresponding to the fact that E^2 is imaginary. Some of the theorems which run parallel to the corresponding theorems of hyperbolic geometry are put down in the following list of exercises.

The formula for the measure of angle used in hyperbolic geometry may be taken over without change, i.e.

$$\theta = m(l_1 l_2) = -\frac{i}{2}\log \text{R}(l_1 l_2,\ i_1 i_2),$$

where l_1 and l_2 are intersecting lines and i_1 and i_2 are tangents to the absolute in the same flat pencil with l_1 and l_2. The formula for distance may also be taken from hyperbolic geometry:

$$d = \text{Dist}(PQ) = \gamma \log \text{R}(PQ,\ P_\infty Q_\infty).$$

In order that this shall give a real value for the distance between two real points, γ must be a pure imaginary. So we write

$$\gamma = -\frac{ki}{2};$$

* This geometry can in large part be developed on the basis of Assumptions A, E, S, P alone, the imaginary conic being replaced by the corresponding elliptic polar system, the existence and properties of which are studied in § 89. As a matter of fact there is considerable interest attached to the elliptic geometry in a modular plane, but the point of view which we are taking in this chapter puts order relations in the foreground.

and in order to have formulas in the simplest possible form, we may choose $k = 1$, so that

$$d = -\frac{i}{2} \log R(PQ, P_\infty Q_\infty).$$

The discussion in § 138 is applicable at once to elliptic geometry if $f(X, X')$ be taken to be a bilinear form in three variables such that $f(X, X) = 0$ is the equation of the absolute of elliptic geometry. Thus we have

$$(20)\quad d = \text{Dist}(YZ) = \frac{-ik}{2} \log \frac{\left(f(Y,Z) + \sqrt{f^2(Y,Z) - f(Y,Y) f(Z,Z)}\right)^2}{f(Y,Y)\, f(Z,Z)},$$

$$(21)\quad \theta = m(uv) = \frac{-i}{2} \log \frac{\left(F(u,v) + \sqrt{F^2(u,v) - F(u,u)\, F(v,v)}\right)^2}{F(u,u)\, F(v,v)},$$

$$(22)\qquad \cos\frac{d}{k} = \sqrt{\frac{f^2(Y,Z)}{f(Y,Y)\, f(Z,Z)}},$$

$$(23)\qquad \cos\theta = \sqrt{\frac{F^2(u,v)}{F(u,u)\, F(v,v)}}.$$

EXERCISES

1. The principle of duality holds good in the elliptic geometry.

2. The elliptic geometry is identical with the set of theorems about the geometry of the plane at infinity in three-dimensional Euclidean geometry.

3. The pairs of perpendicular lines at any point are pairs of an elliptic involution.

4. The lines perpendicular to a line l all meet in the pole of l with respect to the absolute. Through any point except the pole of l there is one and but one line perpendicular to l.

5. Defining a *ray* as a segment whose ends are conjugate with respect to the absolute, prove that Assumption X, § 66, holds in the single elliptic geometry if the restrictions be added that A and B are on the same ray.

6. Assumptions XI and XIII of § 66 hold for single elliptic geometry.

7. How may Assumptions XII, XIV, and XV be modified so as to be valid for single elliptic geometry?

8. A circle is a conic touching the absolute in two conjugate imaginary points.

9. A circle is the locus of a point at a fixed distance from a fixed line.

10. If A, B, C are three collinear points,

$$\text{Dist}(A, B) + \text{Dist}(BC) + \text{Dist}(CA) = \pi.$$

In other words, the total length of a line is π.

11. The sum of the angles of a triangle is less than π.

12. Let K^2 be a circle in a Euclidean plane, and let $[C^2]$ be the set of circles which meet K^2 in pairs of points on its diameters. An elliptic plane is determined by defining as "elliptic points" all the Euclidean points interior to K^2 and all the pairs of Euclidean points in which K^2 is met by its diameters, and defining as collinear any set of elliptic points on a circle C^2.

142. Elliptic geometry of three dimensions. The three-dimensional elliptic geometry is the set of theorems about a three-dimensional projective space which state properties undisturbed by the projective collineations leaving invariant an arbitrary but fixed projective polar system, called the *absolute polar system,* in which no point is on its polar plane. It is a direct generalization of the elliptic geometry of the plane and may be based on a similar set of assumptions.

In a real space this polar system is that of an imaginary quadric (called the *absolute quadric*) with respect to which each real point has a real polar plane, and the equation of the absolute quadric may be taken to be

$$x_0^2 + x_1^2 + x_2^2 + x_3^2 = 0.$$

A *displacement* is defined as a direct* projective collineation (cf. § 32) which leaves the absolute polar system invariant; a *symmetry* is defined as a nondirect projective collineation leaving the absolute polar system invariant. The definitions of congruence, perpendicularity, distance, etc. follow the pattern of the hyperbolic and parabolic geometries, and the same method may be used, as in those geometries, to extend the theorems on congruence from the plane to space.

It can easily be proved by means of the theorems on the quadric in Chap. VI that any displacement is a product of two line reflections whose axes are polar with regard to the absolute. From this proposition a series of theorems on displacements can be derived, just as in the parabolic and hyperbolic geometries.

Through a given point not on a given line l there is no line parallel to l in the sense in which the term is used in parabolic or hyperbolic geometry. There is, however, a generalization of the Euclidean notion of parallelism to elliptic three-dimensional space which preserves many of the properties of Euclidean parallelism and is, if possible, more interesting.

* Without appealing to order relations, the direct collineations may be characterized as those which do not interchange the reguli on the absolute quadric.

Any real line l meets the absolute in two conjugate imaginary points, and through these points there are two lines p_1, p_2 of one regulus and two lines q_1, q_2 of the other regulus. The lines p_1, p_2 are conjugate imaginary lines of the second kind (§ 109), and l is one line of an elliptic congruence of which p_1, p_2 are directrices. A similar remark applies to the conjugate imaginary lines q_1, q_2. Any line of the elliptic congruences having p_1, p_2 or q_1, q_2 as directrices is called a *Clifford parallel** of l or a *paratactic*† of l. Thus there are two Clifford parallels to l through any point not on l, and l is a Clifford parallel to itself.

The two Clifford parallels to any line through any point not on it may be distinguished as follows: Let R_1^2 and R_2^2 be the two reguli on the absolute. Two real lines l, m meeting two conjugate imaginary lines p_1, p_2 of R_1^2 are *right-handed* Clifford parallels, or paratactics; and two real lines l', m' meeting two conjugate imaginary lines q_1, q_2 of R_2^2 are *left-handed* Clifford parallels, or paratactics.

The distinction between right-handed and left-handed Clifford parallels may be drawn entirely in terms of real elements by means of the notion of sense-class (§ 32), and thus connected with the intuitive distinction between right and left. This matter will be taken up again in the next chapter. In the meantime it may be remarked that the definition in terms of the two reguli on the absolute is independent of all question of order relations and is based on Assumptions A, E, P alone.

From the definition it follows immediately that if l is a right-handed Clifford parallel to m, m is a right-handed Clifford parallel to l; that if m is also a right-handed Clifford parallel to n, l is a right-handed Clifford parallel to n. In general, two lines have one and only one common intersecting perpendicular; but if they are right-handed Clifford parallels, there is a regulus of common intersecting perpendiculars, and the latter are all left-handed Clifford parallels.

The product of two orthogonal line reflections whose axes are Clifford parallels leaves each line of the congruence of Clifford parallels perpendicular to the axes invariant, and is called a *translation*. A

* Cf. Clifford, A Preliminary Sketch of Biquaternions, Mathematical Papers (London, 1882), p. 181, and Klein, Autographierte Vorlesungen über nicht-euklidische Geometrie, Vol. II (Göttingen, 1892), p. 245.

† E. Study, Jahresbericht der Deutschen Mathematikervereinigung, Vol. XI (1903), p. 319.

translation is right-handed or left-handed according as the congruence of its invariant lines is right-handed or left-handed. Any displacement can be expressed as a product of two translations.

For a discussion of Clifford parallels and related questions see Appendix II of the book by Bonola referred to above, F. Klein, Mathematische Annalen, Vol. XXXVII (1890), p. 544, and the other references given above in this section.

143. Double elliptic geometry. The geometry corresponding to the group of projective collineations transforming a sphere S^2 in a Euclidean three-space into itself is called *spherical* or *double elliptic plane geometry.* The sphere S is called the *double elliptic plane.* The circles in which S^2 is met by planes through its center are called *lines,* and two figures are said to be *congruent* if conjugate under the group of direct projective collineations transforming the sphere into itself.

The plane which is called elliptic in § 141 is sometimes called *single elliptic* to distinguish it from the double elliptic plane here described. Since the plane at infinity π_∞ of a Euclidean space is a single elliptic plane, and since each line through the center of S^2 meets S^2 in two points and π_∞ in one point, there is a correspondence between a single elliptic plane and a double elliptic plane, in which each point of the first corresponds to a pair of points of the latter. By means of this correspondence any result of either geometry can be carried over into the other geometry.

These remarks can all be generalized to n-dimensions. For a set of assumptions for double elliptic geometry as a separate science, see J. R. Kline, Annals of Mathematics, 2d Ser., Vol. XIX (1916), p. 31.

144. Euclidean geometry as a limiting case of non-Euclidean. In the two-dimensional case we have seen that the equation of the absolute may be taken as

$$x_1^2 + x_2^2 - 4\gamma^2 x_0^2 = 0, \tag{24}$$

or in line coördinates, as

$$\frac{u_0^2}{4\gamma^2} - (u_1^2 + u_2^2) = 0. \tag{25}$$

The formulas of hyperbolic geometry arise if γ is real and not zero, and of elliptic geometry if γ is imaginary. If we set $c = \frac{1}{4\gamma^2} = 0$, (25) may be regarded as the equation of the circle at infinity of the

Euclidean geometry in the form used in § 72. Moreover, if we set $c = 0$ in the formulas of §§ 138 and 141, we obtain

$$\cos\theta = \frac{u_1v_1 + u_2v_2}{\sqrt{(u_1^2 + u_2^2)(v_1^2 + v_2^2)}}$$

and

$$\theta = -\frac{i}{2}\log\frac{u_1v_1 + u_2v_2 + i(u_1v_2 - u_2v_1)}{u_1v_1 + u_2v_2 - i(u_1v_2 - u_2v_1)},$$

which agree with the formulas of Euclidean geometry given in § 72. In like manner, if we set $c = 0$ in the formula for the differential of distance in § 139, we obtain $ds^2 = du^2 + dv^2$. The generalization of these remarks to three or n dimensions is of course obvious.

If c changes by continuous variation from a positive to a negative value, it must pass through zero. Since the corresponding geometry is elliptic while c is positive, parabolic when c is zero, and hyperbolic while c is negative, the parabolic geometry is often spoken of as a limiting case both of elliptic and of hyperbolic geometry.

This point of view is reënforced by observing that the formula (10) makes the measure of a fixed angle a continuous function of c, so that for a small variation of c the value given by (10) for θ suffers a correspondingly small variation. A like remark can be made about the distance between a fixed pair of points.

This has the consequence that for a given figure F consisting of a finite number of points and lines, and for a given number ϵ, a number δ can be found such that if c varies between $-\delta$ and δ, the distance of point-pairs and the angular measure of line-pairs of F do not vary more than ϵ. Nevertheless, in this interval of variation of c the geometry according to which the distances and angles are measured changes from elliptic through parabolic to hyperbolic.

For example, if F were a triangle, and the sum of the angles were found by physical measurement to be between $\pi + \epsilon$ and $\pi - \epsilon$, the geometry according to which the measurements were made might be either parabolic, hyperbolic, or elliptic. Further refinements of experimental methods might decrease ϵ, but according to current physical doctrine could not reduce it to zero. Hence, while experiment might conceivably prove that the geometry at the bottom of the system of measurements was elliptic or hyperbolic, it could not prove it to be parabolic.

For the details of showing that the Euclidean formula for distance is a limiting case of the non-Euclidean formula, see Clebsch-Lindemann, loc. cit., Vol. II, p. 530.

145. Parameter representation of elliptic displacements. Suppose the coördinate system so chosen that the equation of the absolute is

$$x_0^2 + x_1^2 + x_2^2 + x_3^2 = 0.$$

The projective collineations which leave the lines of a regulus on the absolute invariant have been proved to have matrices of the form (50) or (51) in § 126. Let R_1^2 be the regulus on the absolute left invariant by the transformations of type (50), and R_2^2 that left invariant by those of type (51). The transformations of type (50) are the translations leaving systems of right-handed Clifford parallels invariant, and those of type (51) the translations leaving systems of left-handed Clifford parallels invariant.

Since any transformation leaving the quadric invariant is a product of one leaving the lines of R_1^2 invariant by one leaving the lines of R_2^2 invariant, any displacement is a product of a transformation of type (50) by one of type (51). Denoting (50) by A and (51) by B, the matrix Δ of any displacement can be written

$$(26)\quad \Delta = B \cdot A = \begin{pmatrix} \beta_0 & \beta_1 & \beta_2 & \beta_3 \\ -\beta_1 & \beta_0 & \beta_3 & -\beta_2 \\ -\beta_2 & -\beta_3 & \beta_0 & \beta_1 \\ -\beta_3 & \beta_2 & -\beta_1 & \beta_0 \end{pmatrix} \cdot \begin{pmatrix} \alpha_0 & \alpha_1 & \alpha_2 & \alpha_3 \\ -\alpha_1 & \alpha_0 & -\alpha_3 & \alpha_2 \\ -\alpha_2 & \alpha_3 & \alpha_0 & -\alpha_1 \\ -\alpha_3 & -\alpha_2 & \alpha_1 & \alpha_0 \end{pmatrix}$$

$$= \left(\begin{matrix} \beta_0\alpha_0 - \beta_1\alpha_1 - \beta_2\alpha_2 - \beta_3\alpha_3 & \beta_0\alpha_1 + \beta_1\alpha_0 + \beta_2\alpha_3 - \beta_3\alpha_2 \\ -\beta_1\alpha_0 - \beta_0\alpha_1 - \beta_3\alpha_2 + \beta_2\alpha_3 & -\beta_1\alpha_1 + \beta_0\alpha_0 + \beta_3\alpha_3 + \beta_2\alpha_2 \\ -\beta_2\alpha_0 + \beta_3\alpha_1 - \beta_0\alpha_2 - \beta_1\alpha_3 & -\beta_2\alpha_1 - \beta_3\alpha_0 + \beta_0\alpha_3 - \beta_1\alpha_2 \\ -\beta_3\alpha_0 - \beta_2\alpha_1 + \beta_1\alpha_2 - \beta_0\alpha_3 & -\beta_3\alpha_1 + \beta_2\alpha_0 - \beta_1\alpha_3 - \beta_0\alpha_2 \end{matrix} \right.$$

$$\left. \begin{matrix} \beta_0\alpha_2 - \beta_1\alpha_3 + \beta_2\alpha_0 + \beta_3\alpha_1 & \beta_0\alpha_3 + \beta_1\alpha_2 - \beta_2\alpha_1 + \beta_3\alpha_0 \\ -\beta_1\alpha_2 - \beta_0\alpha_3 + \beta_3\alpha_0 - \beta_2\alpha_1 & -\beta_1\alpha_3 + \beta_0\alpha_2 - \beta_3\alpha_1 - \beta_2\alpha_0 \\ -\beta_2\alpha_2 + \beta_3\alpha_3 + \beta_0\alpha_0 + \beta_1\alpha_1 & -\beta_2\alpha_3 - \beta_3\alpha_2 - \beta_0\alpha_1 + \beta_1\alpha_0 \\ -\beta_3\alpha_2 - \beta_2\alpha_3 - \beta_1\alpha_0 + \beta_0\alpha_1 & -\beta_3\alpha_3 + \beta_2\alpha_2 + \beta_1\alpha_1 + \beta_0\alpha_0 \end{matrix} \right).$$

If $\Delta' = B'A'$ is the matrix of a second displacement, and B' and A' are of the types (50) and (51) respectively,

$$(27)\qquad \Delta' \cdot \Delta = B'A'BA = B'B \cdot A'A,$$

because any displacement leaving all lines of R_1^2 invariant is commutative with any displacement leaving all lines of R_2^2 invariant.

Thus any displacement

$$
(28)\qquad
\begin{aligned}
x_0' &= a_{00}x_0 + a_{01}x_1 + a_{02}x_2 + a_{03}x_3,\\
x_1' &= a_{10}x_0 + a_{11}x_1 + a_{12}x_2 + a_{13}x_3,\\
x_2' &= a_{20}x_0 + a_{21}x_1 + a_{22}x_2 + a_{23}x_3,\\
x_3' &= a_{30}x_0 + a_{31}x_1 + a_{32}x_2 + a_{33}x_3
\end{aligned}
$$

is given parametrically in terms of two sets of homogeneous parameters α_0, α_1, α_2, α_3 and β_0, β_1, β_2, β_3 by means of the formulas obtained by equating a_{ij} to the corresponding element of the last matrix in Equation (26).

The formulas for the parameters of the product of two displacements are determined by (27), for if $\Delta'' = B''A'' = \Delta'\Delta$, then $B'' = B'B$ and $A'' = A'A$, and hence

$$
(29)\qquad
\begin{aligned}
\alpha_0'' &= \alpha_0'\alpha_0 - \alpha_1'\alpha_1 - \alpha_2'\alpha_2 - \alpha_3'\alpha_3,\\
\alpha_1'' &= \alpha_0'\alpha_1 + \alpha_1'\alpha_0 + \alpha_2'\alpha_3 - \alpha_3'\alpha_2,\\
\alpha_2'' &= \alpha_0'\alpha_2 - \alpha_1'\alpha_3 + \alpha_2'\alpha_0 + \alpha_3'\alpha_1,\\
\alpha_3'' &= \alpha_0'\alpha_3 + \alpha_1'\alpha_2 - \alpha_2'\alpha_1 + \alpha_3'\alpha_0,
\end{aligned}
$$

$$
(30)\qquad
\begin{aligned}
\beta_0'' &= \beta_0'\beta_0 - \beta_1'\beta_1 - \beta_2'\beta_2 - \beta_3'\beta_3,\\
\beta_1'' &= \beta_0'\beta_1 + \beta_1'\beta_0 - \beta_2'\beta_3 + \beta_3'\beta_2,\\
\beta_2'' &= \beta_0'\beta_2 + \beta_1'\beta_3 + \beta_2'\beta_0 - \beta_3'\beta_1,\\
\beta_3'' &= \beta_0'\beta_3 - \beta_1'\beta_2 + \beta_2'\beta_1 + \beta_3'\beta_0.
\end{aligned}
$$

The formulas for the α's are, by § 127, the same as for the multiplication of quaternions, and the formulas for the β's are given by the following quaternion formula:

$$(\beta_0' - \beta_1'i - \beta_2'j - \beta_3'k)(\beta_0 - \beta_1 i - \beta_2 j - \beta_3 k) = \beta_0'' - \beta_1''i - \beta_2''j - \beta_3''k.$$

Now let λ_1 and λ_2 be two symbols defined by the multiplication table

(31)

	λ_1	λ_2
λ_1	λ_1	0
λ_2	0	λ_2

and the conditions $\lambda_1 q = q\lambda_1$, $\lambda_2 q = q\lambda_2$, where q is any quaternion. If we write

$$
\begin{aligned}
(32)\quad &[\lambda_1(\alpha_0' + \alpha_1'i + \alpha_2'j + \alpha_3'k) + \lambda_2(\beta_0' - \beta_1'i - \beta_2'j - \beta_3'k)]\\
&\cdot [\lambda_1(\alpha_0 + \alpha_1 i + \alpha_2 j + \alpha_3 k) + \lambda_2(\beta_0 - \beta_1 i - \beta_2 j - \beta_3 k)]\\
&= \lambda_1(\alpha_0'' + \alpha_1''i + \alpha_2''j + \alpha_3''k) + \lambda_2(\beta_0'' - \beta_1''i - \beta_2''j - \beta_3''k),
\end{aligned}
$$

the α'''s and β'''s are given in terms of the α's, β's, α''s, and β''s by the equations (29) and (30).

The number system whose elements are $\lambda_1 q_1 + \lambda_2 q_2$, where q_1 and q_2 are quaternions, is one of the systems of biquaternions referred to in the footnote of § 130. It is often given a form which may be derived as follows:

Let

$$(33)\qquad \begin{aligned} e_1 &= \lambda_1 + \lambda_2, & \lambda_1 &= \frac{e_1 + e_2}{2},\\ e_2 &= \lambda_1 - \lambda_2, & \lambda_2 &= \frac{e_1 - e_2}{2}. \end{aligned}$$

Then e_1 and e_2 obey the multiplication table

(34)

	e_1	e_2
e_1	e_1	e_2
e_2	e_2	e_1

and we have

$$\begin{aligned} 2(\lambda_1 q_1 + \lambda_2 q_2) &= (e_1 + e_2) q_1 + (e_1 - e_2) q_2 \\ &= e_1(q_1 + q_2) + e_2(q_1 - q_2), \end{aligned}$$

or

$$\begin{aligned} &\lambda_1(\alpha_0 + \alpha_1 i + \alpha_2 j + \alpha_3 k) + \lambda_2(\beta_0 - \beta_1 i - \beta_2 j - \beta_3 k) \\ &\quad = e_1\left(\frac{\alpha_0 + \beta_0}{2} + \left(\frac{\alpha_1 - \beta_1}{2}\right)i + \left(\frac{\alpha_2 - \beta_2}{2}\right)j + \left(\frac{\alpha_3 - \beta_3}{2}\right)k\right) \\ &\qquad + e_2\left(\frac{\alpha_0 - \beta_0}{2} + \left(\frac{\alpha_1 + \beta_1}{2}\right)i + \left(\frac{\alpha_2 + \beta_2}{2}\right)j + \left(\frac{\alpha_3 + \beta_3}{2}\right)k\right). \end{aligned}$$

Let us write

$$(35)\qquad \begin{aligned} \gamma_0 &= \frac{\alpha_0 + \beta_0}{2}, & \gamma_1 &= \frac{\alpha_1 - \beta_1}{2}, & \gamma_2 &= \frac{\alpha_2 - \beta_2}{2}, & \gamma_3 &= \frac{\alpha_3 - \beta_3}{2},\\ \delta_0 &= \frac{\alpha_0 - \beta_0}{2}, & \delta_1 &= \frac{\alpha_1 + \beta_1}{2}, & \delta_2 &= \frac{\alpha_2 + \beta_2}{2}, & \delta_3 &= \frac{\alpha_3 + \beta_3}{2}. \end{aligned}$$

The rule for multiplying biquaternions,

$$\begin{aligned} &[e_1(\gamma_0' + \gamma_1' i + \gamma_2' j + \gamma_3' k) + e_2(\delta_0' + \delta_1' i + \delta_2' j + \delta_3' k)] \\ &\quad \cdot [e_1(\gamma_0 + \gamma_1 i + \gamma_2 j + \gamma_3 k) + e_2(\delta_0 + \delta_1 i + \delta_2 j + \delta_3 k)] \\ &\quad = e_1(\gamma_0'' + \gamma_1'' i + \gamma_2'' j + \gamma_3'' k) + e_2(\delta_0'' + \delta_1'' i + \delta_2'' j + \delta_3'' k), \end{aligned}$$

gives the following equations:

$$(36)\qquad \begin{aligned} \gamma_0'' &= \gamma_0'\gamma_0 - \gamma_1'\gamma_1 - \gamma_2'\gamma_2 - \gamma_3'\gamma_3 + \delta_0'\delta_0 - \delta_1'\delta_1 - \delta_2'\delta_2 - \delta_3'\delta_3,\\ \gamma_1'' &= \gamma_0'\gamma_1 + \gamma_1'\gamma_0 + \gamma_2'\gamma_3 - \gamma_3'\gamma_2 + \delta_0'\delta_1 + \delta_1'\delta_0 + \delta_2'\delta_3 - \delta_3'\delta_2,\\ \gamma_2'' &= \gamma_0'\gamma_2 - \gamma_1'\gamma_3 + \gamma_2'\gamma_0 + \gamma_3'\gamma_1 + \delta_0'\delta_2 - \delta_1'\delta_3 + \delta_2'\delta_0 + \delta_3'\delta_1,\\ \gamma_3'' &= \gamma_0'\gamma_3 + \gamma_1'\gamma_2 - \gamma_2'\gamma_1 + \gamma_3'\gamma_0 + \delta_0'\delta_3 + \delta_1'\delta_2 - \delta_2'\delta_1 + \delta_3'\delta_0,\\ \delta_0'' &= \gamma_0'\delta_0 - \gamma_1'\delta_1 - \gamma_2'\delta_2 - \gamma_3'\delta_3 + \delta_0'\gamma_0 - \delta_1'\gamma_1 - \delta_2'\gamma_2 - \delta_3'\gamma_3,\\ \delta_1'' &= \gamma_0'\delta_1 + \gamma_1'\delta_0 + \gamma_2'\delta_3 - \gamma_3'\delta_2 + \delta_0'\gamma_1 + \delta_1'\gamma_0 + \delta_2'\gamma_3 - \delta_3'\gamma_2,\\ \delta_2'' &= \gamma_0'\delta_2 - \gamma_1'\delta_3 + \gamma_2'\delta_0 + \gamma_3'\delta_1 + \delta_0'\gamma_2 - \delta_1'\gamma_3 + \delta_2'\gamma_0 + \delta_3'\gamma_1,\\ \delta_3'' &= \gamma_0'\delta_3 + \gamma_1'\delta_2 - \gamma_2'\delta_1 + \gamma_3'\delta_0 + \delta_0'\gamma_3 + \delta_1'\gamma_2 - \delta_2'\gamma_1 + \delta_3'\gamma_0. \end{aligned}$$

The γ's and δ's given by (36) may be regarded as a new set of parameters for the elliptic displacements. Since the α's and β's are separate sets of homogeneous variables, they may be subjected to the relation

$$(37) \qquad \alpha_0^2+\alpha_1^2+\alpha_2^2+\alpha_3^2=\beta_0^2+\beta_1^2+\beta_2^2+\beta_3^2.$$

By means of (35) the relation (37) becomes

$$(38) \qquad \gamma_0\delta_0+\gamma_1\delta_1+\gamma_2\delta_2+\gamma_3\delta_3=0.$$

The formulas for the coefficients of a displacement (28) in terms of the new parameters are found by substituting

$$\begin{array}{llll}\alpha_0=\gamma_0+\delta_0, & \alpha_1=\ \ \gamma_1+\delta_1, & \alpha_2=\ \ \gamma_2+\delta_2, & \alpha_3=\ \ \gamma_3+\delta_3,\\ \beta_0=\gamma_0-\delta_0, & \beta_1=-\gamma_1+\delta_1, & \beta_2=-\gamma_2+\delta_2, & \beta_3=-\gamma_3+\delta_3\end{array}$$

in the formulas for a_{ij} in terms of the α's and β's. In other words, the matrix of the displacement corresponding to $(\gamma_0, \gamma_1, \gamma_2, \gamma_3;\ \delta_0, \delta_1, \delta_2, \delta_3)$ is

$$\left[\begin{pmatrix}\gamma_0 & -\gamma_1 & -\gamma_2 & -\gamma_3\\ \gamma_1 & \gamma_0 & -\gamma_3 & \gamma_2\\ \gamma_2 & \gamma_3 & \gamma_0 & -\gamma_1\\ \gamma_3 & -\gamma_2 & \gamma_1 & \gamma_0\end{pmatrix}-\begin{pmatrix}\delta_0 & -\delta_1 & -\delta_2 & -\delta_3\\ \delta_1 & \delta_0 & -\delta_3 & \delta_2\\ \delta_2 & \delta_3 & \delta_0 & -\delta_1\\ \delta_3 & -\delta_2 & \delta_1 & \delta_0\end{pmatrix}\right]$$

$$\cdot\left[\begin{pmatrix}\gamma_0 & \gamma_1 & \gamma_2 & \gamma_3\\ -\gamma_1 & \gamma_0 & -\gamma_3 & \gamma_2\\ -\gamma_2 & \gamma_3 & \gamma_0 & -\gamma_1\\ -\gamma_3 & -\gamma_2 & \gamma_1 & \gamma_0\end{pmatrix}+\begin{pmatrix}\delta_0 & \delta_1 & \delta_2 & \delta_3\\ -\delta_1 & \delta_0 & -\delta_3 & \delta_2\\ -\delta_2 & \delta_3 & \delta_0 & -\delta_1\\ -\delta_3 & -\delta_2 & \delta_1 & \delta_0\end{pmatrix}\right],$$

and the formulas for the composition of two displacements are (36).

EXERCISE

The elliptic displacements are orthogonal transformations in four homogeneous variables. Work out the parameter representation determined by the formula

$$R=(1-S)(1+S)^{-1}$$

of § 125.

146. Parameter representation of hyperbolic displacements. Let the equation of the absolute be taken in the form

$$(39) \qquad x_0^2+\mu^2(x_1^2+x_2^2+x_3^2)=0.$$

If μ is real, the corresponding geometry is elliptic; and if μ is a pure imaginary, the corresponding geometry is hyperbolic. No generality is lost by taking $\mu=1$ (as in the section above) for the elliptic case and $\mu=\sqrt{-1}$ in the hyperbolic case. For the sake of the limiting process referred to at the end of the section, we shall, however, carry out the discussion for an arbitrary μ.

By precisely the reasoning used in § 126 it is seen that any collineation leaving one regulus on the absolute invariant has the matrix

$$A=\begin{pmatrix} \alpha_0 & \mu\alpha_1 & \mu\alpha_2 & \mu\alpha_3 \\ -\frac{1}{\mu}\alpha_1 & \alpha_0 & -\alpha_3 & \alpha_2 \\ -\frac{1}{\mu}\alpha_2 & \alpha_3 & \alpha_0 & -\alpha_1 \\ -\frac{1}{\mu}\alpha_3 & -\alpha_2 & \alpha_1 & \alpha_0 \end{pmatrix},$$

and any collineation leaving the other regulus invariant has the matrix

$$B=\begin{pmatrix} \beta_0 & \mu\beta_1 & \mu\beta_2 & \mu\beta_3 \\ -\frac{1}{\mu}\beta_1 & \beta_0 & \beta_3 & -\beta_2 \\ -\frac{1}{\mu}\beta_2 & -\beta_3 & \beta_0 & \beta_1 \\ -\frac{1}{\mu}\beta_3 & \beta_2 & -\beta_1 & \beta_0 \end{pmatrix}.$$

Hence any displacement has a matrix BA. In other words, if

$$\begin{aligned}
&a_{00}=\beta_0\alpha_0-\beta_1\alpha_1-\beta_2\alpha_2-\beta_3\alpha_3,\\
&a_{01}=\mu(\beta_0\alpha_1+\beta_1\alpha_0+\beta_2\alpha_3-\beta_3\alpha_2),\\
&a_{02}=\mu(\beta_0\alpha_2-\beta_1\alpha_3+\beta_2\alpha_0+\beta_3\alpha_1),\\
&a_{03}=\mu(\beta_0\alpha_3+\beta_1\alpha_2-\beta_2\alpha_1+\beta_3\alpha_0),\\
&a_{10}=-\frac{1}{\mu}(\beta_1\alpha_0+\beta_0\alpha_1+\beta_3\alpha_2-\beta_2\alpha_3),\\
&a_{11}=-\beta_1\alpha_1+\beta_0\alpha_0+\beta_3\alpha_3+\beta_2\alpha_2,\\
&a_{12}=-\beta_1\alpha_2-\beta_0\alpha_3+\beta_3\alpha_0-\beta_2\alpha_1,\\
&a_{13}=-\beta_1\alpha_3+\beta_0\alpha_2-\beta_3\alpha_1-\beta_2\alpha_0,\\
(40)\qquad &a_{20}=-\frac{1}{\mu}(\beta_2\alpha_0-\beta_3\alpha_1+\beta_0\alpha_2+\beta_1\alpha_3),\\
&a_{21}=-\beta_2\alpha_1-\beta_3\alpha_0+\beta_0\alpha_3-\beta_1\alpha_2,\\
&a_{22}=-\beta_2\alpha_2+\beta_3\alpha_3+\beta_0\alpha_0+\beta_1\alpha_1,\\
&a_{23}=-\beta_2\alpha_3-\beta_3\alpha_2-\beta_0\alpha_1+\beta_1\alpha_0,\\
&a_{30}=-\frac{1}{\mu}(\beta_3\alpha_0+\beta_2\alpha_1-\beta_1\alpha_2+\beta_0\alpha_3),\\
&a_{31}=-\beta_3\alpha_1+\beta_2\alpha_0-\beta_1\alpha_3-\beta_0\alpha_2,\\
&a_{32}=-\beta_3\alpha_2-\beta_2\alpha_3-\beta_1\alpha_0+\beta_0\alpha_1,\\
&a_{33}=-\beta_3\alpha_3+\beta_2\alpha_2+\beta_1\alpha_1+\beta_0\alpha_0,
\end{aligned}$$

the transformation (28) is a displacement.

As we have already seen in the elliptic case, if A' and B' are matrices analogous to A and B,

$$B'A' \cdot BA = B'B \cdot A'A.$$

Hence the product of two displacements BA and $B'A'$ is a displacement $B''A''$ such that

$$A'' = A'A$$

and

$$B'' = B'B.$$

On multiplying out the two matrix products $A'A$ and $B'B$, it is evident that the elements of A'' and B'' are given by the formulas (29) and (30) found above for the elliptic case. These formulas are associated with the biquaternions determined by the table (31).

The remark must now be made that if $\mu = \sqrt{-1}$, the parameter representation above does not give real values of a_{ij} for real values of the α's and β's. Suppose, however, that we transform the biquaternions $\lambda_1 q_1 + \lambda_2 q_2$ as follows:

$$\epsilon_1 = \lambda_1 + \lambda_2, \qquad \lambda_1 = \frac{\mu\epsilon_1 + \epsilon_2}{2\mu},$$

$$\epsilon_2 = \mu(\lambda_1 - \lambda_2), \qquad \lambda_2 = \frac{\mu\epsilon_1 - \epsilon_2}{2\mu}.$$

Then ϵ_1 and ϵ_2 obey the multiplication table

(41)

	ϵ_1	ϵ_2
ϵ_1	ϵ_1	ϵ_2
ϵ_2	ϵ_2	$\mu^2\epsilon_1$

and we have
$$2\mu(\lambda_1 q_1 + \lambda_2 q_2) = (\mu\epsilon_1 + \epsilon_2) q_1 + (\mu\epsilon_1 - \epsilon_2) q_2$$
$$= \mu(q_1 + q_2)\epsilon_1 + (q_1 - q_2)\epsilon_2,$$

or
$$\lambda_1(\alpha_0 + \alpha_1 i + \alpha_2 j + \alpha_3 k) + \lambda_2(\beta_0 - \beta_1 i - \beta_2 j - \beta_3 k)$$
$$= \epsilon_1(\gamma_0 + \gamma_1 i + \gamma_2 j + \gamma_3 k) + \epsilon_2(\delta_0 + \delta_1 i + \delta_2 j + \delta_3 k),$$

where

(42)
$$\gamma_0 = \frac{(\alpha_0 + \beta_0)}{2}, \quad \gamma_1 = \frac{(\alpha_1 - \beta_1)}{2}, \quad \gamma_2 = \frac{(\alpha_2 - \beta_2)}{2}, \quad \gamma_3 = \frac{(\alpha_3 - \beta_3)}{2},$$
$$\delta_0 = \frac{\alpha_0 - \beta_0}{2\mu}, \quad \delta_1 = \frac{\alpha_1 + \beta_1}{2\mu}, \quad \delta_2 = \frac{\alpha_2 + \beta_2}{2\mu}, \quad \delta_3 = \frac{\alpha_3 + \beta_3}{2\mu}.$$

The rule for multiplying biquaternions

$$\epsilon_1(\gamma_0''+\gamma_1''i+\gamma_2''j+\gamma_3''k)+\epsilon_2(\delta_0''+\delta_1''i+\delta_2''j+\delta_3''k)$$
$$=[\epsilon_1(\gamma_0'+\gamma_1'i+\gamma_2'j+\gamma_3'k)+\epsilon_2(\delta_0'+\delta_1'i+\delta_2'j+\delta_3'k)]$$
$$\cdot[\epsilon_1(\gamma_0+\gamma_1 i+\gamma_2 j+\gamma_3 k)+\epsilon_2(\delta_0+\delta_1 i+\delta_2 j+\delta_3 k)],$$

according to (41), gives the following equations:

$$(43)\quad \begin{aligned}
\gamma_0'' &= \gamma_0'\gamma_0-\gamma_1'\gamma_1-\gamma_2'\gamma_2-\gamma_3'\gamma_3+\mu^2(\delta_0'\delta_0-\delta_1'\delta_1'-\delta_2'\delta_2-\delta_3'\delta_3),\\
\gamma_1'' &= \gamma_0'\gamma_1+\gamma_1'\gamma_0+\gamma_2'\gamma_3-\gamma_3'\gamma_2+\mu^2(\delta_0'\delta_1+\delta_1'\delta_0+\delta_2'\delta_3-\delta_3'\delta_2),\\
\gamma_2'' &= \gamma_0'\gamma_2-\gamma_1'\gamma_3+\gamma_2'\gamma_0+\gamma_3'\gamma_1+\mu^2(\delta_0'\delta_2-\delta_1'\delta_3+\delta_2'\delta_0+\delta_3'\delta_1),\\
\gamma_3'' &= \gamma_0'\gamma_3+\gamma_1'\gamma_2-\gamma_2'\gamma_1+\gamma_3'\gamma_0+\mu^2(\delta_0'\delta_3+\delta_1'\delta_2-\delta_2'\delta_1+\delta_3'\delta_0),\\
\delta_0'' &= \gamma_0'\delta_0-\gamma_1'\delta_1-\gamma_2'\delta_2-\gamma_3'\delta_3+\delta_0'\gamma_0-\delta_1'\gamma_1-\delta_2'\gamma_2-\delta_3'\gamma_3,\\
\delta_1'' &= \gamma_0'\delta_1+\gamma_1'\delta_0+\gamma_2'\delta_3-\gamma_3'\delta_2+\delta_0'\gamma_1+\delta_1'\gamma_0+\delta_2'\gamma_3-\delta_3'\gamma_2,\\
\delta_2'' &= \gamma_0'\delta_2-\gamma_1'\delta_3+\gamma_2'\delta_0+\gamma_3'\delta_1+\delta_0'\gamma_2-\delta_1'\gamma_3+\delta_2'\gamma_0+\delta_3'\gamma_1,\\
\delta_3'' &= \gamma_0'\delta_3+\gamma_1'\delta_2-\gamma_2'\delta_1+\gamma_3'\delta_0+\delta_0'\gamma_3+\delta_1'\gamma_2-\delta_2'\gamma_1+\delta_3'\gamma_0.
\end{aligned}$$

For $\mu=0$ these equations reduce to (64) and (65) of § 130, and for $\mu^2=1$ they reduce to (36). For $\mu^2=-1$ they give the standard formulas for combining hyperbolic displacements. Thus there are three essentially distinct systems of biquaternions, determined respectively by the conditions $\mu^2=1$, $\mu^2=-1$, $\mu=0$. The first corresponds to the elliptic, the second to the hyperbolic, and the third to the parabolic geometry. The geometry in each case is determined by an absolute whose equation in point coördinates is (39), and in plane coördinates,

$$(44)\qquad \mu^2u_0^2+u_1^2+u_2^2+u_3^2=0.$$

Since the same geometry corresponds to any two real values of μ, there must be a simple isomorphism between any two systems of biquaternions corresponding to positive values of μ^2; and a like statement holds with regard to the systems of biquaternions corresponding to negative values of μ^2. The biquaternions for which $\mu=0$ may be regarded as a limiting case between those for which μ^2 is positive and those for which μ^2 is negative, just as the parabolic geometry is regarded as a limiting case between the hyperbolic and elliptic (§ 144).

In these remarks it is understood that the coefficients $\gamma_0, \gamma_1, \gamma_2, \gamma_3, \delta_0, \delta_1, \delta_2, \delta_3$ are always real. From the geometrical discussion above it is clear that if these coefficients were taken as complex, the biquaternions for which $\mu^2=1$ would be isomorphic with those for which $\mu^2=-1$.

The multiplication table (41), in case $\mu^2=-1$, is satisfied if we take $\epsilon_1=1$ and $\epsilon_2=\sqrt{-1}$. Hence the biquaternions with real coefficients,

$$\epsilon_1(\gamma_0+\gamma_1 i+\gamma_2 j+\gamma_3 k)+\epsilon_2(\delta_0+\delta_1 i+\delta_2 j+\delta_3 k),$$

are equivalent, in case $\mu^2=-1$, to the quaternions with ordinary complex coefficients,

$$\alpha_0+\beta_0\sqrt{-1}+(\alpha_1+\beta_1\sqrt{-1})i+(\alpha_2+\beta_2\sqrt{-1})j+(\alpha_3+\beta_3\sqrt{-1})k.$$

The biquaternions for which $\mu=0$, when taken with complex coefficients, may be regarded as a number system of sixteen units with real coefficients. This is the number system (§ 130) which is needed to study the displacements in the complex Euclidean geometry, and it may be regarded as containing the other systems of real biquaternions.

CHAPTER IX

THEOREMS ON SENSE AND SEPARATION

147. Plan of the chapter. The theorems and definitions of Chapter II are for the most part special cases of more general concepts of Analysis Situs. The present chapter develops these ideas further, so that the two chapters together lay the foundation for the class of theorems which are particularly of use in the application of geometry to analysis, and vice versa.

In most of the chapter attention is confined to theorems which can be proved without the use of the continuity assumptions (C, R). Many of the theorems are proved on the basis of A, E, S alone and others on the basis of A, E, S, P.

In the first sections (§§ 148–153) of this chapter we prove some of the general theorems about convex regions. These are followed (§§ 154–157) by the definitions of some very general concepts, such as curve, region, continuous group, etc. It will not be necessary (or possible in the remaining pages) to develop the corresponding general theory to any considerable extent. Nevertheless, these general notions underlie and give unity to the rest of the chapter, which may in fact be regarded as a study of certain continuous families of figures by special methods.

In §§ 158–181 the theory of sense-classes is developed in considerable detail for the various cases considered in earlier chapters and for other cases, the principal idea involved being that of an elementary transformation. Finally (§§ 182–199), we prove the fundamental theorems on the regions determined in a plane by polygons and in space by polyhedra.

148. Convex regions. THEOREM 1. *If l is a line coplanar with a triangular region* R *and containing a point of* R, *the points of* R *on l constitute a segment.*

Proof. A line coplanar with a triangle and not containing more than one vertex meets the sides of the triangle in at least two and at most three points. These points, by § 22, are the ends of two or three segments. By Theorem 20, Chap. II, the points of any one of these segments are in the same one of the triangular regions determined by the triangle, and two points in different segments are in different triangular regions.

COROLLARY. *The points common to a tetrahedral region and a line containing one of its points constitute a linear segment.*

Proof. A line not on one of the planes of a tetrahedron meets these planes in at least two and at most four points. The rest of the argument is the same as for the theorem above, replacing Theorem 20, Chap. II, by Theorem 21 of the same chapter.

Convex regions on a line have been defined and studied in § 23.

DEFINITION. A set of points in a plane is said to be a *two-dimensional* (or *planar*) *convex region* if and only if it satisfies the following conditions: (1) Any two points of the set are joined by an interval consisting entirely of points of the set, (2) every point of the set is interior to a triangular region containing no point not in the set, and (3) there is at least one line coplanar with and not containing any point of the set.

A triangular region, a Euclidean plane, and the interior of a conic are examples of planar convex regions.

THEOREM 2. *If l is a line coplanar with a two-dimensional convex region* R *and containing a point of* R, *the points of* R *on l constitute a linear convex region.*

Proof. The definition of a linear convex region is given in § 23. That the points of R on l satisfy (1) of that definition follows directly from (1) of the definition of a planar convex region. To prove (2) that any point P of R on l is interior to a segment of points of R on l, we observe that by (2) of the definition of a planar convex region P is interior to a triangular region consisting entirely of points of R and that by Theorem 1 the points common to l and this triangular region are a linear segment. Condition (3) of the definition of a linear convex region is satisfied by the points of R on l because l contains one point of the line coplanar with R and not containing any point of R.

DEFINITION. A set of points in space is said to be a *three-dimensional* (or *spatial*) *convex region* if and only if it satisfies the following conditions: (1) Any two points of the set are joined by an interval consisting entirely of points of the set, (2) every point of the set is interior to a tetrahedral region containing no points not in the set, and (3) there is at least one plane containing no point of the set.

A tetrahedral region, a Euclidean space, and a hyperbolic space are examples of three-dimensional convex regions.

THEOREM 3. *If a line l contains a point of a three-dimensional convex region* R, *the points of* R *on l constitute a linear convex region.*

The proof of this theorem follows the same lines as that of Theorem 2, the corollary of Theorem 1 being used instead of Theorem 1 in showing that the points of l in R satisfy Condition (2) of the definition of linear convex region.

In consequence of Theorems 2 and 3 the definitions (*between, precede, ray, sense,* etc.) and theorems of § 23 are applicable to collinear sets of points in two- and three-dimensional convex regions. In the rest of this chapter the segment AB where A and B are in a given convex region R always means the segment AB of points of R.

THEOREM 4. *If ABC are three noncollinear points of a convex region* R, *D a point of* R *in the order $\{BCD\}$, and E a point of* R *in the order $\{CEA\}$, there exists a point F of* R *in the orders $\{AFB\}$ and $\{DEF\}$.*

Proof. Let F be defined as the point of intersection of the lines DE and AB (fig. 77, p. 351). By (3) of the definition of a two- or three-dimensional convex region there is a line l_∞ coplanar with A, B, and C and containing no point of R. Hence l_∞ does not meet any of the segments AB, BC, CA. Hence (Theorem 19, Chap. II) the line DE which meets the segment CA and does not meet BC must meet AB. Hence $\{AFB\}$.

The line l_∞ does not meet any of the segments FB, BD, DF, and the line AC meets the segment BD and does not meet the segment BF. Hence AC meets the segment DF. Hence $\{DEF\}$.

THEOREM 5. *A three-dimensional convex region* R *satisfies Assumptions I–VIII of the set given for a Euclidean space in § 29.*

Proof. Assumptions I, II, III, V, VIII are direct consequences of Theorem 3 and the theorems of § 23. Assumptions VI and VII are consequences of Condition (2) of the definition of a three-dimensional convex region. Assumption IV is a consequence of Theorem 4.

The theory of order relations in convex regions can be based entirely on Theorem 5. This amounts to developing the consequences of Assumptions I–VIII of § 29. Since both the Euclidean and the hyperbolic spaces satisfy these assumptions, this method of treating convex regions is of considerable interest from the point of view of foundations of geometry (cf. references in § 29). The methods required to prove the theorems on this basis are but little different from those used in the next section.

COROLLARY. *In a real projective space a convex region also satisfies Assumption XVII of § 29.*

EXERCISES

1. The set of all points common to a set of convex regions which are all contained in a single convex region is, if existent, a convex region. (In other words, the logical product of a set of convex regions contained in a convex region is a convex region.)

2. Prove on the basis of Assumptions I–VIII of § 29 that for any set of points $P_1, P_2, \cdots, P_n$, finite in number, there is a line l such that $P_1, P_2, \cdots, P_n$ are all on the same side of l.

***3.** A set of points in a projective space such that any two points of the set are joined by *one and only one* segment consisting entirely of points of the set and such that every point of the set is interior to at least one tetrahedral region consisting entirely of points of the set, is a convex region.

***4.** Study the set of assumptions for projective geometry consisting of A, E and the assumption that in the projective space there is a set of points satisfying the Assumptions I–VIII, XVII for a convex region.

149. Further theorems on convex regions. THEOREM 6. *If A, B, C are three noncollinear points of a convex region* R, *they are the vertices of one and only one triangular region consisting entirely of points of* R. *This triangular region consists of all points on the segments joining A to the points of the segment BC.*

Proof. By Theorem 4 a line joining B to a point of the segment CA meets a segment joining A to any point A_1 of the segment BC; and by the same theorem any point of the segment AA_1 is joined to B by a line meeting the segment CA. Hence the set of points $[P]$ on the segments joining A to the points of the segment BC is identical with the set of points of intersection of lines joining A to points of the segment BC with lines joining B to points of the segment CA. By similar reasoning $[P]$ is the set of points of intersection of lines joining A to points of the segment BC with lines joining C to points of the segment AB. The points $[P]$ form a triangular region because they are all the points not separated from a particular P by any pair of the three lines AB, BC, CA.

The other three triangular regions having A, B, C as vertices contain points of the line which by (3) of the definition of a convex region is coplanar with ABC and contains no point of R. Hence $[P]$ is the only triangular region satisfying the conditions of the theorem.

In the rest of this section the triangular region determined by three noncollinear points A, B, C of a convex region R according to Theorem 6 shall be called *the triangular region* ABC. It is also called the *interior* of the triangle ABC.

COROLLARY. *If* $ABCD$ *are four noncoplanar points of a convex region* R, *they are the vertices of one and only one tetrahedral region consisting entirely of points of* R. *This tetrahedral region consists of the segments of points of* R *joining* A *to points of the triangular region* BCD.

Proof. Let $[\alpha]$ be the set of segments joining A to points of the triangular region BCD and $[P]$ the set of all points on the segments $[\alpha]$. Any P is also on a segment joining B to a point of the triangular region ACD, as is seen by applying the theorem above to the figure obtained by taking a section of the tetrahedron $ABCD$ by the plane ABP. In like manner any P is on a segment joining C to a point of the triangular region DAB, and on a segment joining D to a point of the triangular region ABC.

The same argument shows that any point of intersection of a line joining A to a point of the triangular region BCD with a line joining B to a point of the triangular region CAD is in the set $[P]$ and that every P is a point of this description. From this it follows that $[P]$ contains all points not separated from a particular P by the faces of the tetrahedron $ABCD$. Hence by Theorem 21, Chap. II, $[P]$ is a tetrahedral region.

Any tetrahedral region having $ABCD$ as vertices and distinct from $[P]$ contains points not in R, because it either contains points on the segments complementary to $[\alpha]$ or on the lines joining A to the points of the triangular regions different from BCD in the plane BCD.

THEOREM 7. *If a plane π contains a point of a three-dimensional convex region* R, *the points of* R *on π constitute a planar convex region.*

Proof. The points of R on π satisfy Conditions (1) and (3) of the definition of a planar convex region because R satisfies Conditions (1) and (3) of the definition of a three-dimensional convex region. To prove that the points of R on π satisfy (2) of the definition of a planar convex region, let P be a point of R on π and l a line on P and π. By Theorem 3 there are two points A, A_1 of R on l such that the segment APA_1 is composed entirely of points of R. Let a be a line on A_1 and π but distinct from l. By the same reasoning as before there are two points B, C of R on a such that the segment BA_1C is composed entirely of points of R. By Theorem 6 the triangular region having A, B, C as vertices and containing P contains no points not in R. Hence the points of R on π satisfy Condition (2) of the definition of a planar convex region.

THEOREM 8. *If l is any line coplanar with and containing a point of a planar convex region* R, *the points of* R *not on l constitute two convex regions such that the segment joining any point of one to any point of the other meets the linear convex region which l has in common with* R.

Proof. By definition there is a line m coplanar with R and containing no point of R. By Theorem 18, Cor. 1, Chap. II, all points of the plane not on l or m fall into two classes $[O]$ and $[P]$ such that (1) two points O, P of different classes are separated by l and m and (2) two points of the same class are not separated by l and m. The region R contains points of both of these classes. For let I be any point of R on l. By Theorem 2 any line through I coplanar with R and distinct from l contains a segment of points of R of which I is one point. If A and B are two points of this segment in the order $\{AIB\}$, A and B are separated by l and m and also are points of R. Hence there exist two mutually exclusive classes $[O']$ and $[P']$, subsets of $[O]$ and $[P]$ respectively, which contain all points of R not on l.

Since any O' and any P' are separated by l and m and no segment $O'P'$ contains a point of m, every segment $O'P'$ contains a point of l.

Since two points of the same class ($[O']$ or $[P']$) are not separated by l and m, and since the segment joining them does not contain a point of m, it does not contain a point of l.

It remains to show that any point of either of the classes, say $[O']$, is interior to a triangular region consisting entirely of points of this class. Let p be any line on a point O' and coplanar with R. Let O'_1 and O'_2 be two points of R on p in the order $\{O'_1 O' O'_2\}$ and such that the segment $O'_1 O'_2$ does not contain a point of l. Let q be any line distinct from p, coplanar with R and on O'_2, and let O'_3, O'_4 be two points of R on q in the order $\{O'_3 O'_2 O'_4\}$ and such that the segment $O'_3 O'_4$ does not contain a point of l. By Theorem 6 there is a unique triangular region with O'_1, O'_3, O'_4 as vertices consisting only of points of R and containing all points of the segment $O'_1 O_2$. Since l does not meet any of the segments $O'_1 O'_2$, $O'_2 O'_3$, $O'_2 O'_4$, it cannot meet any segments joining O'_1 to a point of the segment $O'_3 O'_4$ (Theorem 4). Hence the triangular region $O'_1 O'_3 O'_4$ consists entirely of points of $[O']$.

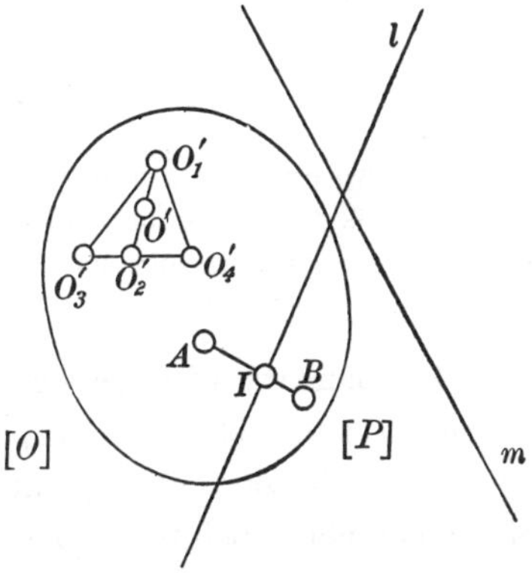

FIG. 80

COROLLARY 1. *If π is any plane containing a point of a three-dimensional convex region* R, *the points of* R *not on π constitute two three-dimensional convex regions such that the segment joining any point of one to any point of the other meets the planar convex region which π has in common with* R.

Proof. The proof is a strict generalization of that of the theorem above to space, using the corollary of Theorem 6 instead of Theorem 6.

COROLLARY 2. *For a given line l (or plane π) and a given convex region* R, *there is only one pair of regions of the sort described in Theorem 8 (or Cor. 1).*

Proof. If O is any point of R not on l, the class containing O must include all points joined to O by segments not meeting l. Hence it must be identical with one of the classes given by the theorem.

DEFINITION. The two convex regions determined according to Theorem 8 by a line in a planar convex region are called the *sides* of the line relative to the convex region. The two convex regions determined according to Cor. 1 by a plane in a convex region are called the two *sides* of the plane relative to the convex region.

DEFINITION. Two sets of points [*P*], [*Q*] in a convex region or in a projective plane or space are said to be *separated* by a set [*S*] if every segment of the convex region or of the projective plane or space which joins a *P* to a *Q* contains an *S*.

EXERCISE

Given two lines containing points of a convex region but intersecting in a point *P* outside the region. Construct the line joining *P* to a point *Q* in the region by means of linear constructions involving only points and lines in the region. Cf. Ex. 4, § 20, Vol. I.

150. Boundary of a convex region. DEFINITION. A point *B* is a *boundary point* of a set of points [*P*] if every tetrahedral region containing *B* contains a point *P* and a point not in [*P*]. The set of all boundary points of [*P*] is called the *boundary* of [*P*].

THEOREM 9. *All boundary points of a set of points on a line l are on l. All boundary points of a set of points on a plane π are on π.*

Proof. If *Q* is a point not on a line *l*, any tetrahedron one of whose faces contains *l* and none of whose faces contains *Q* will determine a tetrahedral region (§ 26) which contains *Q* and does not contain any point of *l*. Hence *Q* is not a boundary point of any set of points on *l*. A like argument proves the second statement in the theorem.

COROLLARY 1. *A boundary point B of a set of points [P] on a line l is any point such that any segment of l containing B contains a P and a point not in [P].*

COROLLARY 2. *A boundary point B of a set of points [P] on a plane π is any point such that any triangular region of π containing B contains a P and a point not in [P].*

THEOREM 10. *Let σ be the convex region common to a line l and a planar convex region* R *and let* R_1 *and* R_2 *be the convex regions formed by the points of* R *which are not on σ. The boundaries of* R_1 *and of* R_2 *contain σ and all boundary points of σ. Each boundary point of* R *is a boundary point of* R_1 *or of* R_2, *and each boundary point of* R_1 *or of* R_2 *which is not on* l *is a boundary point of* R.

Proof. If Q is any point of σ, and m a line on Q coplanar with R_1 and distinct from l, any segment of m containing Q contains points both of R_1 and of R_2. Since any triangular region containing Q contains a segment of m containing Q, it contains points both of R_1 and of R_2. Hence Q is a boundary point both of R_1 and of R_2. If B is a boundary point of σ, any triangular region containing B contains a point Q of σ, and hence, by the argument just given, contains points both of R_1 and of R_2. Hence B is a boundary point both of R_1 and of R_2.

Let A be a boundary point of R. Any triangular region T containing A contains at least one point not in R_1 or R_2, namely, A itself. Since A is a boundary point of R, T contains at least one point of R, which may be in R_1 or in R_2 or in σ. In the latter case T contains points of R_1 and R_2 both, by the paragraph above. Hence in every case T contains points of R_1 or R_2. If every triangular region containing A contains points of R_1 and of R_2, A is a boundary point of both R_1 and R_2. If this does not happen, some triangular region T_0 containing A contains points of one of R_1 and R_2 (say R_1) and not of the other. Any triangular region T containing A then contains points of R_1 because by an easy construction we obtain a triangular region T' containing A and contained in both T and T_0; and since T' contains A, it contains points of R, which because they are in T_0 must be points of R_1. Hence A is a boundary point of R_1.

Let C be a boundary point of R_1 which is not on l. Any triangular region T containing C contains points of R, because it contains points of R_1. It also contains points not in R_1. One of these points is not in R unless T consists entirely of points of R_1, R_2, and l. If the latter case should arise, since C is not on l a triangular region T' could be constructed containing C, interior to T, and not containing any point of l. T' then would contain points of both R_1 and R_2 and hence would contain a segment joining a point of R_1 to a point of R_2; which segment, by Theorem 8, would contain a point of l, contrary to hypothesis. Hence T contains points not in R, and C is a boundary point of R.

COROLLARY. *Let σ be the convex region common to a plane π and a three-dimensional convex region* R, *and let* R_1 *and* R_2 *be the convex regions formed by the points of* R *which are not on* π. *The boundaries of* R_1 *and* R_2 *contain* σ *and all boundary points of* σ. *Each boundary point of* R *is a boundary point of* R_1 *or of* R_2, *and each boundary point of* R_1 *or of* R_2 *which is not on* π *is a boundary point of* R.

It is to be noted that we have not proved that a convex region always has a boundary. Cf. Ex. 7, below.

EXERCISES

1. If A and B are two points of the boundary of a convex region R, one of the segments joining them consists entirely of points of R or entirely of points of the boundary of R.

2. A line has no points, one point, two points, or one interval in common with the boundary of a convex region.

3. If a segment consists of boundary points of a given set, its ends are also boundary points.

4. Using the notation of Theorem 10, no point of l not in σ or its boundary can be a boundary point of R. Hence if P is a point of a two- or three-dimensional convex region R, and B a boundary point of R, the points P and B are joined by a segment consisting entirely of points of R.

5. Using the notation of the corollary of Theorem 10, no point of π not in σ or its boundary can be a boundary point of R.

6. Using the notation of Theorem 10, if R and its boundary are contained in another convex region R′, then no point of the boundary of R_1 not on σ or its boundary can be on the boundary of R_2.

7. Give an example of a space containing a convex region which has no boundary.

8. A ray whose origin is in the interior of a triangle meets the boundary of this triangular region in one and only one point.

***9.** Let O be an arbitrary point of a Euclidean plane, and R_0 an arbitrary convex region containing O and having a boundary which is met in two points by every line which contains a point of R_0. Let any set of points into which the boundary of R_0 can be transformed by a homothetic transformation (§ 47) be called a *circle*. Let the point to which O is transformed by the homothetic transformation which carries the boundary of R_0 into any circle be called the *center* of this circle. Let two point-pairs AB and $A'B'$ be said to be *congruent* if and only if there is a circle with A as center and passing through B which can be carried by a translation into one with A' as center and passing through B'. The geometry based on these definitions is analogous to the Euclidean plane geometry. Develop its main theorems. Cf. the memoir of H. Minkowski by D. Hilbert, Mathematische Annalen, Vol. LXVIII (1910), p. 445.

151. Triangular regions. The theorems of the last sections can be used to complete the discussion of the regions determined by a triangle. We shall continue to use the notation of § 26 and shall denote the sides AB, BC, CA by c, a, and b respectively. The points of the plane which are not on a form a convex region, of which a is the boundary. By Theorem 8 the points not on a or b fall into two convex regions, of each of which a and b together (by Theorem 10) constitute the boundary. The line c meets a and b in the points B and A respectively and hence has the segment γ in common with one of the regions and $\bar{\gamma}$ in common with the other. By Theorem 8 the region containing γ is separated into two convex regions, each having γ on its boundary, and the other into two, each having $\bar{\gamma}$ on its boundary. Thus the three lines a, b, c determine four planar convex regions which are identical with the four triangular regions of Theorem 20, Chap. II. Since the lines enter symmetrically, each of the segments α, β, γ, $\bar{\alpha}$, $\bar{\beta}$, $\bar{\gamma}$ is on the boundary of two and only two of the triangular regions.

The three vertices A, B, C are on the boundaries of all four triangular regions, because every point of the plane can be joined to these three points by segments not meeting the lines a, b, c. No point not on a, b, or c can be a boundary point of any of the triangular regions, because such a point is an interior point of one of them.

Since any line m which meets one of the four planar convex regions meets it in a segment the ends of which are the only points of m on the boundary, the three segments which bound one of the four triangular regions cannot be met by the same line. The boundaries of the four regions therefore consist respectively (cf. fig. 16) of the vertices of the triangle, together with

$\bar{\alpha}$, $\bar{\beta}$, $\bar{\gamma}$ for Region I,
α, β, $\bar{\gamma}$ for Region II,
$\bar{\alpha}$, β, γ for Region III,
α, $\bar{\beta}$, γ for Region IV.

In addition to what has already been stated in Theorem 2, the discussion above gives us the following information:

THEOREM 11. *A triangular region is bounded by the three vertices of the triangle, together with three segments joining them which cannot all be met by a line.*

If $\overline{AOB}$ and $\overline{APC}$ are two noncollinear segments they may be denoted by α and β. The two segments whose ends are B and C may be denoted by γ and $\bar{\gamma}$, γ being the one met by the line OP. As we have just seen, α, β, and $\bar{\gamma}$, together with the vertices of the triangle, are the boundary of a convex region, and there is one and only one of the four convex regions of whose boundary α and β form part. Hence

THEOREM 12. *For any two noncollinear segments α, β having a common end there is a unique triangular region and a unique segment $\bar{\gamma}$ such that α, β, and $\bar{\gamma}$, together with the ends of α and β, form the boundary of the triangular region.*

COROLLARY 1. *On any point coplanar with but not in a given triangular region* T, *there is at least one line composed entirely of points not in* T.

COROLLARY 2. *The triangular region determined according to Theorem 12 by two noncollinear segments $\overline{CB'A}$ and $\overline{CA'B}$ consists of the points of intersection of the lines joining B to the points of the first segment with the lines joining A to the points of the second segment.*

The complete set of relations among the points, segments, and triangular regions determined by three noncollinear parts A, B, C may be indicated by the following tables,

H_1:

	α	$\bar{\alpha}$	β	$\bar{\beta}$	γ	$\bar{\gamma}$
A	0	0	1	1	1	1
B	1	1	0	0	1	1
C	1	1	1	1	0	0

H_2:

	I	II	III	IV
α	0	1	0	1
$\bar{\alpha}$	1	0	1	0
β	0	1	1	0
$\bar{\beta}$	1	0	0	1
γ	0	0	1	1
$\bar{\gamma}$	1	1	0	0

where in the first table a "1" or a "0" is placed in the ith row and jth column according as the point whose name appears at the beginning of the ith row is or is not an end of the segment whose name appears at the top of the jth column; and where in the second table a "1" or a "0" is placed in the ith row and jth column according as the segment whose name appears at the beginning of the ith row is or is not a part of the boundary of the triangular region whose name appears at the top of the jth column.

EXERCISES

1. The lines polar (§ 18, Vol. I) with respect to a triangle ABC to the points of one of the four triangular regions determined by ABC constitute one of the four sets of lines determined by ABC, according to the dual of Theorem 20, Chap. II. The points on these lines constitute the set of all points coplanar with but not on the given triangular region or its boundary.

2. Divide the lines of the plane of a complete quadrangle into classes according as the point pairs in which they meet the pairs of opposite sides separate one another or not. Apply the results to the problem: When can a real conic be drawn through four given points and tangent to a given line? Dualize.

152. The tetrahedron. The discussion in § 151 generalizes at once to space. Let us use the notation of § 26. The points not on α_1 constitute a convex region of which α_1 is the boundary. By Theorem 8, Cor. 1, the points not on α_1 and α_2 constitute two convex regions, of each of which, by Theorem 10, α_1 and α_2 form the boundary.

The plane α_3 has points in each of the three-dimensional convex regions bounded by α_1 and α_2 and hence by Theorem 7 has a planar convex region in common with each of them. By Theorem 8, Cor. 1, each of these planar convex regions separates the spatial convex region in which it lies into two spatial convex regions, of each of which (Theorem 10, Cor.) it forms part of the boundary. Thus the points not on α_1, α_2, α_3 form four spatial convex regions. Since any plane not on A_4 meets α_1, α_2, and α_3 in a triangle, it meets each of these four spatial convex regions in a triangular region. Thus, since the planes α_1, α_2, α_3 enter symmetrically, we have

THEOREM 13. DEFINITION. *Three planes α_1, α_2, α_3 meet by pairs in three lines, and each pair of these lines bounds two planar convex regions. The points not on α_1, α_2, and α_3 form four spatial convex regions (called* trihedral regions) *each bounded by the three lines and three of the planar convex regions. The relations among these regions are fully represented by the matrices of § 151 if the three lines are denoted by A, B, C, the planar convex regions by α, β, γ, $\bar{\alpha}$, $\bar{\beta}$, $\bar{\gamma}$, and the three-dimensional regions by* I, II, III, IV.

Each of the four spatial convex regions determined by α_1, α_2, α_3 is met by α_4 in a triangular region and separated by it into two convex regions each of which is partially bounded by the triangular region. Hence the points not on α_1, α_2, α_3, α_4 form eight convex spatial regions which must be identical with the tetrahedral regions of Theorem 21, Chap. II. Since the planes α_1, α_2, α_3, α_4 enter symmetrically, there are sixteen triangular regions each of which is on the boundary of two and only two three-dimensional regions; and, moreover, each tetrahedral region has one and only one triangular region from each of the four planes on its boundary.

Since any point not on α_1, α_2, α_3, α_4 can be joined to any of the points A_1, A_2, A_3, A_4 by a segment not containing any point of α_1, α_2, α_3, or α_4, the points A_1, A_2, A_3, A_4 are on the boundary of all eight tetrahedral regions; and by similar reasoning each segment which bounds a triangular region also bounds each of the tetrahedral regions bounded by the triangular region.

THEOREM 14. *The boundary of a tetrahedral region consists of its four vertices, together with four triangular regions and the six segments bounding the four triangular regions and bounded by the four vertices.*

COROLLARY. *Three noncoplanar segments having a common end are on the boundary of one and only one of the tetrahedral regions having their ends as vertices.*

The complete set of relations among the points, segments, triangular regions, and tetrahedral regions determined by A_1, A_2, A_3, A_4 may be indicated by three matrices analogous to those employed in § 151. That the points A_i and A_j are ends of the segments σ_{ij} and $\bar{\sigma}_{ij}$ is indicated in the first matrix, a "1" in the ith row and jth column signifying that the point whose name appears at the beginning of the ith row is an end of the segment whose name appears at the top of the jth column, and a "0" signifying that it is not.

H_1 :

	σ_{12}	$\bar{\sigma}_{12}$	σ_{13}	$\bar{\sigma}_{13}$	σ_{14}	$\bar{\sigma}_{14}$	σ_{23}	$\bar{\sigma}_{23}$	σ_{24}	$\bar{\sigma}_{24}$	σ_{34}	$\bar{\sigma}_{34}$
A_1	1	1	1	1	1	1	0	0	0	0	0	0
A_2	1	1	0	0	0	0	1	1	1	1	0	0
A_3	0	0	1	1	0	0	1	1	0	0	1	1
A_4	0	0	0	0	1	1	0	0	1	1	1	1

The four triangular regions in the plane $\alpha_i (i=1, 2, 3, 4)$ determined by the lines in which the other three planes meet α_i may be denoted by τ_{i1}, τ_{i2}, τ_{i3}, τ_{i4}. Applying the results of

§ 151 to each plane we have the following matrix, in which a "1" or a "0" appears in the ith row and jth column according as the segment whose name is at the beginning of the ith row is or is not on the boundary of the triangular region whose name is at the top of the jth column.

H_2:

	τ_{11}	τ_{12}	τ_{13}	τ_{14}	τ_{21}	τ_{22}	τ_{23}	τ_{24}	τ_{31}	τ_{32}	τ_{33}	τ_{34}	τ_{41}	τ_{42}	τ_{43}	τ_{44}
σ_{12}	0	0	0	0	0	0	0	0	0	1	0	1	0	1	0	1
$\bar{\sigma}_{12}$	0	0	0	0	0	0	0	0	1	0	1	0	1	0	1	0
σ_{13}	0	0	0	0	0	1	0	1	0	0	0	0	0	1	1	0
$\bar{\sigma}_{13}$	0	0	0	0	1	0	1	0	0	0	0	0	1	0	0	1
σ_{14}	0	0	0	0	0	1	1	0	0	1	1	0	0	0	0	0
$\bar{\sigma}_{14}$	0	0	0	0	1	0	0	1	1	0	0	1	0	0	0	0
σ_{23}	0	1	0	1	0	0	0	0	0	0	0	0	0	0	1	1
$\bar{\sigma}_{23}$	1	0	1	0	0	0	0	0	0	0	0	0	1	1	0	0
σ_{24}	0	1	1	0	0	0	0	0	0	0	1	1	0	0	0	0
$\bar{\sigma}_{24}$	1	0	0	1	0	0	0	0	1	1	0	0	0	0	0	0
σ_{34}	0	0	1	1	0	0	1	1	0	0	0	0	0	0	0	0
$\bar{\sigma}_{34}$	1	1	0	0	1	1	0	0	0	0	0	0	0	0	0	0

Let us denote the eight tetrahedral regions by $T_1, \cdots, T_8$ and construct a matrix analogous to the preceding ones, in which a "1" or a "0" appears in the ith row and jth column according as the triangular region whose name is at the beginning of the ith row is or is not on the boundary of the tetrahedral region whose name is at the top of the jth column. By definition there is a plane π which meets all the six segments σ_{ij} and none of the segments $\bar{\sigma}_{ij}$. There is one and only one tetrahedral region not met by π. Let us assign the notation so that this region is called T_1. As π cannot meet the segments and triangular regions on the boundaries of T_1, these segments must be the six segments $\bar{\sigma}_{ij}$ and these triangular regions must be those bounded by $\bar{\sigma}_{ij}$. The latter can be found by means of the matrix H_2. This determines the first column of the matrix to be constructed. The other columns are found by considering successively the planes of the seven other classes of planes described in

§ 26. Thus, for example, T_2 is the region on whose boundary are the segments $\bar{\sigma}_{12}$, $\bar{\sigma}_{13}$, σ_{14}, $\bar{\sigma}_{23}$, σ_{24}, σ_{34}.

H_8 :

	T_1	T_2	T_3	T_4	T_5	T_6	T_7	T_8
τ_{11}	1	0	0	0	0	0	0	1
τ_{12}	0	0	0	1	1	0	0	0
τ_{13}	0	1	0	0	0	0	1	0
τ_{14}	0	0	1	0	0	1	0	0
τ_{21}	1	0	0	0	1	0	0	0
τ_{22}	0	0	0	1	0	0	0	1
τ_{23}	0	1	0	0	0	1	0	0
τ_{24}	0	0	1	0	0	0	1	0
τ_{31}	1	0	1	0	0	0	0	0
τ_{32}	0	0	0	0	0	1	0	1
τ_{33}	0	1	0	1	0	0	0	0
τ_{34}	0	0	0	0	1	0	1	0
τ_{41}	1	1	0	0	0	0	0	0
τ_{42}	0	0	0	0	0	0	1	1
τ_{43}	0	0	1	1	0	0	0	0
τ_{44}	0	0	0	0	1	1	0	0

EXERCISE

The planes polar (§ 18, Vol. I) with respect to a tetrahedron $ABCD$ to the points of one of the tetrahedral regions determined by $ABCD$ constitute one of the four sets of planes determined by $ABCD$ according to § 26. The points on these planes constitute the set of all points not on the given tetrahedral region or its boundary.

*** 153. Generalization to *n* dimensions.** The generalization to n dimensions of the point pair, triangle, and tetrahedron is the *$(n+1)$-point in n-space.* This is any set of $n+1$ points no n of which are in the same $(n-1)$-space, together with the lines, planes, 3-spaces, etc. which they determine by pairs, triads, tetrads, etc. By a direct generalization of § 26 one proves that the points not on the $n-1$ spaces of an $(n+1)$-point fall into 2^n mutually exclusive sets $R_1, \cdots, R_{2^n}$ such that any two points of the same set are joined by a segment of points of the set and that any segment joining two points not in the same set contains at least one point on an $(n-1)$-space of the $(n+1)$-point. Any one of the sets $R_1, \cdots, R_{2^n}$ is called a *simplex* or *n-dimensional segment.*

Thus the simplex is a generalization of the linear segment, triangular region, and tetrahedral region. By replacing triangular and tetrahedral regions by simplexes throughout §§ 148–152 we obtain immediately the theory of n-dimensional convex regions. A like process applied to §§ 154–157, below, gives the theory of n-dimensional connected sets, regions, continuous families of sets of points, continuous families of transformations, continuous groups, etc. We leave both series of generalizations to the reader.

154. Curves. DEFINITION. Let $[T]$ be the set of all points on an interval T_0T_1 of a line l. A set of points $[P]$ is called a *continuous curve* or, more simply, a *curve*, if it is in such a correspondence Γ with $[T]$ that

(1) for every T there is one and only one P such that $P = \Gamma(T)$;

(2) for every P there is at least one T such that $P = \Gamma(T)$;

(3) for every T, say T', and for every tetrahedral region R containing $\Gamma(T')$, there is a segment σ of l containing T' and such that for every T in σ, $\Gamma(T)$ is in R.

A curve is said to be *closed* if $\Gamma(T_0) = \Gamma(T_1)$. It is said to be *simple* if Γ can be chosen so as to satisfy (1), (2), (3) and so that if $T' \neq T''$, $\Gamma(T') \neq \Gamma(T'')$ unless the pair $T'T''$ is identical with the pair T_0T_1.

The point $\Gamma(T)$ is said to *describe* the curve as T varies. The curve is said to *join* the points $\Gamma(T_0)$ and $\Gamma(T_1)$.

In view of the definition of the geometric number system in Chap. VI, Vol. I, and the theorems in Chap. I, Vol. II, this definition could also be stated in the following form: Let (t) be the set of numbers such that $0 \leqq t \leqq 1$. A set of points $[P]$ is called a *curve* if it is in such a correspondence Γ with $[t]$ that (1) for every t there is one and only one $P = \Gamma(t)$, (2) for every P there is at least one t such that $P = \Gamma(t)$, and (3) for every t, say t', and for every tetrahedral region R containing $\Gamma(t')$ there is a number $\delta > 0$ such that if $t' - \delta < t < t' + \delta$, $\Gamma(t)$ is in R.

In the Euclidean or non-Euclidean spaces (3) may be replaced by the condition: For every t' and every positive number ϵ there is a positive number δ such that if $t' - \delta < t < t' + \delta$, the distance between $\Gamma(t)$ and $\Gamma(t')$ is less than ϵ.

The most obvious examples of simple closed curves are the projective line and the point conic. The proof that these are simple closed curves will be given for the planar case, and may be extended at once to the three-dimensional case by substituting tetrahedral regions for triangular ones.

THEOREM 15. *A projective line is a simple closed curve.*

Proof. Let $[P]$ be the set of points on a projective line and let P_0, P_1, P_2, P_3 be four particular values of $[P]$ in the order $\{P_0P_1P_2P_3\}$. Let T_0, T_1, T_2, T_3, T_4 be five collinear points in the order $\{T_0T_1T_2T_3T_4\}$, and let $[T]$ be the set of all points of the interval $T_0T_1T_4$. If T is on the interval $T_0T_1T_2$, let $\Gamma(T)$ be the point to which T is carried by a projective correspondence* which takes the points T_0, T_1, T_2 into P_0, P_1, P respectively; and if T is on the interval $T_2T_3T_4$, let $\Gamma(T)$ be the point to which T is carried by a projectivity which carries the points T_2, T_3, T_4 into P_2, P_3, P_0 respectively.

The correspondence Γ is defined so that there is one and only one point $P=\Gamma(T)$ for each T; and also so that $\Gamma(T')\neq\Gamma(T'')$, unless $T'=T''$, or $T'=T_0$ and $T''=T_4$, or $T'=T_4$ and $T''=T_4$. Thus $[P]$ satisfies conditions (1) and (2) of the definition of a curve and the condition that a curve be simple.

Let R be any triangular region containing a point $P'=\Gamma(T')$. By Theorem 1 there is a segment of the projective line $[P]$ containing P' and contained in R; let $P''=\Gamma(T'')$ and $P'''=\Gamma(T''')$ be the ends of this segment. This segment is the image either of the points T between T'' and T''' or of the points T not between T'' and T'''. Hence if σ be any segment of the line T_0T_1 containing T' and not containing T'' or T''', every point T on σ is such that $\Gamma(T)$ is in R. Hence $[P]$ satisfies Condition (3) of the definition of a curve.

THEOREM 16. *A point conic is a simple closed curve.*

Proof. The proof is precisely the same as that of Theorem 15 except that $[P]$ is the set of points on a conic, and the following lemma is used instead of Theorem 1.

*This does not use Assumption P, because it requires only the *existence* of a projectivity, and this may be set up as a series of perspectivities (cf. Chap. III, Vol. I).

Lemma. *If a point P of a conic C^2 is in a triangular region* R *coplanar with C^2, there is a segment σ of C^2 which contains P and is contained in* R.

Proof. If C^2 is entirely in R the conclusion of the theorem is obvious. If not, let Q be a point of C^2 not in R. By § 75 the points of the line PQ interior to C^2 constitute a segment having P and Q as ends. Let R be a point of this segment which is also on the segment containing P (Theorem 1), which the line PQ has in common with R (fig. 81).

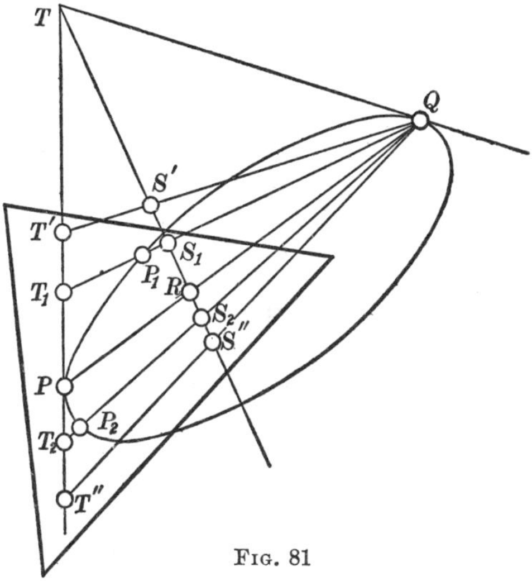

Fig. 81

Let T be the common point of the tangents at P and Q and let T' and T'' be points of R in the order $\{TT'PT''\}$. Let S' and S'' be the points in which QT' and QT'' meet TR; so that $\{TS'RS''\}$. Let S_1 and S_2 be points interior to R, interior to C^2, and in the order $\{TS'S_1RS_2S''\}$ (Theorem 1). The lines QS_1 and QS_2 meet TP in two points T_1 and T_2 respectively in the order $\{TT'T_1PT_2T''\}$. Since these points are on the segment $T'PT''$ they are in R. Since Q is on the conic C^2 the lines QT_1 and QT_2 meet C^2 in two points P_1 and P_2 respectively.

Since S_1 is interior and T_1 (a point of a tangent) exterior to C^2, we have the order $\{QS_1P_1T_1\}$. But S_1 and T_1 are in R and Q is not in R. Hence by Theorem 1, P_1 is in R. In like manner P_2 is in R.

The segment $\overline{P_1PP_2}$ of the conic C^2 is now easily seen to consist entirely of points of R. For if $\bar{P}$ is any point of this segment, and $\bar{T}$ and $\bar{S}$ the points in which $Q\bar{P}$ meets PT and RT respectively,

$$P\bar{P}P_1P_2 \barwedge P\bar{T}T_1T_2 \overset{Q}{\underset{\wedge}{=}} R\bar{S}S_1S_2.$$

Hence $\bar{T}$ is on the segment $\overline{T_1PT_2}$, and $\bar{S}$ is on the segment $\overline{S_1RS_2}$. Hence $\bar{T}$ and $\bar{S}$ are interior to R, and $\bar{S}$ interior to C^2. Since $\bar{T}$ is exterior to C^2, it follows that $\bar{S}$ and $\bar{T}$ separate $\bar{P}$ and Q. Therefore, as Q is not in R, $\bar{P}$ is in R.

EXERCISE

The boundary of a triangular region is a simple closed curve.

155. Connected sets, regions, etc. A set of points is said to be *connected* if and only if any two points of the set are joined by a curve consisting entirely of points of the set. A connected set is sometimes called a *continuous family of points.* In a space satisfying Assumptions A, E, H, C (or A, E, K or A, E, J) a connected set is also called a *continuum.* A connected set in a plane such that every point of the set is in a triangular region containing no points not in the set is called a *planar region.* A connected set of points in space such that every point of the set is in a tetrahedral region containing no points not in the set is called a *three-dimensional region.*

A one-to-one transformation Γ carrying a set of points $[X]$ into a set of points $[Y]$ is said to be *continuous* if and only if for every X, say X', and every tetrahedral region T containing $\Gamma(X')$, there is a tetrahedral region R containing X' and such that for every X in R, $\Gamma(X)$ is in T.

If a linear interval joining two points A, B is subjected to a continuous one-to-one reciprocal transformation, it goes into a curve joining the transforms of A and B (§ 154). The set of points on the curve, excluding the transforms of A and B, is called a *1-cell.*

If a triangular region and its boundary are subjected to a continuous one-to-one reciprocal transformation, the set of points into which the triangular region goes is called a *simply connected element of surface*, or a *2-cell.*

If a tetrahedral region and its boundary are subjected to a continuous one-to-one reciprocal transformation, the set of points into which the boundary goes is called a *simply connected surface*, or *simple surface*, and the set of points into which the tetrahedral region goes is called a *simply connected three-dimensional region*, or a *3-cell.*

EXERCISES

1. A region contains no point of its boundary.

2. If A and B are any two points of a planar region R, there exists a finite number of triangular regions $t_1, t_2, \cdots, t_n$ such that t_i has a point in common with t_{i+1} $(i = 1, \cdots, n-1)$ and t_1 contains A and t_n contains B. This property could be taken as the definition of a region in a plane.

3. Given any set of regions all contained in a convex region. The set of all points in triangular regions whose vertices are in the given regions is a convex region. This region is contained in every convex region containing the given set of regions (J. W. Alexander).

4. The set of all points on segments joining pairs of points of an arbitrary region R contained in a convex region constitutes a convex region R′. The region R′ is contained in every convex region containing R.

5. The boundary (§ 150) of a region in a plane (space) separates (§ 149) the set of all points in the region from the set of all points of the plane (space) not in the region.

6. A continuous one-to-one reciprocal transformation of space transforms any region into a region.

156. Continuous families of sets of points. The notion of continuous curve has the following direct generalization:

Definition. Let $[T]$ be the set of all points on an interval T_0T_1 of a line l. A set of sets of coplanar points [S] is called a *continuous one-parameter family of sets of points* if it is in such a correspondence Γ with T that

(1) for every T there is one and only one set S such that $\mathsf{S}=\Gamma(T)$;

(2) for every set S there is at least one T such that $\mathsf{S}=\Gamma(T)$;

(3) for every T, say T', and for every triangular region R including a point of the set $\Gamma(T')$, there is a segment σ of l containing T' and such that if T is in σ at least one point of the set $\Gamma(T)$ is in R.

The definition of a continuous one-parameter family of sets of points in space is obtained by replacing the triangular region R in the statements above by a tetrahedral region.

If the sets S are taken to be lines, planes, conics, quadrics, etc., this gives the definition of one-parameter continuous families of lines, planes, conics, quadrics, etc., respectively. Cf. Exs. 1–5, below.

Definition. *A connected set of sets of points* or a *continuous family of sets of points* is a set of sets of points [S] such that any two sets S_1, S_2 are members of a continuous one-parameter family of sets of [S].

For example, the discussions given below in terms of elementary transformations establish in each case that a sense-class is a connected set of sets of points. Cf. also Exs. 6–7, below.

The definition of a continuous family may be extended in an obvious way so as to include sets whose elements are points, sets of points, sets of sets of points, etc.

EXERCISES

1. Defining an *envelope* of lines as the plane dual of a curve, prove that an envelope is a continuous one-parameter family of lines.

2. The space dual of a curve is a continuous one-parameter family of planes.

3. Pencils of lines and planes are continuous one-parameter families.

4. A line conic or a regulus is a continuous one-parameter family of lines.

5. A pencil of point conics is a continuous one-parameter family of curves.

6. The set of all lines in a plane or space or in a linear congruence or a linear complex is a connected set of sets of points.

7. The set of all planes in space or of all planes tangent to a quadric is a connected set of sets of points.

157. Continuous families of transformations. Let $[T]$ be the set of all points on an interval T_0T_1 of a line l. Let $[\Pi_T]$ be a set of transformations of a set of points $[P]$. If (1) to every T there corresponds one and only one transformation Π_T, and (2) for every point P the set of points $[\Pi_T(P)]$ is a curve for which the defining correspondence Γ (in the notation of § 154) may be taken to be the correspondence between T and $\Pi_T(P)$, then $[\Pi_T]$ is said to be a *continuous one-parameter family of transformations.* The curves $[\Pi_T(P)]$ are called the *path curves* of $[\Pi_T]$.

The term "continuous one-parameter family of transformations" may also be applied to a set of transformations $[\Pi_T]$ of a set S of points P and of sets of points S (e.g. S may be a set of figures as defined in § 13, Vol. I). In this case (1) and (2) must be satisfied, and also the following condition: (3) For every set of points S, $[\Pi_T(\mathsf{S})]$ is a one-parameter continuous family of sets of points for which the defining correspondence Γ (in the notation of § 156) may be taken to be the correspondence between T and $\Pi_T(\mathsf{S})$.

If the set of correspondences $[\Pi_T]$ is both a group and a continuous one-parameter family of transformations, it is called a *one-parameter continuous group.*

A set of transformations $[\Pi]$ of a set of points and of sets of points, such that any two transformations of $[\Pi]$ are members of a continuous one-parameter family of transformations of $[\Pi]$, is called a *continuous family of transformations.* If $[\Pi]$ is also a group, it is called a *continuous group.*

If $[\Pi_T]$ is a continuous one-parameter family of one-to-one reciprocal transformations of a figure F, and if Π_{T_0} is the identity, then F is said to be *moved*, or *deformed, to the figure* $\Pi_{T_1}(F)$ *through the set of intermediate positions* $[\Pi_T(F)]$. Any one of the transformations Π_T is called a *deformation*; if F is a set of points and all the transformations of the family $[\Pi_T]$ are continuous, the deformation is said to be a *continuous deformation.*

158. Affine theorems on sense. Let us recapitulate some of the main propositions about sense-classes in Euclidean spaces by enumerating the one-dimensional propositions of which they are generalizations.

The group of all projectivities $x' = ax + b$ on a Euclidean line has a subgroup of *direct projectivities* for which $a > 0$. This subgroup is self-conjugate, because if a transformation of the group be denoted by Σ, and any other transformation $x' = \alpha x + \beta$ by T, then $\mathrm{T}\Sigma\mathrm{T}^{-1}$ is

$$x' = \alpha\left(a\left(\frac{1}{\alpha}x - \frac{\beta}{\alpha}\right) + b\right) + \beta,$$

a transformation in which the coefficient of x is positive. From the fact that the subgroup is self-conjugate, it follows as in § 18 that the same subgroup is defined by the condition $a > 0$, no matter how the scale is chosen, so long as P_∞ is the point at infinity. These statements are generalized to the plane in § 30 and to spaces of any dimensionality in § 31. The generalization consists in replacing a by the determinant

$$\begin{vmatrix} a_{11} & a_{12} \\ a_{21} & a_{22} \end{vmatrix}$$

for the two-dimensional case, and by the corresponding n-rowed determinant in the n-dimensional case.

A sense-class $S(AB)$ is the set of all ordered pairs of points into which a pair of distinct points can be carried by direct projectivities (§ 23). This proposition is generalized to the plane in § 30 and to n-space in § 31.

A particular arbitrarily chosen sense-class shall be called *positive* and the other sense-class shall be called *negative.* This statement reads the same for any number of dimensions. In the three-dimensional case the positive sense-class is also called *right-handed* and the negative sense-class *left-handed* (see the fine print in § 162).

In the one-dimensional case a nonhomogeneous coördinate system is called *positive* if $S(P_0P_1)$ is positive. In the two-dimensional case a nonhomogeneous coördinate system is called *positive* if $S(OXY)$ is positive when $O=(0, 0)$, $X=(1, 0)$, and $Y=(0, 1)$. In the three-dimensional case a nonhomogeneous coördinate system is called *positive* or *right-handed* if $S(OXYZ)$ is positive when $O=(0, 0, 0)$, $X=(1, 0, 0)$, $Y=(0, 1, 0)$, and $Z=(0, 0, 1)$.

On the Euclidean line two ordered pairs of points AB and $A'B'$ are in the same sense-class if and only if

$$\begin{vmatrix} 1 & a \\ 1 & b \end{vmatrix} \quad \text{and} \quad \begin{vmatrix} 1 & a' \\ 1 & b' \end{vmatrix}$$

have the same sign, a, b, a', b' being the nonhomogeneous coördinates of A, B, A', B' respectively. Hence, if the coördinate system is positive, $S(AB)$ is positive or negative according as $(b-a)$ is positive or negative. Similar criteria for the plane and space are given in §§ 30, 31. It follows immediately that if the coördinate system in the plane is positive, $S(ABC)$ is positive or negative according as the determinant

$$\begin{vmatrix} 1 & a_1 & a_2 \\ 1 & b_1 & b_2 \\ 1 & c_1 & c_2 \end{vmatrix}$$

is positive or negative, where $A=(a_1, a_2)$, $B=(b_1, b_2)$, $C=(c_1, c_2)$. If the coördinate system in space is positive, $S(ABCD)$ is positive or negative according as the determinant

$$\begin{vmatrix} 1 & a_1 & a_2 & a_3 \\ 1 & b_1 & b_2 & b_3 \\ 1 & c_1 & c_2 & c_3 \\ 1 & d_1 & d_2 & d_3 \end{vmatrix}$$

is positive or negative, where $A=(a_1, a_2, a_3)$, $B=(b_1, b_2, b_3)$, $C=(c_1, c_2, c_3)$, $D=(d_1, d_2, d_3)$.

In the one-dimensional case B is on one or the other of the rays having A as origin according as $S(AB)$ is positive or negative. In a Euclidean plane C is on one side of the line AB or the other according as $S(ABC)$ is positive or negative (§ 30). In a Euclidean space D is on one side or the other of the plane ABC according as $S(ABCD)$ is positive or negative.

The projectivities $x'=ax+b$ of the Euclidean line are in one-to-one reciprocal correspondence with the points (a, b) of the Euclidean plane. The direct projectivities correspond to the points on one side of the line $a=0$ and the opposite ones to those on the other side. From this it readily follows that the set of all direct projectivities forms a continuous group, whereas the set of all projectivities is a group which is not continuous.

In like manner the transformations

$$x' = a_{11}x + a_{12}y + a_{10},$$
$$y' = a_{21}x + a_{22}y + a_{20}$$

can be set in correspondence with the points of a six-dimensional Euclidean space, the direct and opposite collineations respectively corresponding to points of two regions separated by the locus

$$a_{11}a_{22} - a_{12}a_{21} = 0.$$

Similarly, the direct and opposite collineations in a Euclidean space of three dimensions may be represented by points of two regions in a space of twelve dimensions. In all three cases the set of all direct collineations forms a continuous group, but the set of all collineations does not.

Another way of coming at the same result is this: Let the ordered pairs of points AB of a Euclidean line be represented by the points (a, b) of a Euclidean plane, a being the nonhomogeneous coördinate of A, and b that of B. Under this convention the points representing pairs of the positive sense-class are on one side of the line $b - a = 0$ and those representing pairs of the negative sense-class on the other side of this line. The one-dimensional affine projectivities are in one-to-one reciprocal correspondence with the ordered point pairs to which they carry a fixed ordered point pair PQ. The direct projectivities thus correspond to point pairs represented by points on one side of the line $b - a = 0$ and the opposite projectivities to point pairs represented by points on the other side.

159. Elementary transformations on a Euclidean line. DEFINITION. Given an ordered pair of points AB of a Euclidean line, the operation of replacing one of the points by a second point not separated from it by the other point is called an *elementary transformation* of the pair AB.*

Thus AB may be transformed into AB' if $\{ABB'\}$ or $\{AB'B\}$. In other words (cf. § 23) B can be transformed to any point B' such that $S(AB) = S(AB')$, and into no other. Hence it follows that if AB is transformable to $A'B'$ by any sequence of elementary transformations, $S(AB) = S(A'B')$.

Conversely, if $S(AB) = S(A'B')$, it is easy to see, as follows, that by a sequence of elementary transformations AB can be transformed

* The transformations which we have considered heretofore have usually been transformations of the line, plane, or space as a whole. Here we are considering a transformation of a single pair of points.

to $A'B'$. From the theorems on linear order in Chap. II it follows that there are two points A'' and B'' satisfying the order relations

$$\{ABA''B''\} \quad \text{and} \quad \{A'B'A''B''\}.$$

By elementary transformations AB goes to AB''; AB'' to $A''B''$; $A''B''$ to $A'B''$; and $A'B''$ to $A'B'$. Hence we have

THEOREM 17. *On a Euclidean line the set of all ordered pairs of points into which an ordered pair of distinct points AB can be transformed by elementary transformations is the sense-class $S(AB)$.*

An elementary transformation may be regarded as a special type of *continuous deformation* (§ 157). If AB is carried by an elementary transformation to AB', the point B may be thought of as moved (§ 157) along the segment BB' from B to B', and since this segment does not contain A, the motion is such that the pair of distinct points never degenerates into a coincident pair. Thus we may say that a sense-class consists of all pairs obtainable from a fixed pair by deformations in which no pair ever degenerates.

When the ordered point pairs are represented by points in a Euclidean plane, as explained at the end of the last section, an elementary transformation corresponds to moving a point (a, b) parallel to the a-axis or the b-axis in such a way as not to intersect the line $a = b$.

DEFINITION. An elementary transformation of a pair of points AB is said to be *restricted with respect to a set of points* $[P]$ if and only if it carries one of the pair, say B, into a point B' such that the segment BB' does not contain any one of the points P. (Any one of these points may, however, be an end of the segment BB'.)

It is evident that any elementary transformation can be effected as a resultant of a sequence of elementary transformations which are restricted with respect to an arbitrary finite set of points. Hence Theorem 17 has the following corollary:

COROLLARY. *Let $P_1, P_2, \cdots, P_n$ be any finite set of points on a line l. Two ordered pairs of points are in the same sense-class if and only if one can be carried into the other by a sequence of elementary transformations restricted with respect to $P_1, P_2, \cdots, P_n$.*

The concept of a restricted elementary transformation is intimately connected with the idea of a "small motion." In the metric geometry the points $P_1, P_2, \cdots, P_n$ can be chosen so as to be in the order $\{P_1, P_2, \cdots, P_n\}$ and so that the segments P_iP_{i+1} are arbitrarily small. Any elementary transformation of a pair of points on the interval P_iP_{i+1} will be effected by a small motion of one of the points in the pair.

160. Elementary transformations in the Euclidean plane and space. DEFINITION. Given an ordered set of three noncollinear points in a Euclidean plane, an *elementary transformation* is the operation of replacing one of them by a point which is joined to it by a segment not meeting the line on the other two.

As in the one-dimensional case, an elementary transformation may be regarded as effected by a continuous deformation of a point triad. A path is specified along which a point may be moved without allowing the triad to degenerate into a collinear one.

Let A, B, C be three noncollinear points and let C' and B' be points of the segments AB and CA respectively. Then by elementary transformations (cf. fig. 84, p. 423) ABC goes to $C'BC$; and this to $C'BB'$; and this to $C'CB'$; and this to BCB'; and this to BCA. In like manner it can be shown that ABC can be carried to CAB by a sequence of elementary transformations. Hence any even permutation of three noncollinear points can be effected by elementary transformations.

By Theorem 27, § 30, an elementary transformation leaves the sense of an ordered triad invariant. Hence, by Theorem 26, § 30, no odd permutation can be effected by elementary transformations.

If A', B', C' are any three noncollinear points, ABC can be carried into some permutation of $A'B'C'$ by elementary transformations. For since at most one side of the triangle $A'B'C'$ is parallel to the line AB, this line meets two of the sides in points which we may denote by A'' and B''. By one-dimensional elementary transformations on the line AB, the ordered pair AB can be carried either to $A''B''$ or to $B''A''$. These one-dimensional elementary transformations determine a sequence of two-dimensional elementary transformations leaving C invariant and carrying ABC to $A''B''C$ or to $B''A''C$. The point C can be carried by an obvious elementary transformation to a point C'' such that $A''C''$ is not parallel to any side of $A'B'C'$, and then $A''C''$ can be carried to two of the points, say $A'''C'''$, in which the line $A''C''$ meets the sides of the triangle $A'B'C'$. The points $A'''B''C'''$ are on the sides of the triangle $A'B'C'$, and the one-dimensional elementary transformations on the sides which carry them into the vertices determine two-dimensional elementary transformations which carry $A'''B''C'''$ to some permutation of $A'B'C'$.

Since ABC cannot be carried into $A'B'C'$ if $S(ABC) \neq S(A'B'C')$, and since all even permutations of $A'B'C'$ can be effected by elementary transformations, it follows that ABC can be carried into $A'B'C'$ by a sequence of elementary transformations if $S(ABC) = S(A'B'C')$. Hence we have

Theorem 18. *In a Euclidean plane $S(ABC) = S(A'B'C')$ if and only if there exists a finite set of elementary transformations carrying the noncollinear points A, B, C into the points A', B', C' respectively.*

Definition. Given an ordered set of four noncoplanar points, an *elementary transformation* is the operation of replacing one of them by another point which is joined to it by a segment containing no point of the plane on the other three.

Let $ABCD$ be four noncoplanar points. Holding D fixed, ABC may be subjected to precisely the sequence of elementary transformations given above in the planar case for carrying ABC into BCA. This effects the permutation

$$\begin{pmatrix} A & B & C & D \\ B & C & A & D \end{pmatrix},$$

the symbol for each point being written above that for the point into which it is transformed. In like manner we obtain the permutations

$$\begin{pmatrix} A & B & C & D \\ B & D & C & A \end{pmatrix}, \quad \begin{pmatrix} A & B & C & D \\ C & B & D & A \end{pmatrix}, \quad \begin{pmatrix} A & B & C & D \\ A & C & D & B \end{pmatrix},$$

and it is easily verifiable that any even permutation of $ABCD$ is a product of these permutations. Hence any even permutation of a set of four points may be effected by elementary transformations.

By Theorem 23, § 27, an elementary transformation of four points (a_1, a_2, a_3), (b_1, b_2, b_3), (c_1, c_2, c_3), (d_1, d_2, d_3) leaves the sign of

$$\begin{vmatrix} a_1 & a_2 & a_3 & 1 \\ b_1 & b_2 & b_3 & 1 \\ c_1 & c_2 & c_3 & 1 \\ d_1 & d_2 & d_3 & 1 \end{vmatrix}$$

invariant, and hence leaves their sense-class invariant. Hence (§ 31) no odd permutations of four noncoplanar points can be effected by elementary transformations.

An ordered tetrad $ABCD$ of noncoplanar points can be carried into some permutation of an ordered tetrad $A'B'C'D'$ of noncoplanar points. For the line AB is not parallel to more than two planes of the tetrahedron, and hence by the one-dimensional case AB can be carried into two points $A''B''$ of the planes of the tetrahedron $A'B'C'D'$. By repeating this argument it is easily proved that C and D can also be carried to points $C''D''$ on these planes. By the two-dimensional case it follows that the ordered tetrad $A''B''C''D''$ of points on the planes of the tetrahedron $A'B'C'D'$ can be carried into some permutation of its vertices. Since $ABCD$ cannot be carried into $A'B'C'D'$, if $S(ABCD) \neq S(A'B'C'D')$ it follows by the last paragraph but one that it can be carried into $A'B'C'D'$ if $S(ABCD) = S(A'B'C'D')$. Thus we have

THEOREM 19. *In a Euclidean space $S(ABCD) = S(A'B'C'D')$ if and only if there exists a finite set of elementary transformations carrying the noncoplanar points A, B, C, D into the points A', B', C', D' respectively.*

The theorems and definitions of the last two sections can be regarded as based on any one of the sets of assumptions A, E, H, C, R or A, E, K or A, E, P, S. Assumption P is used wherever coördinates are employed, but it is possible to make the argument without the aid of coördinates and thus to base it on A, E, S alone (cf. Ex. 2, § 161).

161. Sense in a convex region. DEFINITION. Given a set of three noncollinear points of a planar convex region R, the operation of replacing any one of them by any other point of R on the same side of the line joining the other two is called an *elementary transformation.* The set of all ordered triads obtainable by finite sequences of elementary transformations from one noncollinear ordered triad of points ABC is called a *sense-class* and is denoted by $S(ABC)$.

This definition is in agreement with the propositions about sense given for the special case of a Euclidean plane. Moreover, if R is any convex region, and l_∞ is any line coplanar with R but containing no point of R, two triads of points of R are in the same sense with respect to R if and only if they are in the same sense with respect to the Euclidean plane containing R and having l_∞ as singular line. Hence the theorems of § 160 may be taken over at once to convex regions in general. This result may be stated as follows:

THEOREM 20. *In a planar convex region there are two and only two senses. Sense is preserved by even and altered by odd permutations of three noncollinear points. Two points C and D are on opposite sides of a line AB if and only if $S(ABC) \neq S(ABD)$.*

DEFINITION. Given a set of four noncoplanar points of a three-dimensional convex region R, the operation of replacing any one of them by any point of R on the same side of the plane of the other three is called an *elementary transformation.* The set of all ordered tetrads obtainable by finite sequences of elementary transformations from one noncoplanar ordered tetrad of points $ABCD$ is called a *sense-class* and is denoted by $S(ABCD)$.

The theories of sense in a three-dimensional convex region and in a three-dimensional Euclidean space are related in just the same way as the corresponding planar theories. Hence we have

THEOREM 21. *In a three-dimensional convex region there are two and only two senses. Sense is preserved by even and altered by odd permutations of four points. Two points D and E are on opposite sides of a plane ABC if and only if $S(ABCD) \neq S(ABCE)$.*

EXERCISES

1. The whole theory of order relations can be developed by defining sense-class on a line by means of elementary transformations instead of as in Chap. II.

* **2.** Develop the theory of order in two- and three-dimensional convex regions, defining sense-class in terms of elementary transformations and using Assumptions A, E, S or Assumptions I–VIII of § 29 (cf. Theorem 5, § 148) as basis.

3. An elementary transformation of a triad of points ABC is said to be *restricted with respect to a set of points* $P_1, P_2, \cdots, P_n$ if it carries a point of the triad, say C, into a point C' such that the segment CC' does not contain any point collinear with two of the points $P_1, P_2, \cdots, P_n$. Two ordered triads of points are in the same sense-class if and only if there is a sequence of restricted elementary transformations carrying the one triad into the other.

4. Generalize the notion of restricted elementary transformation to space.

162. Euclidean theorems on sense. The involutions which leave the point at infinity of a Euclidean line invariant may be called *point reflections.* The product of two point reflections is a parabolic projectivity leaving the point at infinity invariant, and may be called a *translation.* A point reflection has an equation of the form

$$x' = -x + b, \tag{1}$$

and a translation has one of the form

$$x' = x + b. \tag{2}$$

The point reflections interchange the two sense-classes of the Euclidean line, and the translations leave them invariant.

In generalizing these propositions to the plane, the point reflections may be replaced by the orthogonal line reflections (Chap. IV) or, indeed, by the set of all symmetries, and the one-dimensional translations by the set of all displacements in the plane. Since an orthogonal line reflection in the plane interchanges the two sense-classes, any symmetry interchanges them, but any displacement leaves each of them invariant. The generalization to three-dimensions is similar.

The equations of a displacement in two or three (or any number of) dimensions are a direct generalization of the one-dimensional equations, namely,

$$x_i' = \sum_{j=1}^{n} a_{ij}x_j + b_i, \qquad (i = 1, 2, \cdots, n) \tag{3}$$

where the matrix (a_{ij}) is orthogonal and the determinant $|a_{ij}|$ is $+1$. The equations of a symmetry satisfy the same condition except that the determinant $|a_{ij}|$ is -1 instead of $+1$.

It is worthy of comment that the distinction between displacements and symmetries holds in the complex space just as well as in the real, whereas the distinction between direct and opposite collineations holds only in the real space. Algebraically, this is because the distinction of sense depends merely on the sign of the determinant $|a_{ij}|$, whereas the distinction between displacements and symmetries is between collineations satisfying the condition $|a_{ij}| = +1$ and $|a_{ij}| = -1$. In the representative spaces of six and twelve dimensions referred to in § 158, $|a_{ij}| = 1$ and $|a_{ij}| = -1$ are the equations of nonintersecting loci.

From the point of view of Euclidean geometry, as has been said above, the two sense-classes are indistinguishable.* In the applications of geometry, however, a number of extra-geometrical elements enter which make the two

* This does not contradict the existence of a geometry in which one sense-class is specified absolutely in the assumptions. The group of such a geometry is unlike the Euclidean group in that it does not include symmetries though it does include displacements. Its relation to the Euclidean geometry is similar to that of the geometries mentioned in the fine print in § 116. Those geometries, however, correspond to groups which are not self-conjugate under the Euclidean group, whereas this one corresponds to a self-conjugate subgroup. On the foundations of geometry in terms of sense-relations taken either absolutely or relatively, see the article by Schweitzer referred to in § 15.

sense-classes play essentially different rôles. Thus any normal human being who identifies the abstract Euclidean space with the space in which he views himself and other material objects may single out one of the sense-classes as follows: Let him hold his right hand in such a way that the index finger is in line with his arm, his middle finger at right angles to his index finger, and his thumb at right angles to the two fingers (fig. 82). Let a point in his palm be denoted by O, and the tips of his thumb, index finger, and middle finger by X, Y, Z respectively. The sense-class $S(OXYZ)$ shall be called *right-handed* or *positive*, and the other *left-handed* or *negative*. This designation is unique because of the mechanical structure of the body.

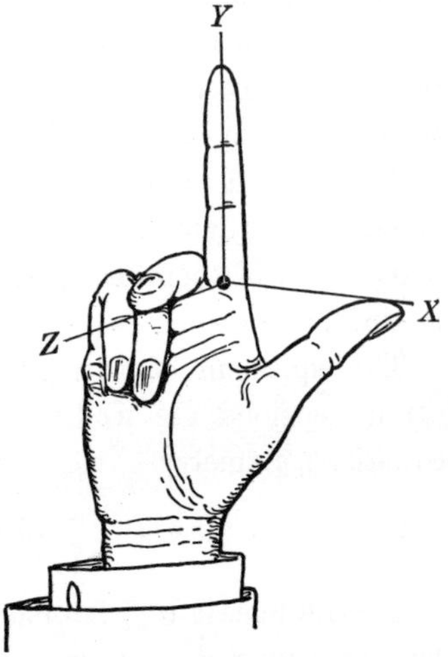

FIG. 82

A nonhomogeneous coördinate system is called *right-handed* or *positive* if and only if $S(OXYZ)$ is positive when $O=(0, 0, 0)$, $X=(1, 0, 0)$, $Y=(0, 1, 0)$, and $Z=(0, 0, 1)$. The reader will find it convenient whenever an arbitrary sense-class is called positive to identify it with the intuitively right-handed sense-class.*

163. Positive and negative displacements. On a Euclidean line, if a translation carries one point A to a point B such that $S(AB)$ is positive, it carries any point A to a point B such that $S(AB)$ is positive. Such a translation is called *positive*. Any other translation is called *negative* and has the property that if it carries C to D, $S(CD)$ is negative. Any translation carries positive translations into positive translations; i.e. if T' is a positive translation and T any translation, $TT'T^{-1}$ is a positive translation. A translation $x' = x + b$ is positive or negative according as b is positive or negative, provided that the scale is such that $S(P_0P_1)$ is positive. The inverse of a positive translation is negative.

The distinction between positive and negative translations is quite distinct from that between direct and opposite projectivities, for all translations are direct.

* An interesting account of the way in which this choice is made in various branches of mathematics and other sciences is to be found in an article by E. Study, Archiv der Mathematik und Physik, 3d series, Vol. XXI (1913), p. 193.

A like subdivision of the Euclidean displacements of a plane which are neither translations nor point reflections nor the identity may be made as follows: A rotation leaving a point O fixed and carrying a point A to a point B not collinear with O and A is said to be *positive* if $S(OAB)$ is positive and to be *negative* if $S(OAB)$ is negative. It is easily proved that if $S(OAB)$ is positive for one value of A it is positive for all values of A. The inverse of a positive rotation is negative. Any displacement transforms a positive rotation into a positive rotation.

A rotation is a product of two orthogonal line reflections $\{lL_\infty\}$ and $\{mM_\infty\}$ such that the lines l and m intersect in O. Hence the ordered pairs of lines which intersect and are not perpendicular fall into two classes, which we shall call *positive* and *negative* respectively, according as the rotations which they determine are positive or negative.

In a three-dimensional Euclidean space let A be a point not on the axis of a given twist which is not a half-twist, let O be the foot of a perpendicular from A on the axis of the twist, and let A' and O' be the points to which A and O respectively are carried by the twist. The twist is said to be *positive* or *right-handed* if $S(OAO'A')$ is positive or right-handed and to be *negative* or *left-handed* if $S(OAO'A')$ is negative.

It is easily seen that $S(OAO'A')$ is the same for all choices of A, so that the definition just made is independent of the choice of A. The inverse of the twist carrying O and A to O' and A' carries O' and A' to O and A, and thus is positive if and only if $S(O'A'OA)$ is positive. Since $S(O'A'OA) = S(OAO'A')$, the inverse of a positive twist is positive. Any direct similarity transformation carries a positive twist into a positive twist.

With the choice of the right-handed sense-class described in the fine print in § 162, the definition here given is such that a right-handed twist is the displacement suffered by a commercial right-handed screw driven a short distance into a piece of wood.

Since a twist is a product of two orthogonal line reflections, $\{ll_\infty\} \cdot \{mm_\infty\}$, it follows that the pairs of ordinary lines lm which are not parallel, intersecting, or perpendicular fall into two classes, according as the twist $\{mm_\infty\} \cdot \{ll_\infty\}$ is positive or negative. We shall call the line pairs of these two classes *positive* and *right-handed* or *negative* and *left-handed* respectively. Since the inverse of a positive twist is positive, the ordered pair ml is positive if lm is positive. Hence a pair of lines is right-handed or left-handed without regard to the order of its members. Any direct similarity transformation carries a right-handed pair of lines into a right-handed pair and a left-handed pair into a left-handed pair.

EXERCISES

1. The collineations which are commutative with a positive displacement (or with a negative displacement) are all direct.

2. By the definition in § 69, $0<\measuredangle AOB<\pi$ or $\pi<\measuredangle AOB<2\pi$ according as $S(OAB)$ is positive or negative, provided that the points O, P_0, $P_{\frac{1}{2}}$ are so chosen that $S(OP_0P_{\frac{1}{2}})$ is positive.

3. By the definition in § 72, $0<m(l_1l_2)<\frac{\pi}{2}$ or $\frac{\pi}{2}<m(l_1l_2)<\pi$ according as the ordered line pair l_1l_2 is positive or negative.

4. Let us define an *elementary transformation* of an ordered line pair l_1l_2 in a plane as being either the operation of replacing l_1 or l_2 by a line parallel to itself, or the operation of replacing l_1 or l_2, say l_1, by a line through the point l_1l_2 which is not separated from l_1 by l_2 and the line through l_1l_2 perpendicular to l_2. Two ordered pairs of nonparallel and nonperpendicular lines are equivalent under elementary transformations if and only if they are both in the positive or both in the negative class.

5. Let us define an *elementary transformation* of a pair of nonparallel and nonperpendicular lines l_1l_2 in space as the operation of replacing one of the lines, say l_1, by a line intersecting l_1 and not separated from l_1 by the plane through the point of intersection perpendicular to l_1 and the plane through this point and l_2. The pair l_1l_2 can be transformed into a pair of lines m_1m_2 by a sequence of elementary transformations if and only if both pairs are right-handed or both pairs are left-handed.

164. Sense-classes in projective spaces. It has been seen in Chap. II (cf. §§ 18 and 32) that the distinction between direct and opposite collineations can be drawn in any projective space of an odd number of dimensions which is real or, more generally, which satisfies *A, E, S*. This depends (§ 32) on the fact that the sign of a determinant $|a_{ij}|$ $(i, j = 0, 1, \cdots, n)$ cannot be changed by multiplying every element by the same factor if n is odd, and can be changed by multiplying every element by -1 if n is even.

In a real projective space of odd dimensionality the direct collineations form a self-conjugate subgroup of the projective group and thus give rise to the definitions of sense-class in §§ 19 and 32. The same remarks are made about the independence of this definition of the frame of reference as in the Euclidean cases, and the criteria for sense in terms of products of determinants are given in §§ 24 and 32. If one forms the analogous determinant products for the projective spaces of even dimensionality, it is found that the sign of the product may be changed by multiplying the coördinates of one point by -1, which verifies in a second way that there is only one sense-class in a projective space of an even number of dimensions.

The projectivity
$$x' = \frac{a_{11}x + a_{12}}{a_{21}x + a_{22}}$$
may be represented by means of a point $(a_{11}, a_{12}, a_{21}, a_{22})$ in a projective space of three dimensions. The points representing direct projectivities are on one side of the ruled quadric
$$\begin{vmatrix} a_{11} & a_{12} \\ a_{21} & a_{22} \end{vmatrix} = 0,$$
and those representing opposite projectivities on the other side. This representation of projectivities by points is in fact identical with that considered in § 129. It can be generalized to any number of dimensions just as are the analogous representations in § 158.

It readily follows that the group of all projective collineations in a real space of n dimensions is continuous if n is even, and not continuous if n is odd. If n is odd the group of direct collineations is continuous.

In the following sections (§§ 165–167) we shall discuss the sense-classes of projective spaces by means of elementary transformations, the latter term being used as before to designate a particular type of continuous deformation. After this (§§ 169–181) similar considerations will be applied to other figures.

165. Elementary transformations on a projective line. DEFINITION. Given a set of three collinear points A, B, C, an *elementary transformation* is the operation of replacing any one of them, say A, by another point A' such that there is a segment AA' not containing B or C.

THEOREM 22. *Two ordered triads of points on a real projective line have the same sense if and only if one is transformable into the other by a finite number of elementary transformations.*

Proof. Comparing the definitions of elementary transformation and of segment (§ 22), it is clear that a single elementary transformation cannot change the sense of a triad of points. Hence two triads of points have the same sense if one can be transformed into the other by a finite number of elementary transformations. The converse statement, namely, that a triad A, B, C can be transformed by elementary transformations into any other triad $A'B'C'$ in the same sense-class, follows at once if we establish (1) that ABC can be transformed by elementary transformations into BCA and CAB and (2) that any ordered triad of points A, B, C can be transformed by elementary transformations into one of the six ordered triads formed by any three points A', B', C'.

(1) Let D be a point in the order $\{ABCD\}$. Then by elementary transformations we can change ABC into ABD, then into ACD, then into BCD, and then into BCA. By repeating these steps once more ABC can be transformed into CAB.

(2) If A' does not coincide with one of the points A, B, C, it is on one of the three mutually exclusive segments (§ 22) of which they are the ends; and by (1) the points ABC may be transformed so that the ends of this segment are B and C. Hence we have $\{ABA'C\}$, and by elementary transformations ABC goes successively into $AA'C$, $BA'C$, $BA'A$, $BA'C$. If A' does coincide with one of the points A, B, C, the triad ABC may be transformed according to (1) so that $A'=A$. In like manner the three points $A'BC$ can be transformed into A', B', C in some order, and then $A'B'C$ into $A'B'C'$ in some order.

The proof given for this theorem holds good without change on the basis of Assumptions A, E, S. Cf. § 15.

DEFINITION. An elementary transformation of a triad of points ABC of a line l is said to be *restricted with respect to a set of points* $P_1, P_2, \cdots, P_n$ if it carries one point of the triad, say C, into a point C' such that C and C' are not separated by any pair of the points $P_1, P_2, \cdots, P_n$. (C or C' may coincide with any of the points $P_1, \cdots, P_n$.)

It is obvious that any elementary transformation whatever is the resultant of a finite number of restricted elementary transformations. Hence Theorem 22 has the following immediate corollary:

COROLLARY. *Let $P_1, P_2, \cdots, P_n$ be any finite set of points on a line l. Two ordered triads of points of l have the same sense if and only if one is transformable into the other by a finite number of elementary transformations restricted with respect to $P_1, P_2, \cdots, P_n$.*

The concept of "restricted elementary transformation" connects with the intuitive idea of "small motions." Let a line be set into projective correspondence with a conic, say a circle. For any n there is a set of points $P_1, P_2, \cdots, P_n$ on the circle such that the intervals P_1P_2, etc. are equal. By increasing n these intervals can be made arbitrarily small, and thus the elementary transformations restricted with respect to $P_1, P_2, \cdots, P_n$ can be made arbitrarily small.

166. Elementary transformations in a projective plane. DEFINITION. Given a set of four points in a projective plane, no three being collinear, an *elementary transformation* is the operation of replacing one of them by a point of the same plane joined to the point replaced by a segment not meeting any side of the triangle of the other three points.

THEOREM 23. *If $ABCD$ and $A'B'C'D'$ are any two complete quadrangles in the same projective plane, there exists a finite set of elementary transformations changing the points A, B, C, D into A', B', C', D' respectively.*

Proof. It can be shown by means of the result for the one-dimensional case, just as in the proof of Theorem 18, first that the ordered tetrad $ABCD$ can be carried by elementary transformations into an

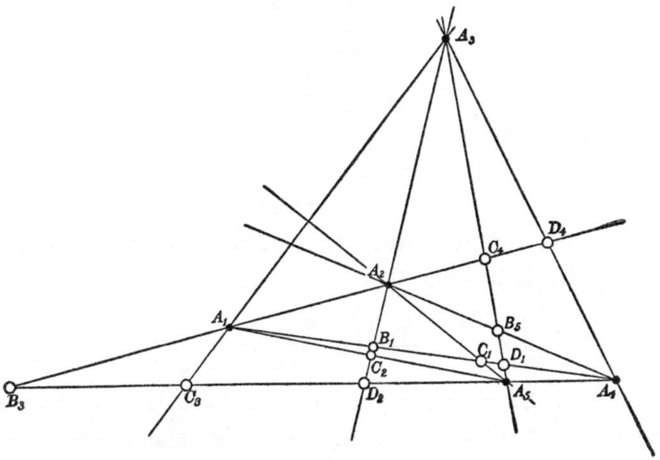

FIG. 83

ordered tetrad $A''B''C''D''$ of points on the sides of the quadrangle $A'B'C'D'$ and then that $A''B''C''D''$ can be carried by elementary transformations into some permutation of $A'B'C'D'$.

To complete the proof it is necessary to show that any permutation of the vertices of a complete quadrangle can be effected by elementary transformations.

Given a complete quadrangle $A_1A_2A_3A_4$, let B_1 be the point of intersection of the lines A_2A_3 and A_1A_4, and let C_1 and D_1 be two points in the order $\{A_1B_1C_1D_1A_4\}$. Let A_5 be the point of intersection of A_2C_1 with A_3D_1 and let C_2, D_2, B_3, C_3, C_4, D_4, B_5 be the points defined by the following perspectivities (fig. 83):

$$A_1B_1C_1D_1A_4 \overset{A_5}{\underset{\wedge}{=}} C_2B_1A_2A_3D_2 \overset{A_1}{\underset{\wedge}{=}} A_5A_4B_3C_3D_2$$
$$\overset{A_3}{\underset{\wedge}{=}} C_4D_4B_3A_1A_2 \overset{A_4}{\underset{\wedge}{=}} C_4A_3A_5D_1B_5.$$

By Theorem 7, Chap. II, it follows that no two of the pairs of points A_1A_4, A_2A_3, A_4A_5, A_1A_2, and A_3A_5 are separated by the lines joining the other three of the points A_1, A_2, A_3, A_4, A_5. Hence there exist elementary transformations changing each of the following sets of four points into the one written below it:

$$\begin{matrix} A_1 & A_2 & A_3 & A_4 \\ A_1 & A_2 & A_3 & A_5 \\ A_4 & A_2 & A_3 & A_5 \\ A_4 & A_1 & A_3 & A_5 \\ A_4 & A_1 & A_2 & A_5 \\ A_4 & A_1 & A_2 & A_3 \end{matrix}$$

Hence the permutation

$$\Pi_1 = \begin{pmatrix} A_1A_2A_3A_4 \\ A_4A_1A_2A_3 \end{pmatrix}$$

can be effected by elementary transformations. By changing the notation in Π_1 it is clear that

$$\Pi_2 = \begin{pmatrix} A_1A_4A_2A_3 \\ A_3A_1A_4A_2 \end{pmatrix}$$

can be effected by elementary transformations. Hence the product $\Pi_2\Pi_1^2$ (i.e. the resultant of Π_1 applied twice and followed by Π_2), which is

$$\begin{pmatrix} A_1A_2A_3A_4 \\ A_2A_1A_3A_4 \end{pmatrix},$$

can also be effected by elementary transformations. Hence any two vertices of the quadrangle can be interchanged by a sequence of elementary transformations, and hence any permutation of the vertices can be effected by means of elementary transformations.

167. Elementary transformations in a projective space. DEFINITION. Given a set of five points in a projective space, no four of the points being coplanar, an *elementary transformation* is the operation of replacing any one of them by a point joined to it by a segment not meeting any plane on three of the other four.

It follows from § 27 that the determinant product (25) of § 32 is unaltered in sign by any sequence of elementary transformations of the points whose coördinates are the columns of (21) in § 32. Hence a sequence of elementary transformations cannot carry an ordered pentad of points from one sense-class into the other.

Hence the odd permutations of the vertices of a complete five-point cannot be effected by elementary transformations. That the even permutations can be thus effected may be seen as follows: Let the vertices be denoted by A, B, C, D, E and let the line DE meet the plane ABC in a point F. This point is not on a side of the triangle ABC. Let A' be the point of intersection of the lines FA and BC, B' that of FB and CA, and C' that of FC and AB. Let A_1 be a point in the order $\{BA_1A'C\}$ (fig. 84) and B_1 the point in which the line FA_1 meets AC, so that $\{AB_1B'C\}$. Let B_2 be a point in the order $\{AB_1B_2B'C\}$.

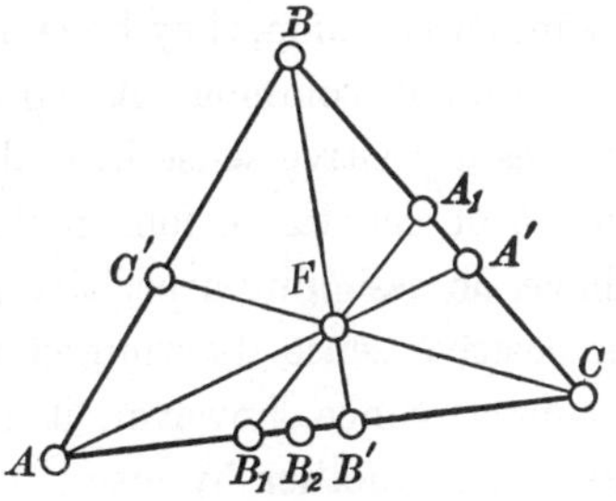

FIG. 84

We now can transform $ABCDE$ by elementary transformations successively into AA_1CDE, AA_1B_2DE, BA_1B_2DE, BCB_2DE, $BCADE$. Thus the even permutation

$$\begin{pmatrix} ABCDE \\ BCADE \end{pmatrix}$$

can be effected by elementary transformations. It is easily verifiable that any even permutation is a product of even permutations of this type.

It can be proved by the same methods as in Theorems 18 and 19 that any five points no four of which are coplanar can be carried into some permutation of any other such set of five points. The details of this proof are left as an exercise to the reader. When this is combined with the paragraph above, we obtain

THEOREM 24. *In a real projective space,* $S(ABCDE)=S(A'B'C'D'E')$ *if and only if there exists a sequence of elementary transformations carrying the points* A, B, C, D, E *into* A', B', C', D', E' *respectively.*

The proof just outlined for this theorem holds good on the basis of Assumptions A, E, S, P. Assumption P comes in because of the use of a coördinate system. This, however, can be avoided; and the construction of a proof on the basis of A, E, S alone is recommended to the reader as an interesting exercise.

***168. Sense in overlapping convex regions.** The discussion of sense in convex regions by means of elementary transformations (as made in §§ 159–161) is essentially the same for any number of dimensions. Now if two regions of the same dimensionality have a point in common, they have at least one convex region of that dimensionality in common. Assigning a positive sense in this region determines a positive sense in each of the given regions. Thus if we have a set of convex regions including all points of a space, we should have, on assigning a positive sense to a tetrad of points in one region, a positive sense determined for any tetrad of points in any of the regions. Since, however, it is in general possible to pass from one region to another by means of different sets of intermediate regions, the possibility arises that this determination of sense may not be unique. In other words, it is logically possible that a given tetrad in a given region might, according to this definition, have both positive and negative senses.

The determination of sense by this method is unique in projective spaces of odd dimensionality and is not unique in projective spaces of even dimensionality. We shall prove this for the two- and three-dimensional cases, but since it reduces merely to a question of even and odd permutations the generalization is obvious.

THEOREM 25. *There exists a unique determination of sense for all three-dimensional convex regions in a real projective three-space, but not for all two-dimensional convex regions in a real projective plane.*

Proof. Consider first the plane and in it a triangle ABC decomposing it into four triangular regions, which we shall denote by the notation of § 26, Chap. II. Any one of these regions, say Region I, is contained in a convex region, say I′ (e.g., a Euclidean plane with line at infinity not meeting Region I), which contains the boundary of the triangular region. So the determination of sense for Region I extends to all the points of its boundary and also to a portion of Region II.

Let the sense of ABC with respect to Region I be positive. The segment $\bar{\gamma}$, one of the segments AB (fig. 16), is common to the boundaries of I and II and hence is contained in Region I′. If C' is any point common to I′ and II, C and C' are on opposite sides of the line AB in Region I′. Hence, according to § 29, $S(BAC')$ is positive in Region II. Hence $S(BAC)$ is positive with respect to Region II.

Regions II and IV have in common a segment BC, and thus by a repetition of this argument $S(CAB)$ is positive with respect to Region IV. The latter region has a segment AC in common with Region I, and hence $S(ACB)$ is positive with respect to Region I. But by hypothesis $S(ABC)$ is positive with respect to Region I. Hence there is not a unique determination of sense in a real projective plane.

To show that there is a unique determination of sense for a real projective three-space, let a given sense-class $S(ABCDE)$ (cf. § 164) be designated as right-handed, and in any convex region let a sense-class $S(A'B'C'D')$ be right-handed if $S(OA'B'C'D')$ is positive, where O is interior to the tetrahedron $A'B'C'D'$. This convention satisfies the requirements laid down above for overlapping convex regions and, by § 167, is unique for the projective three-space.

Any two-dimensional region whatever is, by definition (§ 155), the set of all points in an infinite set of triangular regions, i.e. in an infinite set of convex regions. In like manner, any three-dimensional region is the set of all points in a set of three-dimensional regions. The method given above may be applied to determine the positive sense-class in all convex regions in a given region R, and R may be said to be two-sided or one-sided according as this determination is or is not unique. Another, slightly different, method of treating this question is given in § 173.

***169. Oriented points in a plane.** By the principles of duality the lines of a flat pencil or the planes of an axial pencil satisfy the same theorems on order as the points of a projective line.

This proposition is valid whether the pencils are considered in a projective or in a Euclidean space.*

DEFINITION. In a plane any point associated with one of the sense-classes among the lines on this point is called an *oriented point,* and a line associated with one of the sense-classes among its points is called an *oriented line.* Two oriented points are said to be *similarly oriented with respect to a line* l if their sense-classes are perspective with the same sense-class in the points of l. By Ex. 1, § 26, if two oriented points are similarly oriented with respect to a line l, they are similarly oriented with respect to a line m if and only if l and m do not separate the two points.

By § 30 a direct collineation of a Euclidean plane transforms any oriented point into one which is similarly oriented with respect to the line at infinity. Hence the oriented points fall into two classes such that any two oriented points of the same class are equivalent under direct collineations and that the two classes are interchanged by any nondirect collineation.

No such statement as this can be made about the oriented lines in a Euclidean plane, because any oriented line can be carried by a direct collineation to any other oriented line. This is obvious because (1) an affine collineation exists carrying an arbitrary line to any other line and (2) the two sense-classes on any line are interchanged by a harmonic homology whose center is the point at infinity of the line.

It is a corollary of the last paragraph that any oriented line of a projective plane can be carried into any other oriented line of the projective plane by a direct collineation. By duality the same proposition holds for oriented points in a projective plane.

The oriented points determined by associating the points of a segment γ with sense-classes in the flat pencils of which they are centers fall into two sets, all points of either set being similarly oriented with respect to any line not meeting γ. These two sets shall be called *segments* of oriented points and may be denoted by $\gamma^{(+)}$ and $\gamma^{(-)}$. If A and B are the ends of γ, the two oriented points determined by A and B and oriented similarly to $\gamma^{(+)}$ with respect to a

*In general, the geometry of a Euclidean space or, indeed, of any space of n dimensions involves the study of the projective geometry of $n-1$ dimensions, in order to describe the relations among the lines, planes, etc. on a fixed point.

line l not meeting γ or either of its ends are called the *ends* of $\gamma^{(+)}$ and may be denoted by $A^{(+)}$ and $B^{(+)}$. The other two oriented points determined by A and B are the ends of $\gamma^{(-)}$ and may be denoted by $A^{(-)}$ and $B^{(-)}$.

In terms of these definitions it is clear that each of the two classes of similarly oriented points determined by a Euclidean plane satisfies a set of order relations such that it may be regarded as a Euclidean plane.

The situation in the projective plane is entirely different. Let us first consider a projective line, and let γ and δ be two complementary segments whose ends are A and B. Let $A^{(+)}, B^{(+)}, A^{(-)}, B^{(-)}, \gamma^{(+)}, \gamma^{(-)}$ be defined as above, and let $\delta^{(+)}$ and $\delta^{(-)}$ be the two segments of oriented points determined by δ and oriented similarly to $A^{(+)}$ and $A^{(-)}$ respectively with respect to a line m not meeting δ or either of its ends. Since $A^{(+)}$ and $B^{(+)}$ are similarly oriented with respect to l, and A and B are separated by l and m, $A^{(+)}$ and $B^{(-)}$ are similarly oriented with respect to m (cf. Ex. 1, § 26, and fig. 85). Hence the ends of $\delta^{(+)}$ are $A^{(+)}$ and $B^{(-)}$, and the ends of $\delta^{(-)}$ are $A^{(-)}$ and $B^{(+)}$. Hence the oriented points and segments are arranged as follows:

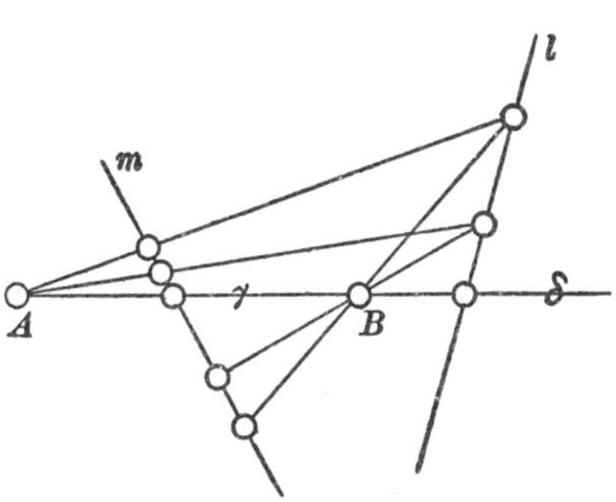

FIG. 85

$$A^{(+)}, \gamma^{(+)}, B^{(+)}, \delta^{(-)}, A^{(-)}, \gamma^{(-)}, B^{(-)}, \delta^{(+)}, A^{(+)},$$

the symbols for segments and their ends being written adjacent.

Let A_1, B_1, A_2, B_2 be four points in the order $\{A_1B_1A_2B_2\}$ on a projective line or on a conic. They separate the line (§ 21) into four mutually exclusive segments $\gamma_1, \delta_1, \gamma_2, \delta_2$ arranged as follows:

$$A_1, \gamma_1, B_1, \delta_2, A_2, \gamma_2, B_2, \delta_1, A_1,$$

the symbols for segments and their ends being written adjacent. Letting A_1 correspond to $A^{(+)}$, γ_1 to $\gamma^{(+)}$, etc., it is obvious that there is a one-to-one reciprocal correspondence preserving order between the points of a real projective line or conic and the oriented points of a real projective line.

Thus, if an oriented point be moved along a projective line in such a way that all oriented points of any segment described are similarly oriented with respect to a line not meeting the segment, the oriented point must describe the line twice before returning to its first position. A motion of this sort will obviously carry any oriented point of the projective plane into any other oriented point. Thus the oriented points either of a projective line or of a projective plane constitute a continuous family in the sense of § 156.

Let π denote the projective plane under consideration here and let us suppose it contained in a projective space S, and let S' be a Euclidean space obtained by removing from S a plane different from π which contains the line AB. Let S^2 be a sphere of S' tangent to π at a point P_1, let O be the center of S^2, and let P_2 be the other point in which the line OP_1 meets the sphere. Let $P^{(+)}$ and $P^{(-)}$ be the two oriented points of π determined by P_1.

A correspondence Γ between the points of the sphere S^2 and the oriented points of the projective plane π may now be set up by the following rule: Let P_1 correspond to $P^{(+)}$, and P_2 to $P^{(-)}$; if X is any point of π not on the line at infinity, denote by X_1 and X_2 the points in which the line OX meets the sphere, assigning the notation so that each of the angles $\measuredangle P_1OX_1$ and $\measuredangle P_2OX_2$ is less than a right angle (i.e. so that the points X_1 are all on the same side as P_1 of the plane through O parallel to π, and the points X_2 are on the other side of this plane); and denote by $X^{(+)}$ the oriented point of π determined by X and joined to $P^{(+)}$ by a segment of oriented points containing no point of the line at infinity AB, and by $X^{(-)}$ the other oriented point determined by X. Let X_1 correspond to $X^{(+)}$, and X_2 to $X^{(-)}$. If Y is any point of the line at infinity AB, and $Y^{(\pm)}$ one of the oriented points determined by it, $Y^{(\pm)}$ is an end of a segment $\sigma^{(+)}$ of points $X^{(+)}$ whose other end is $P^{(+)}$ and of a segment $\sigma^{(-)}$ of points $X^{(-)}$ whose other end is $P^{(-)}$. The line OY meets the sphere in two points one of which, Y_i, is an end both of a segment of points X_1 corresponding to $\sigma^{(+)}$ and of a segment of points X_2 corresponding to $\sigma^{(-)}$. Let Y_i correspond to $Y^{(\pm)}$. This construction evidently makes the oriented point other than $Y^{(\pm)}$ which is determined by Y correspond to the point other than Y_i in which OY meets the sphere.

The correspondence Γ is one-to-one and reciprocal and makes each segment of oriented points of π correspond to a segment of points on S^2. In view of the correspondence between the sphere and the inversion plane, this result may be stated in the following form:

THEOREM 26. *There is a one-to-one reciprocal correspondence preserving order-relations between the oriented points of a real projective plane and the points of a real inversion plane.*

The treatment of oriented points in this section does not generalize directly to three dimensions, because there is only one sense-class in a projective plane and, therefore, also only one in a bundle of lines. The discussion of sense in terms of the set of all lines through a point is therefore possible along these lines only in spaces of an even number of dimensions.

A discussion which is uniform for spaces of any number of dimensions can, however, be made in terms of rays. An outline of the theory of pencils and bundles of rays which may be used for this purpose is given in the next three sections, and an outline of one way of generalizing the contents of the present section is given in § 173.

Another type of generalization of the theory of oriented points in the plane is the theory of doubly oriented lines in three dimensions which is given in § 180, below.

***170. Pencils of rays.** The term "ray"* is defined in § 23 for a linear convex region and extended to any convex region in § 148. The definition of *angle* in § 28 will be carried over to any convex region.

DEFINITION. The set of all rays with a common origin in a planar convex region is called a *pencil* of rays. The common origin is called the *center* of the pencil.

The order relations in a pencil of rays are essentially the same as those among the points of a projective line. This can be shown by setting up a correspondence between the rays through the center of a circle and the points in which they meet the circle, as in § 69. It can also be done on the basis of Assumptions A, E, P alone by proving Theorems 27–33, below. The proofs of the theorems are not given, because they are not very different from those of other theorems in this chapter. A third way of deriving these relations is indicated in Theorems 34, 35, and a fourth in Theorems 37–41.

THEOREM 27. *If a, b, c are three rays of a pencil, and if any segment joining a point of a to a point of c contains a point of b, then every segment joining a point of a to a point of c contains a point of b.*

* In some books the term "ray" is used as synonymous with "projective line," and "pencil of rays" with "pencil of lines."

DEFINITION. If a, b, c are three rays of a pencil, b is said to be *between* a and c if and only if (1) a and c are not collinear and (2) any segment joining a point of a to a point of c contains a point of b.

THEOREM 28. *If b is any ray between two rays a and c, any other ray between a and c is either between a and b or between b and c. No ray is both between a and b and between b and c. Any ray between a and b is between a and c.*

THEOREM 29. *There is a one-to-one reciprocal correspondence preserving all order relations between the points of a segment of a line and the rays between two rays of a pencil.*

THEOREM 30. *If three rays a, b, c of a pencil are such that no two of them are collinear and no one of them is between the other two, then any other ray of this pencil is between a and b or between b and c or between c and a.*

DEFINITION. Given a set of three distinct rays a, b, c of a pencil, by an *elementary transformation* is meant the operation of replacing one of them, say c, by a ray c' not collinear with c and such that neither a nor b is between c and c'. The class consisting of all ordered triads into which abc is transformable by finite sequences of elementary transformations is called a *sense-class* and is denoted by $S(abc)$.

An elementary transformation of abc into abc' is said to be *restricted with respect* to a set of rays $a_1, a_2, \cdots, a_n$ of the pencil if none of the rays $a_1, a_2, \cdots, a_n$ is between c and c'.

THEOREM 31. *Let $a_1, a_2, \cdots, a_n$ be an arbitrary set of rays of a pencil. Two ordered triads of rays of the pencil are in the same sense-class if and only if one can be transformed into the other by a sequence of elementary transformations which are restricted with respect to $a_1, a_2, \cdots, a_n$.*

THEOREM 32. *Let a_1, a_2, a_3 be three distinct rays of a pencil such that no one of the three is between the other two. There exists a one-to-one reciprocal correspondence Γ between the rays of the pencil and the points of a projective line such that to each elementary transformation of the rays which is restricted with respect to a_1, a_2, a_3 there corresponds an elementary transformation on the projective line which is restricted with respect to the points corresponding to a_1, a_2, a_3.*

The correspondence Γ required in this theorem may be set up as follows: Let three arbitrary collinear points A_1, A_2, A_3 be the correspondents of a_1, a_2, a_3 respectively; let Γ_1 be a projectivity which carries the lines which contain the rays between a_1 and a_2 to the points of the segment complementary to $\overline{A_1A_3A_2}$ and carries the line containing a_1 to A_1; for the rays between a_1 and a_2 let Γ be the correspondence in which each ray between a_1 and a_2 corresponds to the point to which the line containing it is carried by Γ_1; let Γ_2 be the projectivity which carries the lines which contain the rays between a_2 and a_3 to the points of the segment complementary to $\overline{A_2A_1A_3}$ and carries the line containing a_2 to A_2; for the rays between a_2 and a_3 let Γ be the correspondence in which each ray corresponds to the point to which the line containing it is carried by Γ_2; let Γ_3 be a projectivity which carries the lines which contain the rays between a_3 and a_1 to the points of the segment complementary to $\overline{A_3A_2A_1}$ and carries the line containing a_3 to A_3; for the rays between a_3 and a_1 let Γ be the correspondence in which each ray corresponds to the point to which the line containing it is carried by Γ_3.

COROLLARY. *There is a one-to-one reciprocal correspondence between the points of a projective line and the rays of a pencil such that two ordered triads of rays of the pencil are in the same sense-class if and only if the corresponding triads of points are in the same sense-class on the line.*

THEOREM 33. *If a, b, c are three rays of a pencil and a', b', c' are the respectively opposite rays,* $S(abc) = S(a'b'c')$.

DEFINITION. If a and b are any two noncollinear rays of a pencil, by an *elementary transformation* of the ordered pair ab is meant the operation of replacing one of them, say b, by another ray, b', of the pencil, such that no ray of the line containing a is between b and b' or coincident with b'. The set of all ordered pairs (i.e. angles) into which an ordered pair of rays ab can be carried by sequences of elementary transformations is called a *sense-class* and is denoted by $S(ab)$.

THEOREM 34. *If O is the center of a pencil of rays and A, B, C, D are points of rays a, b, c, d respectively of the pencil, then $S(ab) = S(cd)$ if and only if $S(OAB) = S(OCD)$.*

THEOREM 35. *If a and b are any two noncollinear rays of a pencil, $S(ab) \neq S(ba)$. Every ordered pair of noncollinear rays in the pencil is either in $S(ab)$ or in $S(ba)$. If a' is the ray opposite to a, $S(ab) \neq S(a'b)$.*

THEOREM 36. *If a, b and a', b' are two ordered pairs of rays of a pencil and c and c' are the rays opposite to a and a' respectively, then $S(ab) = S(a'b')$ if and only if $S(abc) = S(a'b'c')$. The same conclusion holds if c is any ray between a and b and c' any ray between a' and b'.*

THEOREM 37. DEFINITION. *The points not on the sides or vertex of an angle $\measuredangle ab$ fall into two classes having the sides and vertex as boundary and such that any segment joining a point of one class to a point of the other contains a point of the sides or the vertex. If the angle is a straight angle, both of these classes of points are convex regions. If not, one and only one of them is convex and is called the* interior *of the angle; the other is called the* exterior *of the angle.*

THEOREM 38. *If A' is any point of the side OA of an angle $\measuredangle AOB$, and B' is any point of the side OB, then $S(OAB) = S(OA'B')$. If C is any point interior to the angle, $S(OAB) = S(OAC) = S(OCB)$, and any point C satisfying these conditions is interior to the angle.*

THEOREM 39. *Any ray having the vertex of an angle as origin, and not itself a side of the angle, is entirely in one or the other of the two classes of points described in Theorem 37. If it is in the interior it contains one and only one point on each segment joining a point of one side of the angle to a point on the other side.*

DEFINITION. Two rays a, b of a pencil are said to be *separated* by two other rays h, k of the same pencil (or by the angle $\measuredangle hk$) if and only if a is in one and b in the other of the classes of points determined according to Theorem 37 by $\measuredangle hk$. A set of rays having a common origin are said to be in the *order* $\{a_1a_2a_3a_4 \cdots a_n\}$ if no two of the rays are separated by any of the angles $\measuredangle a_1a_2$, $\measuredangle a_2a_3$, $\cdots$, $\measuredangle a_{n-1}a_n$, $\measuredangle a_na_1$.

THEOREM 40. *A set of rays in the order $\{a_1a_2a_3 \cdots a_{n-1}a_n\}$ are also in the orders $\{a_2a_3 \cdots a_na_1\}$ and $\{a_na_{n-1} \cdots a_2a_1\}$.*

COROLLARY. *Any two rays a, b having a common origin are in the orders $\{ab\}$ and $\{ba\}$. Any three rays a, b, c having a common origin are in the orders $\{abc\}$, $\{bca\}$, $\{cab\}$, $\{acb\}$, $\{bac\}$, $\{cba\}$.*

THEOREM 41. *To any finite number $n \geqq 2$ of rays having a common origin may be assigned a notation so that they are in the order* $\{a_1 a_2 a_3 \cdots a_n\}$.

***171. Pencils of segments and directions.** The notion of a ray belongs essentially with that of a convex region, but the theorems of the last section may easily be put into a form which is not limited to convex regions. The proofs are all omitted for the same reasons as in the section above.

DEFINITION. A set of all segments having a common end and lying in the same plane is called a *pencil of segments.* The common end is called the *center* of the pencil. Two segments or intervals having a common end A are said to be *similarly directed at A* if either of them is entirely contained in the other. The set of all segments similarly directed at a given point with a given segment is called a *direction-class* or, more simply, a *direction.* The set of all directions of the segments of a pencil at its center is called a *pencil of directions.* The directions of two collinear segments having a common end A and not similarly directed are said to be *opposite,* and the two segments are said to be *oppositely directed at A.*

Thus if $ABCD$ are four collinear points in the order $\{ABCD\}$ the segments $\overline{ABC}$ and $\overline{ABD}$ are similarly directed, while $\overline{ABC}$ and $\overline{ADC}$ are oppositely directed. At a given point on a given line there are obviously two and only two directions, and these are opposite to each other. Two noncollinear segments with a common end are contained in one and only one pencil, namely, the one having the common end as center and lying in the plane of the two segments.

DEFINITION. A segment σ is said to be *between* two noncollinear segments σ_1, σ_2 if the three segments are in the same pencil and σ is similarly directed with a segment which is in the pencil and contained entirely in the triangular region determined by σ_1 and σ_2 (Theorem 12). A direction d is said to be *between* two noncollinear directions d_1, d_2 if there exist three segments σ, σ_1, σ_2 in the directions d, d_1, d_2 respectively such that σ is between σ_1 and σ_2.

This extension of the notion of betweenness to directions is justified by the following theorem.

THEOREM 42. *If α and β are two noncollinear segments with a common end O, and α' and β' are similarly directed with α and β*

respectively at O, the segments between α and β are similarly directed with the segments between α' and β'.

DEFINITION. Let σ_1, σ_2, σ_3 be three segments of a pencil no two of them being similarly directed. By an *elementary transformation* is meant the operation of replacing one of them, say σ_3, by a segment σ_4, which is in the pencil and such that neither σ_1 nor σ_2 is between σ_3 and σ_4 or similarly directed with σ_4. A class consisting of all ordered triads into which $\sigma_1\sigma_2\sigma_3$ is transformable by finite sequences of elementary transformations is called a *sense-class* and is denoted by $S(\sigma_1\sigma_2\sigma_3)$. If d_1, d_2, d_3 are three directions of a pencil, and σ_1, σ_2, σ_3 three segments in the directions d_1, d_2, d_3 respectively, the *sense-class* $S(d_1d_2d_3)$ is the class of all triads of directions which are the directions of triads of segments in the sense-class $S(\sigma_1\sigma_2\sigma_3)$.

THEOREM 43. *If σ_1, σ_2, σ_3 are three segments of a pencil, no two of them being similarly directed, and σ'_3 is similarly directed with σ_3, $S(\sigma_1\sigma_2\sigma_3) = S(\sigma_1\sigma_2\sigma'_3)$.*

THEOREM 44. *There is a one-to-one reciprocal correspondence between the directions of a pencil and the points of a line such that two triads of directions are in the same sense if and only if the corresponding triads of points have the same sense.*

We now take from §§ 21–23 of Chap. II the definitions of separation, order, etc., and on account of Theorem 44 we have at once

COROLLARY 1. *The Theorems of §§ 21–23 remain valid when applied to the directions of a pencil instead of to the points of a line.*

COROLLARY 2. *Two pairs of opposite directions separate each other.*

DEFINITION. Let σ_1 and σ_2 be two noncollinear segments of a pencil; by an *elementary transformation* is meant the operation of replacing one of them, say σ_2, by any segment σ_3 of the pencil such that no segment collinear with σ_1 is between σ_2 and σ_3. The set of all ordered pairs of segments into which $\sigma_1\sigma_2$ is transformable by sequences of elementary transformations is called a *sense-class* and is denoted by $S(\sigma_1\sigma_2)$.

THEOREM 45. *If a pair of segments σ_1 σ_2 is transformable by elementary transformations into a pair $\sigma'_1\sigma'_2$, then $\sigma'_1\sigma'_2$ is transformable by elementary transformations into $\sigma_1\sigma_2$.*

THEOREM 46. *If a segment* σ_2 *is similarly directed with a segment* σ_2' *and not collinear with a segment* σ_1 *which has the same origin as* σ_2, $S(\sigma_1\sigma_2)=S(\sigma_1\sigma_2')$.

THEOREM 47. *If* $\sigma_1, \sigma_2, \sigma_3, \sigma_4$ *are segments of a pencil and* σ_1 *is not collinear with* σ_2, *nor* σ_3 *with* σ_4, *then either* $S(\sigma_1\sigma_2)=S(\sigma_3\sigma_4)$ *or* $S(\sigma_2\sigma_1)=S(\sigma_3\sigma_4)$. $S(\sigma_1\sigma_2)\neq S(\sigma_2\sigma_1)$. *If* σ_1' *is opposite to* σ_1, *and* σ_3' *to* σ_3, $S(\sigma_1\sigma_2)=S(\sigma_3\sigma_4)$ *if and only if* $S(\sigma_1'\sigma_1\sigma_2)=S(\sigma_3'\sigma_3\sigma_4)$.

DEFINITION. Let d_1 and d_2 be two directions of a pencil and let σ_1 and σ_2 be two segments in the directions d_1 and d_2 respectively. By the *sense-class* $S(d_1d_2)$ is meant the class of all ordered pairs of directions which are the directions of ordered pairs of segments in the sense-class $S(\sigma_1\sigma_2)$.

It is evident that the last two theorems may be restated, without material change, in terms of directions instead of segments.

***172. Bundles of rays, segments, and directions.** DEFINITION. The set of all rays in a three-dimensional convex region which have a common origin O is called a *bundle* of rays. The point O is called the *center* of the bundle.

Let a, b, c be three noncoplanar rays of a bundle. By an *elementary transformation* is meant the operation of replacing one of the rays, say a, by a ray a' such that no ray of the plane containing b and c is between a and a'. The set of all ordered triads of rays into which abc can be carried by sequences of elementary transformations is called a *sense-class* and is denoted by $S(abc)$.

THEOREM 48. *If* abc *and* $a'b'c'$ *are two ordered triads of noncoplanar rays having a common origin* O, *and* A, B, C, A', B', C' *are points of the rays* a, b, c, a', b', c' *respectively, then* $S(abc)=S(a'b'c')$ *if and only if* $S(OABC)=S(OA'B'C')$.

THEOREM 49. *If* a, b, c *are three noncoplanar rays of a bundle,* $S(abc)=S(bca)\neq S(acb)$. *If* a', b', c' *are any other three noncoplanar rays of the bundle, either* $S(a'b'c')=S(abc)$ *or* $S(a'b'c')=S(acb)$.

THEOREM 50. *If* a, b, c *are three noncoplanar rays of a bundle and* a' *is the ray opposite to* a, $S(abc)\neq S(a'bc)$.

THEOREM 51. *If* abc *are three noncoplanar rays of a bundle, the set* $[x]$ *of rays of the bundle which satisfy the relation* $S(xab)=S(xbc)=S(xca)$ *are in such a one-to-one reciprocal correspondence* Γ *with the points of a triangular region that if rays* x_1, x_2, x_3,

x_4, x_5, x_6 correspond to points X_1, X_2, X_3, X_4, X_5, X_6 respectively, $S(x_1x_2x_3) = S(x_4x_5x_6)$ if and only if $S(X_1X_2X_3) = S(X_4X_5X_6)$. If A, B, C are points of the rays a, b, c respectively, and the triangular region is the interior of the triangle ABC, Γ may be taken as the correspondence in which each x corresponds to the point in which it meets the triangular region.

THEOREM 52. *If a, b, c, d are four rays of a bundle such that any plane containing two of them contains a ray between the other two, any other ray of the bundle is between two rays of the set a, b, c, d or in one of four sets $[x]$, $[y]$, $[z]$, $[w]$ such that $[x]$ satisfies the condition $S(xbc) = S(xcd) = S(xdb)$, $[y]$ satisfies $S(yac) = S(ycd) = S(yda)$, $[z]$ satisfies $S(zab) = S(zbd) = S(zda)$, $[w]$ satisfies $S(wab) = S(wbc) = S(wca)$.*

COROLLARY. *Under the conditions of the theorem if A, B, C, D are points of the rays a, b, c, d respectively, the center of the bundle is interior to the tetrahedron $ABCD$.*

DEFINITION. A set of all segments having a common end is called a *bundle of segments.* The set of all directions of the segments of a bundle is called a *bundle of directions.*

DEFINITION. Let σ_1, σ_2, σ_3 be three segments of the same bundle, but not in the same pencil; the operation of replacing any one of them, say σ_3, by a segment σ_4 of the bundle such that no segment of the pencil containing σ_1 and σ_2 is between σ_3 and σ_4 or coincident with σ_4 is called an *elementary transformation.* A class consisting of all ordered triads of segments into which $\sigma_1\sigma_2\sigma_3$ can be carried by finite sequences of elementary transformations is called a *sense-class* and is denoted by $S(\sigma_1\sigma_2\sigma_3)$.

The generalization of Theorems 48–52 to the corresponding theorems for a bundle of segments presents no difficulty.

***173. One- and two-sided regions.** A discussion of the order relations in projective spaces which is closely analogous both to § 168 and to § 169 may be made according to the following outline. The details are left as an exercise for the reader.

Let O be any point of a planar region R. Let A, B, C be the vertices of a triangular region T containing O and contained in R, and let α, β, γ be the segments in R joining O to A, B, C respectively. Then $S(\alpha\beta) = S(\beta\gamma) = S(\gamma\alpha)$.

If O' is any other point of T, and α', β' the segments of R joining O' to A and B respectively, $S(\alpha\beta)$ is said to be *like* $S(\alpha'\beta')$; and if $S(\alpha\beta)$ is like $S(\alpha'\beta')$, and $S(\alpha'\beta')$ like $S(\alpha''\beta'')$, then $S(\alpha\beta)$ is said to be *like* $S(\alpha''\beta'')$. A region for which a given sense-class at one point is like the other sense-class at that point is said to be *one-sided.* Any other region is said to be *two-sided.*

A convex region is two-sided. A projective plane is a one-sided region.

Let O be any point of a three-dimensional region R. Let A, B, C, D be the vertices of a tetrahedral region T containing O and contained in R, and let α, β, γ, δ be the segments in R joining O to A, B, C, D respectively. Then $S(\alpha\beta\gamma)=S(\beta\alpha\delta)=S(\delta\gamma\beta)=S(\gamma\delta\alpha)$.

If O' is any other point of T, and α', β', γ' are the segments of R joining O' to A, B, C respectively, $S(\alpha\beta\gamma)$ is said to be *like* $S(\alpha'\beta'\gamma')$; if $S(\alpha\beta\gamma)$ is like $S(\alpha'\beta'\gamma')$, and $S(\alpha'\beta'\gamma')$ is like $S(\alpha''\beta''\gamma'')$, then $S(\alpha\beta\gamma)$ is said to be *like* $S(\alpha''\beta''\gamma'')$.

One- and two-sided regions are defined as in the two-dimensional case.

Any region in a three-dimensional projective space is two-sided.

174. Sense-classes on a sphere. The theorems in § 172 can be regarded as defining the order relations among the points of a sphere if carried over to the sphere by letting each point of the sphere correspond to the ray joining it to the center of the sphere. Another way of treating the order relations on a sphere and one which connects directly with § 97 is as follows:

DEFINITION. Let A, B, C, D be four points of a sphere not all on the same circle. By an *elementary transformation* is meant the operation of replacing one of them, say A, by a point A' on the same side of the circle BCD. The set of all ordered tetrads into which $ABCD$ is transformable by sequences of elementary transformations is called a *sense-class* and is denoted by $S(ABCD)$.

THEOREM 53. *There are two and only two sense-classes on a sphere.* $S(ABCD)\neq S(ABDC)$.

THEOREM 54. $S(ABCD)=S(A'B'C'D')$ *if and only if* $bb'>0$, *where* $\mathrm{R}(AB,\ CD)=a+b\sqrt{-1}$, $\mathrm{R}(A'B',\ C'D')=a'+b'\sqrt{-1}$, *and* a, a', b, b' *are real.*

175. Order relations on complex lines. In view of the isomorphism between the geometry of the real sphere and the complex projective line (cf. §§ 91, 95, and 100) the theorems of the section above and of § 97 determine the order relations on any complex line.

One very important difference between the situation as to order in the real and the complex spaces is the following: In a real plane or space one sense-class on a line is carried by projectivities of a continuous group into both sense-classes on any other line. So that fixing a particular sense-class on one line as positive does not determine a positive sense-class on all other lines. On a complex line, however, an ordered set of four points $ABCD$ is in one sense-class or the other according as b is positive or negative, where $a+b\sqrt{-1}=R(AB, CD)$ and a and b are real (Theorem 54). In consequence of the invariance of cross ratios under projection, a given sense-class on one line goes by projectivities into one and only one sense-class on any other line. Hence if one sense-class is called positive on one line, the positive sense-class can be determined on every other line as being that sense-class which is projective with the positive sense-class on the initial line.

This connects very closely with the convention for purposes of analytic geometry that by $\sqrt{c}$ is meant that one of the square roots of c which takes the form $a+b\sqrt{-1}$, where a and b are real and $b>0$, or if $b=0$, $a>0$. The symbol $\sqrt{-1}$ is taken to represent that one of the square roots of -1 for which $S(\infty\ 0\ 1\sqrt{-1})$ is positive.

176. Direct and opposite collineations in space. From the algebraic definition of direct collineation in terms of the sign of a determinant, we obtain at once

THEOREM 55. *Any collineation of a real three-dimensional projective space which leaves a Euclidean space invariant is direct if and only if the collineation which it effects in the Euclidean space is direct.*

In a Euclidean space a point D is on the same side of a plane $ABCD$ with a point E if and only if $S(ABCD)=S(ABCE)$. Hence a homology whose center is at infinity is direct or opposite according as a point not on its plane of fixed points is transformed to a point on the same or the opposite side of this plane. Extending this result to the projective space by the aid of the theorem above we have

THEOREM 56. *A homology which carries a point A to a point A', distinct from A, is opposite or direct according as A and A' are separated or not separated by the center of the homology and the point in which its plane of fixed points is met by the line AA'.*

Corollary 1. *A harmonic homology is opposite.*

Corollary 2. *The inverse of a direct homology is direct.*

Since any collineation is expressible as a product of homologies (§ 29, Vol. I), it follows that

Corollary 3. *The inverse of a direct collineation is direct.*

Since an elation is a product of two harmonic homologies having the same plane of fixed points it follows from Cor. 1 that

Corollary 4. *An elation is direct.*

Since a line reflection (§ 101) is a product of two harmonic homologies,

Corollary 5. *A line reflection is direct.*

Theorem 57. *A collineation leaving three skew lines invariant is direct.*

Proof. Denote the lines by l_1, l_2, l_3 and the collineation by Γ. The projectivity on l_1 which is effected by Γ is a product of two or three hyperbolic involutions (§ 74). Each involution on l_1 is effected by a line reflection whose directrices are the lines which pass through the double points of the involution and meet l_2 and l_3. The product Π of these line reflections leaves l_1, l_2, l_3 invariant and effects the same transformation on l_1 as Γ. Hence $\Pi^{-1}\Gamma$ leaves l_2, l_3 and all points on l_1 invariant. It also leaves invariant any line meeting l_1, l_2, and l_3, and hence leaves all points on l_2 and l_3 invariant. Hence $\Pi^{-1}\Gamma$ is the identity, and hence $\Gamma = \Pi$. Since the line reflections are all direct, Γ is direct.

Corollary 1. *Any collineation leaving all points of two skew lines invariant is direct.*

Proof. Such a collineation leaves invariant three skew lines meeting the given pair of invariant lines.

Corollary 2. *Any collineation transforming a regulus into itself is direct.*

Proof. Such a collineation is a product of a collineation leaving all lines of the given regulus invariant by one leaving all lines of the conjugate regulus invariant. Hence it is direct, by the theorem.

Corollary 2 is also a direct consequence of Cor. 5, above, and Theorem 34, Chap. VI.

COROLLARY 3. *Any collineation carrying a regulus into its conjugate regulus is opposite.*

Proof. The two reguli are interchanged by a harmonic homology whose center and axis are pole and polar with regard to the regulus. This harmonic homology is opposite by Cor. 1, Theorem 56, and since its product by any collineation Γ interchanging the two reguli leaves them both invariant and hence is direct by Cor. 2, it follows that Γ is opposite.

DEFINITION. By a *doubly oriented line* is meant a line l associated with one sense-class among the points on l and one sense-class among the planes on l. The doubly oriented line is said to be *on* any point, line, or plane on l.

A doubly oriented line may be denoted by the symbol $(ABC, \alpha\beta\gamma)$ if A, B, C denote collinear points and α, β, γ planes on the line AB. For this symbol determines the line AB and the sense-classes $S(ABC)$ and $S(\alpha\beta\gamma)$ uniquely. Since there are two sense-classes $S(ABC)$ and $S(ACB)$ among the points on a line AB and two sense-classes $S(\alpha\beta\gamma)$ and $S(\alpha\gamma\beta)$ among the planes on AB, there are four doubly oriented lines,

$$(ABC,\ \alpha\beta\gamma),$$
$$(ACB,\ \alpha\gamma\beta),$$
$$(ABC,\ \alpha\gamma\beta),$$
$$(ACB,\ \alpha\beta\gamma),$$

into which AB enters.

THEOREM 58. *The collineations which transform a doubly oriented line into itself are all direct.*

Proof. Let $(ABC, \alpha\beta\gamma)$ be a doubly oriented line, Γ a collineation leaving it invariant, l any line not meeting AB, and $l' = \Gamma(l)$. The line l' cannot meet AB, because AB is transformed into itself by Γ. If l' does not intersect l, let m be the line harmonically separated from AB by l and l' in the regulus containing AB, l, and l'. If l' meets l let m be the line harmonically separated by l and l' from the point in which the plane ll' is met by AB. In either case AB does not intersect m, and if Λ is the line reflection whose directrices are AB and m, $\Lambda(l') = l$. Hence $\Lambda\Gamma$ leaves both AB and m invariant. Since Λ and Γ preserve sense both in the pencil of points AB and in the pencil of planes $\alpha\beta$, $\Lambda\Gamma$ preserves sense both on AB and on m. Hence by § 74, $\Lambda\Gamma$ effects a projectivity on AB which is a product of two hyperbolic involutions, $\{P_4P_3\}\cdot\{P_2P_1\}$, and it effects a projectivity on m which is a product of two hyperbolic involutions, $\{Q_4Q_3\}\cdot\{Q_2Q_1\}$. Let l_1, l_2, l_3, l_4 be the lines $P_1Q_1, P_2Q_2, P_3Q_3, P_4Q_4$ respectively. The product

$$\{l_1l_2\}\cdot\{l_3l_4\}\cdot\Lambda\cdot\Gamma$$

leaves all points on AB and on m invariant and is therefore direct by Cor. 1, Theorem 57. All the collineations in this product except Γ are direct by Cor. 5, Theorem 56. Hence Γ is direct.

COROLLARY 1. *Any collineation which reverses both sense-classes of a doubly oriented line is direct.*

Proof. Let Γ be a collineation reversing both sense-classes of a doubly oriented line $(ABC, \alpha\beta\gamma)$. Let a and b be two lines meeting AB but not intersecting each other. The line reflection $\{ab\}$ reverses both sense-classes of $(ABC, \alpha\beta\gamma)$ and is direct. Hence $\{ab\}\cdot\Gamma$ leaves them both invariant and is direct by the theorem. Hence Γ is direct.

COROLLARY 2. *Any collineation which transforms each of two skew lines into itself and effects a direct projectivity on each is direct.*

COROLLARY 3. *Any collineation which transforms each of two skew lines into itself and effects an opposite projectivity on each is direct.*

177. Right- and left-handed figures. The theorems of the last section can be used in showing that other figures than the ordered pentads of points may be classified as right-handed and left-handed. For this purpose the following theorem is fundamental.

THEOREM 59. *If the collineations carrying a figure F_0 into itself are all direct, the figures equivalent to F_0 under the group of all collineations fall into two classes such that any collineation carrying a figure of one class into a figure of the same class is direct and any collineation carrying it into a figure of the other class is opposite.*

Proof. Let $[F]$ be the set of all figures into which F_0 can be carried by direct collineations. There is no opposite collineation carrying F_0 into an F; for suppose Γ were such an opposite collineation, let P be one of the direct collineations which by definition of $[F]$ carry F_0 into F; then $\mathrm{P}^{-1}\Gamma$ would be an opposite collineation carrying F_0 into itself. In like manner it follows that any collineation carrying any F into itself or any other F is direct.

Let $[F']$ be the set of all figures into which F_0 is carried by opposite collineations. An argument like that above shows (1) that any collineation carrying F_0 into an F' is opposite and (2) that any collineation carrying an F' into itself or another F' is direct. It follows at once that any collineation carrying an F into an F' or an F' into an F is opposite.

Since the direct collineations form a continuous family of transformations, we have

COROLLARY. *The figures conjugate to F_0 under the group of direct collineations form a continuous family.*

The propositions about the sense-classes of ordered tetrads of noncollinear points are corollaries of this theorem because the only collineation carrying an ordered pentad of noncollinear points into itself is the identity.

By Theorems 57 and 59 all triads of noncollinear lines fall into two classes such that any collineation carrying a triad of one class into a triad of the same class is direct and any collineation carrying a triad of one class into a triad of the other class is opposite. It is to be noted particularly that the triads of lines here considered need not be ordered triads, since by Cor. 2, Theorem 57, the collineation effecting any permutation of a set of three noncollinear lines is direct.

Similar propositions hold with regard to doubly oriented lines, reguli, congruences, and complexes (cf. § 178).

Let us now suppose that a particular sense-class $S(ABCD)$ in a Euclidean space has been designated as *right-handed* (cf. § 162). Any ordered tetrad of points in this sense-class is also called *right-handed* and any ordered tetrad in the other sense-class is called *left-handed.*

Let P be a point interior to the triangular region BCD, Q the point at infinity of the line AP, β the plane APB, γ the plane APC, and δ the plane APD. All doubly oriented lines into which $(APQ, \beta\gamma\delta)$ is carried by direct collineations shall be called *right-handed* and all others shall be called *left-handed.*

The set of points $ABCDQ$ and the sense-class $S(ABCDQ)$ in the projective space $ABCD$ shall be called *right-handed* and all other ordered pentads of noncollinear points and the other sense-class shall be called *left-handed.*

These conventions give the same determination of right-handed doubly oriented lines and ordered pentads of points no matter what point of the triangular region BCD is taken as P, because any collineation leaving A, B, C, D invariant and carrying one such P into another is direct. In like manner these conventions are independent of the choice of $ABCD$, so long as $S(ABCD)$ is direct.

A triad of skew lines l_1, l_2, l_3 shall be said to be *right-handed* or *left-handed* according as the doubly oriented line $(ABC, \alpha\beta\gamma)$ is right-handed or left-handed, provided that m is a line meeting l_1, l_2, l_3, and A, B, C are the points ml_1, ml_2, ml_3 respectively, and α, β, γ are the planes ml_1, ml_2, ml_3 respectively.

This convention is independent of the choice of m, by Theorems 57 and 58. By the same theorems any collineation carrying a right-handed triad of noncollinear lines into a right-handed triad of lines is direct, and any collineation carrying a right-handed triad of lines into a left-handed triad is opposite.

The reader should verify that a pair of skew lines lm in a Euclidean space is right-handed or left-handed in the sense of § 163 according as lml_∞ is right-handed or left-handed, l_∞ being the line at infinity which is the absolute polar of the point at infinity of l. If m_∞ is the absolute polar of the point at infinity of m, lmm_∞ is right-handed if and only if lml_∞ is right-handed.

Let A be a point of the axis of a twist Γ in a Euclidean space, let $B = \Gamma(A)$, and let C be the point at infinity of the line AB; let α be any plane on the line AB, $\beta = \Gamma(\alpha)$, and γ the plane on AB perpendicular to α. Then Γ is right-handed in the sense of § 163 if and only if the doubly oriented line $(ABC, \alpha\beta\gamma)$ is right-handed. This is easily verified.

178. Right- and left-handed reguli, congruences, and complexes. By Cor. 2, Theorem 57, every triad of lines in a regulus is right-handed or every triad is left-handed. In the first case the regulus shall be said to be *right-handed* and in the second case to be *left-handed.*

THEOREM 60. *The collineations which leave an elliptic linear congruence invariant are all direct.*

Proof. An elliptic congruence has a pair of conjugate imaginary lines as its directrices (§ 109), and there is one real line of the congruence through each point of a directrix. Any collineation Γ which carries each directrix of the congruence into itself effects a projectivity on that directrix. This projectivity is a product of two involutions (§ 78, Vol. I). Each involution may be effected by a line reflection whose lines of fixed points are the (real) lines of the congruence through the (imaginary) double points of the involution; since such a line reflection leaves both directrices invariant, it leaves the congruence invariant. Hence there exist two line reflections Λ_1, Λ_2, each transforming the congruence into itself, such that $\Lambda_2\Lambda_1\Gamma$ leaves all points on a directrix invariant. Hence $\Lambda_2\Lambda_1\Gamma$ transforms each line of the congruence into itself. By Theorem 57, $\Lambda_2\Lambda_1\Gamma$ is direct, and by Theorem 56, Cor. 5, Λ_1 and Λ_2 are direct. Hence Γ is direct.

If l is any real line not in the congruence, the lines of the congruence meeting l form a regulus, and the directrices are double lines of an involution in the lines of the conjugate regulus. If l' is the line conjugate to l in this involution, the line reflection $\{ll'\}$ must interchange the two directrices. Hence if Γ' is any collineation interchanging the directrices, $\{ll'\} \cdot \Gamma'$ is a collineation which leaves each of them invariant. Hence by the paragraph above $\{ll'\} \cdot \Gamma'$ is direct. Hence Γ' is direct. Hence any real collineation leaving an elliptic linear congruence invariant is direct.

COROLLARY 1. *The triads of lines of an elliptic linear congruence are all right-handed or all left-handed.*

For any triad can be carried into any other triad by a direct collineation.

COROLLARY 2. *If four linearly independent lines are such that all sets of three of them are right-handed or such that all sets of three of them are left-handed, the linear congruence which contains them is elliptic.*

An elliptic congruence shall be said to be *right-handed* if every triad of lines in it is right-handed; otherwise it is said to be *left-handed.*

A pair of conjugate imaginary lines of the second kind (§ 109) is said to be *right-handed* or *left-handed* according as it is determined by a right-handed or a left-handed congruence.

A pair of Clifford parallels (§ 142) is said to be *right-handed* or *left-handed* according as the congruence of Clifford parallels to which they belong is right-handed or left-handed. This distinction is in agreement with that introduced in § 142, because according to both definitions a collineation carrying a system of right-handed Clifford parallels into a system of right-handed ones is direct, and a collineation carrying a system of right-handed Clifford parallels into a system of left-handed ones is opposite.

THEOREM 61. *The collineations which leave a nondegenerate linear complex invariant are all direct.*

Proof. Let Γ be a collineation leaving a complex C invariant, and let l be any line of C and $l' = \Gamma(l)$. Let l'' be any line of C not meeting l or l'. The lines of C which meet l and l'' constitute a regulus, and three lines of this regulus together with l and l'' constitute a set of five linearly independent lines (§ 106, Vol. I) upon which, therefore, all the lines of C are linearly dependent. Hence a collineation Γ' which leaves this regulus invariant and interchanges l and l'' leaves C invariant. Let Γ'' be a collineation, similarly obtained, which interchanges l'' and l' and leaves C invariant. The product $\Gamma'\Gamma''\Gamma$ leaves C and l invariant, and Γ' and Γ'' are direct.

Any collineation leaving C and l invariant leaves invariant the projectivity Π between the points on l and the planes corresponding to them in the null system determined by C. The projectivity Π transforms an arbitrary sense-class among the points on l into an arbitrary sense-class among the planes on l. These two sense-classes determine a doubly oriented line, $\bar{l}$. The other sense-class of the points on l is carried by Π into the other sense-class of planes on l, and these two sense-classes determine a doubly oriented line $\bar{\bar{l}}$. Since any collineation leaving C and l invariant leaves Π invariant, it either transforms this doubly oriented line into itself or into the one obtained by reversing both its sense-classes. Hence any such collineation is direct by Theorem 58 and its first corollary. In particular $\Gamma'\Gamma''\Gamma$ is direct, and since Γ' and Γ'' are direct, it follows that Γ is direct.

By Theorem 61 all the doubly oriented lines analogous to $\bar{l}$ which are determined by C are all right-handed or all left-handed. In the first case C shall be called *right-handed*, and in the second case C shall be called *left-handed.*

The algebraic criteria in the exercises below are taken from the article by E. Study referred to in § 162. See also F. Klein, Autographierte Vorlesungen über nicht-Euclidische Geometrie, Vol. II, Chap. I, Göttingen, 1890.

EXERCISES

1. Classify parabolic congruences (§ 107, Vol. I) as right-handed and left-handed.

2. For two lines p and p' let

$$(p, p') = p_{12}p'_{34} + p_{13}p'_{42} + p_{14}p'_{23} + p_{34}p'_{12} + p_{42}p'_{13} + p_{23}p'_{14},$$

where p_{ij} are the Plücker coördinates (§ 109, Vol. I) of p, and p'_{ij} those of p'. Three lines p, p', p'' are right-handed or left-handed according as

$$(p, p')\cdot(p', p'')\cdot(p'', p)$$

is positive or negative.

3. A pair of conjugate imaginary lines of the second kind whose Plücker coördinates are p_{ij} and $\bar{p}_{ij}$ respectively are right-handed or left-handed according as

$$p_{12}\bar{p}_{12} + p_{13}\bar{p}_{13} + p_{14}\bar{p}_{14} + p_{34}\bar{p}_{34} + p_{42}\bar{p}_{42} + p_{23}\bar{p}_{23}$$

is positive or negative.

4. The linear line complex whose equation in Plücker coördinates is (§ 110, Vol. I)

$$a_{12}p_{12} + a_{13}p_{13} + a_{14}p_{14} + a_{34}p_{34} + a_{42}p_{42} + a_{23}p_{23} = 0$$

is right-handed or left-handed according as

$$a_{12}a_{34} + a_{13}a_{42} + a_{14}a_{23}$$

is positive or negative.

5. A twist given by the parameters of § 130 is right-handed if $\alpha_0\beta_0 > 0$ and the coördinate system is right-handed.

6. The linear complex C determined by a twist according to Ex. 7, § 122, is right-handed or left-handed according as the twist is right-handed or left-handed.

***179. Elementary transformations of triads of lines.** Let F_0 be a figure such that all the collineations which transform it into itself are direct, and let $[F]$ be the set of all figures equivalent to F under direct transformations. From the fact that the group of all direct collineations is continuous, it can be proved that $[F]$ is a continuous family of figures.

This can also be put into evidence by generalizing the notion of elementary transformation to other figures. This is essentially what has been done in §§ 169 and 173. For triads of skew lines the following theorem is fundamental.

THEOREM 62. *If l_1, l_2, l_3 are three skew lines, and l_4 is a line coplanar with l_3 and such that the points in which l_1 and l_2 meet the plane l_3l_4 are not separated by the lines l_3 and l_4, then $l_1l_2l_3$ can be carried to $l_1l_2l_4$ by a direct collineation.*

Proof. Let a be a line meeting l_1, l_3, and l_4 (fig. 86) in points A_1, A_3, A_4 respectively, which are all distinct. Let α be the plane containing l_2 and the point B of intersection of l_3 and l_4. If A_1 is in α, an elation with A_1 as center, α as plane of fixed points, and carrying A_3 to A_4 will carry l_1, l_2, l_3 into l_1, l_2, l_4 respectively. By Theorem 56, Cor. 4, this elation is direct.

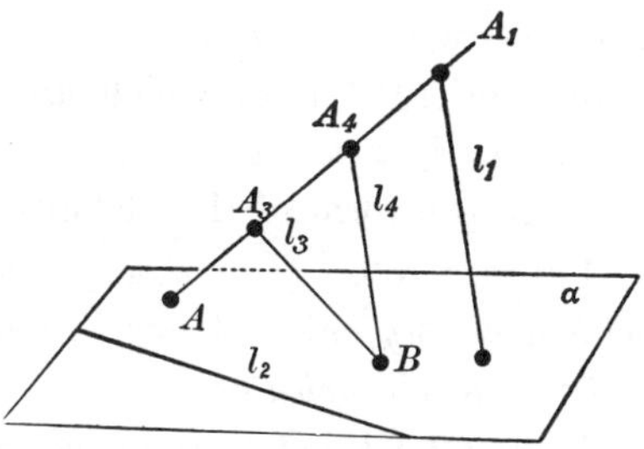

FIG. 86

If A_1 is not in α, the points A_3 and A_4 are not separated by A_1 and the point A in which a meets α; for by hypothesis A_1 and the point in which l_2 meets the line BA are not separated by the lines l_3 and l_4. Hence the homology with A_1 as center and α as plane of fixed points which carries l_3 to l_4 is direct (Theorem 56). This homology carries l_1, l_2, l_3 into l_1, l_2, l_4 respectively.

An *elementary transformation* of a triad of skew lines $l_1l_2l_3$ may be defined as the operation of replacing one of them, say l_3, by a line l_4 which is coplanar with l_3 and such that l_3 and l_4 do not separate the points in which their plane is met by l_1 and l_2.

By Theorem 62 an elementary transformation may be effected by a direct collineation. A sequence of elementary transformations therefore carries a right-handed triad into a right-handed triad and a left-handed triad into a left-handed triad.

Conversely, it can be proved that any right-handed triad can be carried into any right-handed triad by a sequence of elementary transformations and that the two classes of lines determined by a pair of skew lines ab according to Ex. 2, § 25, are the lines $[x]$ such that abx is right-handed and the lines $[y]$ such that aby is left-handed. These propositions are left to the reader.

***180. Doubly oriented lines.** The theory of sense-classes in three dimensions could be based entirely on that of doubly oriented lines (§ 176). We shall prove the earliest theorems of such a theory in this section. The proofs are based on Assumptions A, E, S and do not make use of the preceding discussions of order in three-space.

DEFINITION. Two doubly oriented lines are said to be *doubly perspective* if they can be given the notation $(ABC, \alpha\beta\gamma)$ and $(A'B'C', \alpha'\beta'\gamma')$ respectively in such a way that $A, B, C, \alpha, \beta, \gamma$ are on $\alpha', \beta', \gamma', A', B', C'$ respectively. Two doubly oriented lines l_0 and l are said to be *similarly oriented* if and only if there exists a sequence of doubly oriented lines $l_1, l_2, \cdots, l_n$ such that l_0 is doubly perspective with l_1, l_1 with $l_2, \cdots, l_{n-1}$ with l_n, and l_n with l. Two doubly oriented lines which are not similarly oriented are said to be *oppositely oriented.*

From the form of this definition it follows immediately that

THEOREM 63. *If a doubly oriented line l_1 is similarly oriented with a doubly oriented line l_2, and l_2 with a doubly oriented line l_3, l_1 is similarly oriented with l_3.*

THEOREM 64. *If three doubly oriented lines m_0, m_1, m_2, no two of which are coplanar, are such that m_0 is doubly perspective with m_1, and m_1 with m_2, then m_2 is doubly perspective either with m_0 or with the doubly oriented line obtained by changing both sense-classes on m_0.*

Proof. Let ABC be an ordered set of points of the sense-class of points of m_0 and let l_0, l_1, l_2 be the three lines on A, B, C respectively which meet m_1 and m_2. The sense-class of planes of m_0 contains either the ordered triad of planes l_0m_0, l_1m_0, l_2m_0 or the ordered triad l_0m_0, l_2m_0, l_1m_0. In the first case (fig. 87) let $l_0m_0 = \alpha$, $l_1m_0 = \beta$, $l_2m_0 = \gamma$. In the second case (fig. 88) let $l_0m_0 = \alpha$, $l_2m_0 = \beta$, $l_1m_0 = \gamma$. In both cases let A_1, B_1, C_1 be the points l_0m_1, l_1m_1, l_2m_1 respectively, $\alpha_1, \beta_1, \gamma_1$ the planes l_0m_1, l_1m_1, l_2m_1 respectively, A_2, B_2, C_2 the points l_0m_2, l_1m_2, l_2m_2 respectively, and $\alpha_2, \beta_2, \gamma_2$ the planes l_0m_2, l_1m_2, l_2m_2 respectively.

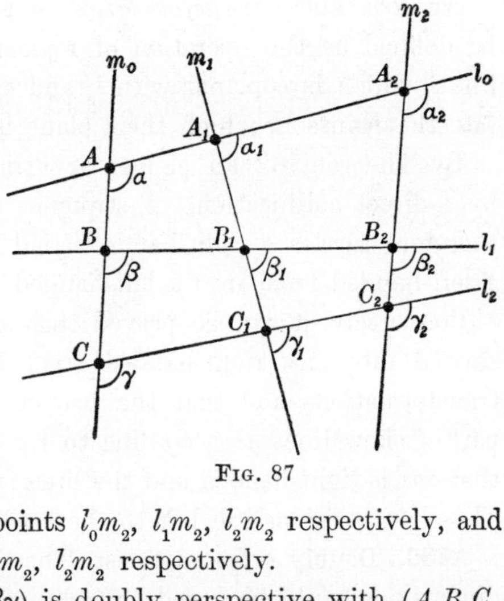

FIG. 87

In the first case $(ABC, \alpha\beta\gamma)$ is doubly perspective with $(A_1B_1C_1, \alpha_1\beta_1\gamma_1)$ and this with $(A_2B_2C_2, \alpha_2\beta_2\gamma_2)$. Since $m_0 = (ABC, \alpha\beta\gamma)$, and

m_0 is doubly perspective with m_1, $m_1 = (A_1B_1C_1, \alpha_1\beta_1\gamma_1)$; and since m_1 is doubly perspective with m_2, $m_2 = (A_2B_2C_2, \alpha_2\beta_2\gamma_2)$. But by construction $(A_2B_2C_2, \alpha_2\beta_2\gamma_2)$ is doubly perspective with $(ABC, \alpha\beta\gamma)$, i.e. m_2 is doubly perspective with m_0.

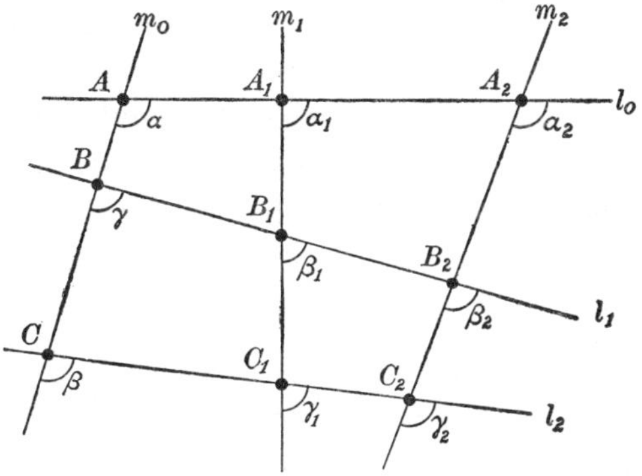

FIG. 88

In the second case $(ABC, \alpha\beta\gamma)$ is doubly perspective with $(A_1C_1B_1, \alpha_1\beta_1\gamma_1)$ and this with $(A_2B_2C_2, \alpha_2\gamma_2\beta_2)$. Since $m_0 = (ABC, \alpha\beta\gamma)$, and m_1 is doubly perspective with m_0, $m_1 = (A_1C_1B_1, \alpha_1\beta_1\gamma_1)$; and since m_1 is doubly perspective with m_2, $m_2 = (A_2B_2C_2, \alpha_2\gamma_2\beta_2)$. But by construction $(A_2B_2C_2, \alpha_2\gamma_2\beta_2)$ is doubly perspective with $(ACB, \alpha\gamma\beta)$; i.e. m_2 is doubly perspective with the doubly oriented line obtained by changing both sense-classes of m_0.

THEOREM 65. *A doubly oriented line $(ABC, \alpha\beta\gamma)$ is similarly oriented with $(ACB, \alpha\gamma\beta)$ and oppositely oriented to $(ABC, \alpha\gamma\beta)$ and $(ACB, \alpha\beta\gamma)$.*

Proof. Let l_0, l_1, l_2 be three lines distinct from AB and such that l_0 is on A and α, l_1 on B and γ, l_2 on C and β. Let m_1 and m_2 be two lines distinct from AB, each of which meets l_0, l_1, and l_2. Let A_1, B_1, C_1 be the points l_0m_1, l_1m_1, l_2m_1 respectively and α_2, β_2, γ_2 the planes l_0m_1, l_1m_1, l_2m_1 respectively; let A_2, B_2, C_2 be the points l_0m_2, l_1m_2, l_2m_2 respectively and α_2, β_2, γ_2 the planes l_0m_2, l_1m_2, l_2m_2 respectively. Then by construction (fig. 88) and definition the oriented line $(ABC, \alpha\beta\gamma)$ is doubly perspective with $(A_1C_1B_1, \alpha_1\beta_1\gamma_1)$, and this with $(A_2B_2C_2, \alpha_2\gamma_2\beta_2)$, and this with $(ACB, \alpha\gamma\beta)$. Hence $(ABC, \alpha\beta\gamma)$ is similarly oriented with $(ACB, \alpha\gamma\beta)$. By a change of notation it is evident that $(ABC, \alpha\gamma\beta)$ is similarly oriented with $(ACB, \alpha\beta\gamma)$. It remains, therefore, to prove that $(ABC, \alpha\beta\gamma)$ is not similarly oriented with $(ACB, \alpha\beta\gamma)$.

If these two oriented lines were similarly oriented, there would be a sequence of doubly oriented lines $m_0, m_1, m_2, \cdots, m_n$ such that

$m_0 = (ABC, \alpha\beta\gamma)$ and $m_n = (ACB, \alpha\beta\gamma)$, and such that each oriented line of the sequence would be doubly perspective with the next one in the sequence. Let m be a doubly oriented line not coplanar with any of $m_0, m_1, \cdots, m_n$, and doubly perspective with m_0; let $\bar{m}$ be the doubly oriented line obtained by changing both sense-classes on m. By Theorem 64 m_1 is doubly perspective with m or $\bar{m}$. By a second application of this theorem m_2 is doubly perspective with m or $\bar{m}$, and by repeating this process n times we find that m_n is doubly perspective with m or $\bar{m}$. But this means that m_n is $(ABC, \alpha\beta\gamma)$ or $(ACB, \alpha\gamma\beta)$.

THEOREM 66. *There are two and only two classes of doubly oriented lines such that any two doubly oriented lines of the same class are similarly oriented and any two of different classes are oppositely oriented.*

Proof. Let $(ABC, \alpha\beta\gamma)$ be an arbitrary fixed doubly oriented line and let K be the class of doubly oriented lines similarly oriented to it. This class contains (Theorem 65) $(ACB, \alpha\gamma\beta)$ but not $(ACB, \alpha\beta\gamma)$ or $(ABC, \alpha\gamma\beta)$. If l is any line and m any line not meeting l or AB, $(ABC, \alpha\beta\gamma)$ is doubly perspective with one of the doubly oriented lines determined by m and this with one of those determined by l. Hence K contains two of the four doubly oriented lines determined by any line of space. Let K' be the class of doubly oriented lines similarly oriented with $(ACB, \alpha\beta\gamma)$. It also contains two of the four doubly oriented lines determined by any line of space. K and K' cannot have a doubly oriented line in common, because this would imply that $(ABC, \alpha\beta\gamma)$ and $(ACB, \alpha\beta\gamma)$ were similarly oriented. Hence every doubly oriented line is either in K or in K'.

There can be no other pair of classes of similarly oriented doubly oriented lines including all doubly oriented lines of space, because one class of such a pair would contain elements both of K and of K', and this would imply, by Theorem 63, that $(ABC, \alpha\beta\gamma)$ was similarly oriented with $(ACB, \alpha\beta\gamma)$.

From the construction which determines whether two doubly oriented lines are similarly oriented or not, it is evident that any collineation carries any two doubly oriented lines which are similarly oriented into two which are similarly oriented. Hence, if a collineation carries one doubly oriented line into a similarly oriented one, it carries every doubly oriented line into a similarly oriented one; and if it carries one into an oppositely oriented one, it carries every doubly oriented line into an oppositely oriented one.

Any collineation which carries a doubly oriented line into a similarly oriented one is said to be *direct*, and any collineation which carries a doubly oriented line into an oppositely oriented one is said to be *opposite*. This definition of direct and opposite collineations is easily seen to be equivalent to that in § 32.

***181. More general theory of sense.** The theory of sense-classes in the preceding pages can be extended to analytic transformations by means of simple limiting considerations. For example, consider a transformation of a part of a Euclidean plane

$$x' = f(xy) = a_{00} + a_{10}x + a_{01}y + a_{20}x^2 + \cdots,$$
$$y' = g(xy) = b_{00} + b_{10}x + b_{01}y + b_{20}x^2 + \cdots,$$

where both series are convergent for all points in a region including the point (0, 0). If the determinant

$$\begin{vmatrix} a_{10} & a_{01} \\ b_{10} & b_{01} \end{vmatrix} = \begin{vmatrix} \dfrac{\partial f(0,0)}{\partial x} & \dfrac{\partial f(0,0)}{\partial y} \\ \dfrac{\partial g(0,0)}{\partial x} & \dfrac{\partial g(0,0)}{\partial y} \end{vmatrix} = J$$

is not zero, it can be shown that there is a region including (0, 0) which is transformed into a region including (a_{00}, b_{00}) in such a way that all ordered point triads of a sense-class in the first region go into ordered point triads of one sense-class in the second region; and if (x', y') is in the same plane as (x, y), the two sense-classes will be the same if and only if $J > 0$.

By a similar limiting process the notions of right- and left-handedness can be extended to curves, ruled surfaces, and other figures having analytic equations. A discussion of some of the cases which arise will be found in the article by Study referred to in § 162.

This sort of theory of sense relations belongs essentially to differential geometry, although the domain to which it applies may be extended by methods of the type used in §§ 168 and 173.

The theory of sense may, however, be extended in a different way so as to apply to the geometry of all continuous transformations instead of merely to the projective geometry or to the geometry of analytic transformations. The main theorems are as follows:

Any one-to-one reciprocal continuous transformation of a curve into itself transforms each sense-class on the curve either into itself or into the other sense-class. A transformation of the first kind is called *direct* and one of the second kind *opposite*. A direct transformation is a *deformation* (§ 157), and an opposite transformation is not a deformation.

Any simple closed curve consisting of points in or on the boundary of a 2-cell R (§ 155) is the boundary of a unique 2-cell which consists entirely of points of R.

A 2-cell can be deformed into itself in such a way as to transform an arbitrary simple closed curve of the cell into an arbitrary simple closed curve of the cell. Any one-to-one reciprocal continuous transformation of a 2-cell and its boundary into themselves is a deformation if and only if it effects a deformation on the boundary; i.e. if and only if it transforms a sense-class on the boundary into itself.

If the sense-classes on one curve j_1 of a 2-cell and its boundary are designated as *positive* and *negative* respectively, any sense-class on any other curve j_1 is called *positive* or *negative* according as it is the transform of the positive or of the negative sense-class on j_1 by a deformation of j_1 into j through intermediate positions which are all simple closed curves on the 2-cell and its boundary. By the theorems above, this gives a unique determination of the positive and negative sense-classes on any curve of the given convex region. A curve associated with its positive sense-class is called a *positively oriented curve*, and a curve associated with its negative sense-class is called a *negatively oriented curve*.

Any transformation of a 2-cell which is one-to-one, reciprocal, and continuous either transforms all positively oriented curves into positively oriented curves or transforms all positively oriented curves into negatively oriented curves. In the first case the transformation is said to be *direct* and in the second case to be *opposite*. The transformation is a deformation if and only if it is direct. A 2-cell associated with its positively oriented curves or with its negatively oriented curves is called an *oriented 2-cell*.

The oriented 2-cells of a simple surface fall into two classes such that any oriented 2-cell of one class can be carried by a continuous deformation of the surface into any other oriented 2-cell of the same class, but not into any oriented 2-cell of the other class. The two oriented 2-cells determined by a given 2-cell are in different classes. A simple surface associated with one of these classes of oriented 2-cells is said to be *oriented.*

A similar theorem does not hold for the oriented 2-cells of a projective plane. Instead we have the theorem that every continuous one-to-one reciprocal transformation of a projective plane is a deformation. Consequently any oriented 2-cell can be carried into any other oriented 2-cell by a deformation.

The oriented simple surfaces in a 3-cell and its boundary fall into two classes such that any member of either class can be deformed into any other member of the same class through a set of intermediate positions which are all oriented simple surfaces, but cannot be deformed in this way into any member of the other class. A continuous one-to-one reciprocal correspondence which carries a 3-cell and its boundary into themselves either interchanges the two classes of oriented simple surfaces or leaves them invariant. In the second case the transformation is a deformation and in the first case it is not. A 3-cell associated with one of its classes of oriented surfaces is called an *oriented 3-cell.*

The oriented 3-cells of a projective space fall into two classes such that any member of one class can be carried by a continuous deformation of the projective space into any member of the same class but not into any member of the other class. A continuous one-to-one reciprocal transformation of the projective space either transforms each class of oriented 3-cells into itself or into the other class. In the first case it is a deformation and in the second it is not. A projective space associated with one of its classes of oriented 3-cells is called an *oriented projective space.*

The one-dimensional theorems outlined above are easily proved on the basis of the discussion of the sense-classes on a line in §§ 159 and 165. The two-dimensional ones, though more difficult, are consequences of known theorems of analysis situs. They involve, however, such theorems as that of Jordan, that a simple closed curve separates a convex region into two regions; and the theorems of this class do not belong (§§ 34, 39, 110) to projective geometry. The Jordan theorem in the special case of a simple closed polygon does, however, belong to projective geometry and is proved below (§ 187).

The three-dimensional propositions outlined here have not all been proved as yet, but are (in form) direct generalizations of the one- and two-dimensional ones.

Let us note that an ordered triad of points as treated in § 160 may be regarded as determining an oriented 2-cell. For the triangular region having the points as vertices is a 2-cell, and a sense-class is determined on its boundary by the order of the vertices. This sense-class determines a sense-class on every curve of the 2-cell and thus determines an oriented 2-cell.

In like manner an ordered tetrad of points as treated in § 160 determines an oriented 3-cell. For the tetrahedral region having points $ABCD$ as vertices is a 3-cell. The triangular region BCD is a 2-cell which does not contain A, and is oriented in view of the order of the points on its boundary. This oriented 2-cell determines an orientation of the boundary of the 3-cell, and thus of the 3-cell.

Likewise an ordered tetrad $ABCD$ of a projective plane determines a 2-cell, i.e. that one of the triangular regions BCD which contains A; and this 2-cell is oriented by the order of the points BCD. Similarly, an ordered pentad $ABCDE$ of points in a projective space determines an oriented 3-cell, i.e. that one of the tetrahedral regions $BCDE$ which contains A, oriented according to the order of the points $BCDE$.

182. Broken lines and polygons. DEFINITION. A set of n points $A_1, A_2, \cdots, A_n$, together with a set of n segments joining A_1 to A_2, A_2 to $A_3, \cdots, A_{n-1}$ to A_n, is called a *broken line* joining A_1 to A_n. The points $A_1, \cdots, A_n$ are called the *vertices* and the segments joining them the *edges* of the broken line. If the vertices are all distinct and no edge contains a vertex or a point on another edge, the broken line is said to be *simple.* If $A_1 = A_n$ the broken line is said to be *closed,* otherwise it is said to be *open.* The set of all points on a closed broken line is called a *polygon.* If the vertices of a polygon are all distinct and no edge contains a vertex or a point on another edge, the polygon is said to be *simple.*

A broken line whose vertices are $A_1, A_2, \cdots, A_n$, and whose edges are the segments joining A_1 to A_2, A_2 to $A_3, \cdots, A_{n-1}$ to A_n, is called the broken line $A_1A_2 \cdots A_n$, and its edges are denoted by $A_1A_2, A_2A_3, \cdots, A_{n-1}A_n$ respectively. If $A_1 = A_n$ the corresponding polygon is denoted by $A_1A_2 \cdots A_{n-1}A_1$; the vertex A_1 is sometimes denoted by A_n, A_2 by A_{n+1}, etc.

The following theorem is an obvious consequence of the definition.

THEOREM 67. *The polygon $A_1A_2 \cdots A_nA_1$ is the same as $A_2A_3 \cdots A_nA_1A_2$ and $A_1A_n \cdots A_2A_1$. If P is any point of the edge A_1A_2 of* *a simple polygon* $A_1A_2 \cdots A_nA_1$, *this polygon is the same as a polygon* $A_1PA_2 \cdots A_nA_1$ *in which the edge* A_1P, *the vertex* P, *and the edge* PA_2 *constitute the same set of points as the edge* A_1A_2. *If a simple polygon* $A_1A_2A_3 \cdots A_nA_1$ *is such that* $A_1A_2A_3$ *are collinear and* $A_3 \neq A_1$, *this polygon is the same as the polygon* $A_1A_3 \cdots A_nA_1$ *in which all the edges but* A_1A_3 *are the same as before and* A_1A_3 *is the segment* $A_1A_2A_3$.

DEFINITION. If A, B, C are any three points on a simple polygon, an *elementary transformation* is the operation of replacing any one of these points, say C, by a point C' such that C and C' are joined by a segment consisting of points of the polygon and not containing either of the other two points. A class consisting of all ordered triads each of which is transformable by a finite number of elementary transformations into a fixed triad ABC is called the *sense-class* ABC and is denoted by $S(ABC)$.

THEOREM. 68. *There exists a one-to-one and reciprocal correspondence between the points of any simple polygon and the points of any line such that two triads of points on the polygon are in the same sense-class with respect to the polygon if and only if the corresponding triads of points on the line are in the same sense-class.*

Proof. Let the vertices of the polygon be denoted by $A_1, A_2, \cdots, A_{n-1}$ and let A_1 be also denoted by A_n. Let $B_1, B_2, \cdots, B_{n-1}$ be n arbitrary points of a line l in the order $\{B_1, B_2, \cdots, B_{n-1}\}$ and let B_n also denote B_1. Let β_i denote that segment B_iB_{i+1}, which contains none of the other points B. Let the edge joining A_i to A_{i+1} correspond projectively to the segment β_i in such a way that A_i and A_{i+1} are homologous with B_i and B_{i+1} respectively. (In general the projectivities by which two sides of the polygon correspond to two segments on the line will be different.) If we also let A_i correspond to B_i $(i = 1, \cdots, n-1)$, there is evidently determined a one-to-one and reciprocal correspondence Γ between the polygon and the line which is such that each side of the polygon with its two ends corresponds with preservation of order relations to a segment of the line and its two ends.

Let P_1, P_2, P_3, P_4 denote points of the polygon and L_1, L_2, L_3, L_4 the points of l to which they respectively correspond under Γ. The correspondence Γ is so defined that if $P_1P_2P_3$ goes into $P_1P_2P_4$ by an elementary transformation with respect to the polygon, then $L_1L_2L_3$ goes into $L_1L_2L_4$ by an elementary transformation restricted with respect to $B_1, B_2, \cdots, B_n$ (cf. § 165), and conversely. Hence the theorem follows at once from the corollary of Theorem 22.

COROLLARY 1. *The theorem above remains true if the words "broken line with distinct ends" be substituted for polygon, and "interval" for line.*

The definitions of separation and order given in § 21 for the points on a line may now be applied word for word to the points on a simple polygon, and in view of the correspondence established in Theorem 68, the theorems about order relations on a line may be applied without change to polygons.

By comparison with the proof of Theorem 15 we obtain immediately

COROLLARY 2. *A simple polygon is a simple closed curve.*

COROLLARY 3. *A simple broken line joining two distinct points A_1, A_n is a simple curve joining A_1 and A_n.*

The order relations on a broken line which is not simple may be studied by the method given above with the aid of a simple device. Suppose we associate an integer with each point of a broken line $A_1A_2 \cdots A_n$ as follows: With A_1 and every point of the segment joining A_1 to A_2 the number 1; with A_2 and every point of the segment joining A_2 to A_3 the number 2; and so on, and, finally, with A_n the number n.

DEFINITION. The object formed by a point of the broken line and the number associated with it by the above process shall be called a *numbered point*; and the numbered point is said to be on any segment, line, plane, etc. which the point is on. If A, B, C are any three numbered points on a polygon, an *elementary transformation* is the operation of replacing any one of these numbered points, say C, by a point C' such that C and C' are joined by a segment of numbered points all having the same number. A class consisting of all ordered triads of numbered points each of which is transformable by a finite sequence of elementary transformations into a fixed triad ABC is called the *sense-class* ABC and is denoted by $S(ABC)$.

By the proof given for Theorem 68 we now have

THEOREM 69. *There exists a one-to-one and reciprocal correspondence between the numbered points of any broken line and the points of any interval such that two triads of numbered points are in the same sense-class if and only if the corresponding triads of points on the interval are in the same sense-class.*

We are therefore justified in applying the theorems and definitions about order relations on an interval to the numbered points of a broken line.

EXERCISE

*Any two points of a region can be joined by a broken line consisting entirely of points of the region.

183. A theorem on simple polygons. In the last section a polygon was defined as the set of points contained in a sequence of points and linear segments. This is the most usual definition and doubtless the most natural. With a view to generalizing so as to obtain the theory of polyhedra in spaces of three and more dimensions, however, we shall find it more convenient to use the property of a simple polygon stated in the following theorem.*

THEOREM 70. *A set of points $[P]$ is a simple polygon if and only if the following conditions are satisfied:* (1) *$[P]$ consists of a set of distinct points, called vertices, and of distinct segments, called edges, such that the ends of each edge are vertices and each vertex is an end of an even number of edges;* (2) *if any points of $[P]$ are omitted, the remaining subset of $[P]$ does not have the property* (1).

Proof. It is obvious that a simple polygon, as defined in § 182, satisfies Conditions (1) and (2), because no edge has a point in common with any other edge or vertex and each vertex is an end of exactly two edges.

Let us now consider a set of points $[P]$ satisfying (1) and (2). If two or more edges have a point in common, this point divides each edge into two segments. Hence the point may be regarded as a vertex at which an even number of edges meet. In like manner, if an edge contains a vertex the two segments into which the edge is divided by the vertex may be regarded as edges. Since there are originally given only a finite number of vertices and edges, this process determines a finite number of vertices and edges such that no edge contains a vertex or any point of another edge.

*This form of the definition of a polygon and a corresponding definition of a polyhedron are due to N. J. Lennes, American Journal of Mathematics, Vol. XXXIII (1911), p. 37.

Now let e_1 be any edge and P_1 one of its ends. Since there are an even number of segments having P_1 as an end, there exists another distinct from e_1; let this be denoted by e_2. Let P_2 be its other end, and let e_3 be a second segment having P_2 as an end, and so on. By this process we obtain a sequence of points and segments

$$e_1, P_1, e_2, P_2, e_3, \cdots.$$

Since the number of vertices is finite, this process must lead by a finite number of steps to a point P_n which coincides with one of the previous points, say P_i. The set of points included in the points and segments

$$P_i, e_{i+1}, P_{i+1}, \cdots, P_{n-1}, e_n$$

satisfies the definition of a simple polygon and has the property that each $P_j (j = i, i+1 \cdots P_{n-1})$ is an end of two and only two e's. Hence it satisfies Condition (1). By Condition (2) it must include all points of the set $[P]$.

COROLLARY. *A set of points satisfying Condition (1) of Theorem 70 consists of a finite number of simple polygons no two of which have any point in common which is not a vertex.*

Proof. In the proof of the second part of the theorem above, Condition (2) is not used before the last sentence. If Condition (2) be not satisfied, the set of points remaining when the segments $e_{i+1}, \cdots, e_n$ (and those of the points $P_i, \cdots, P_{n-1}$ which are not ends of the remaining segments) are removed continues to satisfy Condition (1). For on removing two segments from an even number, an even number remains. Hence the process by which the simple polygon $P_i, e_{i+1}, \cdots, P_{n-1}, e_n$ was obtained may be repeated and another simple polygon removed. Since the total number of edges is finite, this step can be repeated only a finite number of times.

184. Polygons in a plane. In the next three sections we shall prove that the polygons in a projective plane are of two kinds, a polygon of the first kind being such that all points not on it constitute two regions, and a polygon of the second kind being such that all points not on it constitute a single region. The boundary of a triangular region is a polygon of the first kind, and a projective line a polygon of the second kind. In proving that the points not on a polygon constitute one or two regions, we shall need the following:

THEOREM 71. *Any point coplanar with but not on a polygon p in a plane α is in a triangular region of α containing no point of p.*

Proof. Let the polygon be denoted by $A_1A_2 \cdots A_nA_1$ and the point by P. By an obvious construction (the details of which are left to the reader; cf. § 149) a triangular region T_1 may be found containing P and not containing A_1 or A_2 or any point of the edge A_1A_2. In like manner a triangular region T_2 may be constructed which contains P, is contained in T_1, and does not contain A_3 or any point of the edge A_2A_3. By repeating this construction we obtain a sequence of triangular regions $T_1, T_2, \cdots, T_n$, each contained in all the preceding ones, containing P, and such that T_k does not contain any point of the broken line $A_1A_2 \cdots A_{k+1}$. Thus T_n contains P and contains no point of the polygon $A_1A_2 \cdots A_nA_1$.

COROLLARY. *Any point of space not on a polygon p is in a tetrahedral region containing no point of p.*

Let the set of lines containing the edges of a simple polygon in a plane be denoted by $l_1, l_2, \cdots, l_n$. Since more than one edge may be on the same line, n is less than or equal to the number of edges. According to Theorem 67 we can first suppose that the notation is so assigned that no two edges having a common end are collinear except in the case of a polygon of two sides (which is a projective line), for two collinear edges and their common end can be regarded as a single edge. In the second place, according to the same theorem, we can introduce as a vertex any point in which an edge is met by one of the lines $l_1, l_2, \cdots, l_n$ which does not contain it.

Under these conventions the polygon may be denoted by $A_1A_2 \cdots A_mA_1$, where each point $A_i (i = 1, 2, \cdots, m)$ is a point of intersection of two of the lines $l_1, l_2, \cdots, l_n$, and each edge is a segment joining two vertices and containing points of only one of the lines $l_1, l_2, \cdots, l_n$.

In like manner, when two or more simple polygons are under consideration, let us denote the set of lines containing all their edges by $l_1, l_2, \cdots, l_n$. We may first arrange that no two edges of the same polygon which have an end in common are collinear, and then introduce new vertices at every point in which an edge is met by one of the lines $l_1, l_2, \cdots, l_n$ which is not on it. Thus in this case also the polygons may be taken to have all their vertices at points of intersection of the n lines $l_1, l_2, \cdots, l_n$ and to have no edge which contains such a point of intersection.

We are thus led to study the points of intersection of a set of n coplanar lines and the segments of these lines which join the points of intersection.

185. Subdivision of a plane by lines. Consider a set of n lines $l_1, l_2, \cdots, l_n$ all in the same plane π. The number α_0 of their points of intersection is subject to the condition

$$1 \leqq \alpha_0 \leqq \frac{n(n-1)}{2},$$

the two extreme cases being the case where all n lines are concurrent and the case where no three are concurrent. According to § 22, Chap. II, and the definition of boundary (§ 150), the points of intersection bound a number α_1 of linear convex regions upon the lines. The number α_1 is subject to the condition

$$n \leqq \alpha_1 \leqq n(n-1),$$

the two extreme cases being the same as before.

THEOREM 72. *The points of a plane which are not on any one of a finite set of lines $l_1, l_2, \cdots, l_n$ fall into a number α_2 of convex regions such that any segment joining two points of different regions contains at least one point of $l_1, l_2, \cdots, l_n$. The number α_2 satisfies the inequality*

$$n \leqq \alpha_2 \leqq \frac{n(n-1)}{2} + 1.$$

Proof. The proof may be made by induction. If $n = 1$ the theorem follows directly from the definition of a convex region. We suppose that it is true for $n = k$, and prove it for $n = k + 1$.

We are given $k+1$ lines $l_1, l_2, \cdots, l_{k+1}$. The lines $l_1, l_2, \cdots, l_k$ determine a number N_k, not less than k and not more than $\frac{k(k-1)}{2} + 1$, of convex regions. The line l_{k+1} meets the remaining k lines in at least one point and not more than k points. The remaining points of l_{k+1} therefore form at least one and at most k linear convex regions, each of which is the set of all points common to l_{k+1}, and one of the planar convex regions (Theorem 3). By Theorem 8 each convex region which contains points of l_{k+1} is divided into two convex regions such that any segment joining two points of different regions meets l_{k+1} if it does not meet one of the lines $l_1, l_2, \cdots, l_k$. Hence the $k+1$ lines determine a number N_{k+1} of convex regions of the required kind such that $N_k + 1 \leqq N_{k+1} \leqq N_k + k$. Since

$$k \leqq N_k \leqq \frac{k(k-1)}{2} - 1,$$

it follows that

$$k+1 \leqq N_{k+1} \leqq \frac{k(k-1)}{2} - 1 + k = \frac{(k+1)k}{2} - 1.$$

Corollary 1. *If n lines of a plane pass through a point, they determine n convex regions in the plane; if no three of them are concurrent, they determine* $\frac{n(n-1)}{2} + 1$ *convex regions.*

Let us denote the α_0 points of intersection of the lines $l_1, l_2, \cdots, l_n$ by

$$a_1^0,\ a_2^0,\ \cdots,\ a_{\alpha_0}^0,$$

or any one of them by a^0; the α_1 linear convex regions which these points determine upon the lines by

$$a_1^1,\ a_2^1,\ \cdots,\ a_{\alpha_1}^1,$$

or any one of them by a^1; and the α_2 planar convex regions by

$$a_1^2,\ a_2^2,\ \cdots,\ a_{\alpha_2}^2,$$

or any one of them by a^2.

Corollary 2. *If the lines $l_1, l_2, \cdots, l_n$ are not concurrent, any line coplanar with and containing a point of an a^2 has a segment of points in common with it. The ends of this segment are on the boundary of the a^2, and no other point of the line is on this boundary.*

Proof. The given line, which we shall call l, meets the lines $l_1, l_2, \cdots, l_n$ in at least two points, and, as seen in the proof of the theorem, one and only one of the mutually exclusive segments having these points as ends is composed entirely of points of the a^2. Let σ denote this segment. Its ends are boundary points of the a^2 by Theorem 10. Let l_i and l_j be lines of the set $l_1, l_2, \cdots, l_n$ such that l_i contains one end of σ and l_j the other. All points of the a^2 are separated from the points of the segment complementary to σ by the lines l_i and l_j. Hence any point of the complementary segment is in a triangular region containing no point of the a^2 and is therefore not a boundary point of the a^2.

This argument carries with it the proof of

COROLLARY 3. *Any interval joining a point of an* a^2 *to a point not in the* a^2 *contains a point of the boundary of the* a^2.

THEOREM 73. *If the lines* $l_1, l_2, \cdots, l_n$ *are not all concurrent, the boundary of each* a^2 *is a simple polygon whose vertices are* a^0*'s and whose edges are* a^1*'s.*

Proof. The theorem is a direct consequence of § 151 in case $n=3$. Let us prove the general theorem by induction; i.e. we assume it true for $n=k$ and prove it for $n=k+1$.

Let the notation be so assigned that l_1, l_2, l_3 are not concurrent. Then any one of the convex regions, say R, determined by $l_1, l_2, \cdots, l_k$ is contained in a triangular region determined by l_1, l_2, and l_3, because no two points of R are separated by any two of the lines l_1, l_2, l_3. Let m be a line containing no point of this triangular region nor any of its vertices. The segments A_iA_j etc. referred to below do not contain any point of m.

If l_{k+1} contains a point of R, it contains, by Cor. 2, above, a segment of points of R such that the ends of this segment are on the boundary of R. By Theorem 67, the ends of this segment may be taken as vertices of the polygon p which by hypothesis bounds R. Thus we may denote this polygon by $A_1A_2 \cdots A_i \cdots A_jA_1$, where A_1 and A_i are the points in which l_{k+1} meets the polygon.

There are just two simple polygons which are composed of the segment A_1A_i and of sides and vertices of p. For any such polygon which contains A_1A_i contains A_1A_2 or A_1A_j; if it contains A_1A_2 it must contain A_2A_3 and therefore $A_3A_4, \cdots, A_{i-1}A_i$, and since it contains A_iA_1 it must be the polygon $A_1A_2A_3 \cdots A_iA_1$; if it contains A_1A_j it must contain A_jA_{j-1} and therefore $A_{j-1}A_{j-2}, \cdots, A_{i+1}A_i$, and since it contains A_iA_1 it must be $A_1A_jA_{j-1} \cdots A_iA_1$.

Neither of the lines l_{k+1} and m meets any edge of the polygon $A_1A_2A_3 \cdots A_iA_1$ except A_iA_1, which is contained in l_{k+1}. Hence all points of this polygon except A_i, A_1 and those on the edge A_iA_1 are in one of the two regions, which we shall call R′ and R″, bounded by l_{k+1} and m. In like manner all points of the polygon $A_1A_jA_{j-1} \cdots A_iA_1$ except A_i, A_1 and those on the edge A_iA_1 are in one of the two regions R′ and R″.

The points of R on any line coplanar with R and meeting the segment A_iA_1 in one point form a segment σ (Cor. 2. above) which does not contain any point of m. Hence the ends P, Q of σ are separated by l_{k+1} and m. But P and Q are boundary points of R by Cor. 2, above. Hence the boundary of R has points in both of the regions R' and R'' bounded by l_{k+1} and m. By the paragraph above, the points of the boundary of R in the one region, say R', must be the points, exclusive of the interval A_iA_1, of the polygon $A_1A_2 \cdots A_iA_1$; and those in the other, R'', must be the points, exclusive of the interval A_iA_1, of the polygon $A_1A_j \cdots A_iA_1$.

Let R_1 and R_2 be the two convex regions formed by the points of R not on l_{k+1}. Since these two regions are separated by l_{k+1} and m, we may assume that R_1 is in R' and R_2 in R''. Every boundary point of R_1 which is not a point of l_{k+1} is in R'. For if B is a point of the boundary of R_1 it is not on m, by construction, and if it is not on l_{k+1} it can be enclosed in a triangular region containing no point of l_{k+1} or m. Such a triangular region must contain points of R_1 and hence can contain no point of R'', since any segment joining a point of R' to a point of R'' contains a point of l_{k+1} or of m. Hence B is in R'. In like manner any boundary point of R_2 not on l_{k+1} is in R''. But by Theorem 10 every point B of the boundary of R is on the boundary of R_1 or R_2. Hence the boundary of R_1 contains all points of the boundary of R in R'; and by Theorem 10 it contains no other points not on l_{k+1}. Hence it is the polygon $A_1A_2 \cdots A_iA_1$. In like manner the polygon $A_1A_j \cdots A_iA_1$ is the boundary of R_2.

Hence the boundaries of the two planar convex regions into which any one of the planar convex regions determined by $l_1, l_2, \cdots, l_k$ is separated by l_{k+1} are simple polygons. The other planar convex regions determined by $l_1, l_2, \cdots, l_{k+1}$ are identical with regions determined by $l_1, l_2, \cdots, l_k$.

COROLLARY 1. *Each a^1 is on the boundaries of two and only two a^2's.*

COROLLARY 2. *In case all the lines $l_1, l_2, \cdots, l_n$ are concurrent, there is only one a^0, the common point of the lines; there are n a^1's, each consisting of all points except a^0 of one of the lines l_i; and there are n a^2's, each having a pair of the lines as its boundary.*

THEOREM 74. *The numbers $\alpha_0, \alpha_1, \alpha_2$ satisfy the relation*

$$\alpha_0 - \alpha_1 + \alpha_2 = 1.$$

Proof. We shall make the proof by mathematical induction. The theorem is obvious if $n = 2$, for in this case $\alpha_0 = 1$, $\alpha_1 = 2$, $\alpha_2 = 2$.

Let us now assume it to be true for $n=k$ and prove that it follows for $n=k+1$.

The lines $l_1, l_2, \cdots, l_k$ determine a set of α_0' points, α_1' linear convex regions, and α_2' planar convex regions subject to the relation $\alpha_0' - \alpha_1' + \alpha_2' = 1$. The line l_{k+1} meets a number, say r, of the planar convex regions and separates each of these into two planar convex regions. Hence α_2' is increased to $\alpha_2' + r$. The number of one-dimensional convex regions is increased by r for the number of convex regions on l_{k+1} and also by a number* s equal to the number of linear convex regions of the lines $l_1, l_2, \cdots, l_k$ which are met by l_{k+1}. The number of points of intersection of $l_1, l_2, \cdots, l_{k+1}$ also exceeds α_0' by s. Hence for $l_1, l_2, \cdots, l_{k+1}$ the numbers α_0, α_1, α_2 are $\alpha_0' + s$, $\alpha_1' + r + s$, $\alpha_2' + r$. Hence $\alpha_0 - \alpha_1 + \alpha_2 = (\alpha_0' + s) - (\alpha_1' + r + s) + (\alpha_2' + r) = 1$.

186. The modular equations and matrices. The relations among the points, linear convex regions, and planar convex regions may be described by means of two matrices of which those given in § 151 for the triangle are special cases. The first matrix, which we shall denote by H_1, is an array of α_0 rows and α_1 columns, each row being associated with an a^0 and each column with an a^1. The element of the ith row and jth column is 1 or 0 according as a_i^0 is or is not an end of a_j^1. The second matrix, H_2, has α_1 rows and α_2 columns associated respectively with the a^1's and a^2's. The element of the ith row and jth column is 1 or 0 according as a_i^1 is or is not on the boundary of a_j^2.

Since every segment a^1 has two and only two ends, each column of H_1 contains just two 1's; and since each a^1 is on the boundary of two and only two a^2's (Theorem 73, Cor. 1), each row of H_2 contains just two 1's.

For each of the a^1's let us introduce a variable which can take on only the values 0 and 1, these being regarded as marks of the field obtained by reducing modulo 2. We denote these variables by $x_1, x_2, \cdots, x_{\alpha_1}$ respectively. There are 2^{α_1} sets of values which can be given to the symbol† $(x_1, x_2, \cdots x_{\alpha_1})$.

*The number s is less than r if l_{k+1} contains points of intersection of $l_1, l_2, \cdots, l_k$.

†Excluding the one in which all the variables are zero, these symbols constitute the points of a finite projective space of $\alpha_1 - 1$ dimensions in which there are three points on every line (cf. § 72, Vol. I).

Every one of these symbols $(x_1, x_2, \cdots, x_{\alpha_1})$ corresponds to a way of labeling each segment a^1 of the original n lines with a 0 or a 1, the segment a_i^1 being labeled with the value of x_i. We shall regard the symbol as the notation for the set of edges labeled with 1's. By the *sum* of two symbols $(x_1\, x_2, \cdots, x_{\alpha_1})$ and $(y_1, y_2, \cdots, y_{\alpha_1})$ we shall mean $(x_1+y_1, x_2+y_2, \cdots, x_{\alpha_1}+y_{\alpha_1})$, the addition being performed modulo 2. According to our convention the sum represents the set of a^1's which are in either of the sets represented by $(x_1, x_2, \cdots, x_{\alpha_1})$ and $(y_1, y_2, \cdots, y_{\alpha_1})$ but not in both. By a repetition of these considerations it follows that the sum of n symbols of the form $(x_1, x_2, \cdots, x_{\alpha_1})$ for sets of edges is the symbol for a set of edges each of which is in an odd number of the n sets of edges.

In the sequel we shall say that a polygon p is the sum, modulo 2, of a set of polygons $p_1, p_2, \cdots, p_n$ if it is represented by a symbol $(x_1, x_2, \cdots, x_{\alpha_1})$ which is the sum of the symbols for $p_1, p_2, \cdots, p_n$. Let us now inquire what is the condition on a symbol $(x_1, x_2, \cdots, x_{\alpha_1})$ that it shall represent a polygon?

At every vertex of a polygon there meet two and only two edges. Hence, if we add all the x's that correspond to the a^1's meeting in any point, this sum must be zero, modulo 2. This gives α_0 equations, one for each a^0, of the form

$$x_p + x_q + \cdots + x_k = 0 \qquad \text{(mod. 2)} \tag{4}$$

$(a_p^0, a_q^0, \cdots, a_k^0$ being the edges which meet at a given vertex), which must be satisfied by the symbol for any polygon. Obviously the matrix of the coefficients of these equations is H_1. For example, in the case of the triangle these equations are (cf. § 151)

$$\begin{aligned} x_3 + x_4 + x_5 + x_6 &= 0, \\ x_1 + x_2 + x_5 + x_6 &= 0, \\ x_1 + x_2 + x_3 + x_4 &= 0. \end{aligned} \qquad \text{(mod. 2)} \tag{5}$$

We shall denote the set of equations (4) by (H_1). Since each column of H_2 gives the notation for a polygon bounding an a^2, the columns of H_2 are solutions of the equations (H_1). For example, the columns of the matrix H_2 in § 151 are solutions of (H_1).

Any solution whatever of these equations corresponds to a labeling of the a^1's with 0's and 1's in such a way that there are an even number of 1's on the a^1's meeting at each a^0. Hence, by the corollary of Theorem 70 the a's labeled with 1's must constitute one or more simple polygons. *Hence every solution of the equations* (H_1) *represents a simple polygon or a set of simple polygons.*

Since each column of the matrix H_1 contains exactly two 1's, any one of the equations is obtained by adding all the rest. Since the only marks of our field are 0 and 1, any linear combination of the equations (H_1) would be merely the sum of a subset of these equations. Consider such a subset and the points a^0 which correspond to the equations in the subset. Every a^1 joining two points of the subset is represented in two equations, and the corresponding variable disappears in the sum. There remain in this sum the variables corresponding to the a^1's joining the points of the subset to the remaining points of the figure. These cannot all pass through the same point unless the subset consists of all points but one (since any two of the original n lines have a point in common). Hence while any one of the equations is linearly dependent * on all the rest, it is not linearly dependent on any smaller subset. *Hence* $\alpha_0 - 1$ *of the equations* (H_1) *are linearly independent.*

Since the number of variables is α_1, the number of solutions in a set of linearly independent solutions on which all other solutions are linearly dependent is $\alpha_1 - \alpha_0 + 1$. By Theorem 74 this number is α_2.† Thus the total number of polygons and sets of polygons is $2^{\alpha_2} - 1$.

The simple polygons which bound the regions a^2 are a set of solutions, namely, the columns of the matrix H_2. Since each row of the matrix H_2 contains just two 1's, it follows that if we add all the columns we obtain a solution of (H_1) in which all the variables are 0. On the other hand, if we add any subset of the columns of H_2 the sum will be a solution in which not all the variables are zero. For consider a segment joining an interior point A of the region a^2 corresponding to one of the columns in the subset to an interior point B of a region a^2 corresponding to one of the columns not in the subset; this segment may be chosen so as not to pass through a point of intersection of two of the lines $l_1, l_2, \cdots, l_n$. Hence it contains a finite number of points on the polygons corresponding to the columns in the subset. The first one of these in the sense from B

* Since the only coefficients which can enter are 0 and 1, the statement that one solution is linearly dependent on a set of others is equivalent to saying that it is a sum of a number of them.

† In the modular space of $\alpha_1 - 1$ dimensions this means that the $\alpha_0 - 1$ independent ($\alpha_1 - 2$)-spaces intersect in an ($\alpha_2 - 1$)-space.

to A is on an a_2^1 which is on the boundary of a region in the subset and a region not in the subset. The variable corresponding to this interval therefore appears in only one of the α's in the subset and so does not drop out in the sum. Hence *any* α_2-1 *of the boundaries of the* α_2 *convex regions correspond to a set of linearly independent solutions of* (4). In other words, $2^{\alpha_1-\alpha_0}-1$, or one less than half of all the solutions of (H_1), are linearly dependent on the solutions corresponding to the columns of H_2. The solutions of H_1 are thus divided into two classes, those linearly dependent on the columns of H_2 and those not so dependent.

Since each of the lines $l_1, l_2, \cdots, l_n$ is a polygon, it corresponds to a solution of the equations (H_1), but *it does not correspond to a solution which is linearly dependent on the columns of the matrix* H_2. This is a corollary of the argument used in showing that the sum of any subset of the columns of H_2 is not a solution in which all the variables are zero. For in that argument we showed that a certain segment AB contains a point on the polygon represented by the sum of such a subset. The same argument applies to the complementary segment. Hence the line AB has two points, at least, in common with the polygon or polygons represented by the sum of the subset of columns. Hence this sum cannot represent a line.

Thus, if we take the solution of the equations (H_1) corresponding to any one of the lines $l_1, l_2, \cdots, l_n$, together with any α_2-1 of the columns of the matrix H_2, we have a linearly independent set of solutions. But since this set contains α_2 independent solutions, all solutions are linearly dependent on this set.

187. Regions determined by a polygon. If p is any polygon it can, by § 184, be regarded as one whose vertices are a^0's and whose edges are a^1's of a set of lines $l_1, l_2, \cdots, l_n$.

Two cases arise according as p is represented by a symbol which is or is not a sum of a subset of the columns of the matrix H_2. In the first case p corresponds also to the sum of all the remaining columns, because the sum of all the columns is $(0, 0, \cdots, 0)$. It cannot correspond to a third set of columns, for the sum of the columns in the second and third sets, which is also the sum of the columns not common to these two sets, would be $(0, 0, \cdots, 0)$. Hence there would be a linear relation among a subset of the columns of H_2 contrary to what has been proved above.

Let us denote the two sets of columns of H_2, whose sums are the symbol for p, by $c_1, c_2, \cdots, c_k$ and $c_{k+1}, \cdots, c_{\alpha_2}$ respectively, and suppose the notation so assigned that they represent the boundaries of $a_1^2, a_2^2, \cdots, a_k^2$ and $a_{k+1}^2, \cdots, a_{\alpha_2}^2$ respectively. Let the points of the plane in $a_1^2, a_2^2, \cdots, a_k^2$, together with such points of the boundaries as are not points of p, be denoted by $[P]$. Let the set of the points analogously related to $a_{k+1}^2, \cdots, a_{\alpha_2}^2$ be denoted by $[Q]$. Clearly, the sets of points $[P]$, $[Q]$, and p are mutually exclusive and include all points of the plane.

Consider any point P_0 of the convex region a_1^2 corresponding to c_1. It is connected by a segment consisting entirely of points P to every point P in or on the boundary of a_1^2. If $k>1$, c_1 has an edge in common with at least one of $c_2, \cdots, c_k$, and the notation may be assigned so that c_1 has an edge in common with c_2. Then P_0 can be joined to any point P_1 of the common edge by a segment of P-points, and P_1 by another segment of P-points to every P-point of the region a_2^2 and its boundary. If $k>2$ there is a solution which may be called c_3, with an edge in common with c_1 or c_2; for if not, the solution c_1+c_2 would be one in which all the 1's correspond to the edges of p, and as no subset of the edges of p forms a polygon, c_1+c_2 would correspond to p itself. As before, every point of the region a_3^2 and its boundary can be joined to P_0 by a broken line of at most three edges. Since there is no subset of $c_1, \cdots, c_k$ whose sum corresponds to π, this process can be continued till we have any point R of the convex regions $a_1^2, a_2^2, \cdots, a_k^2$ and their boundaries joined by a broken line b to P_0. If R is on π the process of constructing b is such that all points of b except R are in $[P]$, whereas if R is in $[P]$ all points of b are in $[P]$.

Hence any two points of $[P]$ can be joined by a broken line consisting only of such points; and, since every point of p is on the boundary of one of $a_1^2, a_2^2, \cdots, a_k^2$, any P can be joined to any point R of p by a broken line every point of which, except R, is in $[P]$. A precisely similar statement is true of $[Q]$.

Consider now any broken line b' joining a point P to a point Q. The points which are on this broken line and also on any a^1 and its ends constitute a finite number of points and segments. Hence b' meets the lines $l_1, l_2, \cdots, l_n$ in a finite number of points and segments, each of the segments being contained entirely in an a^1.

These points and the ends of these segments we shall denote by $A_1, A_2, \cdots, A_k$ taken in the sense on the broken line from P to Q. Since P and A_1 are within or on the boundary of the same convex region, A_1 is either in $[P]$ or on p. If A_1 is in $[P]$ the same consideration shows that A_2 is in $[P]$ or on p. If none of the A's were on p, this process would lead to the result that A_k is in $[P]$, and hence Q would also be in $[P]$, contrary to hypothesis. Hence one of the A's is on p, and hence any broken line joining a point P to a point Q contains a point on p.

It now follows that $[P]$ and $[Q]$ are both regions. For we have seen that any point P can be joined to any other P by a broken line consisting entirely of points of P. By Theorem 71 any point P is contained in a triangular region containing no points of p. This triangular region contains no Q, because if it did a segment joining it to P would, by the argument just made, contain a point of p. Hence $[P]$ satisfies the definition of a two-dimensional region given in § 155. A similar argument applies to $[Q]$. Hence we have

THEOREM 75. *Any simple polygon p which corresponds to a symbol* $(x_1, x_2, \cdots, x_{\alpha_1})$ *which is the sum of a set of columns of* H_2 *is the boundary of two mutually exclusive regions which include all points of the plane not on p and are such that any two points of the same region can be joined by a broken line which is in the region. Any broken line joining a point of the one region to a point of the other region contains a point of the polygon.*

COROLLARY 1. *Any point R of p can be joined to any point not on p by a broken line containing no other point of p.*

COROLLARY 2. *If a segment ST meets p in a single point O which is not a vertex of p, S and T are in different regions with respect to p.*

Proof. Let S' and T' be two points in the order $\{SS'OT'T\}$ and such that the segment $\overline{S'OT'}$ contains no point of $l_1, l_2, \cdots, l_n$ except O. By § 185, S' and T' are in two convex regions a^2 which have an edge in common. Since this edge is an edge of p, the columns of H_2 corresponding to these two a^2's must be one in the set $c_1, c_2, \cdots, c_k$, and the other in the set $c_{k+1}, \cdots, c_{\alpha_2}$. Hence, if S' and S are in $[P]$, T' and T are in $[Q]$, and vice versa.

THEOREM 76. *Any simple polygon p which corresponds to a symbol* $(x_1, x_2, \cdots, x_{\alpha_1})$ *which is not the sum of a set of columns of* H_2

is the boundary of a region which includes all points of the plane not on p. Any two points not on p can be joined by a broken line not meeting p.

Proof. By Theorem 71 any point not on p can be enclosed in a triangular region containing no point of p. Hence the theorem will be proved if we can show that any two points not on p are joined by a broken line consisting only of such points. If this were not so, we could let P_0 be any point not on p and let $[P]$ be the set of all points not on p which can be joined to P_0 by broken lines not meeting p. As in the proof of Theorem 75, $[P]$ would have to consist of a number of regions a^2, together with those points of their boundaries which were not on p; and the boundary of $[P]$ could consist only of points of p. But the boundary of $[P]$ must consist of the polygon or polygons whose symbol is obtained by adding the columns of H_2 corresponding to the a^2's in $[P]$. By § 183 no subset of the points of p can be a simple polygon. Hence p would be the the boundary of $[P]$ and be expressible linearly in terms of the boundaries of a^2's, contrary to hypothesis.

Every polygon whose edges are on $l_1, l_2, \cdots, l_n$ corresponds to a symbol $(x_1, x_2, \cdots, x_{\alpha_1})$ which either is or is not expressible linearly in terms of the columns of H_2. Hence the arbitrary simple polygon p with which this section starts and which determines the lines $l_1, l_2, \cdots, l_n$ is described either in Theorem 75 or in Theorem 76. Hence we have

THEOREM 77. DEFINITION. *The polygons of a plane α fall into two classes the individuals of which are called* odd *and* even *respectively. A polygon of the first class is the boundary of a single region comprising all points of α not on the polygon. A polygon of the second class is the boundary of each of two regions which contain all points of α not on the polygon, have no point in common, and are such that any broken line joining a point of one region to a point of the other contains a point of the polygon.*

The odd polygons are also called *unicursal*, and the even polygons are also called *bounding*. A line is an example of an odd polygon, and the boundary of a triangular region is an example of an even one. The segments $\bar{\alpha}, \beta, \bar{\gamma}$ as defined in § 26 are the edges of an odd polygon.

THEOREM 78. *Two polygons of which one is even and which are such that neither polygon has a vertex on the other have an even (or zero) number of points in common.*

Proof. Let p_1 be an even polygon, let p_2 be any other polygon, and let the points of intersection of the polygons be $R_1, \cdots, R_n$ in the order $\{R_1 R_2 \cdots R_n\}$ with respect to p_2. If $n = 0$ the theorem is verified. If n were 1 the edge of p_2 containing R_1 would have its ends in different regions with respect to π_1, and hence the broken line composed of all p_2 except the side containing R_1 would have to contain a point of p_1, contrary to hypothesis. If $n > 1$ the interval of p_2 which has R_1 and R_2 as ends and contains no other points R is a broken line which belongs (except for its ends) entirely to one of the two regions $[P]$ and $[Q]$ determined by p_1; and by Cor. 2, Theorem 75, the interval of p_2 similarly determined by R_2 and R_3 belongs entirely to the other of the two regions $[P]$ and $[Q]$. Thus, if $S_1, S_2, \cdots, S_n$ are a set of points of p_2 in the order $\{R_1 S_1 R_2 S_2 R_3 \cdots S_{n-1} R_n S_n\}$, and S_1 is in $[P]$, all the S's with odd subscripts are in $[P]$ and all the S's with even subscripts are in $[Q]$. But by Cor. 2, Theorem 75, S_n is in $[Q]$ since S_1 is in $[P]$. Hence n is even.

COROLLARY. *A line coplanar with and containing no vertex of an even polygon meets it in an even (or zero) number of points.*

THEOREM 79. *Two odd polygons such that neither has a vertex on the other meet in an odd number of points.*

Proof. Let the polygons be p_1 and p_2, let the lines containing the sides of p_1 be $l_1, \cdots, l_{n-1}$, and let l_n be a line containing no vertex of either polygon. According to the results stated at the end of the last section, p_1 is expressible by addition, modulo 2, as the sum of l_n and a number of boundaries of a^2's. The latter combine into a number of even polygons, the edges of which are either edges of p_1 or of l_n. Hence these even polygons have no vertices on p_2 and contain no vertices of p_2. Hence by Theorem 78 they have an even (or zero) number of points in common with p_2. Thus our theorem will follow if we can show that l_n has an odd number of points in common with p_2.

By the argument just used p_2 can be expressed as the sum, modulo 2, of a line m and a number of even polygons which have no vertices on l_n. The latter meet l_n in an even (or zero) number of points, and m meets l_n in one point. Hence p_2 meets l_n in an odd number of points.

COROLLARY 1. *Two odd polygons always have at least one point in common.*

COROLLARY 2. *If p is a simple polygon and there exists an odd polygon p_1 meeting p in an even (or zero) number of points and such that neither polygon has a vertex on the other, then p is even.*

Since the plane of a convex region always contains at least one line not having a point in common with the region, the last result has the following special case, which, on account of its importance, we shall list as a theorem.

THEOREM 80. *Any simple polygon lying entirely in a convex region is even.*

To complete the theory of the subdivision of the plane by a polygon, there are needed a number of other theorems which can be handled by methods analogous to those already developed. They are stated below as exercises.

EXERCISES

1. If a simple polygon p lies entirely in a convex region R, the points of R not on p fall into two regions such that any broken line joining a point of one region to a point of the other has a point on p. One of these regions, called the *interior* of the polygon, has the property that any ray (with respect to R) whose origin is a point of this region meets p in an odd number of points, provided it contains no vertex of p. The other region, called the *exterior* of the polygon with respect to R, has the property that any ray whose origin is one of the points of this region meets p in an even (or zero) number of points, provided it contains no vertex of p.

2. If p is any even polygon in a plane α, one of the two regions determined by p, according to Theorem 77, contains no odd polygon and is called the *interior* of p. The other contains an infinity of odd polygons and is called the *exterior* of p.

3. If one line coplanar with and not containing a vertex of a simple polygon meets it in an odd (even or zero) number of points, every line not containing a vertex and coplanar with it meets it in an odd (even or zero) number of points.

4. If the boundary of a convex region consists of a finite number of linear segments, together with their ends, it is a simple polygon.

5. A simple polygon which is met by every line not containing a vertex in two or no points is the boundary of a convex region.

6. For any simple polygon $A_1A_2 \cdots A_nA_1$, there exists a set of $n-2$ triangular regions such that (1) every point of the interior of the polygon is in or on the boundary of one of the triangular regions, (2) every vertex of one of the triangular regions is a vertex of the polygon, and (3) no two of the triangular regions have a point in common.

***7.** By use of convex regions and matrices analogous to H_1 and H_2, prove Theorem 77 for any curve made up of analytic pieces (i.e. 1-cells which satisfy analytic equations).

188. Polygonal regions and polyhedra. DEFINITION. A *planar polygonal region* is a two-dimensional region R for which there exists a finite number of points and linear regions such that any interval joining a point of R to a point not in R, but coplanar with it, meets one of these points or linear regions. A (three-dimensional) *polyhedral region* is a three-dimensional region R for which there exists a finite number of points, linear regions, and planar polygonal regions such that any interval joining a point of R to a point not in R meets one of these points, linear regions, or planar polygonal regions.

Let R be a planar polygonal region and let $l_1, l_2, \cdots, l_n$ be a set of lines coplanar with R and containing all the points and linear regions such that any interval joining a point in R to a point not in R meets one of these points or one of these linear regions. Let us adopt the notation of § 185.

If a point P of one of the two-dimensional convex regions a^2 is in R, all points of the a^2 are in R, for all such points are joined to P by intervals not meeting $l_1, l_2, \cdots, l_n$.

Since any point not on $l_1, l_2, \cdots, l_n$ is interior to a triangular region containing no points of $l_1, l_2, \cdots, l_n$, no such point can be a boundary point of R.

Let $a^2_{i_1}, \cdots, a^2_{i_k}$ be the a^2's which have points in R. As we have seen, all points of these a^2's are in R. All points of their boundaries are either in R or on its boundary; for every point of the boundary of an $a^2_{i_r}$ $(r=1, \cdots, k)$ may be joined to a point of $a^2_{i_r}$, that is, to a point of R, by a segment of points of R, and hence is either a point of R or of its boundary.

Any point B of the boundary of R is on the boundary of one of $a^2_{i_1}, \cdots, a^2_{i_k}$. For any triangular region T containing B contains points of R and hence contains a triangular region T' of points of R. The region T' must have points in common with at least one a^2. If T be chosen so as to contain no points of any a^2 which does not have B on its boundary, any a^2 having a point in common with T' is one of $a^2_{i_1}, \cdots, a^2_{i_k}$. Hence every boundary point of R is on the boundary of one of $a^2_{i_1} \cdots, a^2_{i_k}$. Hence the set of points of R and its boundary is identical with the set of all points of $a^2_{i_1}, \cdots, a^2_{i_k}$ and their boundaries. In other words,

THEOREM 81. *For any planar polygonal region* R *there is a finite set of convex polygonal regions* $\mathsf{R}_1, \cdots, \mathsf{R}_n$ *such that the set of all points of* $\mathsf{R}_1, \cdots, \mathsf{R}_n$ *and their boundaries is identical with* R *and its boundary.*

As a consequence, any set of points which consists of planar polygonal regions and their boundaries can be described as a set of points in a set of convex polygonal regions and their boundaries. Therefore no generality is lost in the following definition of a polyhedron by stating it in terms of convex polygonal regions.

DEFINITION. A set of points $[P]$ is called a *polyhedron* if it satisfies the following conditions and contains no subset which satisfies them: $[P]$ consists of a set of distinct points $a^0_1, a^0_2, \cdots, a^0_{\alpha_0}$, segments $a^1_1, a^1_2, \cdots, a^1_{\alpha_1}$, and convex planar polygonal regions $a^2_1, a^2_2, \cdots, a^2_{\alpha_2}$ such that each a^1 is bounded by two a^0's and each a^2 by a simple polygon whose vertices are a^0's and whose edges are a^1's; no a^1 or a^2 contains an a^0 and no two of the a^1's or a^2's have a point in common; each a^1 is on the boundary of an even number of a^2's. The points a^0 are called the *vertices*, the segments a^1 the *edges*, and the planar regions a^2 the *faces* of the polyhedron.

Just as any point of a polygon can be regarded as a vertex, so any point of an edge of a polyhedron can be regarded as a vertex, and any segment contained in a face and joining two of its vertices can be regarded as an edge.

The relations among the vertices, edges, and faces of a polyhedron can be described by means of matrices H_1 and H_2 analogous to those of § 186. In the first matrix,

$$\mathsf{H}_1 = (\eta^1_{ij}),$$

the element η^1_{ij} is 0 or 1 according as a^0_i is not or is an end of a^1_j. In the second matrix,

$$\mathsf{H}_2 = (\eta^2_{ij}),$$

the element η^2_{ij} is 0 or 1 according as a^1_i is not or is on the boundary of a^2_j. The theory of the polyhedron can be derived from a discussion of these matrices just as that of the projective plane (a special polyhedron) has been derived in the sections above.

Thus the polygons which can be formed from the vertices and edges of the polyhedron are denoted by symbols of the form $(x_1, x_2, \cdots, x_{\alpha_1})$ as in § 186. They are all expressible as sums, modulo 2, of the boundaries of the faces together with $P-1$ other polygons. The number P is called the *connectivity* of the polyhedron and is the same no matter how the polyhedron is subdivided into faces, edges, and vertices. It is determined by the following relation:

$$\alpha_0 - \alpha_1 + \alpha_2 = 3 - P.$$

EXERCISES

1. Any polygonal region can be regarded as composed of a finite set of triangular regions together with portions of their boundaries, no two of the triangular regions having a point in common.

2. If R is a polygonal region, every broken line joining a point of R to a point not in R has a point on the boundary.

3. For any three-dimensional polyhedral region R there is a finite set of polyhedral regions $R_1, R_2, \cdots, R_n$ such that the set of all points of $R_1, R_2, \cdots, R_n$ and their boundaries is identical with R and its boundary. $R_1, R_2, \cdots, R_n$ may be so chosen as all to be tetrahedral regions.

4. If a polyhedron is the boundary of a convex region, each edge of the polyhedron is on the boundaries of two and only two of its faces.

189. Subdivision of space by planes. The theorems of § 185 generalize at once into the following. The proofs (with one exception) are left to the reader.

THEOREM 82. *The points of space which are not upon any one of a finite set of planes $\pi_1, \pi_2, \cdots, \pi_n$ fall into a finite number α_3 of convex regions such that any segment joining two points of different regions contains at least one point of $\pi_1, \pi_2, \cdots, \pi_n$. The number α_3 satisfies the inequality $n \leqq \alpha_3 \leqq \frac{n(n-1)(n-2)}{6} + n$.*

As in § 185, we indicate the α_0 points of intersection of n planes $\pi_1, \pi_2, \cdots, \pi_n$ by

$$a_1^0, a_2^0, \cdots, a_{\alpha_0}^0,$$

or any one of them by a^0; the α_1 linear convex regions determined by these points upon the lines of intersection, by

$$a_1^1, a_2^1, \cdots, a_{\alpha_1}^1,$$

or any one of them by a^1; the α_2 planar convex regions determined by the lines of intersection upon the planes, by

$$a_1^2,\ a_2^2,\ \cdots,\ a_{\alpha_2}^2,$$

or any one of them by a^2; and the α_3 spatial convex regions determined by the planes, by

$$a_1^3,\ a_2^3,\ \cdots,\ a_{\alpha_3}^3,$$

or any one of them by a^3.

THEOREM 83. *If the planes* $\pi_1, \pi_2, \cdots, \pi_n$ *are not all coaxial, the boundary of each* a^3 *is composed of a finite number of* a^2*'s and of those* a^1*'s and* a^0*'s which bound the* a^2*'s in question. Each* a^2 *is upon the boundary of two and only two* a^3*'s.*

COROLLARY 1. *If the planes* $\pi_1, \pi_2, \cdots, \pi_n$ *are coaxial,* $\alpha_0 = 0$, $\alpha_1 = 0$, *and the boundary of each* a^3 *is composed of two* a^2*'s together with the common line of the planes.*

COROLLARY 2. *If the planes are not all concurrent, any line through a point I of one of the regions* a^3 *meets the boundary in two points P, Q. The segment* $\overline{PIQ}$ *consists entirely of points of the* a^3*, and the complementary segment entirely of points not in the* a^3.

THEOREM 84. *If an* a^1 *is on the boundary of an* a^3*, it is on the boundaries of two and only two* a^2*'s of the boundary of the* a^3*. Any plane section of an* a^3 *is a two-dimensional convex region bounded by a simple polygon which is a plane section of the boundary of the* a^3.

COROLLARY. *The boundary of each* a^3 *is a polyhedron.*

THEOREM 85. *The numbers* $\alpha_0, \alpha_1, \alpha_2, \alpha_3$ *are subject to the relation* $\alpha_0 - \alpha_1 + \alpha_2 - \alpha_3 = 0$.

Proof. The proof is made by induction. In the case of two planes, $\alpha_0 = 0$, $\alpha_1 = 0$, $\alpha_2 = 2$, $\alpha_3 = 2$. Assuming that the theorem is true for n planes, let us see what is the effect of introducing a plane π_{n+1}. This plane is divided by the other planes into a number of convex two-dimensional regions equal to the number of a^3's in which it has points; but it divides each of these a^3's into two a^3's. Hence the adjunction of these new a^2's and a^3's increases α_2 and α_3 by equal amounts. The plane π_{n+1}, according to Theorem 8, Cor. 1, divides in two each a^2 which it meets; but it has a new a^1 in common with each such region. Here, therefore, α_2 and α_1 are increased by equal amounts. The plane π_{n+1} divides in two each a^1 which it meets; but it has a point in common with each such region. Hence, in this case, α_1 and α_0 are increased by equal amounts. Hence, if the formula is true for n planes, it is true for $n+1$.

COROLLARY. *The number of a^1's for $\pi_1, \pi_2, \cdots, \pi_n$ which are not on lines of intersection of pairs of the planes $\pi_1, \pi_2, \cdots, \pi_{n-1}$ is the number by which $\alpha_1-\alpha_0$ for the planes $\pi_1, \pi_2, \cdots, \pi_n$ exceeds $\alpha_1-\alpha_0$ for the planes $\pi_1, \pi_2, \cdots, \pi_{n-1}$.*

Proof. New a^1's are produced by the introduction of π_n in two ways: (1) π_n may meet an a^1 of $\pi_1, \pi_3, \cdots, \pi_{n-1}$ in a point; if so, this a^1 is separated into two a^1's and a new a^0 is introduced; (2) π_n may meet an a^2 of $\pi_1, \pi_2, \cdots, \pi_{n-1}$ in a new a^1. The only new a^0's produced by the introduction of π_n are accounted for under (1). Hence (2) accounts for the increase of $\alpha_1-\alpha_0$, as stated above.

190. The matrices H_1, H_2, and H_3. The relations among the convex regions determined by n planes which are not coaxial may be described by means of three matrices, which we shall call H_1, H_2, and H_3. In the first matrix,

$$H_1=(\eta^1_{ij}),$$

$i=1, 2, \cdots, \alpha_0$; $j=1, 2, \cdots, \alpha_1$; and $\eta^1_{ij}=1$ or 0 according as a^0_i is or is not an end of a^1_j. In the second matrix,

$$H_2=(\eta^2_{ij}),$$

$i=1, 2, \cdots, \alpha_1$; $j=1, 2, \cdots, \alpha_2$; and $\eta^2_{ij}=1$ or 0 according as a^1_i is or is not on the boundary of a^2_j. In the third matrix,

$$H_3=(\eta^3_{ij}),$$

$i=1, 2, \cdots, \alpha_2$; $j=1, 2, \cdots, \alpha_3$; and $\eta^3_{ij}=1$ or 0 according as a^2_i is or is not on the boundary of a^3_j. Examples of these three matrices are those given in § 152 to describe the tetrahedron. It will be noted that H_1 has two 1's in each column, and H_3 two 1's in each row.

Corresponding to the matrix H_1, there is a set of α_0 linear equations (modulo 2)

$$(H_1) \qquad \sum_{j=1}^{\alpha_1} \eta^1_{ij}x_j \qquad (i=1, 2, \cdots, \alpha_0).$$

Let the symbol $(x_0, x_1, \cdots, x_{\alpha_1})$, where the x_k's are 0 or 1, be taken to represent a set of a^1's containing a^1_k if $x_k=1$ and not containing it if $x_k=0$. Just as in § 186, this set of a^1's will be the edges of a polygon or set of polygons if and only if $(x_0, x_1, \cdots, x_{\alpha_1})$ is a solution of (H_1).

Just as in § 186, the sum of two sets of polygons (modulo 2) will be taken to be the set of polygons represented by the sum of the symbols $(x_1, x_2, \cdots, x_{\alpha_1})$ for the two sets of polygons. The sum, modulo 2, of two sets of polygons p_1 and p_2 is therefore the set of polygons whose edges appear either in p_1 or in p_2 but not in both p_1 and p_2.

By the reasoning in § 186, $\alpha_0 - 1$ of the equations (H_1) are linearly independent, and the other one is linearly dependent on these. The columns of H_2 are the symbols $(x_0, x_1, \cdots, x_{\alpha_1})$ for the boundaries of the a^2's and hence are solutions of (H_1).

Corresponding to the matrix H_2, there is a set of α_1 linear equations (modulo 2)

$$(\mathrm{H}_2) \qquad \sum_{j=1}^{\alpha_2} \eta_{ij}^2 x_j \qquad (i = 1, 2, \cdots, \alpha_1).$$

Let the symbol $(x_1, x_2, \cdots, x_{\alpha_1})$, where the x_k's are 0 or 1, be taken to represent a set of a^2's containing a_k^2 if $x_k = 1$ and not containing it if $x_k = 0$. If this symbol is a solution of (H_2), it represents a set of a^2's such that each a^1 is on the boundaries of an even number (or zero) of them; i.e. it represents the faces of a polyhedron or a set of polyhedra.

The columns of H_3 represent the boundaries of the a^3's. By Theorem 84 any a^1 of the boundary of an a^3 is on the boundaries of two and only two a^2's of this boundary. Hence the columns of H_3 are solutions of (H_2).

Corresponding to the matrix H_3, there is a set of α_2 linear equations (modulo 2)

$$(\mathrm{H}_3) \qquad \sum_{j=1}^{\alpha_3} \eta_{ij}^3 x_j \qquad (i = 1, 2, \cdots, \alpha_2)$$

Let the symbol $(x_1, x_2, \cdots, x_{\alpha_3})$, where the x_k's are 0 or 1, be taken to represent a set of a^3's containing a_k^3 if $x_k = 1$ and not containing it if $x_k = 0$. If this symbol is a solution of (H_3), it represents a set of a^3's of which there is an even number on each a^2. It is easily seen that the only such set of a^3's is the set of all a^3's in space. Hence the only solutions of (H_3) are $(0, 0, \cdots, 0)$ and $(1, 1, \cdots, 1)$. Hence there are $\alpha_3 - 1$ linearly independent equations in (H_3) on which all the rest are linearly dependent.

Let the ranks* of the matrices H_1, H_2, H_3 be r_1, r_2, r_3 respectively.

* The rank of a matrix is the number of rows (or columns) in a set of linearly independent rows (or columns) on which all the other rows (or columns) are linearly dependent.

By what has been seen above

$$r_1 = \alpha_0 - 1,$$
$$r_3 = \alpha_3 - 1.$$

The discussion in the next section will establish that

$$r_2 = \alpha_1 - \alpha_0.$$

191. The rank of H_2. Let us now suppose that $\pi_1, \pi_2, \cdots, \pi_n$ are not all on the same point and that the notation is so assigned that $\pi_1, \pi_2, \pi_3, \pi_4$ are the faces of a tetrahedron. By inspection of the matrices given in § 152, it is clear that for the case $n = 4$, $\alpha_0 = 4$, $\alpha_1 = 12$, $\alpha_2 = 16$, $\alpha_3 = 8$, and $r_2 = 8$ (a set of linearly independent columns of H_2 upon which the rest depend linearly is the set of columns corresponding to $\tau_{11}, \tau_{12}, \tau_{13}, \tau_{21}, \tau_{22}, \tau_{23}, \tau_{31}$, and τ_{32}). The number of solutions of (H_1) in a linearly independent set upon which all the other solutions depend is $\alpha_1 - \alpha_0 + 1 = 9$. Hence one solution which does not depend linearly upon the columns of H_2, together with a set of eight linearly independent columns of H_2, constitute a set of linearly independent solutions of (H_1) upon which all the others depend linearly. Any solution representing a projective line, e.g. (1, 1, 0, 0, 0, 0, 0, 0, 0, 0, 0, 0), will serve this purpose.

In case $n > 4$, the columns of H_2 fall into three classes: (1) those representing the boundaries of a^2's in π_n; (2) those representing the boundaries of a^2's which are not in π_n but have an a^1 in π_n; and (3) those representing the boundaries of a^2's which have no a^1 in π_n.

Any column of Class (1) is expressible as a sum of columns of Classes (2) and (3). For the a^2 whose boundary it represents is on the boundary of an a^3 whose boundary has no other a^2 in common with π_n (cf. § 150). Since each a^1 on the boundary of an a^3 is on the boundary of two and only two a^2's of the boundary of the a^3 (Theorem 84), it follows that the given column is the sum of the columns which represent the boundaries of the other a^2's on the boundary of the a^3. These columns are all of Classes (2) or (3).

Each a^1 which is not on a line of intersection of two of the planes $\pi_1, \pi_2, \cdots, \pi_{n-1}$ is the linear segment in which one of the a^2's determined by $\pi_1, \pi_2, \cdots, \pi_{n-1}$ is met by π_n. Hence the row of H_2 corresponding to this a^1 contains just two 1's in columns of Class (2), and the sum of these two columns of Class (2) is the symbol for the boundary of one of the a^2's determined by $\pi_1, \pi_2, \cdots, \pi_{n-1}$. Moreover, the columns of H_2 of Class (2) form a set of pairs of this sort, since every a^1 of π_n is either on a line of intersection of two of the planes $\pi_1, \pi_2, \cdots, \pi_{n-1}$ or is an edge of two and only two a^2's not in π_n.

No one of such a pair of columns of H_2 can enter into a linear relation among a set of columns of Classes (2) and (3) unless the other does. For this column would be the only column of the set containing a 1 in the row corresponding to the a^1 common to the boundaries of the a^2's represented by the two columns, and hence the sum of columns could not reduce to $(0, 0, \cdots, 0)$.

Let H_2' be the matrix consisting of the columns of Class (3) of H_2 and the sums of the pairs of columns of Class (2) discussed in the last two paragraphs. According to the last paragraph the rank of H_2' is less than the rank of H_2 by the number of these pairs of columns; and by the corollary of Theorem 85 this number is the difference between the values of $\alpha_1 - \alpha_0$ for $\pi_1, \pi_2, \cdots, \pi_n$ and for $\pi_1, \pi_2, \cdots, \pi_{n-1}$.

The columns of H_2' are the symbols in terms of the a^1's determined by $\pi_1, \pi_2, \cdots, \pi_n$ for the boundaries of the a^2's determined by $\pi_1, \pi_2, \cdots, \pi_{n-1}$. Hence any two rows of this matrix which correspond to a pair of a^1's into which an a^1 determined by $\pi_1, \pi_2, \cdots, \pi_{n-1}$ is separated by π_n must be identical; and if one of each such pair of rows is omitted, H_2' reduces to the H_2 for $\pi_1, \pi_2, \cdots, \pi_{n-1}$. Hence H_2' has the same rank as the H_2 for $\pi_1, \pi_2, \cdots, \pi_{n-1}$.

Since the difference in the ranks of H_2 for $\pi_1, \pi_2, \cdots, \pi_n$ and of H_2' is the same as the difference between the values of $\alpha_1 - \alpha_0$ for $\pi_1, \pi_2, \cdots \pi_n$ and for $\pi_1, \pi_2, \cdots, \pi_{n-1}$, it follows that the introduction of π_n increases the rank of H_2 by the same amount that it increases $\alpha_1 - \alpha_0$. Since $\alpha_1 - \alpha_0 = r_2$ for $n = 4$, the same relation holds for all values of n. Hence we have

THEOREM 86. *For a set of planes $\pi_1, \pi_2, \cdots, \pi_n$ which are not all concurrent,*

$$\alpha_1 - \alpha_0 = r_2.$$

By Theorem 85 this relation is equivalent to

$$\alpha_2 - \alpha_3 = r_2.$$

192. Polygons in space. THEOREM 87. *The symbol $(x_1, x_2, \cdots, x_{\alpha_1})$ for a line is not linearly dependent on the columns of* H_2.

Proof. Let π be any plane not containing any of the points a^0. The boundary of any a^2 is an even polygon in the sense of § 187 and is met by π in two points or none, the two points being on different edges, if existent. The sum, modulo 2, of two sets of polygons p_1, p_2 each of which is met by π in an even number (regarding zero as even) of points is a set of polygons p met by π in an even number of points; for if π meets p_1 in $2k_1$ points and p_2 in $2k_2$ points, and if k_3 of these points are on edges common to p_1 and p_2, π must meet p in $2k_1 + 2k_2 - 2k_3$ points. Hence any polygon which is a sum of the boundaries of the a^2's is met by π in an even number of points; i.e. any polygon represented by a symbol $(x_1, x_2, \cdots, x_{\alpha_1})$ linearly dependent on the columns of H_2 is met by π in an even number of points. Since no line is met by π in an even number of points, the symbol representing it cannot be a sum of any number of columns of H_2.

THEOREM 88. *All solutions of* (H_1) *are linearly dependent on a set of* r_2 *(i.e.* $\alpha_1 - \alpha_0$*) linearly independent columns of* H_2 *and the symbol* $(x_1, x_2, \cdots, x_{\alpha_1})$ *for one line.*

Proof. It has been shown that the rank of H_1 is $\alpha_0 - 1$. The number of variables in the equations (H_1) is α_1. The number of linearly independent solutions in a set on which all the rest are linearly dependent is therefore $\alpha_1 - \alpha_0 + 1$. Since the rank of H_2 is $\alpha_1 - \alpha_0$, and the columns of H_2 are solutions of (H_1), there are $\alpha_1 - \alpha_0$ linearly independent columns of H_2 which are solutions of (H_1); and since the solution of (H_1) which represents a line is not linearly dependent on these, the statement in the theorem follows.

In the proof of Theorem 87 it appeared that any polygon which is a sum, modulo 2, of a set of polygons bounding a^2's is met by a plane which contains none of its vertices in an even number of points. Since a line is met by a plane not containing it in one point, an argument of the same type shows that any polygon which is a sum, modulo 2, of a line and a number of polygons bounding a^2's is met by a plane containing none of its vertices in an odd number of points. Thus we have, taking Theorem 88 into account:

THEOREM 89. DEFINITION. *A polygon which is the sum, modulo 2, of a number of polygons which bound convex planar regions is met by any plane not containing a vertex in an even number of points and is called an* even *polygon. A polygon which is the sum, modulo 2, of a line and a number of polygons which bound convex planar regions is met by any plane not containing a vertex in an odd number of points and is called an* odd *polygon. Any polygon is either odd or even.*

Suppose a polygon p is the sum, modulo 2, of the boundaries of a set of convex regions $a_1^2, \cdots, a_m^2$. The set of points $[P]$ in $a_1^2, \cdots, a_m^2$ or on their boundaries is easily seen (by an argument analogous to that given in the proof of Theorem 75) to be a connected set. By an extension of the definition in § 150 p may be said to be the *boundary* of $[P]$. From this point of view an even polygon is a bounding polygon and an odd polygon is not.

193. Odd and even polyhedra. It has been seen in § 190 that the solutions of (H_2) represent polyhedra or sets of polyhedra. The converse is also true, as is obvious on reference to the definition of a polyhedron. The sum of two symbols $(x_1, x_2, \cdots, x_{\alpha_2})$ which represent sets of polyhedra is a symbol representing a set of polyhedra. This is obvious either geometrically or from the algebraic consideration that the sum of two solutions of (H_2) is a solution of (H_2).

The set of polyhedra p represented by the symbol which is the sum of the symbols for two sets of polyhedra p_1 and p_2 is called the *sum*, modulo 2, of p_1 and p_2. As in the analogous case of polygons, p is a set of polyhedra whose faces are in p_1 or in p_2 but not in both p_1 and p_2.

The number of variables in (H_2) is α_2 and the rank of H_2 is $\alpha_2 - \alpha_3$ by Theorems 86 and 85. Hence the solutions of (H_2) are linearly dependent on a set of α_3 linearly independent solutions. Since any $\alpha_3 - 1$ of the columns of H_3 are linearly independent, such a set of columns, together with one other solution linearly independent of them, will furnish a set of linearly independent solutions of (H_2).

The symbol for any plane is a solution of (H_2) linearly independent of the columns of H_3. For let l be any line meeting no a^0 or a^1. Any column of H_3 represents the polyhedron bounding an a^3, and such a polyhedron is met by l in two points or none. By reasoning analogous to that used in the proof of Theorem 87, it follows that l meets the sum, modulo 2, of the boundaries of any number of a^3's in an even number of points or none. Since l meets each plane π_1 in one point, the symbol for π_i is not linearly dependent on the columns of H_3. By the last paragraph we now have

THEOREM 90. *Any solution of* (H_2) *is linearly dependent on* $\alpha_3 - 1$ *columns of* H_3 *and the symbol for any one of the planes* $\pi_1, \pi_2, \cdots, \pi_n$.

COROLLARY 1. *Any polyhedron is the sum, modulo 2, of a subset of a set of polyhedra consisting of one plane and all polyhedra which bound convex regions.*

Proof. Let $\pi_1, \pi_2, \cdots, \pi_n$ be a set of planes containing all vertices, edges, and faces of a given polyhedron and such that $\pi_1, \pi_2, \pi_3, \pi_4$ are not concurrent. By the theorem the given polyhedron is either expressible as a sum of the boundaries of some of the a^3's determined by $\pi_1, \pi_2, \cdots, \pi_n$ or as a sum of one of these planes and some of the a^3's.

In the course of the argument above it was shown that any polyhedron expressible in terms of the boundaries of the a^3's was met in an even number of points by any line not meeting an a^0 or an a^1. One of the planes $\pi_1, \pi_2, \cdots, \pi_n$ is met by such a line in one point. Hence any polyhedron which is the sum of such a plane and a number of the boundaries of a^3's is met by this line in an odd number of points. Hence

COROLLARY 2. DEFINITION. *A polyhedron which is the sum, modulo 2, of a number of boundaries of convex three-dimensional regions is met in an even number of points by any line not meeting a vertex or an edge. Such a polyhedron is said to be* even. *A polyhedron which is the sum, modulo 2, of a plane and a number of boundaries of convex three-dimensional regions is met in an odd number of points by any line not meeting a vertex or an edge. Such a polygon is said to be* odd.

EXERCISE

Let p be a polygon and π a polyhedron such that π contains no vertex of p and p contains no vertex or edge of π. If p and π are both odd they have an odd number of points in common. If one of them is even they have an even number (or zero) of points in common.

194. Regions bounded by a polyhedron. An even polyhedron p is the sum of the boundaries of a set of convex three-dimensional polyhedral regions, and we may assign the notation so that these regions are denoted by $a_1^3, a_2^3, \cdots, a_k^3$.

The polyhedron p is also the sum of the boundaries of

$$a_{k+1}^3, a_{k+2}^3, \cdots, a_{\alpha_3}^3,$$

because the sum of all the columns of H_3 is $(0, 0, \cdots, 0)$. There is no other linear expression for p in terms of the boundaries of the a^3's, because there is only one linear relation among the columns of H_3.

This is all a direct generalization of what is said at the beginning of § 187. As in § 187, it is easily seen that the points of $a_1^3, a_2^3, \cdots, a_k^3$, together with those points of their boundaries which are not on p, constitute a region bounded by p; and that the points of $a_k^3, a_{k+1}^3, \cdots, a_{\alpha_3}^3$, together with those points of their boundaries which are not on p, constitute a second region bounded by p. With a few additional details (which are generalizations of those given in the proof of Theorem 75) this constitutes the proof of the following theorem:

THEOREM 91. *Any even polyhedron is the boundary of each of two and only two regions which contain all points of space not on the polyhedron. These regions are such that any broken line joining a point of one region to a point of the other contains a point of the polyhedron. Any two points of the same region can be joined by a broken line consisting entirely of points of the region.*

By a similar generalization of Theorem 76, we obtain

THEOREM 92. *Any odd polyhedron is the boundary of a single region containing all points not on the polyhedron. Any two points of this region can be joined by a broken line not containing any point of the polyhedron.*

COROLLARY. *Any point P on a polyhedron can be joined to any point not on it by a broken line containing no point of the polyhedron except P.*

195. The matrices E_1 and E_2 for the projective plane. DEFINITION. A segment, interval, broken line, polygon, two-dimensional convex region, or three-dimensional convex region associated with a sense-class among its points is called an *oriented* or *directed* segment, interval, broken line, polygon, two-dimensional convex region, or three-dimensional convex region.

DEFINITION. Let a^1 be any segment which, with its ends A and B, is contained in a segment s, and let s^1 denote the oriented segment obtained by associating a^1 with one of its sense-classes. The sense-class of s^1 is contained in a sense-class of s which is either $S(AO)$ or $S(OA)$ if O is any point of a^1. In the first case A is said to be *positively related* to s^1 and in the second case A is said to be *negatively related* to s^1.

To aid the intuition, we may think of an oriented segment as marked with an arrow, the head of which is at the end which is positively related to the oriented segment.

Obviously, if one end of an oriented segment is positively related to it, the other end is negatively related to it, and vice versa.

DEFINITION. The sense-class $S(A_1A_2A_3)$ of a polygon $A_1A_2 \cdots A_nA_1$ and the sense-class $S(AB)$ on the edge A_1A_2 are said to *agree* in case of the order $\{A_1ABA_2\}$ and to *disagree* in case of the order $\{A_1BAA_2\}$.

Returning to the notation of § 185, the segments $a_1^1, \cdots, a_{\alpha_1}^1$ may each be associated with two senses. They thus give rise to $2\alpha_1$ directed segments. Assigning an arbitrary one of the two senses to each a^1, we have α_1 oriented segments to which we may assign the notation $s_1^1, \cdots, s_{\alpha_1}^1$. We shall denote the oriented segment obtained by changing the sense-class of s_i^1 by $-s_i^1$ and call it the *negative* of s^1.

The relations of the s^1's to the points $a_1^0, \cdots, a_{\alpha_0}^0$ may be indicated by means of a matrix which we shall call E_1. In the matrix E_1 the element of the ith row and jth column shall be $1, -1$, or 0, according as the point a_i^0 is positively related to, negatively related to, or not an end of, the oriented segment s_j^1.

It is clear that the signs 1 and -1 are interchanged in the jth column of this matrix if the sense-class of s_j^1 is changed. Since the sense-class of each segment is arbitrary, a matrix equivalent to E_1 can be obtained from the matrix H_1, § 186, by arbitrarily changing one and only one 1 in each column to -1.

In the case of the triangle, by letting the segments $\alpha, \bar{\alpha}, \beta, \bar{\beta}, \gamma, \bar{\gamma}$ give rise to $s_1, s_2, \cdots, s_6$ respectively, we derive the following matrix from H_1 of § 151:

E_1 :

	s_1	s_2	s_3	s_4	s_5	s_6
A	0	0	1	1	1	1
B	1	1	0	0	-1	-1
C	-1	-1	-1	-1	0	0

The elements of the matrix E_1 may be regarded as the coefficients of a set of linear equations analogous to the equations (H_1) of § 186, where, however, the variables and coefficients are not reduced with respect to any modulus. These equations arise as follows:

Let $(x_1, x_2, \cdots, x_{\alpha_1})$ be a symbol in which the x's can take on any integral values, positive, negative, or zero, and let this symbol represent a set of oriented segments comprising s_i^1 counted x_i times if x_i is positive, $-s_i^1$ counted $-x_i$ times if x_i is negative, and neither s_i^1 nor $-s_i^1$ if x_i is zero, i taking on the values $1, 2, \cdots, \alpha_1$.

The sense-class of an oriented polygon agrees with a definite sense-class of each of its sides and thus determines a set of oriented segments. The symbol $(x_1, x_2, \cdots, x_{\alpha_1})$ for this set of oriented segments may also be regarded as a symbol for the oriented polygon. Each vertex of the polygon is positively related to one of the oriented segments represented by $(x_1, x_2, \cdots, x_{\alpha_1})$ and negatively related to another. Thus if s_i^1 and s_j^1 meet at a certain vertex to which they are both positively related according to the matrix E_1, we have that $x_i = 1$ and $x_j = -1$ or that $x_i = -1$ and $x_j = 1$ in the symbol $(x_1, \cdots, x_{\alpha_1})$ for any directed polygon containing the sides a_i and a_j. The x's corresponding to the segments not in the polygon must of course be zero. Hence the symbol $(x_1, \cdots, x_{\alpha_1})$ must satisfy the linear equation whose coefficients are given by the row of E_1 corresponding to the vertex in question. If s_i and s_j are oppositely related to a vertex according to the matrix E_1, we must have $x_i = 1$ and $x_j = 1$ or $x_i = -1$ and $x_j = -1$ in the symbol for any directed polygon containing the sides a_i and a_j. Hence in this case also the linear equation given by the corresponding row of E_1 must be satisfied. Finally, the equation given by a row of E_1 corresponding to a point which is not a vertex of the polygon is satisfied because all the x_i's corresponding to edges meeting at that point are zero. Hence *the symbol for a directed polygon must be a solution of the linear equations whose coefficients are the elements of the rows of the matrix* E_1. These equations shall be denoted by (E_1). In the case of the triangle they are

$$\begin{aligned} x_3 + x_4 + x_5 + x_6 &= 0, \\ x_1 + x_2 - x_5 - x_6 &= 0, \\ -x_1 - x_2 - x_3 - x_4 &= 0. \end{aligned} \tag{6}$$

By reasoning entirely analogous to that of § 186, it follows that any solution of (E_1) in integers represents one or more directed simple polygons. The situation here differs from that described in the modulo 2 case, in that the same side may enter into more than one polygon and the same polygon may be counted any number of times in a set of polygons.

Since each column of the matrix E_1 contains just one 1 and one -1, the sum of the left-hand members of the equations (E_1) vanishes identically. There can be no other linear homogeneous relation among the equations (E_1), because the matrix E_1 and the equations (E_1) when reduced modulo 2 are the same as H_1 and (H_1), and so any linear relation among the equations (E_1) would imply one among (H_1).* Hence the number of linearly independent equations of (E_1) is $\alpha_0 - 1$. The number of variables being α_1, the number of linearly independent solutions is $\alpha_1 - \alpha_0 + 1$. In view of Theorem 74, this number is equal to α_2.

It will be recalled that in the modulo 2 case one class of solutions of Equations (H_1) is given by the columns of the matrix H_2. These columns are the notation for the polygons bounding the convex regions $a_1^1, \cdots, a_{\alpha_2}^1$. If each of these polygons be replaced by one of the two corresponding directed polygons, a set of solutions is determined for the equations (E_1). These solutions are obtained directly from the matrix H_2 by introducing minus signs so that the columns become solutions of (E_1). This is possible in just two ways for each column, because each polygon bounding an a^2 has two and only two sense-classes. A matrix so obtained shall be denoted by E_2. In the case of the triangle such a matrix is

$$E_2 \begin{pmatrix} 0 & -1 & 0 & 1 \\ 1 & 0 & -1 & 0 \\ 0 & 1 & 1 & 0 \\ -1 & 0 & 0 & -1 \\ 0 & 0 & 1 & -1 \\ 1 & -1 & 0 & 0 \end{pmatrix}$$

It is evident on inspection that the rank of this matrix is equal to the number of columns. That is to say, unlike those of H_2, *the*

* The coefficients of any linear homogeneous relation among the rows of E_1 may be taken as integers having no common factor. Hence on reducing modulo 2 it would yield a linear relation among the rows of H_1. But as the only linear relation among the rows of H_1 is that the sum of all the rows is zero, there is no linear relation among the rows of E_1 not involving all the rows. There could not be two such relations among all the rows of E_1, because by combining them we could derive a relation involving a subset of the rows.

columns of E_2 *are linearly independent.* The same proposition holds good for the matrix E_2 in the general case. This can be proved as follows:

By the reasoning used above for the rows of E_1 and H_1, it follows that any linear relation among the columns of E_2 implies one among the columns of H_2. Since the only such relation among the columns of H_2 involves all the columns, we need only investigate linear homogeneous relations among the columns of E_2 in which all the coefficients are different from zero. If such a relation existed, two columns of E_2 corresponding to regions having an edge in common would have numerically equal multipliers in the relation, else the elements corresponding to the common edge would not cancel. But since any two of the convex regions a^2 can be joined by a broken line consisting only of points of these regions and of the edges of their bounding polygons, it follows that all the coefficients in the relation would be numerically equal, i.e. they could all be taken as $+1$ or -1.

Now the n lines $l_1, \cdots, l_n$ containing all the points and segments of our figure are not all concurrent; three of them, say l_1, l_2, l_3, form a triangle. Let us add together all the terms of the supposed relation corresponding to regions a^2 in one of the four triangular regions determined by l_1, l_2, l_3. The elements corresponding to edges interior to this triangular region must all cancel, because they cannot cancel against terms corresponding to regions a^2 exterior to the triangular region. The sum must represent an oriented polygon of which the edges are all on the boundary of the triangular region. This oriented polygon, by § 183, must be identical with the boundary of the triangular regions associated with one of its two sense-classes. If we operate similarly with the other three triangular regions determined by l_1, l_2, l_3, we obtain three other oriented polygons. But since the linear combination of the columns of E_2 is supposed to vanish, each edge of the four triangular regions should appear once with one sense and once with the opposite sense, and this would imply that in the case of a triangle there would exist a linear homogeneous relation among the columns of E_2, contrary to the observation above. Hence in every case *the* α_2 *columns of* E_2 *are linearly independent.*

Since there are only α_2 linearly independent solutions of the equations (E_1), it follows that *all the solutions of* (E_1) *are linearly dependent on the columns of* E_2. This is in sharp contrast with the property of the equations (H_1) stated at the end of § 186.

196. Odd and even polygons in the projective plane. Let us apply the results of the section above to the theory of odd and even polygons. Since any polygon is expressible in terms of the columns of E_2, an odd polygon must be so expressible. Let us write this expression in the form

$$\rho p = \sum_{i=1}^{i=\alpha_2} y_i s_i^2, \tag{7}$$

where $s_1^2, \cdots, s_{\alpha_2}^2$ represent the columns of E_2, p is the symbol for the given oriented polygon, and ρ and $y_1, \cdots, y_{\alpha_2}$ are integers which may be taken so as not to have a common factor.

Since the coefficients do not have 2 as a common factor, (7) does not vanish entirely when reduced modulo 2. But since an odd polygon is not expressible in terms of the columns of H_2, ρ must contain the factor 2, and (7) must reduce, modulo 2, to an identity among the columns of H_2. The only such identity is the one involving all the columns of H_2. Hence the y_i's are all odd. But in order that the edges not on the odd polygon p shall vanish, the y's corresponding to s^2's having an edge in common must be equal. Since any two points not on p can be joined by a broken line not meeting p (Theorem 76), it follows that all the y's are equal. If they are all taken equal to $\pm k$, it is obvious that $\rho = 2k$. Hence we have the theorem:

THEOREM 93. *The symbol p for any odd polygon is expressible in the form*

$$2p = \sum_{i=1}^{\alpha_2} e_i s_i^2, \tag{8}$$

where each e_i is $+1$ or -1.

This theorem may be verified in a special case by adding the columns of the matrix E_2 given above for a triangle. The sum is (0, 0, 2, − 2, 0, 0), which represents a line *counted twice*. The number 2 is called the *coefficient of torsion* of the two-sided polygon (cf. Poincaré, Proceedings of the London Mathematical Society, Vol. XXXII (1900), p. 277. The systematic use of the matrices E_1, E_2, etc. is due to Poincaré).

Another form of statement for Theorem 93 is the following: *If the region bounded by an odd polygon p be decomposed into convex regions each bounded by an even polygon, each edge of p is on the boundary of two of these convex regions.*

An even polygon p is also expressible in the form (7). Aside from a common factor of all the coefficients, there is only one expression for p of the form (7), for if not, by eliminating p we could obtain a linear homogeneous relation among the columns of E_2.

Let R be one of the two regions bounded (Theorem 75) by p, which contains one of the convex regions a_i^2 for which the corresponding y_i in (7) is not zero. Any two s^2's corresponding to a^2's having an edge in common must be multiplied by numerically equal y's in (7) in order that the symbol for the common edge shall not appear in p. Since any two points of R can be joined by a broken line consisting entirely of points of R, this implies that the coefficients y_i corresponding to the a^2's in R are all numerically equal to an integer k. From this it follows that the sum of the terms in the right-hand member of (7) which correspond to a^2's in R is equal to p, because each edge of p is an edge of one and only one of the a^2's in R. Since the equality just found is of the form (7), and (7) is unique, we have that ρ and $y_1, \cdots, y_{\alpha_2}$ are all numerically equal to k. Obviously the factor k can be divided out of (7). Hence we have

THEOREM 94. *The symbol p for an even polygon is expressible in the form*

$$p = \sum_{i=1}^{\alpha_2} e_i s_i^2, \tag{9}$$

where e_i is 0 or $+1$ or -1. The a_i^2's such that the e_i's with the same subscripts are not zero are the a_i^2's in one of the regions R referred to in Theorem 75.

DEFINITION. By the *interior* (or *inside*) of an even polygon is meant that one of the two regions determined according to Theorem 94 which contains the a_i^2's having the same subscripts as the non-zero e_i's in (9). The other region is called the *exterior* of the polygon.

EXERCISE

Identify the interior of a two-sided polygon as defined above with the interior as defined in § 187.

197. One- and two-sided polygonal regions. Let $A_1, A_2, \cdots, A_n$ be a polygon which is the boundary of a convex region R for which there is a convex region R′ containing R and its boundary. If O and

O' are any two points of R, then $S(OA_1A_2)=S(O'A_1A_2)$ (cf. § 161) with respect to R$'$ because O and O' are on the same side of the line A_1A_2 in R$'$. Again,

$$S(OA_1A_2)=S(OA_2A_3)=\cdots=S(OA_nA_1)$$

because A_1 and A_3 are on opposite sides of the line OA_2, A_2 and A_4 are on opposite sides of the line OA_3, etc.

A sense-class in R, which we shall call *positive*, determines a positive sense-class in any convex region R$'$ containing R, i.e. the sense-class containing the given sense-class of R. This, in view of the paragraph above, determines a unique sense-class on the polygon bounding R, by the rule that if $S(OA_1A_2)$ is positive, where O is in R, then $S(A_1A_2A_3)$ is positive on the boundary of R; and if $S(OA_2A_1)$ is positive, then $S(A_2A_1A_n)$ is positive on the boundary of R. From § 161 it follows without difficulty that this determination is independent of the choice of the convex region R$'$.

Conversely, it is obvious that by this rule a sense-class on the boundary of R determines a definite sense-class in R.

Definition. Let a^2 be any planar convex region which, with its boundary, is contained in a convex planar region R, and let a^1 be any segment on the boundary of a^2. Let s^1 denote the oriented segment obtained by associating a^1 with one of its sense-classes, and s^2 denote the oriented region obtained by associating a^2 with one of its sense-classes. The sense-class of s^2 is contained in a certain sense-class of R which may be denoted by $S(OAB)$, where O is in a^2 and A and B are on a^1. If $S(AB)$ is the sense-class of s^1, then s^1 and s^2 are said to be *positively related*; and if $S(AB)$ is not the sense-class of s^1, they are said to be *negatively related.*

As pointed out above, this definition is independent of the choice of R. Let R$_1$ and R$_2$ be two convex regions having no point in common and bounded by two polygons $A_1A_2A_3\cdots A_m$ and $A_1A_2B_3\cdots B_m$ respectively which have in common only the vertices A_1 and A_2 and the points of the edge A_1A_2. Suppose, also, that R$_1$, R$_2$ and their boundaries are contained in a convex region R. These conditions are satisfied if R$_1$ and R$_2$ are a^2's, and A_1A_2 is an a^1, determined by a set of lines four of which are such that no three are concurrent.

The rule given above for determining positive sense on the boundaries of R$_1$ and R$_2$ requires that if $S(OA_1A_2)$ is positive for O a point of R$_1$, then $S(A_1AA_2)$ must be positive on the boundary of R_1, where A is a point of the edge A_1A_2. If O' is any point of R_2, it is on the opposite side of the line A_1A_2 from O in R. Hence $S(O'A_2A_1)$ is positive, and hence $S(A_2AA_1)$ must be the positive sense-class on the boundary of R.

Let R_1 and R_2 be two of the a^2's determined by a set of lines $l_1, l_2, \cdots, l_n$; let the boundary of R_1 associated with the positive sense-class as determined in the last paragraph be denoted by $(x_1, x_2, \cdots, x_{\alpha_1})$ according to the notation of § 195; and let the boundary of R_2 associated with the positive sense-class determined at the same time be $(y_1, y_2, \cdots, y_{\alpha_1})$. The notation may be assigned so that x_1 and y_1 refer to the edge A_1A_2 common to the boundaries of R_1 and R_2. In this case, if $x_1 = 1$, $y_1 = -1$, and if $x_1 = -1$, $y_1 = +1$; for the positive sense for the boundary of R_1 is $S(A_1AA_2)$ and for the boundary of R_2 is $S(A_2AA_1)$. Hence the sum of the two symbols $(x_1, x_2, \cdots, x_{\alpha_1})$ and $(y_1, y_2, \cdots, y_{\alpha_1})$ is the symbol for the boundary of the region R′ composed of R_1, R_2 and the common edge A_1A_2, this boundary being associated with a sense-class S' which agrees with the positive sense-class on any edge of the boundary of R_1 or R_2 which is an edge of the boundary of R′.

By repeated use of these considerations it follows that if a set of a^2's with their boundaries constitute a convex region R and its boundary, the symbol $(x_1, x_2, \cdots, x_{\alpha_1})$ for the boundary of R associated with a sense-class which is designated as positive, is the sum of the symbols for the boundaries of the a^3's, each associated with its positive sense-class. In other words, the symbol for the boundary of R associated with its positive sense-class is the sum of a set of columns of H_2, each multiplied by $+1$ or -1 so that it shall be the symbol for the boundary of the corresponding a^2 associated with the sense-class which is positive relatively to the positive sense-class of R. By comparison with Theorem 94, it follows (as is obvious from other considerations also) that any polygon which is the boundary of a convex region is even.

The argument in the paragraph above applies without essential modification to any region bounded by a polygon and having a unique determination of sense according to § 168. Hence any polygon bounding a two-sided region is even.

Moreover the steps of the argument may be reversed as follows: If the symbol for any oriented polygon p be expressible in terms of the columns of H_2, in the form (7), where the non-zero coefficients are $e_{i_1}, e_{i_2}, \cdots, e_{ik}$, p is the boundary of the region R consisting of $a_{i_1}{}^2, a_{i_2}{}^2, \cdots, a_{ik}{}^2$ and those points of their boundaries which are not on p. If R′ is a convex region contained in R, and its positive sense-class be determined as agreeing with the positive sense-class of one of the regions $a_{i_1}{}^2, a_{i_2}{}^2, \cdots, a_{ik}{}^2$, it must agree with that of every a^2 with which it has a point in common; for otherwise the symbols for the common edges of two of the a^2's would not cancel in (7). If R″ is any other convex region contained in R, and its positive sense-class is also determined by this rule, the positive sense-classes of R′ and R″ must, by definition, agree in any region common to R′ and R″. Hence R is two-sided according to § 168. Thus we have by comparison with § 196

THEOREM 95. *The interior of an even polygon is a two-sided region.*

198. One- and two-sided polyhedra. Let the vertices of a polyhedron be denoted by $a_1{}^0, a_2{}^0, \cdots, a_{\alpha_0}{}^0$, the edges by $a_1{}^1, a_2{}^1, \cdots, a_{\alpha_1}{}^1$ and the faces by $a_1{}^2, a_2{}^2, \cdots, a_{\alpha_2}{}^2$. Assigning an arbitrary one of its sense-classes to each edge, there is determined a set of oriented segments $s_1{}^1, s_2{}^1, \cdots, s_{\alpha_1}{}^1$ and a matrix

$$E_1 = (\epsilon_{ij}{}^1),$$

in which $i = 1, 2, \cdots, \alpha_0$; $j = 1, 2, \cdots, \alpha_1$; and $\epsilon_{ij}{}^1$ is $+1$, -1, or 0, according as $a_i{}^0$ is positively related to, negatively related to, or not an end of $s_j{}^1$.

Assigning an arbitrary one of its sense-classes to each face, there is determined a set of oriented planar convex regions $s_1{}^2, s_2{}^2, \cdots, s_{\alpha_2}{}^2$ and a matrix

$$E_2 = (\epsilon_{ij}{}^2),$$

in which $i = 1, 2, \cdots, \alpha_1$; $j = 1, 2, \cdots, \alpha_2$; and $\epsilon_{ij}{}^2$ is $+1$, -1, or 0, according as $s_i{}^1$ is positively related to (cf. § 197), negatively related to, or not on the boundary of $s_j{}^2$. By the last section each column of E_2 is the symbol $(x_1, x_2, \cdots, x_{\alpha_1})$, in the sense explained in § 195, for an oriented polygon obtained by associating the polygon bounding one of the a^2's with one of its sense-classes. Changing the sense-class assigned to any a^2 to determine the corresponding s^2 amounts to multiplying all elements of the corresponding column of E_2 by -1.

For simplicity let us at first restrict attention to polyhedra in which each edge is on the boundaries of two and only two faces.

In this case there are just two non-zero elements in each row of E_2. Hence the sum of the columns of E_2 will reduce to $(0, 0, \cdots, 0)$ if and only if the sense-classes have been assigned to the faces of the polyhedron in such a way that one of these elements is $+1$ and the other -1 in each row. This means that each s^1 is positively related to one of the s^2's on whose boundary it is and negatively related to the other. Thus the faces are related as are the a^2's which constitute a two-sided region bounded by an even polygon in the plane (§ 197).

DEFINITION. A polyhedron for which the sense-classes can be assigned to the edges and faces in such a way that each edge is positively related to one of the faces on whose boundary it is and negatively related to the other, is said to be *two-sided,* or *bilateral*; and one for which this assignment of sense-classes is not possible is said to be *one-sided,* or *unilateral.*

Changing the assignment of sense-classes on an edge amounts merely to multiplying the corresponding column of E_1 and row of E_2 by -1, and changing the assignment of sense-classes on a face amounts to the same operation on a column of E_2. Consequently the polyhedron is two-sided if there is a linear relation whose coefficients are 1's and -1's among all the columns of E_2, and it is one-sided if there is no such relation. It is also obvious from these considerations that if a polyhedron satisfies the definition of two-sidedness (or of one-sidedness) for one assignment of sense-classes to its edges, it does so for all assignments. We therefore infer at once:

THEOREM 96. *A polyhedron is one- or two-sided according as the rank of* E_2 *is* α_2 *or* $\alpha_2 - 1$.

By reference to § 195 we find

COROLLARY. *The projective plane is a one-sided polyhedron.*

In the case of any polyhedron in which each edge is on the boundary of only two faces, it is seen that the only possible linear relation among the columns of E_2 reduces to one in which each coefficient is $+1$ or -1, for any other relation would imply that a subset of the faces determines a polyhedron.

THEOREM 97. *A polyhedron bounding a convex region* R *which is contained with its boundary in a convex region* R′, *is two-sided.*

Proof. Let sense-classes be assigned to the edges in an arbitrary way, but let sense-classes be assigned to the faces according to the following rule: Let a given sense-class $S(PQRT)$ in R' be designated as positive. Let O be any point of R and A, B, C, three noncollinear points of a face of the polyhedron. The sense-class $S(ABC)$ is assigned to this face if and only if $S(OABC)$ is positive.

There is no difficulty in proving that if C and D are two points of an edge s_i^1 of the polyhedron bounding R, and E and E' points of the two faces having this edge on their boundaries, then E and E' are on opposite sides of the plane OCD. Hence

$$S(OCDE) \neq S(OCDE').$$

Hence the sense-classes are assigned according to the rule above to the two faces having the edge s_i^1 on their boundaries in such a way that s_i^1 is positively related to one and negatively related to the other.

DEFINITION. By an *oriented polyhedron* is meant the set of oriented two-dimensional convex regions $[s^2]$ obtained by associating each face of a two-sided polyhedron with a sense-class in such a way that if sense-classes are assigned arbitrarily to the edges to determine directed segments, each of these directed segments is positively related to one of the oriented two-dimensional convex regions on whose boundary it is and negatively related to the other. The s^2's are called the *oriented faces* of the oriented polyhedron, and the s^1's its *oriented edges.*

COROLLARY. *A given two-sided polyhedron determines two and only two oriented polyhedra according to the definition above.*

DEFINITION. Let a^3 be a three-dimensional convex region which is contained with its boundary in a convex region R, and a^2 a two-dimensional convex region on the boundary of a^3. Let s^3 denote a^3 associated with one of its sense-classes, and let s^2 denote a^2 associated with one of its sense-classes. The sense-class of s^3 is contained in one of the sense-classes, say $\bar{S}$, of R. Let O be a point of a^3, and A, B, C three points of a^2, such that $S(OABC)$ is $\bar{S}$. Then if $S(ABC)$ is the sense-class associated with a^2 to form s^2, s^2 and s^3 are said to be *positively related.* Otherwise they are said to be *negatively related.*

By § 161 this definition is independent of any particular choice of the convex region R containing a^3 and its boundary. From what has been proved above it follows that if each a^2 on the boundary of an a^3 is associated with a sense-class in such a way as to be positively related to the oriented region determined by a^3 and one of its sense-classes, this set of oriented two-dimensional convex regions is an oriented polyhedron.

The definitions made in this section are extended to polyhedra in which each edge is on an even number of faces (instead of only two, as we have been supposing) as follows:

DEFINITION. A polyhedron is said to be *two-sided* if sense-classes can be assigned to the edges and faces in such a way that each resulting oriented edge is positively related and negatively related to equal numbers of the resulting oriented faces.

EXERCISES

1. An odd polyhedron is one-sided and an even polyhedron is two-sided.

2. Make a discussion of one- and two-sided polyhedral regions in space analogous to the discussion for the two-dimensional case in § 197.

199. Orientation of space. The matrices of § 195 can be generalized to the three-dimensional case. Let $s_1^1, s_2^1, \cdots, s_{\alpha_1}^1$, be the oriented segments obtained by associating each of the segments $a_1^1, a_2^1, \cdots, a_{\alpha_1}^1$ with an arbitrary one of its sense-classes. In the first matrix,

$$E_1 = (\epsilon_{ij}^1),$$

$i=1, 2, \cdots, \alpha_0$; $j=1, 2, \cdots, \alpha_1$; and ϵ_{ij}^1 is $+1$, -1, or 0 according as a_i^0 is positively related to, negatively related to, or not an end of s_j^1. E_1 can be formed from H_1 by changing one 1 to a -1 in each column. The choice of the -1 in the jth column amounts to the choice of the sense-class on a_j^1 which determines s_j^1. As an exercise, the reader should form E_1 from the H_1 given for a tetrahedron in § 152.

Sets of oriented segments s^1 are represented as in § 195 by symbols of the form $(x_1, x_2, \cdots, x_{\alpha_1})$, where the x's are positive or negative integers. By the same argument as in § 195, if this symbol represents a set of oriented segments each of which is an edge of a polygon associated with that one of its sense-classes which agrees with a fixed sense-class of the polygon, it is a solution of the equations,

$$(E_1) \qquad \sum_{j=1}^{\alpha_1} \epsilon_{ij}^1 x_j = 0, \qquad (i=1, 2, \cdots, \alpha_0)$$

and, conversely, any solution of these equations is the symbol for one or more such sets of oriented segments. Thus any solution of (E_1) may be regarded as representing one or more oriented polygons.

Let $s_1^2, s_2^2, \cdots, s_{\alpha_2}^2$ be the oriented two-dimensional convex regions obtained by associating each a^2 with an arbitrary one of its sense-classes. The oriented two-dimensional regions obtained by associating the s^2's with the opposite sense-classes may be denoted by $-s_1^2$, $-s_2^2, \cdots, -s_{\alpha_2}^2$ respectively. In the second matrix,

$$E_2 = (\epsilon_{ij}^2),$$

$i=1, 2, \cdots, \alpha_1$; $j=1, 2, \cdots, \alpha_2$; and ϵ_{ij}^2 is $1, -1$, or 0 according as s_i^1 is positively related to, negatively related to, or not on the boundary of s_j^2. E_2 can be formed from H_2 by changing some of the 1's in each column of H_2 to -1's in such a way that each column shall be a symbol $(x_1, x_2, \cdots, x_{\alpha_1})$ for a set of s^1's whose sense-classes all agree with that of the oriented polygon determined by associating the boundary of s^2 with one of its sense-classes. This is possible by the argument at the beginning of § 197, since each column of H_2 is the symbol for the boundary of one and only one a^2. As an exercise, the reader should form E_2 from the H_2 given for a tetrahedron in § 152.

A symbol of the form $(x_1, x_2, \cdots, x_{\alpha_2})$ in which each x is a positive or negative integer or zero may be taken to represent a set of oriented two-dimensional convex regions which includes s_i^2 counted x_i times if x_i is positive, $-s_i^2$ counted $-x_i$ times if x_i is negative, and does not include s_i^2 if x_i is zero. If this symbol represents an oriented polyhedron (§ 197), it is a solution of the equations

$$(E_2) \qquad \sum_{j=1}^{\alpha_2} \epsilon_{ij}^2 x_j = 0, \qquad (i=1, 2, \cdots, \alpha_1).$$

For consider the ith of these equations:

$$\epsilon_{i_1}^2 x_1 + \epsilon_{i_2}^2 x_2 + \cdots + \epsilon_{i\alpha_2}^2 x_{\alpha_2} = 0.$$

If an oriented face of the oriented polyhedron is positively related to s_i^1, it contributes a term $+1$ to the left-hand member of this equation; for if s_k^2 is this oriented face, $x_k = 1$ and $\epsilon_{ik}^2 = 1$; and if $-s_k^2$ is this oriented face, $x_k = -1$ and $\epsilon_{ik}^2 = -1$. An oriented face which is negatively related to s_i^1 contributes a term -1 to the left-hand member of this equation; for if s_k^2 is this oriented face, $x_k = 1$ and $\epsilon_{ik}^2 = -1$; and if $-s_k^2$ is this oriented face, $x_k = -1$ and $\epsilon_{ik} = 1$. Hence there are as many terms equal to $+1$ as there are oriented faces positively related to s_i^1, and as many terms equal to -1 as there are oriented faces negatively related to s_i^1. If neither s_k^2 nor $-s_k^2$ is in the oriented polyhedron, or if s_k^2 does not have s_i^1 on its boundary, the kth term of this equation is zero, for in the first case $x_k = 0$ and in the second case $\epsilon_{ik}^2 = 0$. Hence by the definition of an oriented polyhedron, each of the equations (E_2) is satisfied if $(x_1, x_2, \cdots, x_{\alpha_2})$ represents an oriented polyhedron. In particular (Theorem 97) the symbol for either oriented polyhedron determined by the boundary of an a^3 is a solution of (E_2).

One-sided polyhedra do not give rise to solutions of (E_2).

Let s_1^3 and $-s_1^3$, s_2^3 and $-s_2^3, \cdots, s_{\alpha_3}^3$ and $-s_{\alpha_3}^3$ be the pairs of oriented three-dimensional convex regions determined by $a_1^3, a_2^3, \cdots, a_{\alpha_3}^3$ respectively according to the definition in § 197. In the third matrix,

$$E_3 = (\epsilon_{ij}^3),$$

$i = 1, 2, \cdots, \alpha_2$; $j = 1, 2, \cdots, \alpha_3$; and ϵ_{ij}^3 is $+1, -1$, or 0 according as s_i^2 is positively related to, negatively related to, or not on the boundary of s_j^3. The matrix E_3 can be formed from H_3 by changing 1's to -1's in the columns of H_3 in such a way that the resulting columns are the symbols for oriented polyhedra and therefore solutions of (E_2). This is possible by Theorem 96. As an exercise, the reader should form E_3 from the H_3 given for a tetrahedron in § 152.

The sum of the columns of E_1 is $(0, 0, \cdots, 0)$ because each row of E_1 contains one $+1$ and one -1. There can be no other linear relation among the columns of E_1, because this would imply, on reducing modulo 2, more than one linear relation among the columns of H_1. Hence the rank of E_1 is $\alpha_0 - 1$, and the number of solutions of E_1 in a linearly independent set on which all the solutions are linearly dependent is $\alpha_1 - \alpha_0 + 1$.

Since the rank of H_2 is $\alpha_1 - \alpha_0$, and since every homogeneous linear relation among the columns of E_2 implies one among the columns of H_2, the rank of E_2 is at least $\alpha_1 - \alpha_0$. It is, in fact, at least $\alpha_1 - \alpha_0 + 1$ because, by Theorem 93, the symbols for a set of columns $c_1, c_2, \cdots, c_k$ which represent oriented polygons bounding all the s^2's of a projective plane satisfy a relation of the form

$$(10) \qquad e_1 c_1 + e_2 c_2 + \cdots + e_k c_k = 2\,l,$$

where l is the symbol for a line in this plane and $e_1, e_2, \cdots, e_n$ are $+1$ or -1. Reducing modulo 2, this gives rise to a homogeneous linear relation among the columns of H_2 which is not one of those obtained by reducing the homogeneous linear relations among the columns of E_2.

Thus there are at least $\alpha_1 - \alpha_0 + 1$ linearly independent columns of E_2. These are all solutions of (E_1), and as there are not more than $\alpha_1 - \alpha_0 + 1$ linearly independent solutions of (E_1), there are not more than $\alpha_1 - \alpha_0 + 1$ linearly independent columns of E_2. Hence the rank of E_2 is $\alpha_1 - \alpha_0 + 1$, which by Theorem 85 is the same as $\alpha_2 - \alpha_3 + 1$.

In consequence, the symbol $(x_1, x_2, \cdots, x_{\alpha_1})$ for any oriented polygon is linearly expressible in terms of the symbols for oriented polygons which bound convex planar regions. It can easily be proved that in case of an odd polygon this expression takes the form (10) where, however, the polygons denoted by $c_1, c_2, \cdots, c_k$ are not necessarily all in the same plane.

Since the number of variables in the equations (E_2) is α_2 and the rank of E_2 is $\alpha_2 - \alpha_3 + 1$, the number of solutions in a linearly independent set on which all solutions are linearly dependent is $\alpha_3 - 1$. The columns of E_3 are all solutions of (E_2). Hence the rank of E_3 cannot be greater than $\alpha_3 - 1$. It cannot be less than $\alpha_3 - 1$, because, on reducing modulo 2, this would imply that the rank of H_3 was less than $\alpha_3 - 1$. Hence the rank of E_3 is $\alpha_3 - 1$. Since the symbol for any oriented polyhedron whose oriented faces are s^2's or $-s^2$'s is a solution of (E_2), it follows that it is expressible linearly in terms of the symbols for oriented polyhedra which bound convex three-dimensional regions.

Since the rank of E_3 is $\alpha_3 - 1$, the set of equations

$$(E_3) \qquad \sum_{j=1}^{\alpha_3} \epsilon^3_{ij} x_j = 0 \qquad (i = 1, 2, \cdots, \alpha_2)$$

must have one solution distinct from $(0, 0, \cdots, 0)$. When reduced modulo (2) this solution must satisfy (H_3) and therefore, by § 190, reduce to $(1, 1, \cdots, 1)$. Since each equation in the set (E_3) has only two coefficients different from zero, and these coefficients are ± 1, it follows that all the x's are numerically equal in a solution $(x_1, x_2, \cdots, x_{\alpha_3})$ of (E_3). Since the equations are homogeneous, all the x's may be taken to be $+1$ or -1.

The ith of these equations is of the form

$$\epsilon^3_{ij_1} x_{j_1} + \epsilon^3_{ij_2} x_{j_2} = 0,$$

$\epsilon^3_{ij_1}$ being $+1$ or -1 according as s^2_i is positively or negatively related to $s^3_{j_1}$, and $\epsilon^3_{ij_2}$ being $+1$ or -1 according as s^2_i is positively or negatively related to $s^3_{j_2}$. Hence, if the set of regions represented by a solution in which the x's are ± 1 includes that one of $s^3_{j_1}$ and $-s^3_{j_1}$ to which s^2_i is positively related, it also includes that one of $s^3_{j_2}$ and $-s^3_{j_2}$ to which s^2_i is negatively related; and if it includes that one of $s^3_{j_1}$ and $-s^3_{j_1}$ to which s^2_i is negatively related, it also includes that one of $s^3_{j_2}$ and $-s^3_{j_2}$ to which s^2_i is positively related.

Hence the existence of a solution of (E_3) other than $(0, 0, \cdots, 0)$ implies the existence of a set of s^3's and $-s^3$s such that each s^2 is positively related to one of them and negatively related to another. Since the notation s^3_j and $-s^3_j$ may be interchanged by multiplying the jth column of E_3 by -1, the notation may be so arranged that $(1, 1, \cdots, 1)$ is a solution of E_3. With the notation so arranged, each s^2 is positively related to one s^3 and negatively related to another. We thus have

THEOREM 98. *If each of the a^2's determined by a set of planes $\pi_1, \pi_2, \cdots, \pi_n$ in a projective space is arbitrarily associated with one of its sense-classes to determine an oriented planar convex region s^2, each of the a^3's can be associated with one of its sense-classes to determine a three-dimensional convex region s^3 in such a way that each s^2 is positively related to one s^3 and negatively related to another.*

The set of s^3's described in this theorem is a generalization of an oriented polyhedron as defined in § 198. If the definition of unilateral and bilateral polyhedra be generalized to any number of dimensions, it is a consequence of this theorem that the three-dimensional space is a bilateral polyhedron. In general, it can easily be verified, by generalizing the matrices E_1, E_2, E_3 etc., that projective spaces of even dimensionality are unilateral polyhedra and projective spaces of odd dimensionality are bilateral polyhedra.

EXERCISE

An odd two-dimensional polyhedron in a three-dimensional space is one-sided and an even one is two-sided.

PRINTED IN THE UNITED STATES OF AMERICA
A B C D E F G H I J K L 0 6 9 8 7 6 5

INDEX

About, 159
Absolute conic, 350, 371
Absolute involutions, 119
Absolute polar systems, 293, 373
Absolute quadric, 369, 373
Addition of vectors, 84
Affine classification of conics, 186
Affine collineation, 72, 287
Affine geometry, 72, 147, 287
Affine groups, 71, 72, 287, 305; subgroups of the, 116
Agree (sense-classes), 485
Alexander, J. W., iii, 405
Algebra of matrices, 333
Algebraic cut, 15
Alignment, assumptions of, 2
Analysis, plane of, 268
Angle, 139, 231, 429, 432
Angles, equal, 165; numbered, 154; of rotation, 325, 327; sum of two, 154
Angular measure, 151, 153, 163, 165, 231, 311, 313, 362, 365
Anomaly, eccentric, 198
Antiprojectivities, 250, 251, 253
Apollonius, 235
Arc, differential of, 366
Area, 96, 149, 150, 157, 311, 312; of ellipse, 150
Assumption, Archimedean, 146
Assumption A, 2
Assumption C, 16
Assumption E, 2
Assumption H, 11
Assumption H_0, 2
Assumption $\overline{H}$, 33
Assumption I, 30
Assumption J, 7
Assumption K, 3
Assumption P, 2; commutative law of multiplication equivalent to, 3
Assumption Q, 16
Assumption R, 23
Assumption $\overline{R}$, 29
Assumption S, 32
Assumptions, of alignment, 2; categoricalness of, 23; consistency of, 23; of continuity, 16; for Euclidean geometry, 59, 144, 302; of extension, 2; independence of, 23; of order, 32; of projectivity, 2
Asymptotes of a conic, 73
Axis, of a circle, 354; of a conic, 191; of a line reflection, 258; of a parabola, 193; of a quadric, 316; radical, 159; of a rotation, 299; of a translation, 317; of a twist, 320

Backward, 303
Barycentric calculus, 40, 104, 292, 293
Barycentric coördinates, 106, 108, 292
Base circle, 254
Base points of a pencil, 242
Beltrami, E., 361
Bennett, A. A., iii
Between, 15, 47, 48, 60, 350, 387, 430, 433
Bilateral polyhedron, 494
Bilinear curve, 269
Biquaternions, 347, 379, 382
Bisector, exterior, 179; interior, 179; perpendicular, 123
Bôcher, M., 256, 271
Böger, R., 168
Bolyai, J., 361
Bonola, R., 59, 362, 363, 371, 375
Borel, E., 60
Boundary, 392, 474, 482
Bounding polygons, 470, 482
Broken lines, 454; directed, 484; oriented, 484
Bundle, of circles, 256; center of, 435; of directions, 436; of projectivities, 342; of rays, 435; of segments, 436
Burnside, W., 41

Calculus, barycentric, 40, 104, 292, 293
Carnot, L. N. M., 90
Carslaw, H. S., 362
Cartan, E., 341
Casey, J., 168
Categoricalness of assumptions, 23
Cayley, A., 163, 335, 341, 361
Cells, 404; oriented, 452, 453
Center, of a bundle of rays, 435; of a circle, 131, 394; of a conic, 73; of curvature, 201; of gravity, 94; of a pencil, 429, 433; of a rotation, 122; of similitude, 162, 163; of a sphere, 315
Center circle, 231
Centers, line of, 159
Ceva, 89

Chain, 17, 21, 222, 229, 250; conjugate points with respect to, 243; fundamental theorem for, 22; n-dimensional, 250; three-, 284
Circle, 120, 131, 142, 145, 148, 157, 269, 354, 394; axis of, 354; base, 254; bundle of, 256; center, 231; center of, 131, 394; circumference of, 148; of curvature, 201; degenerate, 253, 266; director, 200; directrix of, 192; Feuerbach, 169, 233; focus of, 192; fundamental, 254; imaginary, 187, 229; at infinity, 293; intersectional properties of, 142; length of, 148; limiting points of pencils of, 159; linearly dependent, 256; nine-point, 169, 233; orthogonal, 161; pencils of, 157, 159, 242; power of a point with respect to, 162; sides of, 245
Circular cone, 317
Circular points, 120, 155
Circular transformations, 225; direct, 225, 452; types of direct, 246, 248
Clebsch, A., 366, 368, 369, 377
Clifford, W. K., 293, 347, 361, 374
Clifford parallel, 374, 375, 377, 444
Clockwise sense, 40
Closed curve, 401
Closed cut, 14
Coble, A. B., iii
Coefficient of torsion, 489
Cole, F. N., 222
Collinear vectors, 84; ratio of, 85
Collineations, affine, 72, 287; direct, 61, 64, 65, 107, 438, 451; direct, of a quadric, 260; equiaffine, 105; focal properties of, 201; involutoric, 257; opposite, 61, 438, 451; in real projective space, 252
Commutative law of multiplication equivalent to Assumption P, 3
Complementary segments or intervals, 46
Complex elements, 156
Complex function plane, 268
Complex geometry, 6, 29
Complex inversion plane, 264, 265
Complex line, 8; order relations on, 437; and real Euclidean plane, correspondence between, 222
Complex plane, 154; inversions in, 235
Complex point, 8, 156
Cone, circular, 317
Confocal conics, 192
Confocal system of quadrics, 348
Congruence of lines, 275, 283; elliptic, 443; right-handed and left-handed elliptic, 444
Congruent figures, 79, 80, 94, 124, 134, 139, 144, 297, 303, 352, 369, 373, 375, 394
Conic, 82, 158, 199; absolute, 350, 371; asymptotes of, 73; axis of, 191; center of, 73; central, 73; confocal, 192; diameter of, 73; directrix of, 191; eccentricity of, 196; eleven-point, 82; equation of, 202, 208; exterior of, 171, 174, 176; focus of, 191; interior of, 171, 174, 176; invariants of, 207; latus rectum of, 198; metric properties of, 81; nine-point, 82; normal to, 173; ordinal and metric properties of, 170; outside of, 171; parameter of, 198; projective, affine, and Euclidean classification of, 186, 210, 212; a simple closed curve, 402; vertex of, 191
Conjugacy under a group, 39
Conjugate imaginary elements, 182
Conjugate imaginary lines, 281, 282, 444
Conjugate points with respect to a chain, 243
Connected set, 404; of sets of points, 405
Connectivity of a polyhedron, 475
Constructions, ruler and compass, 180
Continuity, assumptions of, 16
Continuous, 404
Continuous curve, 401
Continuous deformation, 406, 407, 410, 452
Continuous family of points, 404
Continuous family of sets of points, 405
Continuous family of transformations, 406
Continuous group, 406
Continuum, 404
Convex regions, 385–394; linear, 47; sense in overlapping, 424; oriented or directed three-dimensional, 484; oriented or directed two-dimensional, 484
Coolidge, J. L., 229, 360, 362
Coördinate system, positive, 407, 408, 416; right-handed, 408, 416
Coördinates, barycentric, 106, 108, 292; polar, 249; rectangular, 311; tetracyclic, 253, 254, 255
Correspondence, between the complex line and the real Euclidean plane, 222; between the real Euclidean plane and a complex pencil of lines, 238; between the rotations and the points of space, 328; perspective, 271; projective, 272
Cosines, direction, 314
Cremona, L., 168, 251, 348
Criteria, of sense, 49; of separation, 55
Crossings of pairs of lines, 276
Cross ratio, equianharmonic, 259; of points in space, 55
Curvature, center of, 201; circle of, 201
Curve, 401; bilinear, 269; closed, 401; a conic a simple closed, 402; equidistantial, 356; normal, 286; path, 249, 356, 406; positively or negatively oriented, 452; rational, 286; simple, 401

Cut-point, 14, 21
Cuts, open and closed, 14 ; algebraic, 15
Cyclic projectivity, 258

Darboux, G., 251, 324
Dedekind, R., 60
Deformation, continuous, 406, 407, 410, 452
Degenerate circle, 253, 266
Degenerate sphere, 315
Dehn, M., 290
De Paolis, R., 362
Describe, 401
Diagonals of a quadrangle, 72
Diameter, of a conic, 73 ; end of, 151 ; of a quadrilateral, 81
Dickson, L. E., 35, 339, 341
Differential of arc, 366
Dilation, 95, 348
Direct collineation, 61, 64, 65, 107, 438, 451 ; of a quadric, 260
Direct projectivities, 37, 38, 407
Direct similarity transformations, 135
Direct transformations, 225, 452
Directed, oppositely, 433 ; similarly, 433
Directed broken line, 484
Directed interval, 484
Directed polygon, 484
Directed segment, 484
Directed three-dimensional convex region, 484
Directed two-dimensional convex region, 484
Direction-class, 433
Direction cosines, 314
Directions, bundle of, 436 ; pencil of, 433
Director circle, 200
Directrices of a skew involution or line reflection, 258
Directrix, of a circle, 192 ; of a conic, 191 ; of a parabola, 193
Disagree (sense-classes), 485
Displacement, 123, 129, 138, 143, 297, 317, 325, 352, 369, 373 ; parameter representation of, 344 ; parameter representation of elliptic, 377 ; parameter representation of hyperbolic, 380 ; types of hyperbolic, 355
Distance, 147, 157, 311, 364, 373 ; algebraic formulas for, 365 ; of translation, 325, 327 ; unit of, 147
Doehlemann, K., 229, 230
Double elliptic plane, 375
Double elliptic plane geometry, 375
Double points of projectivities, 5, 114, 177
Doubly oriented line, 440, 442, 445, 447, 449
Doubly perspective, 448
Down, 303

Eccentric anomaly, 198
Eccentricity of a conic, 196
Edges, of a broken line, 454 ; of a polyhedron, oriented, 495
Eisenhart, L. P., 368
Elementary transformations, 409, 411–414, 418, 419, 421, 423, 430, 431, 434–437, 447, 455, 456 ; restricted, 410, 414, 420, 430
Elements, complex, 156 ; imaginary, 7, 156, 182 ; ideal, 71, 287 ; improper, 71
Eleven-point conic, 82
Ellipse, 73, 140 ; area of, 150 ; foci of, 189 ; imaginary, 187
Elliptic congruence, 443
Elliptic displacements, parameter representation of, 377
Elliptic geometry, double, 375
Elliptic geometry of three dimensions, 373
Elliptic pencils of circles, 242
Elliptic plane, 371 ; double, 375 ; single, 371, 375
Elliptic plane geometry, 371
Elliptic points, 373
Elliptic polar systems, 218
Elliptic projectivity, 5, 171
Elliptic transformations, direct circular, 248
Emch, A., 230
End of a diameter, 151
Ends of a segment or interval, 45, 427
Enriques, F., 302
Envelope of lines, 406
Equation of a conic, 202, 208
Equations of the affine and Euclidean groups, 116, 135, 305 ; linearly independent, 466 ; and matrices, modular, 464
Equiaffine collineations, 105
Equiaffine group, 105, 291
Equianharmonic cross ratio or set of points, 259
Equidistantial curves, 356
Equilateral hyperbola, 169
Equivalence, of ordered point triads, 96, 288, 290 ; of ordered tetrads, 290 ; with respect to a group, 39
Euclid, 360
Euclidean classification of conics, 186, 210
Euclidean geometry, 117, 118, 119, 135, 144, 287, 300, 302 ; assumptions for, 59, 144, 302 ; as a limiting case of non-Euclidean, 375
Euclidean group, 117, 118, 135, 144 ; equations of, 116, 135, 305
Euclidean line, 58
Euclidean plane, 58, 60–63, 71 ; and complex line, correspondence between, 222, 238 ; inversion group in the real, 225 ; sense in, 61
Euclidean spaces, 58, 287 ; sense in, 63
Euler, L., 332, 337

Even polygons, 470, 482, 489; in the projective plane, 489
Even polyhedra, 482, 483
Expansion, 348
Extension, assumptions of, 2
Exterior, of an angle, 432; of a conic, 171, 174, 176; of a polygon, 472; of an even polygon, 490; of a quadric, 344
Exterior bisector, 179

Faces of a polyhedron, 474; oriented, 495
Family of points, continuous, 404
Family of sets of points, continuous, 405
Family of transformations, continuous, 406
Fano, G., 11, 285, 286
Feuerbach, 169, 233
Field, Galois, 35
Fine, H. B., 3, 18
Finzel, A., 369
Focal involution, 195
Focal properties of collineations, 201
Foci of an ellipse or hyperbola, 189
Focus, of a circle, 192; of a conic, 191; of a parabola, 193
Follow, 13, 37, 47, 48
Forward, 303
Foundations, of complex geometry, 29; of general projective geometry, 1
Fubini, G., 362
Function plane, 268
Functions, trigonometric, 154
Fundamental circles, 254
Fundamental theorem of projectivity for a chain, 22

Galois field, 35
Gauss, C. F., 40, 361
Generalization, by inversion, 231; by projection, 167, 231
Geometrical order, 46
Geometries, projective, 36
Geometry, affine, 72, 147, 287; assumptions for Euclidean, 59, 144, 302; complex, 6, 29; corresponding to a group, 70, 71, 78, 199, 285, 302; double elliptic, 375; elliptic, 371; Euclidean, 117, 118, 119, 135, 144, 287, 300, 302; Euclidean, as a limiting case of non-Euclidean, 375; foundations of general projective, 1; generalized, 285; history of non-Euclidean, 360; hyperbolic plane, 350; inversion, 219; inversion plane and hyperbolic, 357; modular, 253; of nearness, 303; non-Euclidean, 350; parabolic metric group and, 119, 130, 135, 144, 293; real inversion, 241; of reals, 140; three-dimensional elliptic, 373; three-dimensional hyperbolic, 369
Grassman, H. 168, 290
Gravity, center of, 94
Group, affine, 71, 72, 287, 305; conjugacy under, 39; continuous, 406; of displacements, 129; equiaffine, 105, 291; equivalence with respect to, 39; Euclidean, 116, 117, 118, 135, 144, 305; geometry corresponding to, 70, 71, 78, 199, 285, 302; homothetic, 95; inversion, in the real Euclidean plane, 225, 226; one-parameter continuous, 406; parabolic metric, and geometry, 119, 130, 135, 144, 293; the projective, of a quadric, 259; special linear, 291; subgroups of the affine, 116
Groups, algebraic formulas for certain parabolic metric, 135; equations of the affine and Euclidean, 116, 135, 305

Half turn, 299, 370
Half twist, 324
Halstead, G. B., 361
Hamel, G., 28
Hamilton, W. R., 339
Harmonic homology, 257
Harmonic separation, 45
Harmonic sequence, 10, 33, 34; limit point of, 10
Hatton, J. L. S., 168
Heath, T. L., 360
Heine, E., 60
Hermitian forms, 362
Hesse, O., 284
Hilbert, D., 103, 181, 394
Homology, harmonic, 257
Homothetic group, 95
Homothetic transformations, 95
Horocycle, 356
Horosphere, 370
Huntington, E. V., 3, 33
Hyperbola, 73; equilateral, 169; foci of, 189; rectangular, 169
Hyperbolic direct circular transformations, 248
Hyperbolic displacements, parameter representation of, 380; types of, 355
Hyperbolic geometry, of three dimensions, 369; and inversion plane, 357
Hyperbolic lines, 350
Hyperbolic metric geometry in a plane, 350
Hyperbolic pencils of circles, 242
Hyperbolic plane, 350
Hyperbolic points, 350
Hyperbolic projectivity, 5, 171
Hyperbolic space, 369

Ideal elements, 71, 287
Ideal lines, 287, 350
Ideal minimal lines, 265
Ideal plane, 287
Ideal points, 71, 265, 268, 287, 350

Ideal space, 58
Imaginary circle, 187, 229
Imaginary elements, 7, 156, 182; conjugate, 182
Imaginary ellipse, 187
Imaginary one-dimensional form, 156
Imaginary lines, conjugate, 281, 282, 444
Imaginary points, 8, 156
Imaginary sphere, rotations of, 335
Improper elements, 71
Incomplete symbol, 41
Independence of assumptions, 23; proofs of, 24–29
Infinity, circle at, 293; line at, 58, 71; plane at, 287; points at, 71, 241, 268, 287, 352; space at, 58
Inside, of a conic, 171; of a quadric, 344
Interior, of an angle, 432; of a conic, 171, 174, 176; of an interval or segment, 45; of a polygon, 472; of an even polygon, 490; of a quadric, 344; of a triangle, 389
Interior bisector, 179
Intermediate positions, 407
Interval, 45, 46, 47, 60, 456; directed, 484; ends of, 45, 427; oriented, 484
Intervals, complementary, 46
Intuitional description of the projective plane, 67
Invariant subgroup, 39, 78, 106, 124
Invariants of a conic section, 207
Inverse matrix, 308
Inverse points, 162
Inversion, 162, 241, 266; generalization by, 231; in a complex plane, 235
Inversion geometry, 219; real, 241, 268
Inversion group in the real Euclidean plane, 225, 226
Inversion plane, 268; complex, 264, 265; hyperbolic geometry and, 357; real, 241
Inversor, Peaucellier, 229
Involution, absolute, 119; focal, 195; order relations with respect to, 45; orthogonal, 119; skew, 258; axes and directrices of skew, 258
Involutoric collineations, 257
Involutoric projectivities, products of pairs of, 277
Involutoric rotation, 299
Irrational points, 17, 21
Isogonality, 231
Isomorphic, 3
Isotropic lines, 120, 125, 265, 294
Isotropic plane, 294
Isotropic rotation, 299
Isotropic translation, 317

Jordan, C., 453
Juel, C., 250, 251

Klein, F., 71, 249, 278, 284, 285, 361, 362, 374, 375, 446
Kline, J. R., 375
Koenigs, G., 324, 339

Latus rectum of a conic, 198
Left-handed Clifford parallels, 374, 444
Left-handed conjugate imaginary lines, 444
Left-handed doubly oriented lines, 442, 445
Left-handed elliptic congruence, 444
Left-handed ordered pentads of points, 442
Left-handed ordered tetrad of points, 442
Left-handed regulus, 443
Left-handed sense-class, 407, 416
Left-handed triad of skew lines, 443, 447
Left-handed twist, 417, 443
Length of a circle, 148
Lennes, N. J., 18, 457
Lewis, G. N., 96, 138, 362
Lie, S., 341
Like sense-classes of segments, 436, 437
Limit point of harmonic sequence, 10
Limiting points of pencils of circles, 159
Lindemann, F., 366, 368, 369
Line, of centers, 159; complex, 8; doubly oriented, 440, 442, 445, 447, 449; Euclidean, 58, 60; hyperbolic, 350; ideal, 287, 350; imaginary, 156; at infinity, 58, 71; ordinary, 71, 287, 350; oriented, 426; real, 156; sides of, 59, 392; similarly oriented with respect to, 426; translation parallel to, 288
Line pairs, measure of, 163
Line reflections, 109, 115, 258; directrices, or axes of, 258; orthogonal, 120, 122, 126, 299, 317, 352, 370
Linear convex regions, 47
Linear group, special, 291
Linearly dependent circles, 256
Linearly dependent solutions of E_1, 488
Linearly independent columns of E_2, 488
Linearly independent equations (H_1), 466
Lines, broken, 454; congruence of, 275, 383; conjugate imaginary, 281, 282, 444; crossings of pairs of, 276; envelope of, 406; ideal minimal, 265; meetings of pairs of, 276; minimal or isotropic, 120, 125, 265, 294; negative pairs of, 417; ordinary minimal, 265; orthogonal, 120, 138, 293, 350, 352; pairs of, 50, 163; parallel, 72, 287, 351; perpendicular, 120, 138, 293, 369, 373; positive pairs of, 417; singular, 235; elementary transformations of triads of skew, 447; right- and left-handed triads of skew, 443; subdivision of a plane by, 51–53, 460–464; vanishing, 86

Lobachevski, N. I., 361
Logarithmic spirals, 249
Lower side of a cut, 14
Loxodromic direct circular transformations, 248
Lüroth, J., 9

MacGregor, H. H., 250
Magnitude of a vector, 86, 147
Malfatti, G., 235
Manning, H. P., 362
Matrices, algebra of, 333; modular equations and, 464; sum of two, 333
Matrices E_1 and E_2 for the projective plane, 484
Matrices H_1, H_2, and H_3, 396, 398–400, 477
Matrix, inverse, 308; orthogonal, 308; rank of, 478; scalar, 334
Measure, of angles, 151, 153, 163; angular, 163, 165, 231, 311, 313, 362, 365; of line pairs, 163; of ordered tetrads, 290; of ordered point triads, 99, 312; of a simple n-point, 104; of triangles, 99, 149, 312; unit of, 99, 140, 319
Median of a triangle, 80
Meetings of pairs of lines, 276
Menelaus, 89
Metric group and geometry, parabolic, 119, 130, 135, 144, 293
Metric properties of conics, 81
Mid-point, 80, 125
Milne, J. J., 168
Minimal lines, 120, 125, 265, 294
Minimal planes, 294
Minimal rotation, 299
Minimal translation, 317
Minkowski, H., 394
Möbius, A. F., 40, 67, 104, 229, 252, 292, 293
Model for projective plane, 67
Modular equations and matrices, 464
Modular spaces, 33, 35, 36, 253
Moore, E. H., 24, 35
Moore, R. L., 59
Morley, F., 222
Motion, rigid, 144, 297; screw, 320
Moved, 406

N-dimensional chain, 250
N-dimensional segment, 401
N-dimensional space, 58
N-dimensions, generalization to, 304
Nearness, geometry of, 303
Negative ordered pairs of lines, 417, 418
Negative of an oriented segment or region, 485
Negative points, 17
Negative relations between points and segments, 485
Negative rotations, 417
Negative sense-class, 407, 416
Negative translation, 416
Negative twist, 417
Negative of a vector, 84
Negatively oriented curve, 452
Negatively related sense-classes, 485, 491, 495
Net of rationality, 35; cuts in, 14; order in, 13
Neutral throw, 245
Nine-point circle, 169, 233
Nine-point conic, 82
Noncollinear points, 96
Nondegenerate circle, 266
Nondegenerate sphere, 315
Non-Euclidean geometry, 350; Euclidean geometry as a limiting case of, 375; history of, 360
Nonmodular spaces, 34
Normal to a conic, 173
Normal curve, 286
Null vector, 83
Numbered angle, 154
Numbered point, 456
Numbered ray, 154
Numbers, complex, 219

Odd polygons, in a plane, 470, 482; in the projective plane, 489
Odd polyhedra, 482, 483
On, 440
One-dimensional form, imaginary, 156; order in, 46; real, 156
One-dimensional projectivities, 156, 170–173; and quaternions, 339; represented by points, 342
One-sided polygonal regions, 490
One-sided polyhedra, 493
One-sided region, 437
Open cut, 14
Opposite, 433
Opposite collineations in space, 438, 451
Opposite projectivities, 37, 38
Opposite to a ray, 48
Opposite sense, 61
Opposite transformations, 452; of a 2-cell, 452
Oppositely directed, 433
Oppositely oriented, 448, 450
Oppositely sensed, 245
Order, 40; assumptions of, 32; geometrical, 46; in a linear convex region, 47; in a net of rationality, 13; in any one-dimensional form, 46; on a polygon, 456; of a set of rays, 432
Order relations, on complex lines, 437; in a Euclidean plane, 138; in the real inversion plane, 244; with respect to involutions, 45
Ordered pair, of points, 268, 271; of rays, 139
Ordered projective spaces, 32
Ordinary lines, 71, 287, 350

Ordinary minimal lines, 265
Ordinary planes, 287
Ordinary points, 71, 265, 268, 287, 350
Ordinary space, 58
Orientation of space, 496
Oriented, oppositely, 448, 450; similarly, 448; similarly, with respect to a line, 426
Oriented broken line, 484
Oriented 2-cell, 452
Oriented 3-cell, 453
Oriented curve, 452
Oriented edges of a polyhedron, 495
Oriented faces of a polyhedron, 495
Oriented interval, 484
Oriented line, 426; doubly, 440, 442, 445, 447, 449
Oriented points, 426; segments of, 426
Oriented polygon, 484
Oriented polyhedron, 495
Oriented projective space, 453
Oriented segment, 484
Oriented segment or region, negative of, 485
Oriented simple surface, 453
Oriented three-dimensional convex region, 484
Oriented two-dimensional convex region, 484
Origin of a ray, 48
Orthogonal circles, 161
Orthogonal involutions, 119
Orthogonal line reflections, 120, 122, 126, 299, 317, 352, 370; center of, 122; pairs of, 126
Orthogonal lines, 120, 138, 293, 350, 352
Orthogonal matrix, 308
Orthogonal plane reflections, 295
Orthogonal planes, 293
Orthogonal points, 352
Orthogonal polar system, 293
Orthogonal projection, 313
Orthogonal transformations, 308
Outside of a conic, 171
Outside of a quadric, 344
Owens, F. W., 59, 371

Padoa, A., 44
Pairs of lines, 50, 163; crossing of, 276; measure of, 163; meetings of, 276; negative, 417; negative ordered, 418; positive, 417; positive ordered, 417; separation of plane by, 50
Pairs, of orthogonal line reflections, 126; of planes, 50; of points, ordered, 268, 271; of points, unordered, 271
Paolis, R. De, 362
Pappus, 5, 103, 118
Parabola, 73; axis of, 193; directrix of, 193; focus of, 193; Steiner, 196; vertex of, 193
Parabolic metric group and geometry, 119, 130, 135, 144, 293
Parabolic pencils of circles, 242
Parabolic projectivities, 5, 171
Parabolic direct circular transformations, 248
Parallel to a line, translation, 288
Parallel lines, 72, 287, 351
Parallel planes, 287
Parallelogram, 72
Parallels, Clifford, 374, 375, 377, 444
Parameter of a conic, 198; continuous one-parameter family of sets of points, 405; continuous one-parameter family of transformations, 406; continuous one-parameter group, 406
Parameter representation, 344; of elliptic displacements, 377; of hyperbolic displacements, 380; of parabolic displacements, 344
Paratactic, 374
Pascal, E., 186, 235, 279, 280
Path curve, 249, 356, 406
Peaucellier inversor, 229
Peirce, B., 341
Pencil, base point of, 242; center of, 429, 433; of directions, 433; of lines, correspondence between the real Euclidean plane and a complex, 238; of rays, 429; of segments, 433
Pencils of circles, 157, 159, 242; limiting points of, 159
Pencils of projectivities, 343
Pentads of noncollinear points, right- and left-handed, 442
Permutations, even and odd, 41
Perpendicular bisector, 123; foot of a perpendicular, 123
Perpendicular lines, 120, 138, 293, 369, 373
Perpendicular planes, 293, 369, 373
Perpendicular points, 352, 369, 373
Perspective, doubly, 448
Perspective correspondence, 271
Pieri, M., 244
Pierpont, J., 3
Planar convex regions, 386
Planar region, 404
Plane, of analysis, 268; complex, 154; complex inversion, 264–268; correspondence between a complex line and the real Euclidean, 222, 238; double elliptic, 375; elliptic, 371; Euclidean, 58–63, 71; function, 268; hyperbolic, 350; hyperbolic geometry and inversion, 357; ideal, 287; at infinity, 287; intuitional description of the projective, 67; inversion, 268; inversion group in the complex Euclidean, 235; inversion group in the real Euclidean, 225, 236; isotropic, 294; minimal, 294; model for

projective, 67 ; order relations in a Euclidean, 138 ; order relations in the real inversion, 244 ; ordinary, 287 ; orthogonal, 293 ; projective, 268 ; real, 140, 156 ; real inversion, 241, 268 ; reflections, orthogonal, 295 ; sense in a Euclidean, 61 ; sides of, 59, 392 ; single elliptic, 371, 375 ; subdivision of a plane by lines, 51, 53, 460–464 ; of symmetry, 295
Planes, pairs of, 50 ; parallel, 287 ; perpendicular, 293, 369, 373 ; subdivision of space by, 50, 54, 475–477 ; vanishing, 348
Plücker, J., 292, 326
Poincaré, H., 341, 362, 489
Point pairs, congruence of parallel, 80 ; mid-point of, 80 ; separation of, 44–47
Point-plane reflection, 257
Point reflection, 92, 122, 300, 352, 414
Point triads, measure of ordered, 99 ; equivalence of ordered, 96, 288, 290 ; sum of ordered, 96
Points, complex, 8, 156 ; circular, 120, 155 ; double, of a projectivity, 5, 114, 177 ; elliptic, 373 ; equianharmonic set of, 259 ; hyperbolic, 350 ; ideal, 71, 265, 268, 287, 350 ; imaginary, 8, 156 ; at infinity, 71, 241, 268, 287, 352 ; inverse, 162 ; irrational, 17, 21 ; negative, 17 ; noncollinear, 96 ; numbered, 456 ; one-dimensional projectivities represented by, 342 ; ordered pairs of, 268, 271 ; ordinary, 71, 265, 268, 287, 350 ; oriented, 426 ; orthogonal, 352 ; of a pencil, base, 242 ; of pencils of circles, limiting, 159 ; perpendicular, 352, 369, 373 ; positive, 17 ; projection of a set of, 291 ; rational, 17 ; real, 8, 156 ; rotations represented by, 342, 343 ; segments of oriented, 426 ; singular, 235 ; in space, correspondence between the rotations and the, 328 ; in space, cross ratios of, 55 ; ultra-infinite, 352 ; unordered pairs of, 271 ; vanishing, 86
Polar coördinates, 249
Polar system, 215 ; absolute, 293, 373 ; elliptic, 218 ; orthogonal, 293
Polygon, 454–459, 480, 481 ; bounding, 470, 482 ; directed, 484 ; even, 470, 482, 489 ; interior and exterior of, 472, 490 ; odd, 470, 482, 489 ; order on, 456 ; oriented, 484 ; regions determined by, 467 ; sum modulo 2 of, 481 ; unicursal, 470
Polygonal regions, 473 ; one- and two-sided, 490
Polyhedra, odd and even, 482, 483 ; one- and two-sided, 493 ; oriented, 495 ; oriented edges of, 495 ; oriented faces of, 495 ; sum modulo 2 of, 482
Polyhedral regions, 473
Polyhedron, 474 ; bilateral, 494 ; connectivity of, 475 ; edges of, 474 ; faces of, 474 ; one-sided, 494 ; oriented edges and faces of, 495 ; two-sided, 494, 496 ; unilateral, 494 ; vertices of, 474
Positions, intermediate, 407
Positive coördinate system, 407, 408, 416
Positive ordered pairs of lines, 417
Positive pairs of lines, 417
Positive points, 17
Positive relation between points and oriented segments, 485
Positive rotation, 417
Positive sense-class, 40, 407, 416, 491
Positive translation, 416
Positive twist, 417
Positively oriented curve, 452
Positively related sense-classes, 485, 491, 495
Power, of a point with respect to a circle, 162 ; of a transformation, 87, 230
Precede, 13, 15, 37, 47, 48, 350, 387
Product, of pairs of involutoric projectivities, 277 ; of two vectors, 220
Projection, generalization by, 167, 231 ; orthogonal, 313 ; of a set of points, 291
Projective classification of conics, 186
Projective correspondence, 272
Projective geometry, 36 ; foundations of general, 1
Projective group of a quadric, 259
Projective plane, 268 ; intuitional description of, 67 ; matrices E_1 and E_2 for, 484
Projective space, collineations in a real, 252 ; sense in, 64
Projective spaces, ordered, 32 ; sense-classes in, 418
Projectivities, bundle of, 342 ; cyclic, 258 ; direct, 37, 38, 407 ; double points of, 5, 114, 177 ; elliptic, 5, 171 ; hyperbolic, 5, 171 ; one-dimensional, 170, 171 ; opposite, 37, 38 ; parabolic, 5, 171 ; pencil of, 343 ; powers of, 87 ; products of pairs of involutoric, 277 ; of a quadric, 273 ; real, 156, 170–173 ; representation by points of one-dimensional, 342 ; representation by quaternions of one-dimensional, 339
Projectivity, assumption of, 2
Prolongation of a segment, 48
Proofs, independence, 24–29

Quadrangle, diagonals of, 72
Quadrics, absolute, 369, 373 ; axes of, 316 ; confocal system of, 348 ; direct collineations of, 260 ; interior and exterior of, 344 ; projective group of, 259 ; projectivities of, 273 ; real, 262 ;

ruled, 259; sides of, 344; sphere and other, 315; unruled, 259
Quadrilateral, diameter of, 81
Quaternions, 337–341, 378; and the one-dimensional projective group, 339

Radical axis, 159
Radii, transformation by reciprocal, 162
Rank, of H_2, 479; of a matrix, 478
Rational curve, 286
Rational modular space, 35, 36
Rational points, 17
Rationality, net of, 35; order in a net of, 13
Ratios of collinear vectors, 85
Rays, 48, 60, 143, 350, 372, 387, 429; bundle of, 435; numbered, 154; opposite, 48; order of a set of, 432; ordered pair of, 139; origin of, 48
Real and imaginary elements and transformations, 156
Real inversion geometry, 241
Real inversion plane, 241, 268; order relations in, 244
Real line, 156
Real one-dimensional form, 156
Real plane, 140, 156
Real points, 8, 156
Real projective transformations, 156
Real quadrics, 262
Reals, geometry of, 140
Reciprocal radii, transformation by, 162
Rectangle, 123
Rectangular coördinates, 311
Rectangular hyperbola, 169
Reflections, axes of line, 258; center of orthogonal line, 122; directrices of line, 258; line, 109, 115, 258; orthogonal line, 120, 122, 126, 299, 317, 352, 370; orthogonal plane, 295; pairs of orthogonal line, 126; point, 92, 122, 300, 352, 414; point-plane, 257; in a three-chain, 284
Region, convex, 385–394; negative of an oriented segment or, 485; one-sided, 437; order in a linear convex, 47; planar, 404; polygonal, 473; polyhedral, 473; sense in overlapping convex, 424; simply connected three-dimensional, 404; tetrahedral, 54, 398, 399; three-dimensional, 404; triangular, 53, 389, 395; trihedral, 397; two-sided region, 437; vertices of a triangular, 53
Regions, bounded by a polyhedron, 483; determined by a polygon, 467
Regulus, right- and left-handed, 443
Restricted elementary transformations, 410, 414, 420, 430
Reye, T., 168
Rhombus, 125
Ricordi, E., 360
Riemann, B., 361
Right angles, 153
Right-handed Clifford parallels, 374, 444
Right-handed conjugate imaginary lines, 444
Right-handed coördinate system, 408, 416
Right-handed doubly oriented lines, 442, 445
Right-handed elliptic congruence, 444
Right-handed ordered pentad of points, 442
Right-handed ordered tetrad of points, 442
Right-handed regulus, 443
Right-handed sense-class, 40, 407, 416, 442
Right-handed triad of skew lines, 443, 447
Right-handed twist, 417, 443
Rigid motion, 144, 297
Rodrigues, O., 330
Rotation, angle of, 325, 327; axis of, 299; center of a, 122; involutoric, 299; isotropic, 299; minimal, 299; negative, 417; positive, 417; sense of, 142
Rotations, 122, 128, 141, 299, 321, 328–337; correspondence between the points of space and, 328; of an imaginary sphere, 335; represented by points, 342, 343
Ruled quadric, 259
Ruler-and-compass constructions, 180
Russell, B., 41
Russell, J. W., 168, 201

Saccheri, G., 361
Same sense, 61
Scalar matrix, 334
Schilling, M., 67
Schweitzer, A. R., 32, 415
Screw motion, 320
Segment, 45, 46, 47, 60, 350; or interval, complementary, 46; directed, 484; ends of, 45, 427; interior of interval or, 45; *n*-dimensional, 401; oriented, 484; prolongation of, 248
Segments, bundle of, 436; of oriented points, 426; pencil of, 433; sense-classes of, 436, 437
Segre, C., 9, 250, 251
Self-conjugate subgroup, 39, 78, 106, 124
Sense, 32, 41, 61, 387, 413; clockwise, 40; criteria for, 49; in a Euclidean plane, 61; in Euclidean spaces, 63; in a linear region, 47; more general theory of, 451; in a one-dimensional form, 40, 43; opposite, 61; in overlapping convex regions, 424; positive, 40, 407, 416; in a projective space, 64; right-handed, 40, 407, 416, 442; of rotation, 142; same, 61

Sense-class, 61, 64, 66, 413, 414, 430, 431, 434, 437, 455, 456; of a 2-cell, 452; of a curve, 452; left-handed, 407, 416; in a linear region, 47; negative, 407, 416, 452; on a one-dimensional form, 40, 43; positive, 40, 407, 416, 452, 491; right-handed, 40, 407, 416, 442
Sense-classes, agree or disagree, 485; negatively related, 485, 491, 495; positively related, 485, 491, 495; in projective space, 418
Sensed, oppositely, 245; similarly, 245
Separated, 392, 432
Separation, algebraic criteria of, 55; harmonic, 45; by pairs of lines, 51; by pairs of planes, 51; of point pairs, 44, 47
Sequence, harmonic, 10, 33, 34; limit point of, 10
Sets of points, connected, 404, 405; continuous family of, 405
Shear, simple, 112, 293
Sheffers, G., 341
Sides, of a circle, 245; of a line, 59, 392; of a plane, 59, 392; of a quadric, 344
Similar, 119
Similar and similarly placed, 95
Similar figures, 293
Similar triangles, 134, 139
Similarity transformations, 117, 119, 293; direct, 135
Similarly directed, 433
Similarly oriented, 448; with respect to a line, 426
Similarly sensed, 245
Similitude, center of, 162, 163
Simple broken line, 454
Simple curve, 401
Simple polygon, 454–457
Simple shear, 112, 293
Simple surface, 404; oriented, 453
Simplex, 401
Simply connected element of surface, 404
Simply connected surface, 404
Simply connected three-dimensional region, 404
Singular lines, 235
Singular points, 235
Singular space, 58
Skew involutions, 258; directrices or axes of, 258
Skew lines, elementary transformations of triads of, 447; right- and left-handed triads of, 443
Smith, H. J. S., 201
Sommerville, D. M. Y., 362
Space, assumptions for a Euclidean, 59; collineations in a real projective, 252; correspondence between the rotations and the points of, 328; cross ratio of points in, 55; direct collineations in, 438, 451; Euclidean, 58, 287; hyperbolic, 369; ideal, 58; at infinity, 58; modular and nonmodular, 33, 34, 36, 253; n-dimensional, 58; opposite collineations in, 438, 451; ordered projective, 32; ordinary, 58; orientation of, 496; oriented projective, 453; polygons in, 480, 481; rational modular, 35, 36; sense in a Euclidean, 63; sense in a projective, 64; sense-classes in projective, 418; singular, 58
Spatial convex regions, 386
Special linear group, 291
Sphere, center of, 315; degenerate, 315; and other quadrics, 315; rotations of an imaginary, 335
Spirals, logarithmic, 249
Square, 125
Statements, vacuous, 24
Staudt, K. G. C. von, 9, 40, 251, 283
Steiner, J., 196, 229
Steinitz, E., 35, 69
Stephanos, C., 286, 324, 342, 344
Study, E., 40, 327, 341, 347, 362, 374, 416, 446
Sturm, R., 168
Subdivision, of a plane by lines, 51–53, 460–464; of a space by planes, 50, 54, 475–477
Subgroup, self-conjugate or invariant, 39, 78, 106, 124
Subgroups of the affine group, 116
Sum, modulo 2, of polygons, 481; modulo 2, of polyhedra, 482; of ordered point-triads, 96; of two angles, 154; of two matrices, 333; of two vectors, 83
Surface, simple, 404; simply connected, 404; simply connected element of, 404
Symbol, incomplete, 41
Symmetric, 124, 297, 300, 352
Symmetry, 123, 124, 129, 138, 297, 300, 352, 373; plane of, 295; with respect to a point, 300

Tait, P. G., 341
Taylor, C., 168
Taylor, W. W., 82
Tetracyclic coördinates, 253, 254, 255
Tetrad, measure of an ordered, 290; of points, right- and left-handed ordered, 442
Tetrads, equivalence of ordered, 290
Tetrahedral region, 54, 398, 399
Tetrahedron, 52, 397; volume of, 290, 311
Three-dimensional affine geometry, 287
Three-dimensional convex region, 386
Three-dimensional directed convex region, 484
Three-dimensional elliptic geometry, 373

Three-dimensional Euclidean geometry, 287
Three-dimensional hyperbolic geometry, 369
Three-dimensional region, 404; simply connected, 404
Throws, 40; neutral, 245; similarly or oppositely sensed, 245
Torsion, coefficient of, 489
Touch, 158
Transference, the principle of, 284
Transformations, of a 2-cell, circular, 225; continuous family of, 406; direct, 225, 452; direct similarity, 135; elliptic direct circular, 248; elementary, 409, 411–414, 418, 419, 421, 423, 430, 431, 434–437, 447, 455, 456; homothetic, 95; loxodromic direct circular, 248; opposite, 452; orthogonal, 308; parabolic direct circular, 248; power of a projective, 87; power of a circular, 230; real and imaginary, 156; by reciprocal radii, 162; restricted elementary, 410, 414, 420, 430; similarity, 117, 119, 293
Translation, 74, 117, 122, 288, 321, 374, 414; axis of, 317; distance of, 325, 327; isotropic, 317; minimal, 317; negative, 416; parallel to a line, 288; positive, 416
Transposition, 41
Transversals, 91
Triads of lines, elementary transformations of, 447; right-handed and left-handed, 443
Triangle, area of, 149, 312; interior of, 389; measure of, 99, 149, 312; median of, 80; separation of a plane by, 52; unit, 99, 149, 312
Triangles, congruent, 134, 139; similar, 134, 139
Triangular region, 53, 389, 395; vertices of, 53
Trigonometric functions, 154
Trihedral regions, 397
Turn, half, 299, 370
Twist, 320, 321; axis of, 320; half, 324; left-handed, 417, 443; negative, 417; positive, 417; right-handed, 417, 443
Two-dimensional convex region, 386; directed, 484
Two-sided polygonal regions, 490
Two-sided polyhedra, 493
Two-sided polyhedron, 494, 496
Two-sided region, 437

Ultra-infinite points, 352
Unicursal polygons, 470
Unilateral polyhedron, 494
Unit of distance, 147
Unit triangle, 99, 149, 312
Unit vector, 220
Unordered pairs of points, 271
Unruled quadric, 259
Up, 303
Upper side of a cut, 14

Vacuous statements, 24
Vailati, G., 44
Vanishing lines, 86
Vanishing planes, 348
Vanishing points, 86
Vector, magnitude of, 86, 147; negative of, 84; null, 83; unit, 220; zero, 83, 220
Vectors, 82, 83, 85, 147, 219, 288; addition of, 84; collinear, 84; product of two, 220; ratios of collinear, 85; sum of, 83
Vertex, of a conic, 191; of a parabola, 193
Vertices, of a broken line, 454; of a polyhedron, 474; of a triangular region, 53
Volume, 290, 311

Whitehead, A. N., 32, 41
Wiener, H., 94, 280, 322, 327
Wilson, E. B., 96, 113, 138, 362

Young, J. W., iii, 250
Young, J. W. A., 146

Zermelo, E., 27
Zero vector, 83, 220